HANDBOOK ON COMPUTATIONAL INTELLIGENCE

Volume 1: Fuzzy Logic, Systems, Artificial Neural Networks, and Learning Systems

HANDBOOK ON COMPUTATIONAL INTELLIGENCE

Volume 1: Fuzzy Logic, Systems, Artificial Neural Networks, and Learning Systems

Editor

Plamen Parvanov Angelov

Lancaster University, UK

World Scientific

NEW JERSEY • LONDON • SINGAPORE • BEIJING • SHANGHAI • HONG KONG • TAIPEI • CHENNAI • TOKYO

Published by

World Scientific Publishing Co. Pte. Ltd.
5 Toh Tuck Link, Singapore 596224
USA office: 27 Warren Street, Suite 401-402, Hackensack, NJ 07601
UK office: 57 Shelton Street, Covent Garden, London WC2H 9HE

British Library Cataloguing-in-Publication Data
A catalogue record for this book is available from the British Library.

HANDBOOK ON COMPUTATIONAL INTELLIGENCE
In 2 Volumes

Volume 1: Fuzzy Logic, Systems, Artifical Neural Networks, and Learning Systems
Volume 2: Evolutionary Computation, Hybrid Systems, and Applications

ISBN 978-981-4675-00-0 (Set)
ISBN 978-981-4675-03-1 (Vol. 1)
ISBN 978-981-4675-04-8 (Vol. 2)

In-house Editors: Dipasri Sardar/Amanda Yun

Typeset by Stallion Press
Email: enquiries@stallionpress.com

Printed in Singapore

Dedication

Computational Intelligence is only possible if we have a *Computer*. This work is dedicated to the inventor of the digital computer, John Vincent Atanasoff.

Contents

Introduction by the Editor

The term *Computational Intelligence* was coined more recently (at the end of the last century when a series of high profile conferences were organized by the Institute of Electrical and Electronics Engineers (IEEE) leading to the formation of the Computational Intelligence Society within the IEEE), however, the disciplines and problems it covers have been in existence for a much longer period of time. The very idea of developing systems, devices, algorithms, techniques that possess characteristics of "*intelligence*" and are computational (not just conceptual) dates back to the middle of the 20th century or even earlier and is broadly associated with the so-called "*artificial intelligence*". However, "artificial intelligence" is nowadays rather linked with logic, cognition, natural language processing, induction and so on, while "*computational intelligence*" has been developed in a direction that can be described as "nature-inspired" alternatives to the conventional/traditional computing approaches. This includes, but is not limited to:

- Fuzzy logic (as a more human-oriented approach to reasoning);
- Artificial neural networks (mimicking the human brain);
- Evolutionary algorithms (mimicking the population-based genetic evolution), and
- Dynamically evolving systems based on the above.

Some authors also attribute other areas of research such as belief-based Depmster–Shafer theory, chaos theory, swarm and collective intelligence, etc. on the margins of *Computational Intelligence.* It is also often the case that the application areas such as pattern recognition, image processing, business and video analytics and so on are also attributed or linked closely to *Computational Intelligence*; areas of research that are closer to Statistical Learning (e.g., Support Vector Machines), probability theory, Bayesian, Markov models etc. are also sometimes considered to be a part of *Computational Intelligence.*

In this handbook, while not closing the door to all possible methods and alternatives, we keep clear the picture of *Computational Intelligence* as a distinct area of research that is based on the above mentioned pillars and we assume that the other areas are either applications of *Computational Intelligence* methods, techniques or approaches or research areas that gravitate around Statistical Learning.

The primary goal of the area of *Computational Intelligence* is to provide efficient computational solutions to the existing open problems from theoretical and application points of view in understanding, representation, modeling, visualization, reasoning, decision, prediction, classification, analysis and control of physical objects, environmental or social processes and phenomena to which the traditional methods, techniques and theories (primarily, so-called "first principles", deterministic, often expressed as differential equations and stemming from mass- and energy-balance) cannot provide a valid or useful/practical solution.

Another specific feature of *Computational Intelligence* is that it offers solutions that bear characteristics of "intelligence" which is usually attributed to humans only. This has to be considered broadly rather than literally as in the area of "artificial intelligence". For example, fuzzy logic systems can make decisions like humans do. This is in a stark contrast with the deterministic type expert systems as well as with the probabilistic associative rules. For artificial neural networks, one can argue that they process the data in a manner which is more like what human Brain does. In evolutionary computation, the population of candidate solutions "evolves" towards the optimum in a manner similar to the way species and living organisms evolve in Nature. Finally, in dynamically evolving systems, self-development is very much like in the real life, where we, humans, learn individually from experience in a supervised (from parents, teachers, peers etc.) or unsupervised (self-learning) manner. Learning from experience, we can develop a rule-base starting from "scratch" and constantly update this rule-base by adding new rules or removing the outdated ones; or similarly, the strengths of the links between neurons in our brain can dynamically evolve and new areas of the brain can be activated or deactivated (thus, dynamically evolving neural networks).

In this handbook, a mix of leading academics and practitioners in this area as well as some of the younger generation researchers contributed to cover the main aspects of the exciting area of *Computational Intelligence*. The overall structure and invitations to a much broader circle of contributors were set up initially. After a careful peer review process, a selected set of contributions was organized in a coherent end product aiming to cover the main areas of *Computational Intelligence*; it also aims to cover both, the theoretical basis and, at the same time, to give a flavor of the possible efficient applications.

This handbook is composed of two volumes and five parts which contain 26 chapters.

Volume 1 includes Part I (Fuzzy Logic) and Part II (Artificial Neural Networks and Learning Systems).

Volume 2 includes Part III (Evolutionary Computation), Part IV (Hybrid Systems) and Part V (Applications).

In Part I, the readers can find seven chapters, including:

- Fundamentals of Fuzzy Set Theory
  This chapter sets the tone with a thorough, step by step introduction to the theory of fuzzy sets. It is written by one of the foremost experts in this area, Dr. Fernando Gomide, Professor at University of Campinas, Campinas, Brazil.
- Granular Computing
  Granular computing became a cornerstone of *Computational Intelligence* and the chapter offers a thorough review of the problems and solutions. It is written by two of the leading experts in this area, Dr. Andrzej Bargiela, Professor at Nottingham University, UK (now in Christchurch University, New Zealand) and Dr. Witold Pedrycz, Professor at University of Alberta, Canada.
- Evolving Fuzzy Systems — Fundamentals, Reliability, Interpretability, Useability, Applications
  Since its introduction around the turn of the centuries by the Editor, the area of evolving fuzzy systems is constantly developing and this chapter offers a review of the problems and some of the solutions. It is written by Dr. Edwin Lughofer, Key Researcher at Johannes Kepler University, Linz, Austria, who quickly became one of the leading experts in this area following an exchange of research visits with Lancaster University, UK.
- Modeling of Fuzzy Rule-based Systems
  This chapter covers the important problem of designing fuzzy systems from data. It is written by Dr. Rashmi Dutta Baruah of Indian Institute of Technology, Guwahati, India and Diganta Baruah of Sikkim Manipal Institute of Technology, Sikkim, India. Rashmi recently obtained a PhD degree from Lancaster University, UK in the area of evolving fuzzy systems.
- Fuzzy Classifiers
  This chapter covers the very important problem of fuzzy rule-based classifiers and is written by the expert in the field, Dr. Hamid Bouchachia, Associate Professor at Bournemouth University, UK.
- Fuzzy Model based Control: Predictive and Adaptive Approach
  This chapter covers the problems of fuzzy control and is written by the experts in the area, Dr. Igor Škrjanc, Professor and Dr. Sašo Blažič, Professor at the University of Ljubljana, Slovienia.

- Fuzzy Fault Detection and Diagnosis

  This chapter is written by Dr. Bruno Costa, Professor at IFRN, Natal, Brazil who specialized recently in Lancaster, UK.

Part II consists of six chapters, which cover:

- The ANN and Learning Systems in Brains and Machines

  This chapter is written by Dr. Leonid Perlovsky from Harvard University, USA.

- Introduction to Cognitive Systems

  This chapter is written by Dr. Peter Erdi, Professor at Kalamazoo College, USA, co-authored by Dr. Mihaly Banyai (leading author) from Wigner RCP, Hungarian Academy of Sciences.

- A New View on Economics with Recurrent Neural Networks

  This chapter offers a rather specific view on the recurrent neural networks from the point of view of their importance for modeling economic processes and is written by a team of industry-based researchers from Siemens, Germany including Drs. Hans Georg Zimmermann, Ralph Grothmann and Christoph Tietz.

- Evolving Connectionist Systems for Adaptive Learning and Pattern Recognition: From Neuro-Fuzzy, to Spiking and Neurogenetic

  This chapter offers a review of one of the cornerstones of *Computational Intelligence*, namely, the evolving connectionist systems, and is written by the pioneer in this area Dr. Nikola Kasabov, Professor at Auckland University of Technology, New Zealand.

- Reinforcement Learning with Applications in Automation Decision and Feedback Control

  This chapter offers a thorough and advanced analysis of the reinforcement learning from the perspective of decision-making and control. It is written by one of the world's leading experts in this area, Dr. Frank L. Lewis, Professor at The University of Texas, co-authored by Dr. Kyriakos Vamvoudakis from the same University (the leading author) and Dr. Draguna Vrabie from the United Technologies Research Centre, USA.

- Kernel Models and Support Vector Machines

  This chapter offers a very skilful review of one of the hottest topics in research and applications linked to classification and related problems. It is written by a team of young Russian researchers who are finishing their PhD studies at Lancaster University, UK (Denis Kolev and Dmitry Kangin) and by Mikhail Suvorov. All three graduated from leading Moscow Universities (Moscow State University and Bauman Moscow State Technical University).

Part III consists of four chapters:

- History and Philosophy of the Evolutionary Computation

  This chapter lays the basis for one of the pillars of *Computational Intelligence*, covering its history and basic principles. It is written by one of the well-known experts in this area, Dr. Carlos A. Coello-Coello from CINVESTAV, Mexico and co-authored by Dr. Carlos Segura from the Centre of Research in Mathematics, Mexico and Dr. Gara Miranda from the University of La Laguna, Tenerife, Spain.

- A Survey of Recent Works in Artificial Immune Systems

  This chapter covers one of the important aspects of *Computational Intelligence* which is associated with the Evolutionary Computation. It is written by the pioneer in the area Dr. Dipankar Dasgupta, Professor at The University of Memphis, USA and is co-authored by Dr. Guilherme Costa Silva from the same University who is the leading author.

- Swarm Intelligence: An Introduction, History and Applications

  This chapter covers another important aspect of Evolutionary Computation and is written by Dr. Fevrier Valdez from The Institute of Technology, Tijuana, Mexico.

- Memetic Algorithms

  This chapter reviews another important type of methods and algorithms which are associated with the Evolutionary Computation and is written by a team of authors from the University of Aizu, Japan led by Dr. Qiangfu Zhao who is a well-known expert in the area of *Computational Intelligence*. The team also includes Drs. Yong Liu and Yan Pei.

Part IV consists of five chapters:

- Multi-objective Evolutionary Design of Fuzzy Rule-Based Systems

  This chapter covers one of the areas of hybridization where Evolutionary Computation is used as an optimization tool for automatic design of fuzzy rule-based systems from data. It is written by the well-known expert in this area, Dr. Francesco Marcelloni, Professor at the University of Pisa, Italy, supported by Dr. Michaela Antonelli and Dr. Pietro Ducange from the same University.

- Bio-inspired Optimization of Type-2 Fuzzy Controllers

  The chapter offers a hybrid system where a fuzzy controller of the so-called type-2 is being optimized using a bio-inspired approach. It is written by one of the leading experts in type-2 fuzzy systems, Dr. Oscar Castillo, Professor at The Institute of Technology, Tijuana Mexico.

- Nature-inspired Optimization of Fuzzy Controllers and Fuzzy Models

  This chapter also offers a hybrid system in which fuzzy models and controllers are being optimized using nature-inspired optimization methods. It is written by the well-known expert in the area of fuzzy control, Dr. Radu-Emil Precup, Professor at The Polytechnic University of Timisoara, Romania and co-authored by Dr. Radu Codrut David.

- Genetic Optimization of Modular Neural Networks for Pattern Recognition with a Granular Approach

  This chapter describes a hybrid system whereby modular neural networks using a granular approach are optimized by a genetic algorithm and applied for pattern recognition. It is written by Dr. Patricia Melin, Professor at The Institute of Technology, Tijuana, Mexico who is well-known through her work in the area of hybrid systems.

- Hybrid Evolutionary-, Constructive-, and Evolving Fuzzy Neural Networks

  This is another chapter by the pioneer of evolving neural networks, Professor Dr. Nikola Kasabov, co-authored by Dr. Michael Watts (leading author), both from Auckland, New Zealand.

Part V includes four chapters:

- Applications of Computational Intelligence to Decision-Making: Modeling Human Reasoning/Agreement

  This chapter covers the use of *Computational Intelligence* in decision-making applications, in particular, modeling human reasoning and agreement. It is authored by the leading expert in this field, Dr. Jonathan Garibaldi, Professor at The Nottingham University, UK and co-authored by Drs. Simon Miller (leading author) and Christian Wagner from the same University.

- Applications of Computational Intelligence to Process Industry

  This chapter offers the industry-based researcher's point of view. Dr. Jose Juan Macias Hernandez is leading a busy Department of Process Control at the largest oil refinery on the Canary Islands, Spain and is also Associate Professor at the local University of La Laguna, Tenerife.

- Applications of Computational Intelligence to Robotics and Autonomous Systems

  This chapter describes applications of *Computational Intelligence* to the area of Robotics and Autonomous Systems and is written by Dr. Adham Atyabi and Professor Dr. Samia Nefti-Meziani, both from Salford University, UK.

- Selected Automotive Applications of Computational Intelligence

  Last, but not least, the chapter by the pioneer of fuzzy systems area Dr. Dimitar Filev, co-authored by his colleagues, Dr. Mahmoud Abou-Nasr (leading author) and Dr. Fazal Sayed (all based at Ford Motors Co., Dearborn, MI, USA) offers the industry-based leaders' point of view.

In conclusion, this Handbook is composed with care aiming to cover all main aspects of *Computational Intelligence* area of research offering solid background knowledge as well as end-point applications from the leaders in the area supported by younger researchers in the field. It is designed to be a one-stop-shop for interested readers, but by no means aims to completely replace all other sources in this dynamically evolving area of research.

Enjoy reading it.

Plamen Angelov
Lancaster, UK

About the Editor

Professor Plamen Angelov (www.lancs.ac.uk/staff/angelov) holds a Personal Chair in Intelligent Systems and leads the Data Science Group at Lancaster University, UK. He has PhD (1993) and Doctor of Sciences (DSc, 2015) degrees and is a Fellow of both the IEEE and IET, as well as a Senior Member of the International Neural Networks Society (INNS). He is also a member of the Boards of Governors of both bodies for the period 2014–2017. He also chairs the Technical Committee (TC) on Evolving Intelligent Systems within the Systems, Man and Cybernetics Society, IEEE and is a member of the TCs on Neural Networks and on Fuzzy Systems within the Computational Intelligence Society, IEEE. He has authored or co-authored over 200 peer-reviewed publications in leading journals, peer-reviewed conference proceedings, five patents and a dozen books, including two research monographs by Springer (2002) and Wiley (2012), respectively. He has an active research portfolio in the area of data science, computational intelligence and autonomous machine learning and internationally recognized results into online and evolving learning and algorithms for knowledge extraction in the form of human-intelligible fuzzy rule-based systems. Prof. Angelov leads numerous projects funded by UK research councils, EU, industry, UK Ministry of Defence, The Royal Society, etc. His research was recognized by 'The Engineer Innovation and Technology 2008 Special Award' and 'For outstanding Services' (2013) by IEEE and INNS. In 2014, he was awarded a Chair of Excellence at Carlos III University, Spain sponsored by Santander Bank. Prof. Angelov is the founding Editor-in-Chief of Springer's journal on *Evolving Systems* and Associate Editor of the leading international scientific journals in this area, including *IEEE Transactions on Cybernetics*, *IEEE Transactions on Fuzzy Systems* and half a dozen others. He was General, Program or Technical co-Chair of prime IEEE conferences

(IJCNN-2013, Dallas; SSCI2014, Orlando,WCCI2014, Beijing; IS'14, Warsaw; IJCNN2015, Killarney; IJCNN/ WCCI2016, Vancouver; UKCI 2016, Lancaster; WCCI2018, Rio de Janeiro) and founding General co-Chair of a series of annual IEEE conferences on Evolving and Adaptive Intelligent Systems. He was a Visiting Professor in Brazil, Germany, Spain, France, Bulgaria. Prof. Angelov regularly gives invited and plenary talks at leading conferences, universities and companies.

Acknowledgments

The Editor would like to acknowledge the support of the Chair of Excellence programme of Carlos III University, Madrid, Spain.

The Editor would also like to acknowledge the unwavering support of his family (Rosi, Lachezar and Mariela).

Prologue

The *Handbook on Computational Intelligence* aims to be a one-stop-shop for the various aspects of the broad research area of Computational Intelligence. The *Handbook* is organized into five parts over two volumes:

(1) Fuzzy Sets and Systems (Vol. 1)
(2) Artificial Neural Networks and Learning Systems (Vol. 1)
(3) Evolutionary Computation (Vol. 2)
(4) Hybrid Systems (Vol. 2)
(5) Applications (Vol. 2)

In total, 26 chapters detail various aspects of the theory, methodology and applications of *Computational Intelligence*. The authors of the different chapters are leading researchers in their respective fields or "rising stars" (promising early career researchers). This mix of experience and energy provides an invaluable source of information that is easy to read, rich in detail, and wide in spectrum. In total, over 50 authors from 16 different countries including USA, UK, Japan, Germany, Canada, Italy, Spain, Austria, Bulgaria, Brazil, Russia, India, New Zealand, Hungary, Slovenia, Mexico, and Romania contributed to this collaborative effort. The scope of the *Handbook* covers practically all important aspects of the topic of Computational Intelligence and has several chapters dedicated to particular applications written by leading industry-based or industry-linked researchers.

Preparing, compiling and editing this Handbook was an enjoyable and inspirational experience. I hope you will also enjoy reading it and will find answers to your questions and will use this book in your everyday work.

Plamen Angelov
Lancaster, UK

Volume 1

Part I

Fuzzy Logic and Systems

Chapter 1

Fundamentals of Fuzzy Set Theory

Fernando Gomide

The goal of this chapter is to offer a comprehensive, systematic, updated, and self-contained tutorial-like introduction to fuzzy set theory. The notions and concepts addressed here cover the spectrum that contains, we believe, the material deemed relevant for computational intelligence and intelligent systems theory and applications. It starts by reviewing the very basic idea of sets, introduces the notion of a fuzzy set, and gives the main insights and interpretations to help intuition. It proceeds with characterization of fuzzy sets, operations and their generalizations, and ends discussing the issue of information granulation and its key constituents.

1.1. Sets

A set is a fundamental concept in mathematics and science. Classically, a set is defined as "any multiplicity which can be thought of as one and any totality of definite elements which can be bound up into a whole by means of a law" or being more descriptive "any collection into a whole M of definite and separate objects m of our intuition or our thought" (Cantor, 1883, 1895).

Intuitively, a set may be viewed as the class M of all objects m satisfying any particular property or defining condition. Alternatively, a set can be characterized by an assignment scheme to define the objects of a domain that satisfy the intended property. For instance, an indicator function or a characteristic function is a function defined on a domain X that indicates membership of an object of X in a set A on X, having the value 1 for all elements of A and the value 0 for all elements of X not in A. The domain can be either continuous or discrete. For instance, the closed interval $[3, 7]$ constitutes a continuous and bounded domain whereas the set $N = \{0, 1, 2, \ldots\}$ of natural numbers is discrete and countable, but with no bound.

In general, a characteristic function of a set A defined in X assumes the following form

$$A(x) = \begin{cases} 1, & \text{if } x \in A \\ 0, & \text{if } x \notin A \end{cases}. \tag{1}$$

The empty set $\emptyset$ has a characteristic function that is identically equal to zero, $\emptyset(x) = 0$ for all x in X. The domain X itself has a characteristic function that is identically equal to one, $X(x) = 1$ for all x in X. Also, a singleton $A = \{a\}$, a set with only a single element, has the characteristic function $A(x) = 1$ if $x = a$ and $A(x) = 0$ otherwise.

Characteristic functions $A : X \rightarrow \{0, 1\}$ induce a constraint with well-defined boundaries on the elements of the domain X that can be assigned to a set A.

1.2. Fuzzy Sets

The fundamental idea of a fuzzy set is to relax the rigid boundaries of the constraints induced by characteristic functions by admitting intermediate values of class membership. The idea is to allow assignments of intermediate values between 0 and 1 to quantify our perception on how compatible the objects of a domain are with the class, with 0 meaning incompatibility, complete exclusion, and 1 compatibility, complete membership. Membership values thus express the degrees to which each object of a domain is compatible with the properties distinctive to the class. Intermediate membership values mean that no natural threshold exists and that elements of a universe can be a member of a class and at the same time belong to other classes with different degrees. Gradual, less strict membership degrees is the essence of fuzzy sets.

Formally, a fuzzy set A is described by a membership function mapping the elements of a domain X to the unit interval [0, 1] (Zadeh, 1965)

$$A : X \rightarrow [0, 1]. \tag{2}$$

Membership functions fully define fuzzy sets. Membership functions generalize characteristic functions in the same way as fuzzy sets generalize sets. Fuzzy sets can be also be seen as a set of ordered pairs of the form $\{x, A(x)\}$ where x is an object of X and $A(x)$ is its corresponding degree of membership. For a finite domain $X = \{x_1, x_2, \ldots, x_n\}$, A can be represented by an n-dimensional vector $A = (a_1, a_2, \ldots, a_n)$ with each component $a_i = A(x_i)$.

Being more illustrative, we may view fuzzy sets as elastic constraints imposed on the elements of a universe. Fuzzy sets deal primarily with the concepts of elasticity, graduality, or absence of sharply defined boundaries. In contrast, sets are concerned with rigid boundaries, lack of graded belongingness, and sharp binary constraints. Gradual membership means that no natural boundary exists and that some elements of the domain can, contrary to sets, coexist (belong) to different fuzzy sets with different degrees of membership. For instance, in Figure 1.1, $x_1 = 1.5$ is compatible with the concept of *short* and $x_2 = 2.0$ belongs to the category of *tall* people, when assuming the model of sets, but x_1 simultaneously is 0.8 *short*

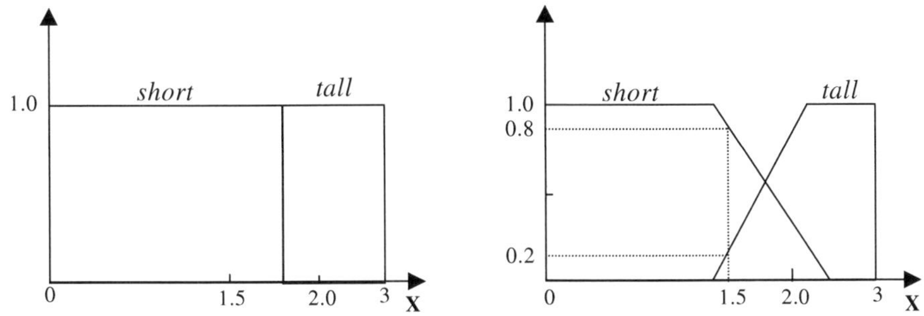

Figure 1.1: Two-valued membership in characteristic functions (sets) and gradual membership represented by membership functions (fuzzy sets).

and 0.2 *tall* and x_2 simultaneously is 0.2 *short* and 0.8 *tall* under the perspective of fuzzy sets.

1.2.1. *Interpretation of Fuzzy Sets*

In fuzzy set theory, fuzziness has a precise meaning. Fuzziness primarily means lack of precise boundaries of a collection of objects and, as such, it is a manifestation of imprecision and a particular type of uncertainty.

First, it is worth noting that fuzziness is both conceptually and formally different from the fundamental concept of probability. In general, it is difficult to foresee the result of tossing a fair coin as it is impossible to know if either head or tail will occur for certain. We may, at most, say that there is a 50% chance to have a head or tail, but as soon as the coin falls, uncertainty vanishes. On the contrary, when we say that a person is tall we are not being precise, and imprecision remains independently of any event. Formally, probability is a set function, a mapping whose universe is a set of subsets of a domain. In contrast, fuzzy sets are membership functions, mappings from some given universe of discourse to the unit interval.

Secondly, fuzziness, generality, and ambiguity are distinct notions. A notion is general when it applies to a multiplicity of objects and keeps only a common essential property. An ambiguous notion stands for several unrelated objects. Therefore, from this point of view, fuzziness does not mean neither generality nor ambiguity and applications of fuzzy sets exclude these categories. Fuzzy set theory assumes that the universe is well defined and has its elements assigned to classes by means of a numerical scale.

Applications of fuzzy set in areas such as data analysis, reasoning under uncertainty, and decision-making suggest different interpretations of membership grades in terms of similarity, uncertainty, and preference (Dubois and Prade, 1997, 1998). Membership value $A(x)$ from the point of view of similarity means the degree of compatibility of an element $x \in X$ with representative elements of A. This is

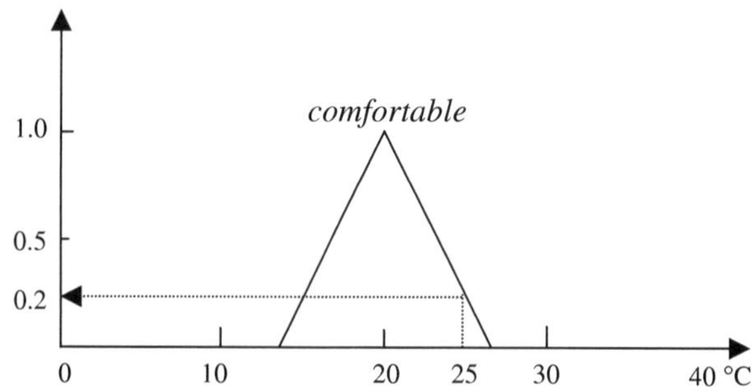

Figure 1.2: Membership function for a fuzzy set of *comfortable* temperature.

the primary and most intuitive interpretation of a fuzzy set, one that is particularly suitable for data analysis. An example is the case when we question on how to qualify an environment as *comfortable* when we know that current temperature is 25°C. Such quantification is a matter of degree. For instance, assuming a domain $X = [0, 40]$ and choosing 20°C as representative of *comfortable* temperature, we note, in Figure 1.2, that 25°C is comfortable to the degree of 0.2. In the example, we have adopted piecewise linearly decreasing functions of the distance between temperature values and the representative value 20° C to determine the corresponding membership degree.

Now, assume that the values of a variable x is such that $A(x) > 0$. Then given a value v of X, $A(v)$ expresses a possibility that $x = v$ given that x is in A is all that is known. In this situation, the membership degree of a given tentative value v to the class A reflects the degree of plausibility that this value is the same as x. This idea reflects a type of uncertainty because if the membership degree is high, our confidence about the value of x may still be low, but if the degree is low, then the tentative value may be rejected as an implausible candidate. The variable labeled by the class A is uncontrollable. This allows assignment of fuzzy sets to possibility distributions as suggested in possibility theory (Zadeh, 1978). For instance, suppose someone said he felt comfortable in an environment. In this situation the membership degree of a given tentative temperature value, say 25°C, reflects the degree of plausibility that this value of temperature is the same as the one under which the individual felt comfortable. Note that the actual value of the temperature value is unknown, but there is no question if that value of temperature did occur or not. Possibility concerns whether an event may occur and with what degree. On the contrary, probability concerns whether an event will occur.

Finally, assume that A reflects a preference on the values of a variable x in X. For instance, x can be a decision variable and fuzzy set A, a flexible constraint characterizing feasible values and decision-maker preferences. In this case $A(v)$

denotes the grade of preference in favor of v as the value of x. This interpretation prevails in fuzzy optimization and decision analysis. For instance, we may be interested in finding a comfortable value of temperature. The membership degree of a candidate temperature value v reflects our degree of satisfaction with the particular temperature value chosen. In this situation, the choice of the value is controllable in the sense that the value being adopted depends on our choice.

1.2.2. *Rationale for Membership Functions*

Generally speaking, any function $A : X \to [0, 1]$ is qualified to serve as a membership function describing the corresponding fuzzy set. In practice, the form of the membership functions should reflect the environment of the problem at hand for which we construct fuzzy sets. They should mirror our perception of the concept to be modeled and used in problem solving, the level of detail we intend to capture, and the context in which the fuzzy set are going to be used. It is essential to assess the type of fuzzy set from the standpoint of its suitability when handling the design and optimization issues. Given these reasons in mind, we review the most commonly used categories of membership functions. All of them are defined in the universe of real numbers, that is $\boldsymbol{X} = \boldsymbol{R}$.

1.2.2.1. *Triangular membership function*

It is described by piecewise linear segments of the form

$$A(x, a, m, b) = \begin{cases} 0 & \text{if } x \leq a \\ \dfrac{x-a}{m-a} & \text{if } x \in [a, m] \\ \dfrac{b-x}{b-m} & \text{if } x \in [m, b] \\ 0 & \text{if } x \geq b \end{cases}.$$

Using more concise notation, the above expression can be written down in the form $A(x, a, m, b) = \max\{\min[(x-a)/(m-a), (b-x)/(b-m)], 0\}$, as in Figure 1.3. The meaning of the parameters is straightforward: m is the modal (typical) value of the fuzzy set while a and b are the lower and upper bounds, respectively. They could be sought as those elements of the domain that delineate the elements belonging to A with non-zero membership degrees.

Triangular fuzzy sets (membership functions) are the simplest possible models of grades of membership as they are fully defined by only three parameters. The semantics of triangular fuzzy sets reflects the knowledge of the typical value of the concept and its spread. The linear change in the membership grades is the

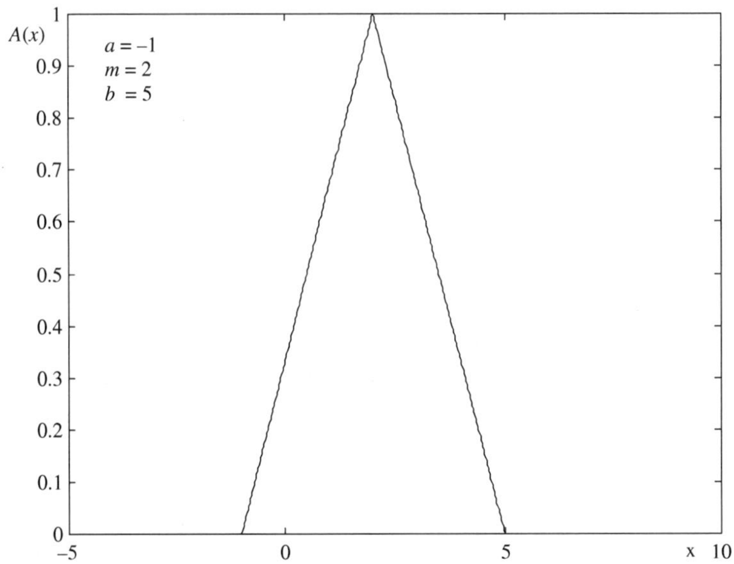

Figure 1.3: Triangular membership function.

simplest possible model of membership one could think of. If the derivative of the triangular membership function could be sought as a measure of sensitivity of A, then its sensitivity is constant for each of the linear segments of the fuzzy set.

1.2.2.2. *Trapezoidal membership function*

A piecewise linear function characterized by four parameters, a, m, n, and b each of which defines one of the four linear parts of the membership function, as in Figure 1.4. It has the following form

$$A(x) = \begin{cases} 0 & \text{if } x < a \\ \dfrac{x-a}{m-a} & \text{if } x \in [a, m] \\ 1 & \text{if } x \in [m, n] \\ \dfrac{b-x}{b-n} & \text{if } x \in [n, b] \\ 0 & \text{if } x > b \end{cases}.$$

We can rewrite A using an equivalent notation as follows

$$A(x, a, m, n, b) = \max\{\min[(x-a)/(m-a), 1, (b-x)/(b-n)], 0\}.$$

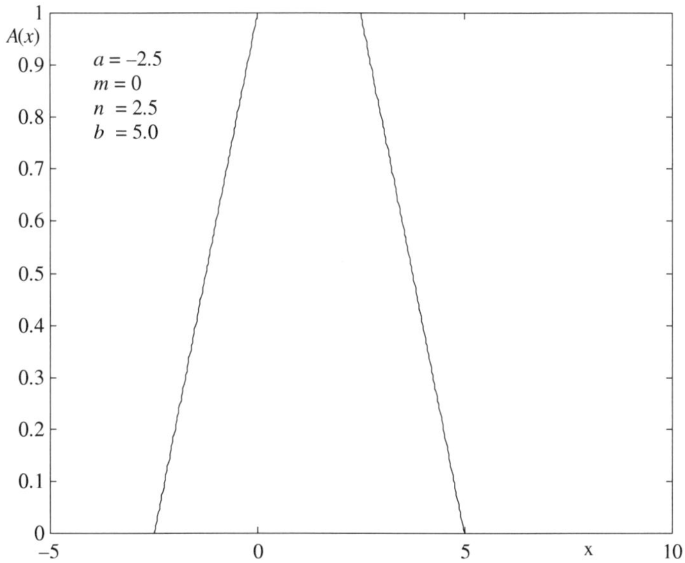

Figure 1.4: Trapezoidal membership function.

1.2.2.3. Γ*-membership function*

This function has the form

$$A(x) = \begin{cases} 0 & \text{if } x \le a \\ 1 - e^{-k(x-a)^2} & \text{if } x > a \end{cases} \quad \text{or} \quad A(x) = \begin{cases} 0 & \text{if } x \le a \\ \dfrac{k(x-a)^2}{1+k(x-a)^2} & \text{if } x > a \end{cases},$$

where $k > 0$, as in Figure 1.5.

1.2.2.4. *S-membership function*

The function is expressed by

$$A(x) = \begin{cases} 0 & \text{if } x \le a \\ 2\left(\dfrac{x-a}{b-a}\right)^2 & \text{if } x \in [a, m] \\ 1 - 2\left(\dfrac{x-b}{b-a}\right)^2 & \text{if } x \in [m, b] \\ 1 & \text{if } x > b \end{cases}.$$

The point $m = (a+b)/2$ is the crossover point of the S-function, as in Figure 1.6.

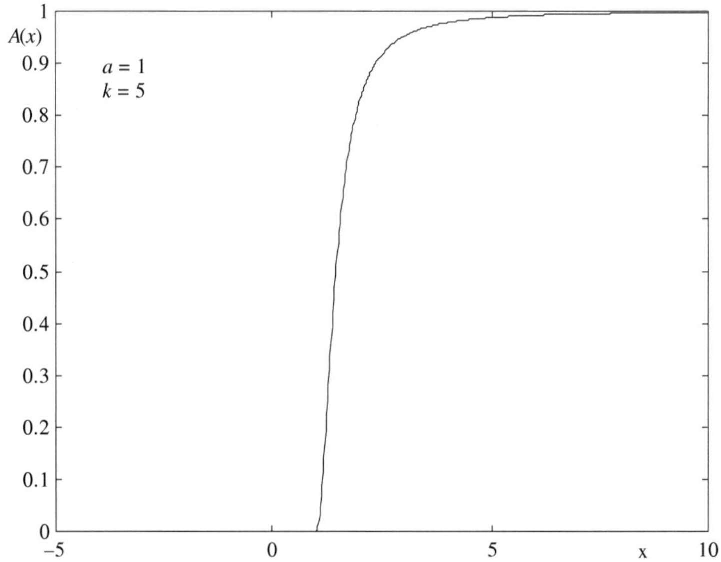

Figure 1.5: Γ-membership function.

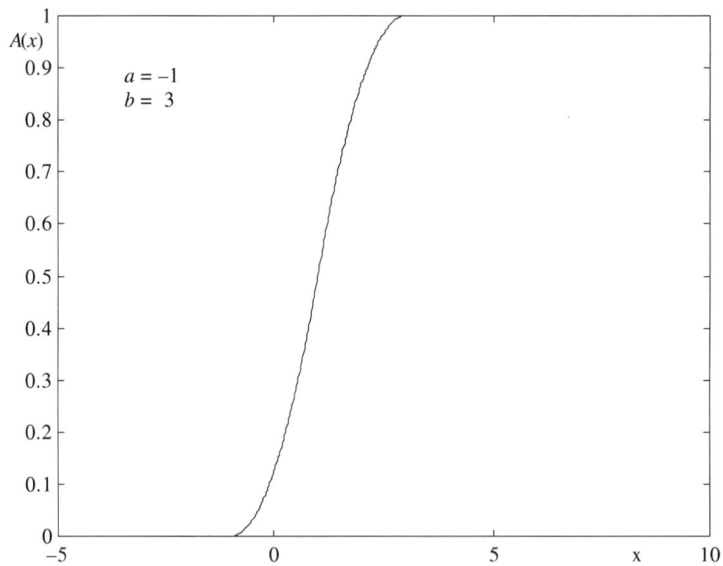

Figure 1.6: S-membership function.

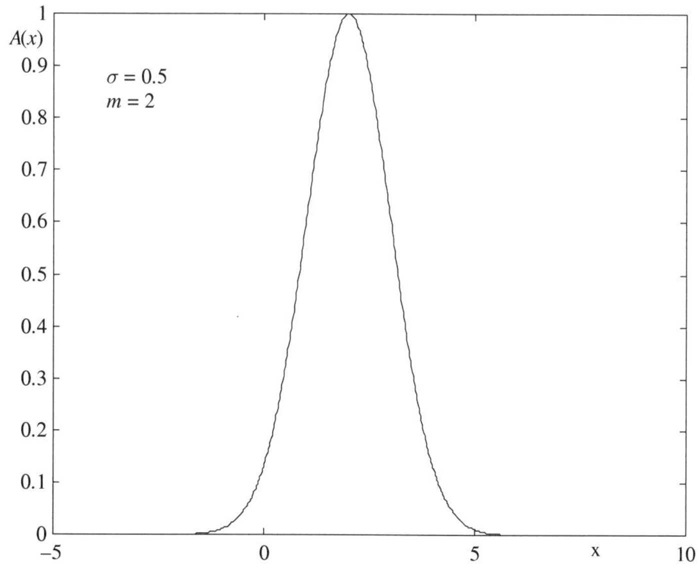

Figure 1.7: Gaussian membership function.

1.2.2.5. *Gaussian membership function*

This membership function is described by the following relationship

$$A(x, m, \sigma) = \exp\left(-\frac{(x-m)^2}{\sigma^2}\right).$$

An example of the membership function is shown in Figure 1.7. Gaussian membership functions have two important parameters. The modal value m represents the typical element of A while σ denotes a spread of A. Higher values of σ corresponds to larger spreads of the fuzzy sets.

1.2.2.6. *Exponential-like membership function*

It has the following form, as in Figure 1.8.

$$A(x) = \frac{1}{1+k(x-m)^2} \quad k > 0.$$

The spread of the exponential-like membership function increases as the value of k gets lower.

1.3. Characteristics of Fuzzy Sets

Given the diversity of potentially useful and semantically sound membership functions, there are certain common characteristics or descriptors that are conceptually

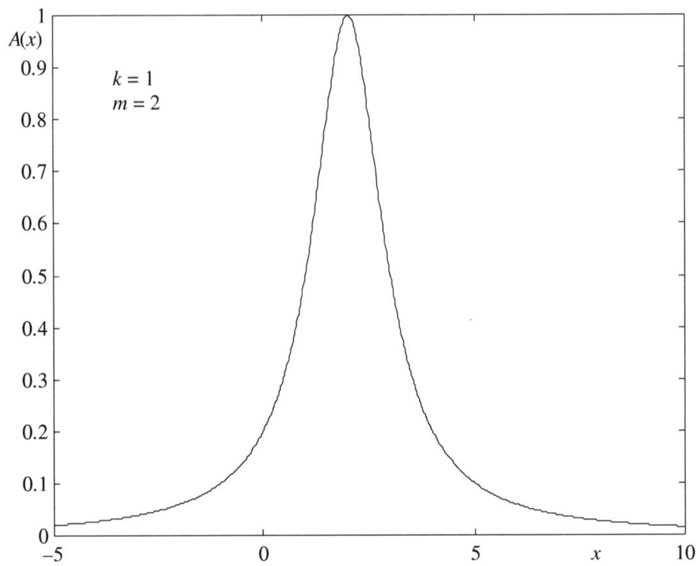

Figure 1.8: Example of the exponential-like membership function.

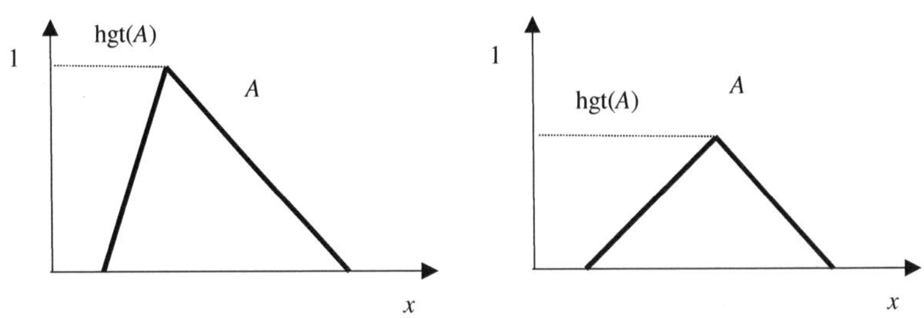

Figure 1.9: Examples of normal and subnormal fuzzy sets.

and operationally useful to capture the essence of fuzzy sets. We provide next a list of the descriptors commonly encountered in practice.

1.3.1. *Normality*

We say that the fuzzy set A is *normal* if its membership function attains 1, that is,

$$\sup_{x \in X} A(x) = 1. \tag{3}$$

If this property does not hold, we call the fuzzy set *subnormal*. An illustration of the corresponding fuzzy set is shown in Figure 1.9. The supremum (sup) in the above expression is also referred to as a height of the fuzzy set A. Thus, the fuzzy set is normal if $hgt(A) = 1$. The normality of A has a simple interpretation: by determining the height of the fuzzy set, we identify an element of the domain whose membership degree is the highest. The value of the height being equal to 1 states that there is at least one element in X fully typical with respect to A and which could be sought as entirely compatible with the semantic category presented by A. A subnormal fuzzy set has height lower than 1, viz. $hgt(A) < 1$, and the degree of typicality of elements in this fuzzy set is somewhat lower (weaker) and we cannot identify any element in X which is fully compatible with the underlying concept. In practice, while forming a fuzzy set we expect its normality.

1.3.2. *Normalization*

The normalization, denoted by $Norm(\cdot)$, is a mechanism to convert a subnormal non-empty fuzzy set A into its normal counterpart. This is done by dividing the original membership function by its height

$$Norm(A) = \frac{A(x)}{hgt(A)}. \tag{4}$$

While the height describes the global property of the membership grades, the following notions offer an interesting characterization of the elements of X regarding their membership degrees.

1.3.3. *Support*

Support of a fuzzy set A, $Supp(A)$, is a set of all elements of X with non-zero membership degrees in A

$$Supp(A) = \{x \in X \mid A(x) > 0\}. \tag{5}$$

In other words, support identifies all elements of X that exhibit some association with the fuzzy set under consideration (by being allocated to A with non-zero membership degrees).

1.3.4. *Core*

The core of a fuzzy set A, $Core(A)$, is a set of all elements of the universe that are typical to A: they come with unit membership grades.

$$Core(A) = \{x \in X \mid A(x) = 1\}. \tag{6}$$

The support and core are related in the sense that they identify and collect elements belonging to the fuzzy set, yet at two different levels of membership. Given the character of the core and support, we note that all elements of the core of A are

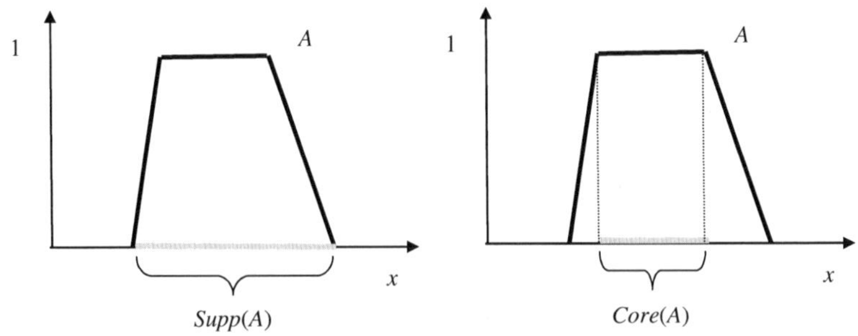

Figure 1.10: Support and core of A.

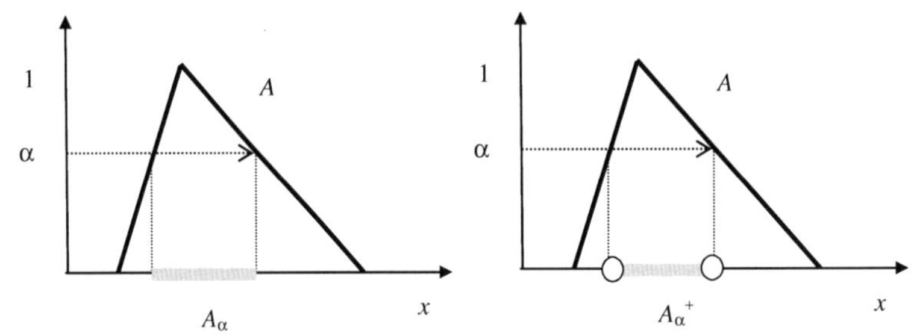

Figure 1.11: Example of α-cut and of strong α-cut.

subsumed by the elements of the support of this fuzzy set. Note that both support and core, are sets, not fuzzy sets. In Figure 1.10, they are intervals. We refer to them as the set-based characterizations of fuzzy sets.

While core and support are somewhat extreme, in the sense that they identify the elements of A that exhibit the strongest and the weakest links with A, we may be also interested in characterizing sets of elements that come with some intermediate membership degrees. The notion of **α-cut** offers here an interesting insight into the nature of fuzzy sets.

1.3.5. *α-Cut*

The **α-cut** of a fuzzy set A, denoted by A_α, is a set consisting of the elements of the domain whose membership values are equal to or exceed a certain threshold level $\boldsymbol{\alpha} \in [0, 1]$. Formally $A_\alpha = \{x \in \boldsymbol{X} \mid A(x) \geq \alpha\}$. A strong **$\alpha$-cut** identifies all elements in $\boldsymbol{X}$ for which $A_\alpha^+ = \{x \in \boldsymbol{X} \mid A(x) > \alpha\}$. Figure 1.11 illustrates the notion of **α-cut** and strong **α-cut**. Both support and core are limit cases of **α-cuts** and strong **α-cuts**. From $\boldsymbol{\alpha} = 0$ and the strong **α-cut**, we arrive at the concept of the support of A. The value $\boldsymbol{\alpha} = 1$ means that the corresponding **α-cut** is the core of A.

1.3.6. *Representation Theorem*

Any fuzzy set can be viewed as a family of fuzzy sets. This is the essence of a result known as the representation theorem. The representation theorem states that any fuzzy set A can be decomposed into a family of **α-cuts**,

$$A = \bigcup_{\alpha \in [0,1]} \alpha A_\alpha$$

or, equivalently in terms of membership functions,

$$A(x) = \sup_{\alpha \in [0,1]} \alpha A_\alpha(x).$$

1.3.7. *Convexity*

We say that a fuzzy set is convex if its membership function satisfies the following condition:

$$A[\lambda x_1 + (1-\lambda)x_2] \geq \min[A(x_1), A(x_2)], \quad \forall x_1, x_2 \in \boldsymbol{X}, \ \lambda \in [0, 1]. \quad (7)$$

Relationship (7) says that, whenever we choose a point x on a line segment between x_1 and x_2, the point (x, $A(x)$) is always located above or on the line passing through the two points (x_1, $A(x_1)$) and (x_2, $A(x_2)$), as in Figure 1.12. Note that the membership function is not a convex function in the conventional sense (Klir and Yuan, 1995).

The set S is convex if, for all $x_1, x_2 \in$ S, then $x = \lambda x_1 + (1-\lambda)x_2 \in S$ for all $\lambda \in [0, 1]$. Convexity means that any line segment identified by any two points in S is contained in S. For instance, intervals of real numbers are convex sets. Therefore, if a fuzzy set is convex, then all of its **α-cuts** are convex, and conversely, if a fuzzy set has all its **α-cuts** convex, then it is a convex fuzzy set, as in Figure 1.13. Thus we may say that a fuzzy set is convex if all its **α-cuts** are convex.

Fuzzy sets can be characterized by counting their elements and using a single numeric quantity as a descriptor of the count. While in case of sets this sounds clear,

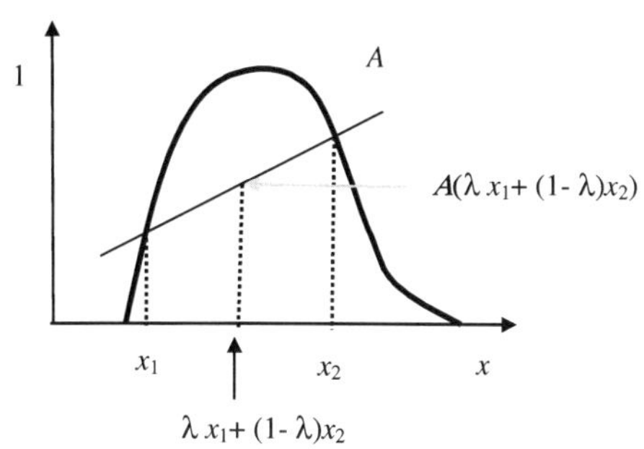

Figure 1.12: Convex fuzzy set A.

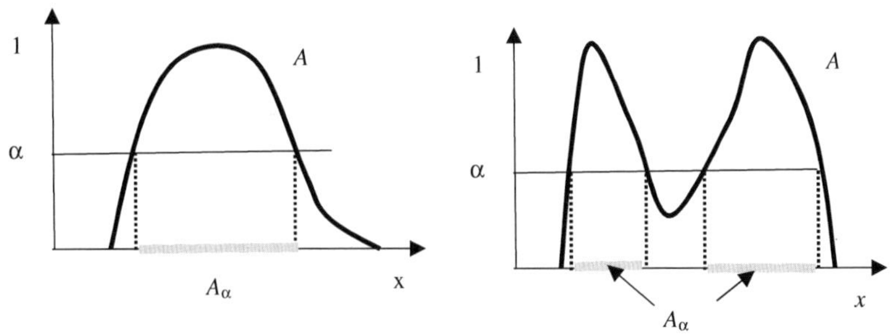

Figure 1.13: Convex and non-convex fuzzy sets.

with fuzzy sets we have to consider different membership grades. In the simplest form this counting comes under the name of cardinality.

1.3.8. *Cardinality*

Given a fuzzy set A defined in a finite or countable universe X, its cardinality, denoted by $Card(A)$ is expressed as the following sum

$$Card(A) = \sum_{x \in X} A(x) \tag{8}$$

or, alternatively, as the integral

$$Card(A) = \int_X A(x)\mathrm{d}x, \tag{9}$$

assuming that the integral is well-defined. We also use the alternative notation $Card(A) = |A|$ and refer to it as a sigma count (σ-count).

The cardinality of fuzzy sets is explicitly associated with the concept of granularity of information granules realized in this manner. More descriptively, the more the elements of A we encounter, the higher the level of abstraction supported by A and the lower the granularity of the construct. Higher values of cardinality come with the higher level of abstraction (generalization) and the lower values of granularity (specificity).

So far we discussed properties of a single fuzzy set. Next we look at the characterizations of relationships between two fuzzy sets.

1.3.9. *Equality*

We say that two fuzzy sets A and B defined in X are equal if and only if their membership functions are identical, that is

$$A(x) = B(x) \quad \forall x \in X. \tag{10}$$

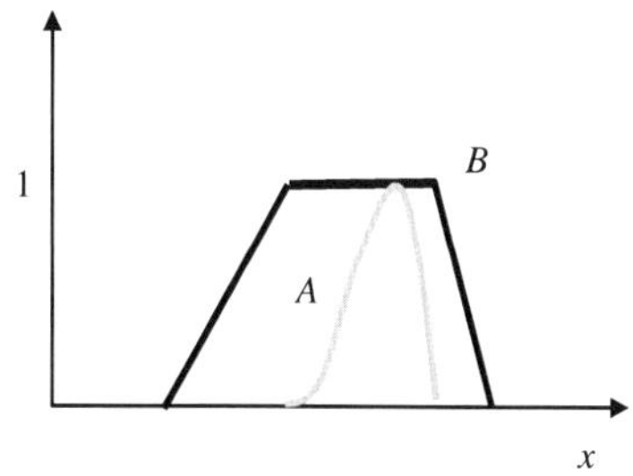

Figure 1.14: Inclusion $A \subseteq B$.

1.3.10. *Inclusion*

Fuzzy set A is a subset of B (A is included in B), $A \subseteq B$, if and only if every element of A also is an element of B. This property expressed in terms of membership degrees means that the following inequality is satisfied

$$A(x) \leq B(x) \quad \forall x \in X. \tag{11}$$

An illustration of these two relationships in the case of sets is shown in Figure 1.14. To satisfy the relationship of inclusion, we require that the characteristic functions adhere to Equation (11) for all elements of X. If the inclusion is not satisfied even for a single point of X, the inclusion property does not hold. See (Pedrycz and Gomide, 2007) for alternative notion of inclusion that captures the idea of degree of inclusion.

1.3.11. *Specificity*

Often, we face the issue to quantify how much a single element of a domain could be viewed as a representative of a fuzzy set. If this fuzzy set is a singleton, then

$$A(x) = \begin{cases} 1 & \text{if } x = x_0 \\ 0 & \text{if } x \neq x_0 \end{cases}, \tag{12}$$

and there is no hesitation in selecting x_o as the sole representative of A. We say that A is very *specific* and its choice comes with no hesitation. On the other extreme, if A covers the entire domain X and has all elements with the membership grade equal to 1, the choice of the only one representative of A becomes more problematic once it is not clear which element to choose. These two extreme situations are shown in Figure 1.15. Intuitively, we see that the specificity is a concept that relates with the cardinality of a set. The higher the cardinality of the set (the more evident its abstraction) is, the lower its specificity.

One approach to quantify the notion of specificity of a fuzzy set is as follows (Yager, 1983). The specificity of a fuzzy set A defined in X, denoted by $Spec(A)$, is

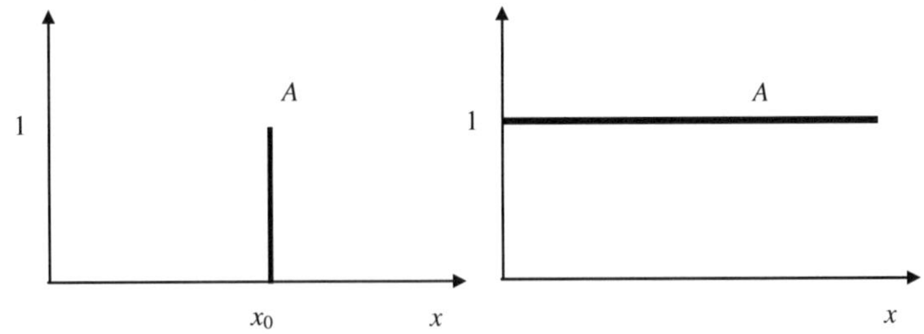

Figure 1.15: Two extreme cases of sets with distinct levels of specificity.

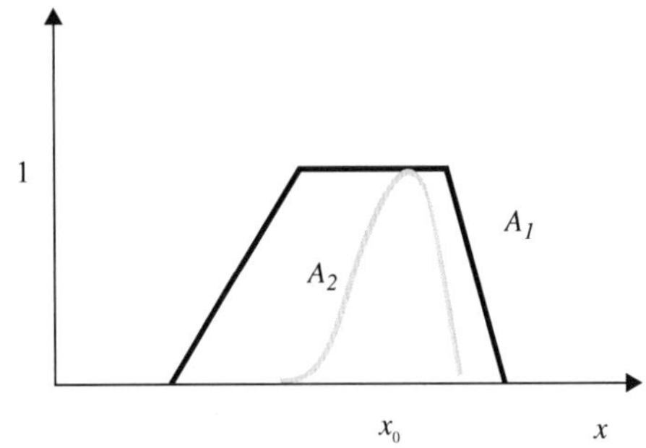

Figure 1.16: Specificity of fuzzy sets: Fuzzy set A_1 is less specific than A_2.

a mapping from a family of normal fuzzy sets in X into nonnegative numbers such that the following conditions are satisfied, as in Figure 1.16.

1. $Spec(A) = 1$ if and only if there exists only one element x_o of X for which $A(x_o) = 1$ and $A(x) = 0 \; \forall x \neq x_o$;
2. $Spec(A) = 0$ if and only if $A(x) = 0 \; \forall x \in X$;
3. $Spec(A_1) \leq Spec(A_2)$ if $A_1 \supset A_2$.

A particular instance of specificity measure is (Yager, 1983)

$$Spec(A) = \int_0^{\alpha_{\max}} \frac{1}{Card(A_\alpha)} d\alpha,$$

where $\alpha_{max} = hgt(A)$. For finite domains, the integration is replaced by the sum

$$Spec(A) = \sum_{i=1}^{m} \frac{1}{Card(A_{\alpha i})} \Delta\alpha_i,$$

where $\Delta\alpha_i = \alpha_i - \alpha_{i-1}$ with $\alpha_o = 0$; m stands for the number of the membership grades of A.

1.4. Operations with Fuzzy Sets

As in set theory, we may combine fuzzy sets to produce new fuzzy sets. Generally, combination must possess properties to match intuition, to comply with the semantics of the intended operation, and to be flexible to fit application requirements. Next we provide an overview of the main operations and their generalizations, interpretations, and examples of realizations.

1.4.1. *Standard Operations on Sets and Fuzzy Sets*

To start, we review the familiar operations of intersection, union and complement of set theory. Consider two sets $A = \{x \in \boldsymbol{R} | 1 \leq x \leq 3\}$ and $B = \{x \in \boldsymbol{R} | 2 \leq x \leq 4\}$, closed intervals of the real line. Their intersection is the set $A \cap B = \{x \in \boldsymbol{R} | 2 \leq x \leq 3\}$. Figure 1.17 shows the intersection operation in terms of the characteristic functions of A and B. Looking at the values of the characteristic function of $A \cap B$ that results when comparing the individual values of $A(x)$ and $B(x)$ for each $x \in \boldsymbol{R}$, we note that they correspond to the minimum between the values of $A(x)$ and $B(x)$.

In general, given the characteristic functions of A and B, the characteristic function of their intersection $A \cap B$ is computed using

$$(A \cap B)(x) = \min[A(x), B(x)] \quad \forall x \in \boldsymbol{X}, \tag{13}$$

where $(A \cap B)(x)$ denotes the characteristic function of the set $A \cap B$.

The union of sets A and B in terms of the characteristic functions proceeds similarly. If A and B are the same intervals as above, then $A \cup B = \{x \in \boldsymbol{R} | 1 \leq x \leq 4\}$. In this case the value of the characteristic function of the union is the maximum of corresponding values of the characteristic functions $A(x)$ and $B(x)$ taken point wise, as in Figure 1.18.

Therefore, given the characteristic functions of A and B, we determine the characteristic function of the union as

$$(A \cup B)(x) = \max[A(x), B(x)] \quad \forall x \in \boldsymbol{X}, \tag{14}$$

where $(A \cup B)(x)$ denotes the characteristic function of the set $A \cup B$.

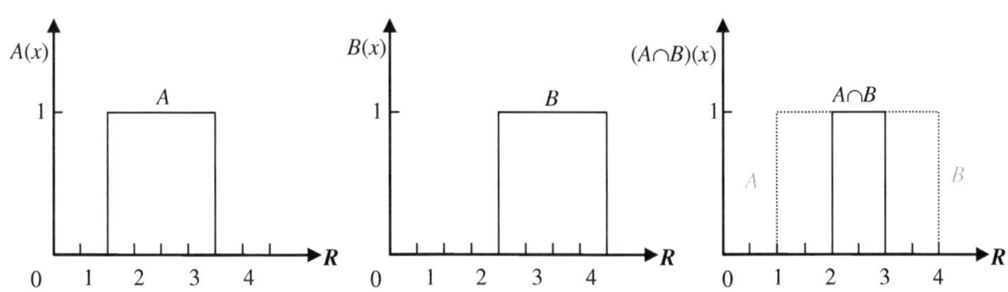

Figure 1.17: Intersection of sets in terms of their characteristic functions.

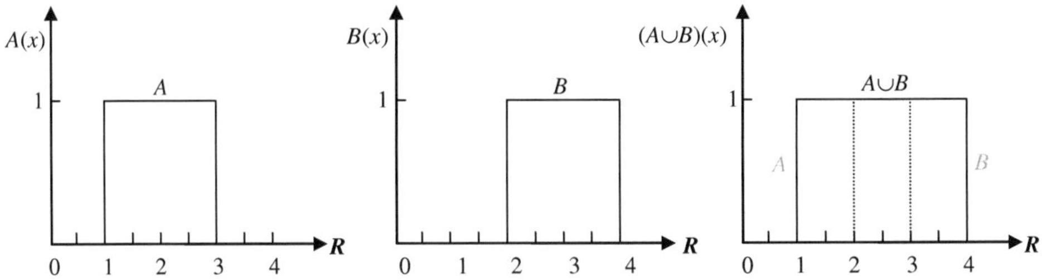

Figure 1.18: Union of two sets in terms of their characteristic functions.

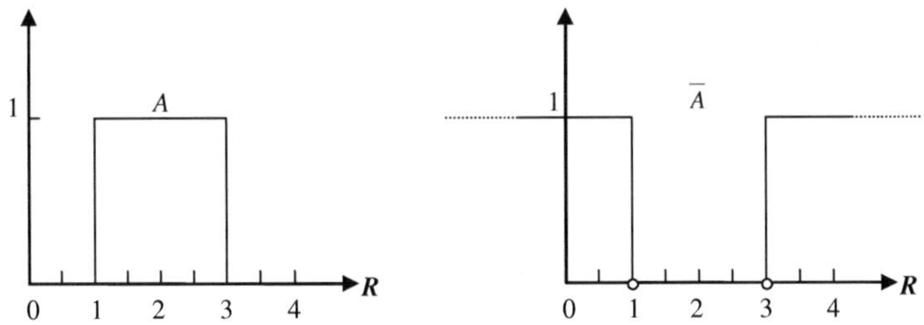

Figure 1.19: Complement of a set in terms of its characteristic function.

Likewise, as Figure 1.19 suggests, the complement $\bar{A}$ of A, expressed in terms of its characteristic function, is the one-complement of the characteristic function of A. For instance, if $A = \{x \in \boldsymbol{R} | 1 \leq x \leq 3\}$, then $\bar{A} = \{x \in \boldsymbol{R} | 4 < x < 1\}$.

Thus, the characteristic function of the complement of a set A is

$$\bar{A}(x) = 1 - A(x), \quad \forall x \in \boldsymbol{X}. \tag{15}$$

Because sets are particular instances of fuzzy sets, the operations of intersection, union and complement should equally well apply to fuzzy sets. Indeed, when we use membership functions in expressions (13)–(15), these formulae serve as standard definitions of intersection, union, and complement of fuzzy sets. Examples are shown in Figure 1.20. Standard set and fuzzy set operations fulfill the properties of Table 1.1.

Figures 1.19 and 1.20 show that the laws of non-contradiction and excluded middle hold for sets, but not for fuzzy sets under the standard operations. See also Table 1.2. Particularly worth noting is a violation of the non-contradiction law once it shows the issue of fuzziness from the point of view of the coexistence of a class and its complement, one of the main source of fuzziness. This coexistence is impossible in set theory and means a contradiction in conventional logic. Interestingly, if we consider a particular subnormal fuzzy set A whose membership function is constant and equal to 0.5 for all elements of the universe, then from Equations (13)–(15) we see that $A = A \cup \bar{A} = A \cap \bar{A} = \bar{A}$, a situation in which there is no way to

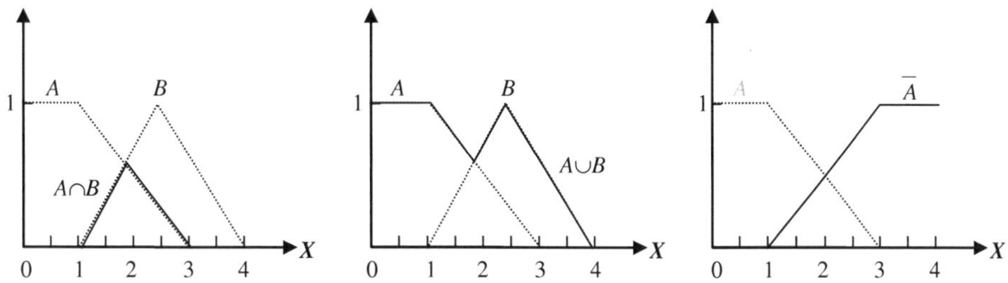

Figure 1.20: Standard operations on fuzzy sets.

Table 1.1: Properties of operations with sets and fuzzy sets.

(1) Commutativity	$A \cup B = B \cup A$
	$A \cap B = B \cap A$
(2) Associativity	$A \cup (B \cup C) = (A \cup B) \cup C$
	$A \cap (B \cap C) = (A \cap B) \cap C$
(3) Distributivity	$A \cup (B \cap C) = (A \cup B) \cap (A \cup C)$
	$A \cap (B \cup C) = (A \cap B) \cup (A \cap C)$
(4) Idempotency	$A \cup A = A$
	$A \cap A = A$
(5) Boundary conditions	$A \cup \phi = A$ and $A \cup \mathbf{X} = \mathbf{X}$
	$A \cap \phi = \phi$ and $A \cap \mathbf{X} = A$
(6) Involution	$\bar{\bar{A}} = A$
(7) Transitivity	if $A \subset B$ and $B \subset C$, then $A \subset C$

Table 1.2: Non-contradiction and excluded middle for standard operations.

	Sets	Fuzzy sets
8-Non-contradiction	$A \cap \bar{A} = \phi$	$A \cap \bar{A} \neq \phi$
9-Excluded middle	$A \cup \bar{A} = \mathbf{X}$	$A \cup \bar{A} \neq \mathbf{X}$

distinguish the fuzzy set from its complement and any fuzzy set that results from standard operations with them. The value 0.5 is a crossover point representing a balance between membership and non-membership at which we attain the highest level of fuzziness. The fuzzy set and its complement are indiscernible.

As we will see next, there are types of operations for which non-contradiction and excluded middle are recovered. While for sets these types produce the same result as the standard operators, this is not the case with fuzzy sets. Also, $A = A \cup \bar{A} = A \cap \bar{A} = \bar{A}$ does not hold for any choice of intersection, union and complement operators.

Operations on fuzzy sets concern manipulation of their membership functions. Therefore, they are domain dependent and different contexts may require their different realizations. For instance, since operations provide ways to combine information, they can be performed differently in image processing, control, and diagnostic systems applications for example. When developing realizations of intersection and union of fuzzy sets it is useful to require commutativity, associativity, monotonicity, and identity. The last requirement (identity) has different forms depending on the operation. For instance, the intersection of any fuzzy set with domain *X* should return the fuzzy set itself. For the union, identity implies that the union of any fuzzy set and an empty fuzzy set returns the fuzzy set itself. Thus, in principle, any two place operator $[0, 1] \times [0, 1] \rightarrow [0, 1]$ which satisfies the collection of the requirements can be regarded as a potential candidate to realize the intersection or union of fuzzy sets, identity acting as boundary conditions meaning. In general, idempotency is not strictly required, however the realizations of union and intersection could be idempotent as this happens with the minimum and maximum operators ($\min [a, a] = a$ and $\max [a, a] = a$).

1.4.2. *Triangular Norms and Conorms*

Triangular norms and conorms constitute general forms of operations for intersection and union. While t-norms generalize intersection of fuzzy sets, t-conorms (or s-norms) generalize the union of fuzzy sets (Klement *et al.*, 2000).

A triangular norm is a two place operation t: $[0, 1] \times [0, 1] \rightarrow [0, 1]$ that satisfies the following properties

1. Commutativity: $a \text{ t } b = b \text{ t } a$,
2. Associativity: $a \text{ t } (b \text{ t } c) = (a \text{ t } b) \text{ t } c$,
3. Monotonicity: if $b \leq c$ then $a \text{ t } b \leq a \text{ t } c$,
4. Boundary conditions: $a \text{ t } 1 = a$ $a \text{ t } 0 = 0$,

where $a, b, c \in [0, 1]$.

There is a one-to-one correspondence between the general requirements outlined above and the properties of t-norms. The first three reflect the general character of set operations. Boundary conditions stress the fact that all t-norms attain the same values at boundaries of the unit square $[0, 1] \times [0, 1]$. Thus, for sets, any t-norm produces the same result.

Examples of t-norms are

Minimum: $a \text{ t}_m b = \min(a, b) = a \wedge b$,

Product: $a \text{ t}_p b = a\ b$,

Lukasiewicz: $a \text{ t}_l b = \max(a + b - 1, 0)$,

Drastic product: $a \text{ t}_d b = \begin{cases} a & \text{if } b = 1 \\ b & \text{if } a = 1 \\ 0 & \text{otherwise} \end{cases}$.

The minimum(t_m), product(t_p), Lukasiewicz(t_l), and drastic product(t_d) operators are shown in Figure 1.21, with examples of the union of the triangular fuzzy sets on $X = [0, 8]$, $A = (x, 1, 3, 6)$ and $B = (x, 2.5, 5, 7)$.

Triangular conorms are functions s: $[0, 1] \times [0, 1] \to [0, 1]$ that serve as generic realizations of the union operator on fuzzy sets.

One can show that s: $[0, 1] \times [0, 1] \to [0, 1]$ is a t-conorm if and only if there exists a t-norm, called dual t-norm, such that for $\forall\, a, b \in [0, 1]$ we have

$$a \,\mathrm{s}\, b = 1 - (1 - a)\mathrm{t}(1 - b). \tag{16}$$

For the corresponding dual t-norm, we have

$$a \,\mathrm{t}\, b = 1 - (1 - a)\mathrm{s}(1 - b). \tag{17}$$

The duality expressed by Equations (16) and (17) can be viewed as alternative definition of t-conorms. Duality allows us to deduce the properties of t-conorms on the basis of the analogous properties of t-norms. From Equations (16) and (17), we get

$$(1 - a)\mathrm{t}(1 - b) = 1 - a \,\mathrm{s}\, b$$

and

$$(1 - a)\mathrm{s}(1 - b) = 1 - a \,\mathrm{t}\, b.$$

These two relationships can be expressed symbolically as

$$\bar{A} \cap \bar{B} = \overline{A \cup B},$$
$$\bar{A} \cup \bar{B} = \overline{A \cap B},$$

which are the De Morgan laws. Commonly used t-conorms include

Maximum: $a \mathrm{s}_m b = \max(a, b) = a \vee b$,

Algebraic sum: $a \mathrm{s}_p b = a + b - a\, b$,

Lukasiewicz: $a \mathrm{s}_l b = \min(a + b, 1)$,

Drastic sum: $$a \mathrm{s}_d b = \begin{cases} a & \text{if } b = 0 \\ b & \text{if } a = 0 \\ 1 & \text{otherwise} \end{cases}.$$

The maximum(s_m), algebraic sum(s_p), Lukasiewicz(s_l), and drastic sum(s_d) operators are shown in Figure 1.22, which also include the union of the triangular fuzzy sets on $[0, 8]$, $A = (x, 1, 3, 6)$ and $B = (x, 2.5, 5, 7)$.

The properties $A \cup \bar{A} = X$ and the excluded middle hold for the drastic sum.

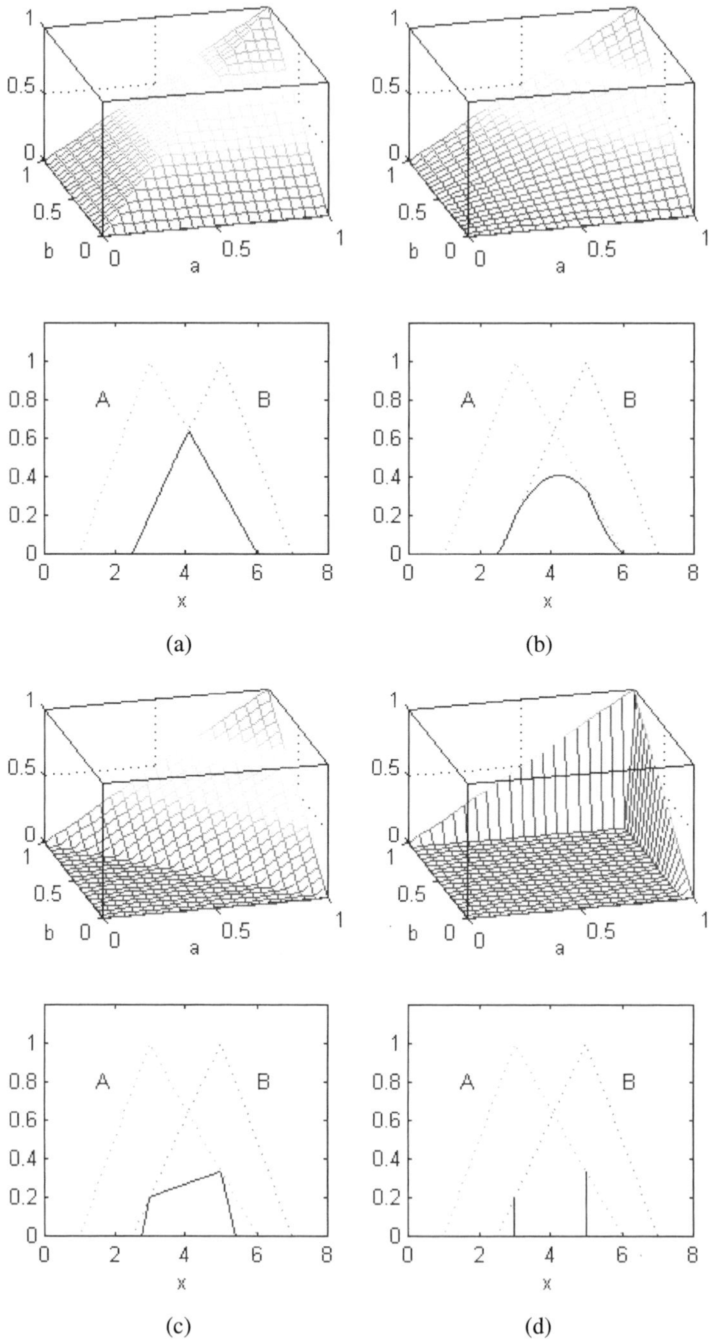

Figure 1.21: The (a) minimum, (b) product, (c) Lukasiewicz, (d) drastic product t-norms and the intersection of fuzzy sets A and B.

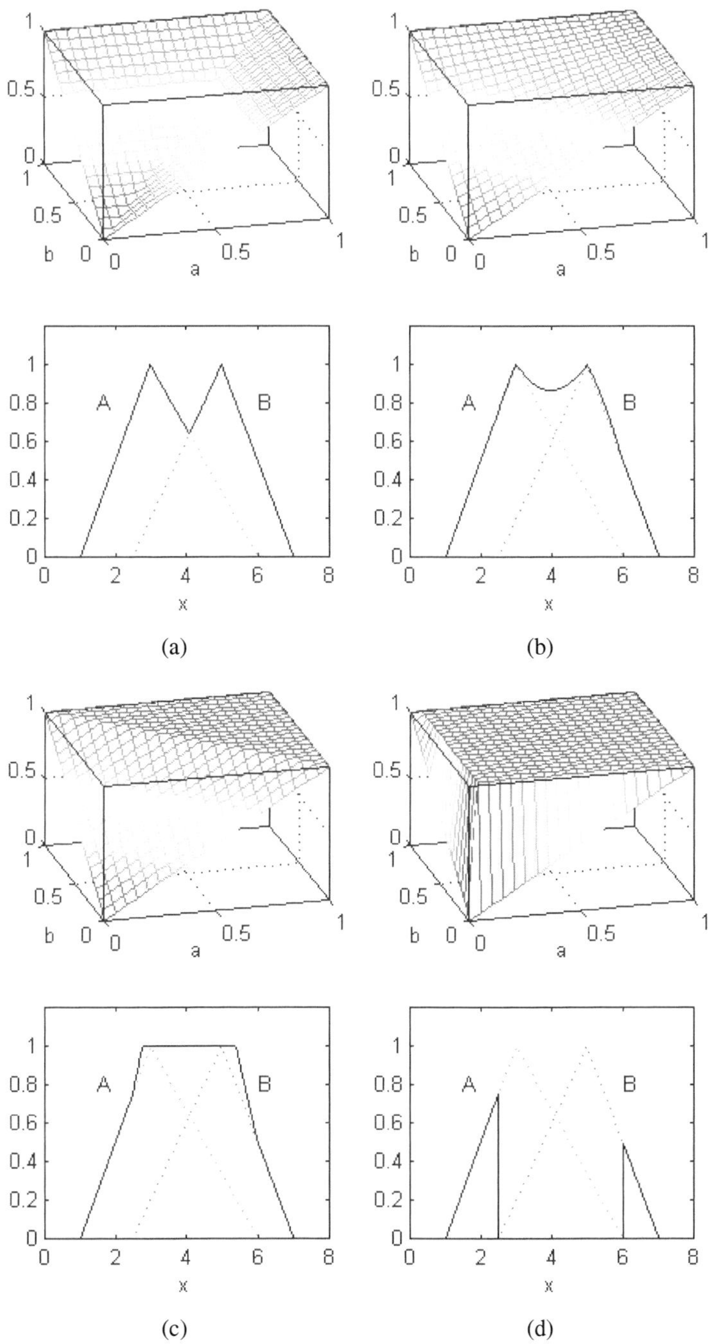

Figure 1.22: The (a) maximum, (b) algebraic sum, (c) Lukasiewicz, (d) drastic sum s-norms and the union of fuzzy sets A and B.

1.4.3. *Triangular Norms as Categories of Logical Operators*

Fuzzy propositions involve combination of linguistic statements (or their symbolic representations) such as in

(1) temperature is *high* and humidity is *low*,
(2) velocity is *low* or noise level is *high*.

These sentences use logical operations $\wedge$ (*and*), $\vee$ (*or*) to combine linguistic statements into propositions. For instance, in the first example we have a conjunction (*and*, $\wedge$) of linguistic statements while in the second there is a disjunction (*or*, $\vee$) of the statements. Given the truth values of each statement, the question is how to determine the truth value of the composite statement or, equivalently, the truth value of the proposition.

Let truth $(P) = p \in [0, 1]$, the truth value of proposition P. Thus, $p = 0$ means that the proposition is false, while $p = 1$ means that P is true. Intermediate values $p \in (0, 1)$ indicate partial truth of the proposition. To compute the truth value of composite propositions coming in the form of $P \wedge Q$, $P \vee Q$ given the truth values p and q of its components, we have to come up with operations that transforms truth values p and q into the corresponding truth values $p \wedge q$ and $p \vee q$. To make these operations meaningful, we require that they satisfy some basic requirements. For instance, it is desirable that $p \wedge q$ and $q \wedge p$ (similarly, $p \vee q$ and $q \vee p$) produce the same truth values. Likewise, we require that the truth value of $(p \wedge q) \wedge r$ is the same as the following combination $p \wedge (q \wedge r)$. In other words, the conjunction and disjunction operations are commutative and associative. Also, when the truth value of an individual statement increases, the truth values of their combinations also increase. Moreover, if P is absolutely false, $p = 0$, then $P \wedge Q$ should also be false no matter what the truth value of Q is. Furthermore, the truth value of $P \vee Q$ should coincide with the truth value of Q. On the other hand, if P is absolutely true, $p = 1$, then the truth value of $P \wedge Q$ should coincide with the truth value of Q, while $P \vee Q$ should also be true. Triangular norms and conorms are the general families of logic connectives that comply with these requirements. Triangular norms provide a general category of logical connectives in the sense that t-norms are used to model conjunction operators while t-conorms serve as models of disjunctions.

Let $L = \{P, Q, \ldots, \}$ be a set of single (atomic) statements $P, Q, \ldots,$ and truth: $L \rightarrow [0, 1]$ a function which assigns truth values $p, q, \ldots, \in [0, 1]$ to each element of L. Thus, we have:

$$\textit{truth}(P \text{ and } Q) \equiv \textit{truth}(P \wedge Q) \rightarrow p \wedge q = p \,\mathrm{t}\, q,$$
$$\textit{truth}(P \textit{ or } Q) \equiv \textit{truth}(P \vee Q) \rightarrow p \vee q = p \,\mathrm{s}\, q.$$

Table 1.3 shows examples of truth values for $P, Q, P \wedge Q$ and $P \vee Q$, when we selected the minimum and product t-norms, and the maximum and albegraic

Table 1.3: Triangular norms as generalized logical connectives.

p	q	$\text{Min}(p, q)$	$\text{Max}(p, q)$	$p\,q$	$p+q-p\,q$
1	1	1	1	1	1
1	0	0	1	0	1
0	1	0	1	0	1
0	0	0	0	0	0
0.2	0.5	0.2	0.5	0.1	0.6
0.5	0.8	0.5	0.8	0.4	0.9
0.8	0.7	0.7	0.8	0.56	0.94

Table 1.4: φ operator for binary values of its arguments.

a	b	$a \Rightarrow b$	$a \varphi b$
0	0	1	1
0	1	1	1
1	0	0	0
1	1	1	1

sum t-conorms, respectively. For $p, q \in \{0, 1\}$, the results coincide with the classic interpretation of conjunction and disjunction for any choice of the triangular norm and conorm. The differences are present when $p, q \in (0, 1)$.

A point worth noting here concerns the interpretation of set operations in terms of logical connectives. By being supported by the isomorphism between set theory and propositional two-valued logic, the intersection and union can be identified with conjunction and disjunction, respectively. This can also be realized with triangular norms viewed as general conjunctive and disjunctive connectives within the framework of multivalued logic (Klir and Yuan, 1995). Triangular norms also play a key role in different types of fuzzy logic (Klement and Navarra, 1999).

Given a continuous t-norm t, let us define the following φ operator

$$a \,\varphi\, b = sup\{c \in [0, 1] | a \text{ t } c \leq b\} \quad \text{for all } a, b \in [0, 1].$$

This operation can be interpreted as an implication induced by some t-norm,

$$a \,\varphi\, b = a \Rightarrow b,$$

and therefore it is, like implication, an inclusion. The operator φ generalizes the classic implication. As Table 1.4 suggests, the two-valued implication arises as a special case of the φ operator in case when $a, b \in \{0, 1\}$.

Note that $a \varphi b(a \Rightarrow b)$, returns 1, whenever $a \leq b$. If we interpret these two truth values as membership degrees, we conclude that $a \varphi b$ models a multivalued inclusion relationship.

1.4.4. *Aggregation of Fuzzy Sets*

Several fuzzy sets can be combined (aggregated) to provide a single fuzzy set forming the result of such an aggregation operation. For instance, when we compute intersection and union of fuzzy sets, the result is a fuzzy set whose membership function captures the information carried by the original fuzzy sets. This fact suggests a general view of aggregation of fuzzy sets as a certain transformations performed on their membership functions. In general, we encounter a wealth of aggregation operations (Dubois and Prade, 1985; Bouchon-Meunier, 1998; Calvo *et al.*, 2002; Dubois and Prade, 2004; Beliakov *et al.*, 2007).

Aggregation operations are n-ary functions $g\colon [0, 1]^n \rightarrow [0, 1]$ with the following properties:

1. Monotonicity $\quad g(x_1, x_2, \ldots, x_n) \geq g(y_1, y_2, \ldots, y_n) \quad \text{if } x_i > y_i$
2. Boundary conditions $\quad g(0, 0, \ldots, 0) = 0$

$$g(1, 1, \ldots, 1) = 1.$$

Since triangular norms and conorms are monotonic, associative, satisfy the boundary conditions, and then they provide a class of associative aggregation operations whose neutral elements are equal to 1 and 0, respectively. We are, however, not restricted to those as the only available alternatives. The following operators constitute important examples.

1.4.4.1. *Averaging operations*

In addition to monotonicity and the satisfaction of the boundary conditions, averaging operations are idempotent and commutative. They can be described in terms of the generalized mean (Dyckhoff and Pedrycz, 1984)

$$g(x_1, x_2, \ldots, x_n) = \sqrt[p]{\frac{1}{n}\sum_{i=1}^{n}(x_i)^p} \quad p \in \boldsymbol{R}, \ p \neq 0.$$

Generalized mean subsumes well-known averages and operators such as

$$p = 1 \quad g(x_1, x_2, \ldots, x_n) = \frac{1}{n}\sum_{i=1}^{n} x_i \quad \text{arithmetic mean,}$$

$$p \rightarrow 0 \quad g(x_1, x_2, \ldots, x_n) = \sqrt[n]{\prod_{i=1}^{n} x_i} \quad \text{geometric mean,}$$

$$p = -1 \qquad g(x_1, x_2, \ldots, x_n) = \frac{n}{\sum_{i=1}^{n} 1/x_i} \qquad \text{harmonic mean,}$$

$$p \to -\propto \qquad g(x_1, x_2, \ldots, x_n) = \min(x_1, x_2, \ldots, x_n) \qquad \text{minimum,}$$

$$p \to \propto \qquad g(x_1, x_2, \ldots, x_n) = \max(x_1, x_2, \ldots, x_n) \qquad \text{maximum.}$$

The following relationship holds

$$\min(x_1, x_2, \ldots, x_n) \leq g(x_1, x_2, \ldots, x_n) \leq \max(x_1, x_2, \ldots, x_n).$$

Therefore, generalized means range over the values not being covered by triangular norms and conorms.

1.4.4.2. *Ordered weighted averaging (OWA) operations*

OWA is a weighted sum whose arguments are ordered (Yager, 1988). Let $\boldsymbol{w} = [w_1, w_2, \ldots, w_n]^T$, $w_i \in [0, 1]$, be weights such that

$$\sum_{i=1}^{n} w_i = 1.$$

Let a sequence of membership values $\{A(x_i)\}$ be ordered as follows $A(x_1) \leq A(x_2) \leq \cdots \leq A(x_n)$. The family of OWA$(A, \boldsymbol{w})$ is defined as the

$$\text{OWA}(\text{A}, \boldsymbol{w}) = \sum_{i=1}^{n} w_i A(x_i).$$

By choosing certain forms of $\boldsymbol{w}$, we can show that OWA includes several special cases of aggregation operators mentioned before. For instance

1. If $\boldsymbol{w} = [1, 0, \ldots, 0]^T$ then OWA$(A, \boldsymbol{w}) = \min(A(x_1), A(x_2), \ldots, A(x_n))$,
2. If $\boldsymbol{w} = [0, 0, \ldots, 1]^T$ then OWA$(A, \boldsymbol{w}) = \max(A(x_1), A(x_2), \ldots, A(x_n))$,
3. If $\boldsymbol{w} = [1/n, \ldots, 1/n]^T$ then OWA$(A, \boldsymbol{w}) = \frac{1}{n}\sum_{i=1}^{n} A(x_i) =$ arithmetic mean.

Varying the values of the weights w_i results in aggregation values located in between minimum and maximum,

$$\min(A(x_1), A(x_2), \ldots, A(x_n)) \leq \text{OWA}(A, \boldsymbol{w}) \leq \max(A(x_1), A(x_2), \ldots, A(x_n)),$$

and OWA behaves as a compensatory operator, similar to the generalized mean.

1.4.4.3. *Uninorms and nullnorms*

Triangular norms provide one of possible ways to aggregate membership grades. By definition, the identity elements are 1 (t-norms) and 0 (t-conorms). When used in the aggregation operations, these elements do not affect the result of aggregation (that is, $a \text{ t } 1 = a$ and $a \text{ t } 0 = a$).

Uninorms generalize and unify triangular norms by allowing the identity element to be any value in the unit interval that is $e \in (0, 1)$. Uninorms become t-norms when $e = 1$ and t-conorms when $e = 0$. They exhibit some intermediate characteristics for all remaining values of e. Therefore, uninorms share the same properties as triangular norms with the exception of the identity (Yager and Rybalov, 1996).

A uninorm is a two place operation u: $[0, 1] \times [0, 1] \rightarrow [0, 1]$ that satisfies the following

1. Commutativity: $a \text{ u } b = b \text{ u } a$,
2. Associativity: $a \text{ u } (b \text{ u } c) = (a \text{ u } b) \text{ u } c$,
3. Monotonicity: if $b \leq c$ then $a \text{ u } b \leq a \text{ u } c$,
4. Identity: $a \text{ u } e = a, \forall a \in [0, 1]$,

where $a, b, c \in [0, 1]$.

Examples of uninorm include conjunctive u_c and disjuntive u_d forms of uninorms. They can be obtained in terms of a t-norm t and a conorm s as follows:

(a) If $(0 \text{ u } 1) = 0$, then

$$a \text{ u}_c\, b = \begin{cases} e\left(\dfrac{a}{e}\right) \text{t} \left(\dfrac{b}{e}\right) & \text{if } 0 \leq a,\ b \leq e \\ e + (1-e)\left(\dfrac{a-e}{1-e}\right) \text{s} \left(\dfrac{b-e}{1-e}\right) & \text{if } e \leq a,\ b \leq 1 \\ \min(a, b) & \text{otherwise} \end{cases},$$

(b) If $(0 \text{ u } 1) = 1$, then

$$a \text{ u}_d\, b = \begin{cases} e\left(\dfrac{a}{e}\right) \text{t} \left(\dfrac{b}{e}\right) & \text{if } 0 \leq a,\ b \leq e \\ e + (1-e)\left(\dfrac{a-e}{1-e}\right) \text{s} \left(\dfrac{b-e}{1-e}\right) & \text{if } e \leq a,\ b \leq 1 \\ \max(a, b) & \text{otherwise} \end{cases}.$$

1.5. Fuzzy Relations

Relations represent and quantify associations between objects. They provide a mechanism to model interactions and dependencies between variables, components, modules, etc. Fuzzy relations generalize the concept of relation in the same manner as fuzzy set generalizes the fundamental idea of set. Fuzzy relations have applications especially in information retrieval, pattern classification, modeling and control, diagnostics, and decision-making.

1.5.1. *Relations and Fuzzy Relations*

Fuzzy relation is a generalization of the concept of relations by admitting the notion of partial association between elements of domains. Intuitively, a fuzzy relation can be seen as a multidimensional fuzzy set. For instance, if $\boldsymbol{X}$ and $\boldsymbol{Y}$ are two domains of interest, a fuzzy relation R is any fuzzy subset of the Cartesian product of $\boldsymbol{X}$ and $\boldsymbol{Y}$ (Zadeh, 1971). Equivalently, a fuzzy relation on $\boldsymbol{X} \times \boldsymbol{Y}$ is a mapping

$$R : \boldsymbol{X} \times \boldsymbol{Y} \rightarrow [0, 1].$$

The membership function of R for some pair (x, y), $R(x, y) = 1$, denotes that the two objects x and y are fully related. On the other hand, $R(x, y) = 0$ means that these elements are unrelated while the values in between, $0 < R(x, y) < 1$, underline a partial association. For instance, if $d_{fs}, d_{nf}, d_{ns}, d_{gf}$ are documents whose subjects concern mainly fuzzy systems, neural fuzzy systems, neural systems and genetic fuzzy systems, with keywords w_f, w_n and w_g, respectively, then a relation R on $\boldsymbol{D} \times \boldsymbol{W}$, $\boldsymbol{D} = \{d_{fs}, d_{nf}, d_{ns}, d_{gf}\}$ and $\boldsymbol{W} = \{w_f, w_n, w_g\}$ can assume the matrix form with the following entries

$$R = \begin{bmatrix} 1 & 0 & 0.6 \\ 0.8 & 1 & 0 \\ 0 & 0 & 0 \\ 0.8 & 0 & 1 \end{bmatrix}.$$

Since the universes are discrete, R can be represented as a 4×3 matrix (four documents and three keywords) and entries are degrees of memberships. For instance $R(d_{fs}, w_f) = 1$ means that the document content d_{fs} is fully compatible with the keyword w_f whereas $R(d_{fs}, w_n) = 0$ and $R(d_{fs}, w_g) = 0.6$ indicate that d_{fs} does not mention neural systems, but does have genetic systems as part of its content. As with relations, when $\boldsymbol{X}$ and $\boldsymbol{Y}$ are finite with $Card(\boldsymbol{X}) = n$ and $Card(\boldsymbol{Y}) = m$, then R can be arranged into a certain $n \times m$ matrix $R = [r_{ij}]$, with $r_{ij} \in [0, 1]$ being the corresponding degrees of association between x_i and y_j.

The basic operations on fuzzy relations, union, intersection, and complement, are analogous to the corresponding operations on fuzzy sets once fuzzy relations are fuzzy sets formed on multidimensional spaces. Their characterization and representation also mimics fuzzy sets.

1.5.1.1. *Cartesian product*

A procedure to construct fuzzy relations is through the use of Cartesian product extended to fuzzy sets. The concept closely follows the one adopted for sets once they involve pairs of points of the underlying universes, added with a membership degree.

Given fuzzy sets $A_1, A_2, \ldots, A_n$ on the respective domains $\boldsymbol{X}_1, \boldsymbol{X}_2, \ldots, \boldsymbol{X}_n$, their Cartesian product $A_1 \times A_2 \times \cdots \times A_n$ is a fuzzy relation R on $\boldsymbol{X}_1 \times \boldsymbol{X}_2 \times \cdots \times \boldsymbol{X}_n$ with the following membership function

$$R(x_1, x_2, \ldots, x_n) = \min\{A_1(x_1), A_2(x_2), \ldots, A_n(x_n)\} \;\forall x_1 \in \boldsymbol{X}_1, \forall x_2 \in \boldsymbol{X}_2, \ldots, \forall x_n \in \boldsymbol{X}_n.$$

In general, we can generalize the concept of this Cartesian product using t-norms:

$$R(x_1, x_2, \ldots, x_n) = A_1(x_1) \text{ t } A_2(x_2) \text{ t}, \ldots, \text{t } A_n(x_n) \;\forall x_1 \in \boldsymbol{X}_1, \forall x_2 \in \boldsymbol{X}_2, \ldots, \forall x_n \in \boldsymbol{X}_n.$$

1.5.1.2. *Projection of fuzzy relations*

Contrasting with the concept of the Cartesian product, the idea of projection is to construct fuzzy relations on some subspaces of the original relation.

If R is a fuzzy relation on $\boldsymbol{X}_1 \times \boldsymbol{X}_2 \times \cdots \times \boldsymbol{X}_n$, its projection on $\boldsymbol{X} = \boldsymbol{X}_i \times \boldsymbol{X}_j \times \cdots \times \boldsymbol{X}_k$, is a fuzzy relation R_X whose membership function is (Zadeh, 1975a, 1975b)

$$R_{\mathrm{X}}(x_i, x_j, \ldots, x_k) = \mathrm{Pr}\,oj_{\mathrm{X}} R(x_1, x_2, \ldots, x_n) = \sup_{x_t, x_u, \ldots, x_v} R(x_1, x_2, \ldots, x_n),$$

where $I = \{i, j, \ldots, k\}$ is a subsequence of the set of indexes $N = \{1, 2, \ldots, n\}$, and $J = \{t, u, \ldots, v\}$ is a subsequence of N such that $I \cup J = N$ and $I \cap J = \emptyset$. Thus, J is the complement of I with respect to N. Notice that the above expression is computed for all values of $(x_1, x_2, \ldots, x_n) \in \boldsymbol{X}_1 \times \boldsymbol{X}_2 \times \cdots \times \boldsymbol{X}_n$. Figure 1.23 illustrates projection in the two-dimensional $\boldsymbol{X} \times \boldsymbol{Y}$ case.

1.5.1.3. *Cylindrical extension*

The notion of cylindrical extension aims to expand a fuzzy set to a multidimensional relation. In this sense, cylindrical extension can be regarded as an operation complementary to the projection operation (Zadeh, 1975a, 1975b).

The cylindrical extension on $\boldsymbol{X} \times \boldsymbol{Y}$ of a fuzzy set of $\boldsymbol{X}$ is a fuzzy relation *cylA* whose membership function is equal to

$$cylA(x, y) = A(x) \quad \forall x \in \boldsymbol{X}, \;\; y \in \boldsymbol{Y}.$$

Figure 1.24 shows the cylindrical extension of a triangular fuzzy set A.

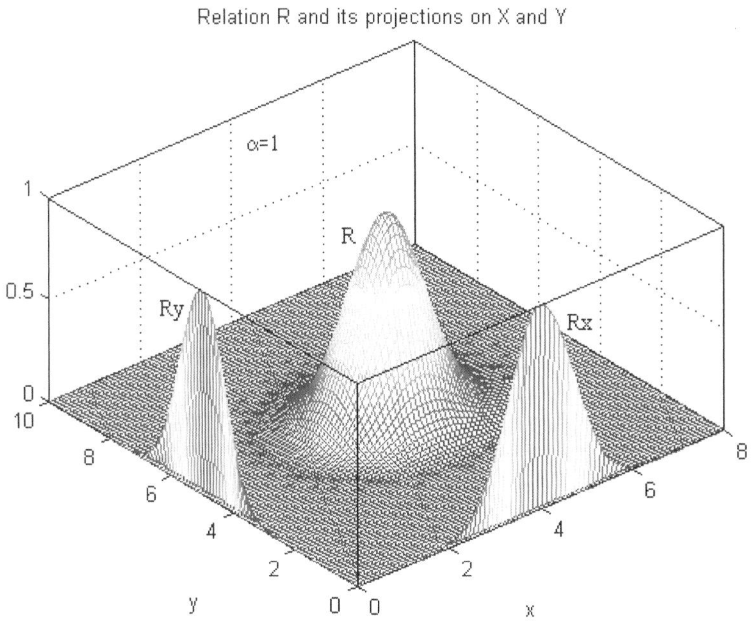

Figure 1.23: Fuzzy relation R and its projections on $\boldsymbol{X}$ and $\boldsymbol{Y}$.

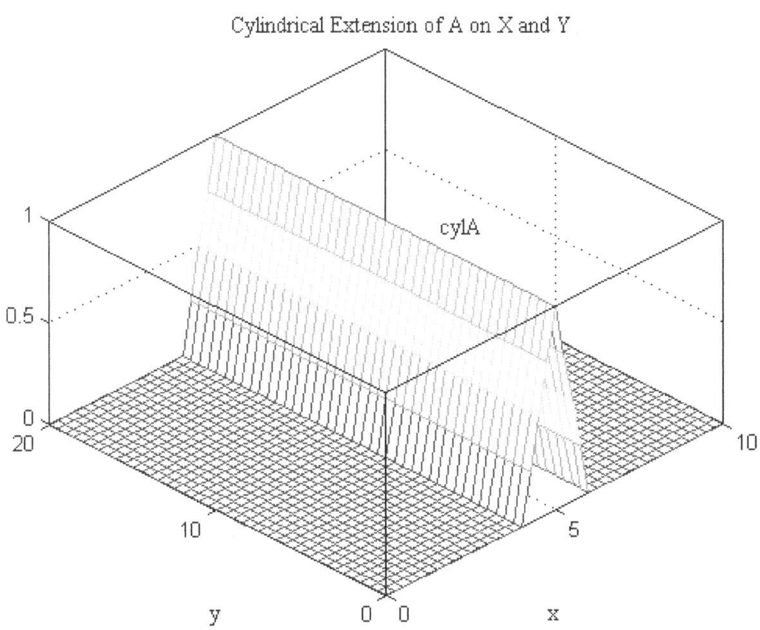

Figure 1.24: Cylindrical extension of a fuzzy set.

1.6. Linguistic Variables

One frequently deals with variables describing phenomena of physical or human systems assuming a finite, quite small number of descriptors.

In contrast to the idea of numeric variables as commonly used, the notion of linguistic variable can be understood as a variable whose values are fuzzy sets. In general, linguistic variables may assume values consisting of words or sentences expressed in a certain language (Zadeh, 1999a). Formally, a linguistic variable is characterized by a quintuple $\langle X, T(X), X, G, M \rangle$ where X is the name of the variable, $T(X)$ is a term set of X whose elements are labels L of linguistic values of X, G is a grammar that generates the names of X, and M is a semantic rule that assigns to each label $L \in T(X)$ a meaning whose realization is a fuzzy set on the universe X with base variable x. Figure 1.25 gives an example.

1.7. Granulation of Data

The notion of granulation emerges as a need to abstract and summarize data to support the processes of comprehension and decision-making. For instance, we often sample an environment for values of attributes of state variables, but we rarely process all details because of our physical and cognitive limitations. Quite often, just a reduced number of variables, attributes, and values are considered because those are

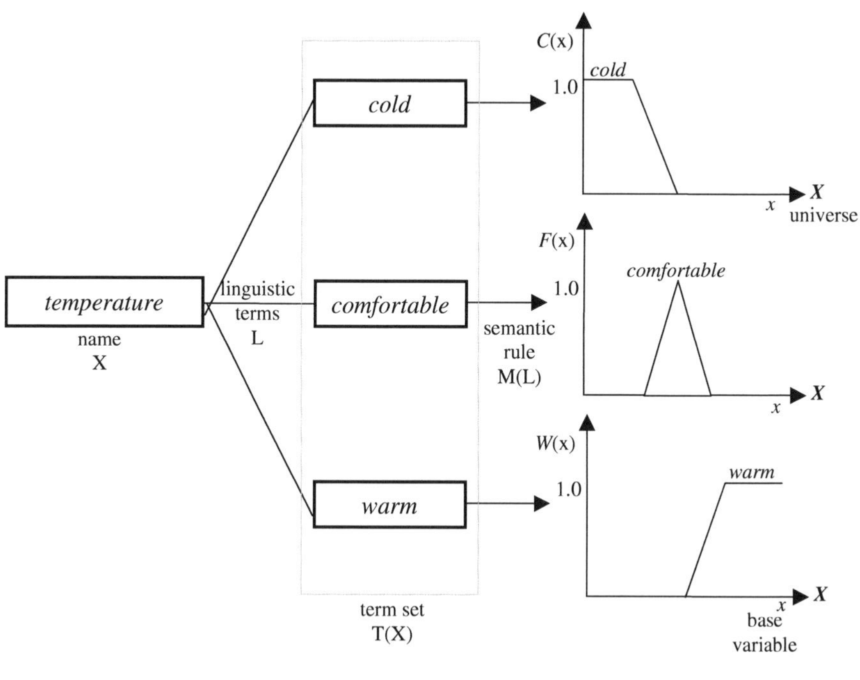

Figure 1.25: An example of the linguistic variable temperature.

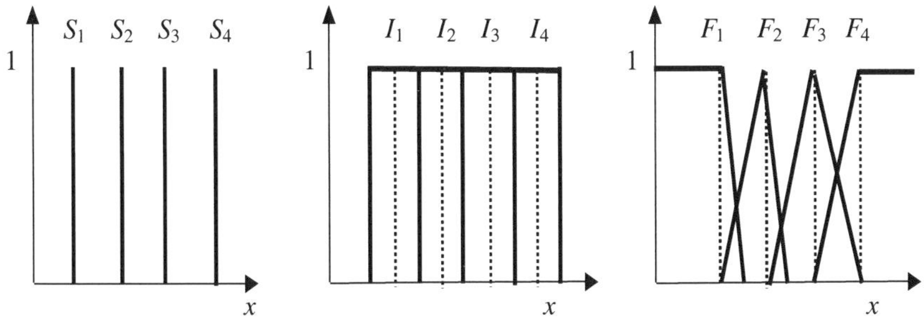

Figure 1.26: Discretization, quantization, and fuzzy granulation.

the only features of interest given the task under consideration. To avoid all necessary and highly distractive details, we require an effective abstraction procedure. Detailed numeric information is aggregated into a format of information granules where the granules themselves are regarded as collections of elements that are perceived as being indistinguishable, similar, close, or functionally equivalent.

There are different formalisms and concepts of information granules. For instance, granules can be realized as sets (intervals), rough sets, probability densities (Lin, 2004). Typical examples of the granular data are singletons and intervals. In these two special cases we typically refer to discretization and quantization, as in Figure 1.26. As the specificity of granules increases, intervals become singletons and in this case limit the quantization results in a discretization process.

Fuzzy sets are examples of information granules. When talking about a family of fuzzy sets, we are typically concerned with fuzzy partitions of X. Given the nature of fuzzy sets, fuzzy granulation generalizes the notion of quantization as in Figure 1.26 and emphasizes a gradual nature of transitions between neighboring information granules (Zadeh, 1999b). When dealing with information granulation we often develop a family of fuzzy sets and move on with the processing that inherently uses all the elements of this families. The existing terminology refers to such collections of data granules as frames of cognition (Pedrycz and Gomide, 2007). In what follows, we briefly review the concept and its main properties.

1.7.1. *Frame of Cognition*

A frame of cognition results from information granulation when we encounter a finite collection of fuzzy sets — information granules that represent the entire universe of discourse and satisfy a system of semantic constraints. The frame of cognition is a notion of particular interest in fuzzy modeling, fuzzy control, classification, and data analysis.

A frame of cognition consists of several labeled, normal fuzzy sets. Each of these fuzzy sets is treated as a reference for further processing. A frame of cognition can be viewed as a codebook of conceptual entities. We may view them as a family of linguistic landmarks, say *small*, *medium*, *high*, etc. More formally, a frame of cognition Φ

$$\Phi = \{A_1, A_2, \ldots, A_m\} \tag{18}$$

is a collection of fuzzy sets defined in the same universe X that satisfies at least two requirements of coverage and semantic soundness.

1.7.2. *Coverage*

We say that Φ covers X if any element $x \in X$ is compatible with at least one fuzzy sets A_i in Φ, $i \in I = \{1, 2, \ldots, m\}$ meaning that it is compatible (coincides) with A_i to some non-zero degree, that is

$$\underset{x \in \mathbf{X}}{\forall} \underset{i \in \mathrm{I}}{\exists} A_i(x) > 0. \tag{19}$$

Being stricter, we may require a satisfaction of the so-called δ-level coverage which means that for any element of X, fuzzy sets are activated to a degree not lower than δ

$$\underset{x \in \mathbf{X}}{\forall} \underset{i \in \mathrm{I}}{\exists} A_i(x) > \delta, \tag{20}$$

where $\delta \in [0, 1]$. From application perspective, the coverage assures that each element of X is represented by at least one of the elements of Φ, and guarantees any absence of gaps, that is, elements of X for which there is no fuzzy set being compatible with it.

1.7.3. *Semantic Soundness*

The notion of semantic soundness is more complicated and difficult to quantify. In principle, we are interested in information granules of Φ that are meaningful. While there is far more flexibility in a way in which a number of detailed requirements could be structured, we may agree upon a collection of several fundamental properties.

Each A_i, $i \in I$, is a unimodal and normal fuzzy set.

Fuzzy sets A_i, $i \in I$, are disjoint enough to assure that they are sufficiently distinct to become linguistically meaningful. This imposes a maximum degree λ of overlap between any two elements of Φ. In other words, given any $x \in X$, there is no more than one fuzzy set A_i such that $A_i(x) \geq \lambda$, $\lambda \in [0, 1]$.

The number of elements of Φ is low; following the psychological findings reported by Miller and others we consider the number of fuzzy sets forming the frame of cognition to be maintained in the range of 7 ± 2 items.

Coverage and semantic soundness (Oliveira, 1993) are the two essential conditions that should be fulfilled by the membership functions of A_i to achieve

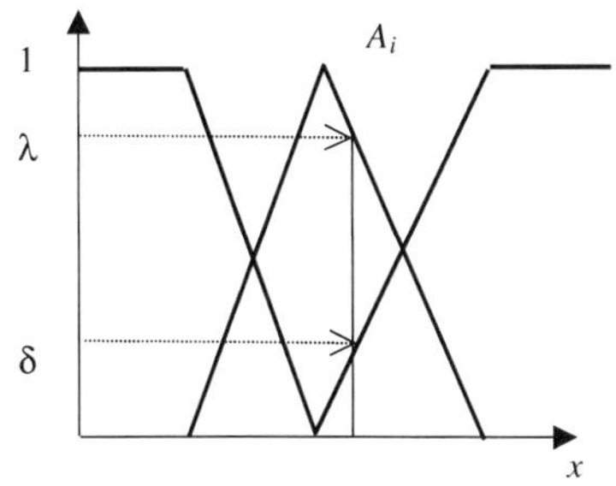

Figure 1.27: Coverage and semantic soundness of a cognitive frame.

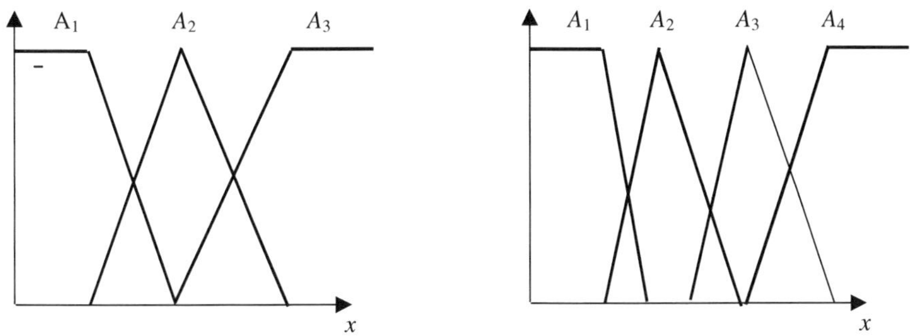

Figure 1.28: Two frames of cognition; Φ_1 is coarser (more general) than Φ_2.

interpretability. In particular, δ-coverage and λ-overlapping induce a minimal (δ) and maximal (λ) level of overlap between fuzzy sets, as in Figure 1.27.

Considering the families of linguistic labels and associated fuzzy sets embraced in a frame of cognition, several characteristics are worth emphasizing.

1.7.3.1. *Specificity*

We say that the frame of cognition Φ_1 is more specific than Φ_2 if all the elements of Φ_1 are more specific than the elements of Φ_2, as in Figure 1.28. Here the specificity $Spec(A_i)$ of the fuzzy sets that compose the cognition frames can be evaluated as suggested in Section 1.3. The less specific cognition frames promotes granulation realized at the higher level of abstraction (generalization). Subsequently, we are provided with the description that captures less details.

1.7.3.2. *Granularity*

Granularity of a frame of cognition relates to the granularity of fuzzy sets used there. The higher the number of fuzzy sets in the frame is, the finer the resulting granulation. Therefore, the frame of cognition Φ_1 is finer than Φ_2 if $|\Phi_1| > |\Phi_2|$. If the converse holds, Φ_1 is coarser than Φ_2, as in Figure 1.28.

1.7.3.3. *Focus of attention*

A focus of attention induced by a certain fuzzy set $A = A_i$ in Φ is defined as a certain **α-cut** of this fuzzy set. By moving A along $\boldsymbol{X}$ while keeping its membership function unchanged, we can focus attention on a certain selected region of $\boldsymbol{X}$, as shown in Figure 1.29.

1.7.3.4. *Information hiding*

Information hiding is closely related to the notion of focus of attention and manifests through a collection of elements that are hidden when viewed from the standpoint of membership functions. By modifying the membership function of $A = A_i$ in Φ we can produce an equivalence of the elements positioned within some region of $\boldsymbol{X}$. For instance, consider a trapezoidal fuzzy set A on $\boldsymbol{R}$ and its 1-cut (core), the closed interval $[a_2, a_3]$, as depicted in Figure 1.30.

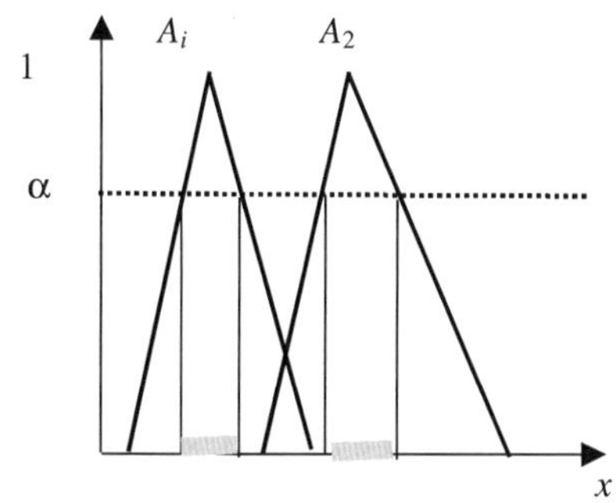

Figure 1.29: Focus of attention; two regions of focus of attention implied by the corresponding fuzzy sets.

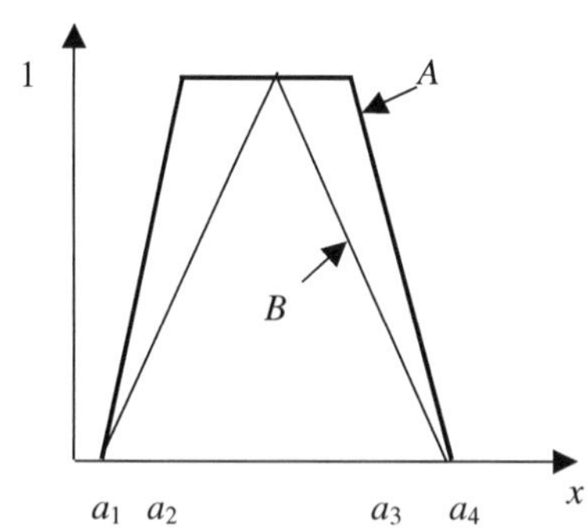

Figure 1.30: A concept of information hiding realized by the use of trapezoidal fuzzy set A. Points in $[a_2, a_3]$ are made indistinguishable. The effect of information hiding is not present in case of triangular fuzzy set B.

All points within the interval $[a_2, a_3]$ are made *indistinguishable* and through the use of this specific fuzzy set they are made equivalent. Hence, more detailed information, a position of a certain point falling within this interval, is *hidden*. In general, by increasing or decreasing the level of the **α-cut**, we can accomplish a so-called α-information hiding through normalization.

1.8. Conclusion

The chapter has summarized the fundamental notions and concepts of fuzzy set theory. The goal was to offer basic and key contents of interest for computational intelligence and intelligent systems theory and applications. Currently, a number of outstanding books and journals are available to help researchers, scientists and engineers to master the fuzzy set theory and the contributions it brings to develop new approaches through hybridizations and new applications. The references section includes some of them. The remaining chapters of this book provide the readers with a clear picture of the current state of the art in the area.

References

Bouchon-Meunier, B. (1998). *Aggregation and Fusion of Imperfect Information*. Heidelberg, Germany: Physica-Verlag.

Beliakov, G., Pradera, A. and Calvo, T. (2007). *Aggregation Functions: A Guide for Practitioners*. Heidelberg, Germany: Springer.

Calvo, T., Kolesárová, A., Komorníková, M. and Mesiar, R. (2002). *Aggregation Operators: Properties, Classes and Construction Methods, in Aggregation Operators: New Trends and Applications*. Heidelberg, Germany: Physica-Verlag.

Cantor, G. (1883). *Grundlagen Einer Allgemeinen Mannigfaltigekeitslehre*. Leipzig: Teubner.

Cantor, G. (1895). Breitraage zur begraundung der transfniten mengernlehre. *Math. Ann.*, 46, pp. 207–246.

Dubois, D. and Prade, H. (1985). A review of fuzzy aggregation connectives. *Info. Sciences*, 36, pp. 85–121.

Dubois, D. and Prade, H. (1997). The three semantics of fuzzy sets. *Fuzzy Sets Syst.*, 2, pp. 141–150.

Dubois, D. and Prade, H. (1998). An introduction to fuzzy sets. *Clin. Chim. Acta*, 70, pp. 3–29.

Dubois, D. and Prade, H. (2004). On the use of aggregation operations in information fusion. *Fuzzy Sets Syst.*, 142, pp. 143–161.

Dyckhoff, H. and Pedrycz, W. (1984). Generalized means as a models of compensative connectives. *Fuzzy Sets Syst.*, 142, pp. 143–154.

Klement, E. and Navarra, M. (1999). Propositional fuzzy logics based on Frank t-norms: A comparison. In D. Dubois, H. Parde and W. Klement (eds.), *Fuzzy Sets, Logics and Reasoning about Knowledge*. Dordrecht, the Netherlands: Kluwer Academic Publishers, pp. 25–47.

Klement, P., Mesiar, R. and Pap, E. (2000). *Triangular Norms*. Dordrecht, Nederland: Kluwer Academic Publishers.

Klir, G. and Yuan, B. (1995). *Fuzzy Sets and Fuzzy Logic: Theory and Applications*. Upper Saddle River, New Jersey, USA: Prentice Hall.

Lin, T. (2004). Granular computing: Rough sets perspectives, *IEEE Connections*, 2, pp. 10–13.

Oliveira, J. (1993). On optimal fuzzy systems with I/O interfaces. *Proc. Second IEEE Int. Conf. on Fuzzy Systems*. San Francisco, California, USA, pp. 34–40.

Pedrycz, W. and Gomide, F. (2007). *Fuzzy Systems Engineering: Toward Human-Centric Computing*. Hoboken, New Jersey, USA: Wiley Intercience.

Yager, R. (1983). Entropy and specificity in a mathematical theory of evidence. *Int. J. Gen. Syst.*, 9, pp. 249–260.

Yager, R. (1988). On ordered weighted averaging aggregation operations in multicriteria decision making. *IEEE Trans. Syst. Man Cyber.*, 18, pp. 183–190.

Yager, R. and Rybalov, A. (1996). Uninorm aggregation operators. *Fuzzy Sets Syst.*, 80, pp. 111–120.

Zadeh, L. (1965). Fuzzy sets. *Inf. Control*, 8, pp. 338–353.

Zadeh, L. (1971). Similarity relations and fuzzy orderings. *Inf. Sci.*, 3, pp. 177–200.

Zadeh, L. (1975a, 1975b). The concept of linguistic variables and its application to approximate reasoning I, II, III. *Info. Sciences*, 8(9), pp. 43–80, 199–251, 301–357.

Zadeh, L. (1978). Fuzzy sets as a basis for a theory of possibility. *Fuzzy Sets Syst.*, 3, pp. 3–28.

Zadeh, L. (1999a). From computing with numbers to computing with words: from manipulation of measurements to manipulation of perceptions. *IEEE Trans. Circ. Syst.*, 45, pp. 105–119.

Zadeh, L. (1999b). Fuzzy logic = computing with words. In Zadeh, L. and Kacprzyk, J. (eds.), *Computing with Words in Information and Intelligent Systems*. Heidelberg, Germany: Physica-Verlag, pp. 3–23.

Chapter 2

Granular Computing

Andrzej Bargiela and Witold Pedrycz

Research into human-centered information processing, as evidenced through the development of fuzzy sets and fuzzy logic, has brought an additional insight into the transformative nature of the aggregation of inaccurate and/or fuzzy information in terms of the semantic content of data aggregates. This insight has led to the suggestion of the development of the granular computing (GrC) paradigm some 15 years ago and takes as a point of departure, an empirical validation of the aggregated data in order to achieve the closest possible correspondence of the semantics of data aggregates and the entities in the problem domain. Indeed, it can be observed that information abstraction combined with empirical validation of abstractions has been deployed as a methodological tool in various scientific disciplines. This chapter is focused on exploring the foundations of GrC and casting it as a structured combination of algorithmic and non-algorithmic information processing that mimics human, intelligent synthesis of knowledge from imprecise and/or fuzzy information.

2.1. Introduction

Granular Computing (GrC) is frequently defined in an informal way as a general computation theory for effectively using granules such as classes, clusters, subsets, groups, and intervals to build an efficient computational model for complex applications which process large volumes of information presented as either raw data or aggregated problem domain knowledge. Though the GrC term is relatively recent, the basic notions and principles of granular computing have appeared under different names in many related fields, such as information hiding in programming, granularity in artificial intelligence, divide and conquer in theoretical computer science, interval computing, cluster analysis, fuzzy and rough set theories, neutrosophic computing, quotient space theory, belief functions, machine learning, databases, and many others. In the past few years, we have witnessed a renewed and fast growing interest in GrC. GrC has begun to play important roles in bioinformatics, e-Business, security, machine learning, data mining, high-performance computing, and wireless mobile computing in terms of efficiency, effectiveness, robustness and structured representation of uncertainty.

With the vigorous research interest in the GrC paradigm (Bargiela and Pedrycz, 2002a, 2002b, 2003, 2005a, 2005b; Bargiela, 2004; Bargiela *et al.*, 2004a, 2004b; Inuiguchi *et al.*, 2003; Lin, 1998; Lin *et al.*, 2002; Pedrycz, 1989; Pedrycz and Gomide, 1998; Pedrycz *et al.*, 2000; Pedrycz and Bargiela, 2002; Skowron and Stepaniuk, 2001; Yao and Yao, 2002; Yao, 2004a, 2004b, 2005; Zadeh, 1965, 1979, 1997, 2002; Dubois *et al.*, 1997), it is natural to see that there are voices calling for clarification of the distinctiveness of GrC from the underpinning constituent disciplines and from other computational paradigms proposed for large-scale/complex information possessing Pawlak (1991). Recent contributions by Yao and Yao (2002), Yao (2004a, 2004b, 2005) attempt to bring together various insights into GrC from a broad spectrum of disciplines and cast the GrC framework as a structured thinking at the philosophical level and structured problem solving at the practical level.

In this chapter, we elaborate on our earlier proposal (Bargiela and Pedrycz, 2006) and look at the roots of GrC in the light of the original insight of Zadeh (1997) stating, "...fuzzy information granulation in an intuitive form underlies human problem solving ...". We suggest that the *human problem solving* has strong foundations in axiomatic set theory and theory of computability and it underlies some recent research results linking intelligence to physical computation (Bains, 2003, 2005). In fact, re-examining human information processing in this light brings GrC from a domain of computation and philosophy to one of physics and set theory.

The set theoretic perspective on GrC adopted in this chapter offers also a good basis for the evaluation of other human-centered computing paradigms such as the generalized constraint-based computation recently communicated by Zadeh.

2.2. Set Theoretical Interpretation of Granulation

The commonly accepted definition of granulation introduced in Inuiguchi *et al.* (2003), Lin *et al.* (2002), and Yao (2004a) is:

Definition 1: *Information granulation is a grouping of elements based on their indistinguishability, similarity, proximity or functionality.*

This definition serves well the purpose of constructive generation of granules but it does little to differentiate granulation from clustering. More importantly however, *Definition 1* implies that the nature of information granules is fully captured by their interpretation as subsets of the original dataset within the Intuitive Set Theory of Cantor (1879). Unfortunately, an inevitable consequence of that is that the inconsistencies (paradoxes) associated with intuitive set theory, such as "cardinality of set of all sets" (Cantor, 1879) or "definition of a set that is not a member of itself" (Russel, 1937) are imported into the domain of information granulation.

In order to provide a more robust definition of information granulation we follow the approach adopted in the development of axiomatic set theory. The key realization there was that the commonly accepted intuition, that one can form any set one wants, should be questioned. Accepting the departure point of intuitive set theory we can say that, normally, sets are not members of themselves, i.e., normally, $\sim(y \text{ in } y)$. But, the axioms of intuitive set theory do not exclude the existence of "abnormal" sets, which are members of themselves. So, if we consider a set of all "normal" sets: $x = \{y| \sim (y \text{ in } y)\}$ we can axiomatically guarantee the existence of set x:

$$\exists x \forall y (y \in x \Leftrightarrow \sim (y \in y)).$$

If we then substitute x for y, we arrive at a contradiction:

$$\exists x \forall x (x \in x \Leftrightarrow \sim (x \in x)).$$

So, the unrestricted comprehension axiom of the intuitive set theory leads to contradictions and cannot therefore serve as a foundation of set theory.

2.2.1. *Zermelo–Fraenkel (ZF) Axiomatization*

An early attempt at overcoming the above contradiction was an axiomatic scheme developed by Ernst Zermelo and Abraham Fraenkel (Zermelo, 1908). Their idea was to restrict the comprehension axiom schema by adopting only those instances of it, which are necessary for reconstruction of common mathematics. In other words, the standard approach, of using a formula $F(y)$ to collect the set y having the property F, leads to generation of an object that is not a set (otherwise we arrive at a contradiction). So, looking at the problem the other way, they have concluded that the contradiction constitutes a *de-facto* proof that there are other semantical entities in addition to sets.

The important observation that we can make here is that the semantical transformation of sets through the process of applying some set-forming formula applies also to the process of information granulation and consequently, information granules should be considered as being semantically distinct from the granulated entities. We therefore arrive at a modified definition of information granulation as follows:

Definition 2: *Information granulation is a semantically meaningful grouping of elements based on their indistinguishability, similarity, proximity or functionality.*

Continuing with the ZF approach we must legalize some collections of sets that are not sets. Let $F(y, z_1, z_2, \ldots, z_n)$ be a formula in the language of set theory (where $z_1, z_2, \ldots, z_n$ are optional parameters). We can say that for any values of parameters $z_1, z_2, \ldots, z_n$ the formula F defines a "class" A

$$A = \{y \mid F(y, z_1, z_2, \ldots, z_n)\},$$

which consists of all y's possessing the property F. Different values of $z_1, z_2, \ldots, z_n$ give rise to different classes. Consequently, the axiomatization of set theory involves formulation of axiom schemas that represent possible instances of axioms for different classes.

The following is a full set of axioms of the ZF set theory:

Z1, Extensionality:

$$\forall x \forall y [\forall z (z \in x \equiv z \in y) \Rightarrow x = y].$$

Asserts that if sets x and y have the same members, the sets are identical.

Z2, Null Set:

$$\exists x \sim \exists y (y \in x).$$

Asserts that there is a unique empty set.

Z3, Pair Set:

$$\forall x \forall y \exists z \forall w (w \in z \equiv w = x \vee w = y).$$

Asserts that for any set x and y, there exists a pair set of x and y, i.e., a set that has only x and y as members.

Z4, Unions:

$$\forall x \exists y \forall z (z \in y \equiv \exists w (w \in x \wedge z \in w).$$

Asserts that for any set x there is a set y containing every set that is a member of some member of x.

Z5, Power Set:

$$\forall x \exists y \forall z [z \in y \equiv \forall w (w \in z \Rightarrow w \in x)].$$

Asserts that for any set x, there is a set y which contains as members all those sets whose members are also elements of x, i.e., y contains all of the subsets of x.

Z6, Infinite Set:

$$\exists x [\emptyset \in x \wedge \forall y (y \in x \Rightarrow \cup\{y, \{y\}\} \in x)].$$

Asserts that there is a set x which contains $\emptyset$ as a member and which is such that, whenever y is a member of x, then $y \cup \{y\}$ is a member of x.

Z7, Regularity:

$$\forall x[x \neq \emptyset \Rightarrow \exists y(y \in x \wedge \forall z(z \in x \Rightarrow \sim (z \in y)))].$$

Asserts that every set is "well-founded", i.e., it rules out the existence of circular chains of sets as well as infinitely descending chains of sets. A member y of a set x with this property is called a "minimal" element.

Z8, Replacement Schema:

$$\forall x \exists y F(x, y) \Rightarrow \forall u \exists v \forall r(r \in v \equiv \exists s(s \in u \wedge F_{x,y}[s, r])).$$

Asserts that given a formula $F(x, y)$ and $F_{x,y}[s, r]$ as a result of substituting s and r for x and y, every instance of the above axiom schema is an axiom. In other words, given a functional formula F and a set u we can form a new set v by collecting all of the sets to which the members of u are uniquely related by F. It is important to note that elements of v need not be elements of u.

Z9, Separation Schema:

$$\forall u \exists v \forall r(r \in v \equiv r \in u \wedge F_x[r]).$$

Asserts that there exists a set v which has as members precisely the members of u which satisfy the formula F. Again, every instance of the above axiom schema is an axiom.

Unfortunately, the presence of the two axiom schemas, Z6 and Z7, implies infinite axiomatization of the ZF set theory. While it is fully acknowledged that the ZF set theory, and its many variants, has advanced our understanding of cardinal and ordinal numbers and has led to the proof of the property of "well-ordering" of sets (with the help of an additional "Axiom of Choice") (ZFC), the theory seems unduly complex for the purpose of set-theoretical interpretation of information granules.

2.2.2. *von Neumann–Bernays–Goedel (NBG) Axiomatization*

A different approach to the axiomatization of set theory designed to yield the same results as ZF but with a finite number of axioms (i.e., without the reliance on axiom schemas) has been proposed by von Neumann in 1920 and subsequently has been refined by Bernays in 1937 and Goedel in 1940 (Goedel, 1940). The defining aspect of NBG set theory is the introduction of the concept of "proper class" among its objects. NBG and ZFC are very closely related and, in fact, NBG is a conservative extension of ZFC.

In NBG, the proper classes are differentiated from sets by the fact that they do not belong to other classes. Thus, in NBG we have

$$x \Leftrightarrow \exists y(x \in y),$$

which can be phrased as x is a set if it belongs to either a set or a class.

The basic observation that can be made about NBG is that it is essentially a two-sorted theory; it involves sets (denoted here by lower-case letters) and classes (denoted by upper-case letters). Consequently, the above statement about membership assumes one of the forms

$$x \in y \quad \text{or} \quad x \in Y,$$

and statements about equality are in the form

$$x = y \quad \text{or} \quad X = Y.$$

Using this notation, the axioms of NBG are as follows

***N*1, Class Extensionality:**

$$\forall x[x \in A \leftrightarrow x \in B) \Rightarrow A = B].$$

Asserts that classes with the same elements are the same.

***N*2, Set Extensionality:**

$$\forall x[x \in a \leftrightarrow x \in b) \Rightarrow a = b].$$

Asserts that sets with the same elements are the same.

***N*3, Pairing:**

$$\forall x \forall y \exists z \forall w(w \in z \equiv w = x \vee w = y).$$

Asserts that for any set x and y, there exists a set $\{x, y\}$ that has exactly two elements x and y. It is worth noting that this axiom allows definition of ordered pairs and taken together with the Class Comprehension axiom, it allows implementation of relations on sets as classes.

***N*4, Union:**

$$\forall x \exists y \forall z(z \in y \equiv \exists w(w \in x \wedge z \in w).$$

Asserts that for any set x, there exists a set which contains exactly the elements of x.

$N5$, Power Set:

$$\forall x \exists y \forall z[z \in y \equiv \exists \forall w(w \in z \Rightarrow w \in x)].$$

Asserts that for any set x, there is a set which contains exactly the subsets of x.

$N6$, Infinite Set:

$$\exists x[\emptyset \in x \wedge \forall y(y \in x \Rightarrow \cup\{y, \{y\}\} \in x)].$$

Asserts there is a set x, which contains an empty set as an element and contains $y \cup \{y\}$ for each of its elements y.

$N7$, Regularity:

$$\forall x[x \neq \emptyset \Rightarrow \exists y(y \in x \wedge \forall z(z \in x \Rightarrow \sim (z \in y)))].$$

Asserts that each non-empty set is disjoined from one of its elements.

$N8$, Limitation of size:

$$\sim x \Leftrightarrow |x| = |V|.$$

Asserts that if the cardinality of x equals to the cardinality of the set theoretic universe V, x is not a set but a proper class. This axiom can be shown to be equivalent to the axioms of Regularity, Replacement and Separation in NBG. Thus the classes that are proper in NBG are in a very clear sense big, while sets are small.

It should be appreciated that the latter has a very profound implication on computation, which processes proper classes. This is because the classes built over countable sets can be uncountable and, as such, do not satisfy the constraints of the formalism of the Universal Turing Machine.

$N9$, Class Comprehension schema:

Unlike in the ZF axiomatization, this schema consists of a finite set of axioms (thus giving finite axiomatization of NBG).

Axiom of Sets: For any set x, there is a class X such that $x = X$.

Axiom of Complement: For any class X, the complement $V - X = \{x \mid x \notin X\}$

Axiom of Intersection: For any class $X$and Y the intersection $X \cap Y = \{x \mid x \in X \wedge x \in Y\}$ is a class.

Axiom of Products: For any classes $X$and Y, the class $X \times Y = \{(x, y) \mid x \in X \wedge x \in Y\}$ is a class. This axiom provides actually for more than what is needed for representing relations on classes. What is actually needed is just that $V \times Y$ is a class.

Axiom of Converses: For any class X, the classes $Conv1(X) = \{(y, x) \mid (x, y) \in X\}$ and $Conv2(X) = \{(y, (x, z)) \mid (x, (y, z)) \in X\}$ exist.

Axiom of Association: For any class X, the classes $Assoc1(X) = \{((x, y), z) \mid (x, (y, z)) \in X\}$ and $Assoc2(X) = \{(w, (x, (y, z))) \mid (w, ((x, y), z)) \in X\}$ exist.

Axiom of Ranges: For any class X, the class $Rng(X) = \{y \mid (\exists x(x, y) \in X\}$ exists.

Axiom of Membership: The class $[\in] = \{(x, y) \mid x \in y\}$ exists.

Axiom of Diagonal: The class $[=] = \{(x, y) \mid x = y\}$ exists. This axiom can be used to build a relation asserting the equality of any two of its arguments and consequently used to handle repeated variables.

With the above finite axiomatization, the NBG theory can be adopted as a set theoretical basis for GrC. Such a formal framework prompts a powerful insight into the essence of granulation namely that **the granulation process transforms the semantics of the granulated entities,** mirroring the semantical distinction between sets and classes.

The semantics of granules is derived from the domain that has, in general, higher cardinality than the cardinality of the granulated sets. Although, at first, it might be a bit surprising to see that such a semantical transformation is an essential part of information granulation, in fact, we can point to a common framework of many scientific disciplines which have evolved by abstracting from details inherent to the underpinning scientific discipline and developing a vocabulary of terms (proper classes) that have been verified by the reference to real-life (ultimately to the laws of physics). An example of granulation of detailed information into semantically meaningful granules might be the consideration of cells and organisms in Biology rather than consideration of molecules, atoms or sub-atomic particles when studying the physiology of living organisms.

The operation on classes in NBG is entirely consistent with the operation on sets in the intuitive set theory. The principle of abstraction implies that classes can be formed out of any statement of the predicate calculus, with the membership relation. Notions of equality, pairing and such, are thus matters of definitions (a specific abstraction of a formula) and not of axioms. In NBG, a set represents a class if every element of the set is an element of the class. Consequently, there are classes that do not have representations.

We suggest therefore that the advantage of adopting NBG as a set theoretical basis for GrC is that it provides a framework within which one can discuss a hierarchy of different granulations without running the risk of inconsistency. For instance, one can denote a "large category" as a category of granules whose collection and collection of morphisms can be represented by a class. A "small category" can be denoted as a category of granules contained in sets. Thus, we can speak of "category of all small categories" (which is a "large category") without the risk of inconsistency.

A similar framework for a set-theoretical representation of granulation is offered by the theory of types published by Russell in 1937 (Russell, 1937). The theory assumes a linear hierarchy of types: with type 0 consisting of objects of undecided type and, for each natural number n, type $n+1$ objects are sets of type n objects. The conclusions that can be drawn from this framework with respect to the nature of granulation are exactly the same as that drawn from the NBG.

2.2.3. *Mereology*

An alternative framework for the formalization of GrC, that of mereology, has been proposed by other researchers. The roots of mereology can be traced to the work of Edmund Husserl (Husserl, 1901) and to the subsequent work of Polish mathematician, Stanislaw Lesniewski, in the late 1920s (Lesniewski, 1929a, 1929b). Much of this work was motivated by the same concerns about the intuitive set theory that have spurred the development of axiomatic set theories (ZF, NBG and others) (Goedel, 1940; Zermelo, 1908).

Mereology replaces talk about "sets" with talk about "sums" of objects, objects being no more than the various things that make up wholes. However, such a simple replacement results in an "intuitive mereology" that is analogous to "intuitive set theory". Such "intuitive mereology" suffers from paradoxes analogous to Russell's paradox (we can ask: If there is an object whose parts are all the objects that are not parts of themselves; is it a part of itself?). So, one has to conclude that the mere introduction of the mereological concept of "partness" and "wholeness" is not sufficient and that mereology requires axiomatic formulation.

Axiomatic formulation of mereology has been proposed as a first-order theory whose universe of discourse consists of *wholes* and their respective *parts*, collectively called objects (Simons, 1987; Tarski, 1983). A mereological system requires at least one primitive relation, e.g., dyadic Parthood, *x is a part of y*, written as Pxy. Parthood is nearly always assumed to partially order the universe. An immediate defined predicate is *x is a proper part of y*, written $PPxy$, which holds if Pxy is true and Pyx is false. An object lacking proper parts is an *atom*. The mereological universe consists of all objects we wish to consider and all of their proper parts. Two other predicates commonly defined in mereology are Overlap and Underlap. These are defined as follows:

— Oxy is an overlap of x and y if there exists an object z such that Pzx and Pzy both hold.

— *Uxy* is an underlap of x and y if there exists an object z such that $x$and y are both parts of z (*Pxz* and *Pyz* hold).

With the above predicates, axiomatic mereology defines the following axioms:

***M*1, Parthood is Reflexive:** Asserts that object is part of itself.

***M*2, Parthood is Antisymmetric:** Asserts that if *Pxy* and *Pyx* both hold, then x and y are the same object.

***M*3, Parthood is Transitive:** Asserts that if *Pxy* and *Pyz* hold then *Pxz* hold.

***M*4, Weak Supplementation:** Asserts that if *PPxy* holds, there exists z such that *Pzy* holds but *Ozx* does not.

***M*5, Strong Supplementation:** Asserts that if *Pyx* does not holds, there exists z such that *Pzy* holds but *Ozx* does not.

***M*5a, Atomistic Supplementation:** Asserts that if *Pxy* does not hold, then there exists an atom z such that *Pzx* holds but *Ozy* does not.

Top: Asserts that there exists a "universal object", designated W, such that PxW holds for any x.

Bottom: Asserts that there exists an atomic "null object", designated N, such that *PNx* hold for any x.

***M*6, Sum:** Asserts that if *Uxy* holds, there exists z, called the "sum of x and y", such that the parts of z are just those objects which are parts of either x or y.

***M*7, Product:** Asserts that if *Oxy* holds, there exists z, called the "Product of x and y", such that the parts of z are just those objects which are parts of both x and y.

***M*8, Unrestricted Fusion:** Let f be a first order formula having one free variable. Then the fusion of all objects satisfying f exists.

***M*9, Atomicity:** Asserts that all objects are either atoms or fusions of atoms.

It is clear that if "parthood" in mereology is taken as corresponding to "subset" in set theory, there is some analogy between the above axioms of *classical extensional mereology* and those of standard ZF set theory. However, there are some philosophical and common sense objections to some of the above axioms; e.g., transitivity of Parthood ($M3$). Also, the set of above axioms is not minimal since it is possible to derive Weak Supplementation axiom ($M4$) from Strong Supplementation axiom ($M5$).

Axiom $M6$ implies that if the universe is finite or if *Top* is assumed, then the universe is closed under sum. Universal closure of product and of supplementation relative to W requires *Bottom*. W and N are evidently the mereological equivalents of the universal and the null sets. Because sum and product are binary operations, $M6$ and $M7$ admit the sum and product of only a finite number of objects. The *fusion* axiom, $M8$, enables taking the sum of infinitely many objects. The same holds for product. If $M8$ holds, then W exists for infinite universes. Hence, *Top* needs to be assumed only if the universe is infinite and $M8$ does not hold. It is somewhat strange that while the *Top* axiom (postulating W) is not controversial, the *Bottom* axiom (postulating N) is. Lesniewski rejected *Bottom* axiom and most mereological systems follow his example. Hence, while the universe is closed under sum, the product of objects that do not overlap is typically undefined. Such defined mereology is equivalent to Boolean algebra lacking a 0. Postulating N generates mereology in which all possible products are definable but it also transforms extensional mereology into a Boolean algebra without a null-element (Tarski, 1983).

The full mathematical analysis of the theories of parthood is beyond the intended scope of this chapter and the reader is referred to the recent publication by Pontow and Schubert (2006) in which the authors prove, by set theoretical means, that there exists a model of general extensional mereology where arbitrary summation of attributes is not possible. However, it is clear from the axiomatization above that the question about the existence of a universal entity containing all other entities and the question about the existence of an empty entity as part of all existing entities are answered very differently by set theory and mereology. In set theory, the existence of a universal entity is contradictory and the existence of an empty set is mandatory, while in mereology the existence of a universal set is stipulated by the respective fusion axioms and the existence of an empty entity is denied. Also, it is worth noting that in mereology there is no straightforward analog to the set theoretical is-element-of relation (Pontow and Schubert, 2006).

So taking into account the above, we suggest the following answer to the underlying questions of this section: Why granulation is necessary? Why the set-theoretical representation of granulation is appropriate?

— The **concept of granulation is necessary** to denote the semantical transformation of granulated entities in a way that is analogous to semantical transformation of sets into classes in axiomatic set theory;
— Granulation interpreted in the context of axiomatic set theory is **very different from clustering**, since it deals with semantical transformation of data and not limits itself to a mere grouping of similar entities; and
— The set-theoretical interpretation of granulation enables **consistent** representation of a hierarchy of information granules.

2.3. Abstraction and Computation

Having established an argument for semantical dimension to granulation, one may ask; how is the meaning (semantics) instilled into real-life information granules? Is the meaning instilled through an algorithmic processing of constituent entities or is it a feature that is independent of algorithmic processing?

The answers to these questions are hinted by von Neumann's *limitation of size principle,* mentioned in the previous section, and are more fully informed by Turing's theoretical model of computation. In his original paper, Turing (1936), he has defined computation as an automatic version of doing what people do when they manipulate numbers and symbols on paper. He proposed a conceptual model which included: (a) an arbitrarily long tape from which one could read as many symbols as needed (from a countable set); (b) means to read and write those symbols; (c) a countable set of states storing information about the completed processing of symbols; and (d) a countable set of rules that governed what should be done for various combinations of input and system state. A physical instantiation of computation, envisaged by Turing, was a human operator (called computer) who was compelled to obey the rules (a)–(d) above. There are several important implications of Turing's definition of computation. First, the model implies that computation explores only a subset of capabilities of human information processing. Second, the constraint that the input and output is strictly symbolic (with symbols drawn from a countable set) implies that the computer does not interact directly with the environment. These are critical limitations meaning that Turing's computer on its own is unable (by definition) to respond to external, physical stimuli. *Consequently, it is not just wrong but essentially meaningless to speculate on the ability of Turing machines to perform human-like intelligent interactions with the real world.*

To phrase it in mathematical terms, the general form of computation, formalized as a Universal Turing Machine (UTM), is defined as mapping of sets that have at most cardinality $\aleph_0$ (infinite, countable) onto sets with cardinality $\aleph_0$. The practical instances of information processing, such as clustering of data, typically involve a finite number of elements both in the input and output sets and represent therefore a more manageable mapping of a finite set with cardinality max_1 onto another finite set with cardinality max_2. The hierarchy of computable clustering can be therefore represented as in Figure 2.1.

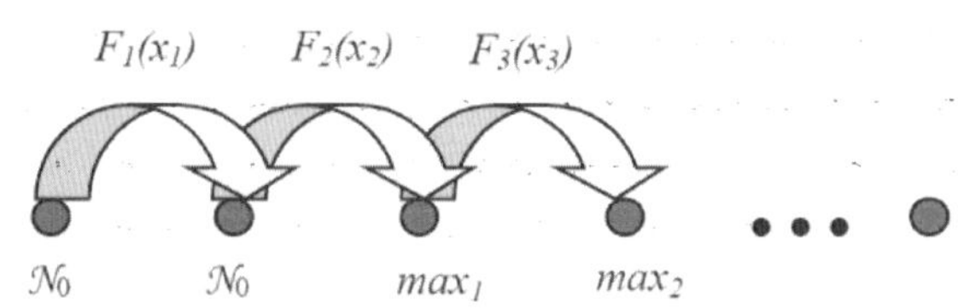

Figure 2.1: Cardinality of sets in a hierarchy of clustering implemented on UTM.

The functions $F_1(x_1) \rightarrow x_2$, $F_2(x_2) \rightarrow x_3$, $F_3(x_3) \rightarrow x_4$ represent mappings of

— infinite (countable) input set onto infinite (countable) output set;
— infinite (countable) input set onto finite output set; and
— finite input set onto finite output set, respectively.

The functional mappings, deployed in the process of clustering, reflect the criteria of similarity, proximity or indistinguishability of elements in the input set and, on this basis, grouping them together into a separate entity to be placed in the output set. In other words, the functional mappings generate data abstractions on the basis of pre-defined criteria and consequently represent UTM computation. However, we need to understand how these criteria are selected and how they are decided to be appropriate in any specific circumstance. Clearly, there are many ways of defining similarity, proximity or indistinguishability. Some of these definitions are likely to have good real-world interpretation, while others may be difficult to interpret or indeed may lead to physically meaningless results.

We suggest that the process of instilling the real-world interpretation into data structures generated by functional mappings $F_1(x_1) \rightarrow x_2$, $F_2(x_2) \rightarrow x_3$, $F_3(x_3) \rightarrow x_4$, involves reference to the real-world, as illustrated in Figure 2.2. This is represented as execution of "experimentation" functions $E_*(x_0)$. These functions map the real-world domain x_0, which has cardinality N_1 (infinite, continuum), onto sets x_1, x_2, x_3, x_4, respectively.

At this point, it is important to underline that the experimentation functions $E_1(x_0) \rightarrow x_1$, $E_2(x_0) \rightarrow x_2$, $E_3(x_0) \rightarrow x_3$, $E_4(x_0) \rightarrow x_4$, are not computational, in UTM sense, because their domain have cardinality N_1. So, the process of defining the criteria for data clustering, and implicitly instilling the meaning into information granules, relies on the laws of physics and not on the mathematical model of computation. Furthermore, the results of experimentation do not depend on whether the experimenter understands or is even aware of the laws of physics. It is precisely because of the fact that we consider the experimentation functions as providing objective evidence.

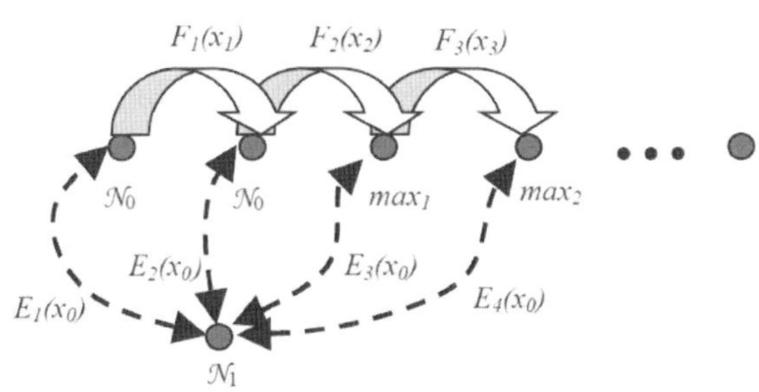

Figure 2.2: Mapping of abstractions from the real-world domain (cardinality N_1) onto the sets of clusters.

2.4. Experimentation as a Physical Computation

Recent research (Siegelmann, 1999) has demonstrated that analog computation, in the form of recurrent analog neural networks (RANN) can exceed the abilities of a UTM, if the weights in such neural networks are allowed to take continuous rather than discrete weights. While this result is significant in itself, it relies on the assumptions about the continuity of parameters that are difficult to verify. So, although the brain looks remarkably like a RANN, drawing any conclusions about the hyper-computational abilities of the brain, purely on the grounds of structural similarities, leads to the same questions about the validity of the assumptions about continuity of weights. Of course, this is not to say that these assumptions are not valid, they may well be valid, but we just highlight that this has not been demonstrated yet in a conclusive way.

A pragmatic approach to bridging the gap between the theoretical model of hyper-computation, as offered by RANN, and the human, intelligent information processing (which by definition is hyper-computational) has been proposed by Bains (2003, 2005). Her suggestion was to reverse the original question about hyper-computational ability of systems and to ask: *if the behavior of physical systems cannot be replicated using Turing machines, how can they be replicated*? The answer to this question is surprisingly simple: *we can use inherent computational ability of physical phenomena in conjunction with the numerical information processing ability of UTM*. In other words, the readiness to refine numerical computations in the light of objective evidence coming from a real-life experiment, instills the ability to overcome limitations of the Turing machine. We have advocated this approach in our earlier work (Bargiela, 2004), and have argued that the hyper-computational power of GrC is equivalent to "keeping open mind" in intelligent, human information processing.

In what follows, we describe the model of physical computation, as proposed in Bains (2003), and cast it in the framework of GrC.

2.4.1. *A Model of Physical Computation*

We define a system under consideration as an identifiable collection of connected elements. A system is said to be *embodied* if it occupies a definable volume and has a collective contiguous boundary. In particular, a UTM with its collection of input/output (I/O) data, states and collection of rules, implementing some information processing algorithm, can be considered a system G whose physical instantiations may refer to specific I/O, processing and storage devices as well as specific energy states. The matter, space and energy outside the boundaries of the embodied system are collectively called the *physical environment* and will be denoted here by P.

A *sensor* is any part of the system that can be changed by physical influences from the environment. Any forces, fields, energy, matter, etc., that may be impinging on the system, are collectively called the *sensor input* ($i \in X$), even where no explicitly-defined sensors exist.

An *actuator* is any part of the system that can change the environment. Physical changes to the embodied system that manifest themselves externally (e.g., emission of energy, change of position, etc.) are collectively called the *actuator output* ($h \in Y$) of G. A coupled pair of sensor input i_t and actuator output h_t represents an instance of experimentation at time t and is denoted here as E_t.

Since the system G, considered in this study, is a computational system (modeled by UTM) and since the objective of the evolution of this system is to mimic human intelligent information processing we will define G_t as the *computational intelligence function* performed by the embodied system G. Function G_t maps the I/O at specific time instances t, resolved with arbitrarily small accuracy $\delta t > 0$, so as not to preclude the possibility of a continuous physical time. We can thus formally define the computational intelligence function as

$$G_t(i_t) \rightarrow h_{t+\delta t}.$$

In the proposed physical model of computation, we stipulate that G_t causes only an immediate output in response to an immediate input. This stipulation does not prevent one from implementing some plan over time but it implies that a controller that would be necessary to implement such plan is part of the intelligence function. The adaptation of G_t in response to evolving input i_t can be described by the *computational learning function*, L_G: $L_G(G_t, i_t) \rightarrow G_{t+\delta t}$.

Considering now the impact of the system behavior on the environment we can define the *environment reaction function* mapping system output h (environment input) to environment output i (system input) as

$$P_t(h_t) \rightarrow i_{t+\delta t}$$

The adaptation of the environment P over time can be described by the *environment learning function*, L_P: $L_P(P_t, h_t) \rightarrow P_{t+\delta t}$.

2.4.2. *Physical Interaction between P and G*

The interaction between the system G and its physical environment P may be considered to fall into one of the two classes: *real interaction* and *virtual interaction*. Real interaction is a pure physical process in which the output from the environment P is in its entirety forwarded as an input to the system G and conversely the output from G is fully utilized as input to P.

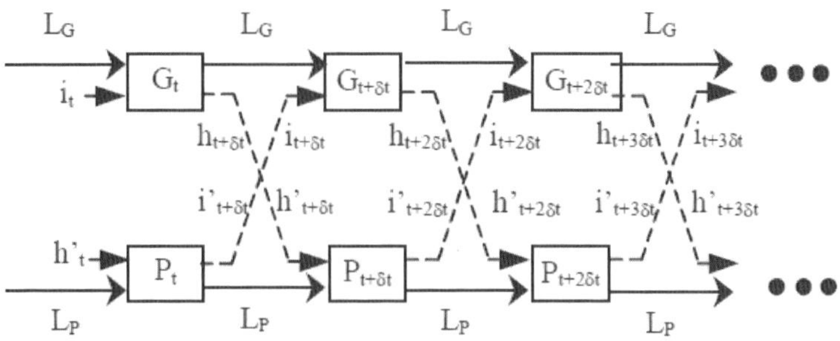

Figure 2.3: Evolution of a system in an experiment with physical interaction.

Referring to the notation in Figure 2.3, real interaction is one in which $h_t = h'_t$ and $i_t = i'_t$ for all time instances t. Unfortunately, this type of interaction does not accept the limitations of the UTM, namely, the processing of only a pre-defined set of symbols rather than a full spectrum of responses from the environment. Consequently, this type of interaction places too high demands on the information processing capabilities of G and, in practical terms, is limited to interaction of physical objects as governed by the laws of physics. In other words the intelligence function and its implementation are one and the same.

2.4.3. *Virtual Interaction*

An alternative mode of interaction is *virtual interaction*, which is mediated by symbolic representation of information. Here, we use the term *symbol* as it is defined in the context of UTM: a letter or sign taken from a finite alphabet to allow distinguishability.

We define V_t as the *virtual computational intelligence function*, analogous to G_t in terms of information processing, and V'_t as the *complementary computational intelligence function*, analogous to G_t in terms of communication with the physical environment. With the above definitions, we can lift some major constraints of physical interactions, with important consequences. The complementary function V'_t can implement an interface to the environment, filtering real-life information input from the environment and facilitating transfer of actuator output, while the virtual intelligence function V_t can implement UTM processing of the filtered information. This means that i_t does not need to be equal to i'_t and h_t does not need to be equal to h'_t. In other words, I/O may be considered selectively rather than in their totality. The implication being that many physically distinguishable states may have the same symbolic representation at the virtual computational intelligence function level. The relationship between the two components of the computational intelligence is illustrated in Figure 2.4.

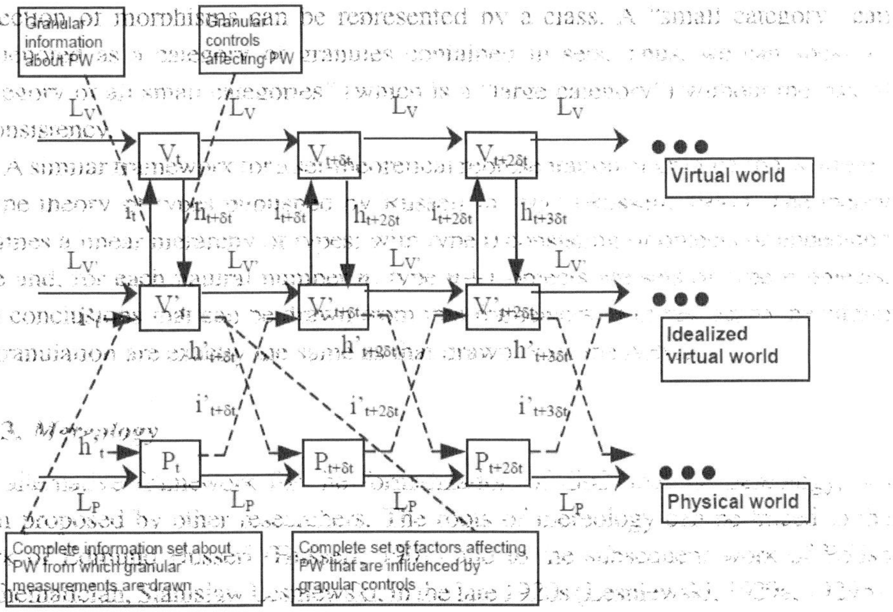

Figure 2.4: Evolution of a system in an experiment with virtual interaction.

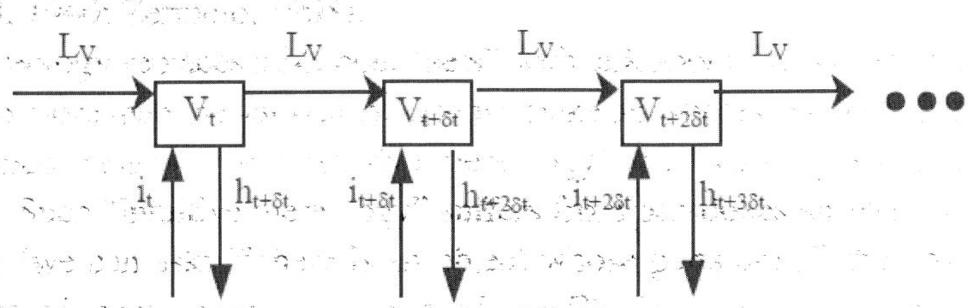

Figure 2.5: The paradigm of computing with perceptions within the framework of virtual interaction.

It should be pointed out that typically we think of the complementary function V_t' as some mechanical or electronic device (utilizing the laws of physics in its interaction with the environment) but a broader interpretation that includes human perception, as discussed by Zadeh (1997), is entirely consistent with the above model. In this broader context, the UTM implementing the virtual computational intelligence function can be referred to as *computing with perceptions* or *computing with words* (see Figure 2.5).

Another important implication of the virtual interaction model is that V and P need not have any kind of conserved relationship. This is because only range/modality of subsets of i_t' and h_t' attach to V and these subsets are defined by the choice of sensor/actuator modalities. So, we can focus on the choice of modalities, within the complementary computational intelligence function, as a mechanism through which one can exercise the assignment of semantics to both I/O of the virtual intelligence function. To put it informally, the complementary function is a facility for defining a "language" in which we chose to communicate with the real world.

Of course, to make the optimal choice (one that allows undistorted perception and interaction with the physical environment), it would be necessary to have a complete knowledge of the physical environment. So, in its very nature the process of defining the semantics of I/O of the virtual intelligence function is iterative and involves evolution of our understanding of the physical environment.

2.5. Granular Computation

An important conclusion from the discussion above is that the discovery of semantics of information abstraction, referred to sometimes as structured thinking, or a philosophical dimension of GrC, can be reduced to physical experimentation. This is a very welcome development as it gives a good basis for the formalization of the GrC paradigm.

We argue here that GrC should be defined as a **structured combination** of algorithmic abstraction of data and non-algorithmic, empirical verification of the semantics of these abstractions. This definition is general in that it neither prescribes the mechanism of algorithmic abstraction nor it elaborates on the techniques of experimental verification. Instead, it highlights the essence of combining computational and non-computational information processing. Such a definition has several advantages:

— it emphasizes the complementarity of the two constituent functional mappings;
— it justifies the hyper-computational nature of GrC;
— it places physics alongside set theory as the theoretical foundations of GrC;
— it helps to avoid confusion between GrC and purely algorithmic data processing while taking full advantage of the advances in algorithmic data processing.

2.6. An Example of Granular Computation

We illustrate here an application of the granular computation, cast in the formalism of set theory, to a practical problem of analyzing traffic queues. A three-way intersection is represented in Figure 2.7. The three lane-occupancy detectors (inductive loops), labeled here as "east", "west" and "south" provide counts of vehicles passing over them. The counts are then integrated to yield a measure of traffic queues on the corresponding approaches to the junction. A representative sample of the resulting three-dimensional time series of traffic queues is illustrated in Figure 2.8.

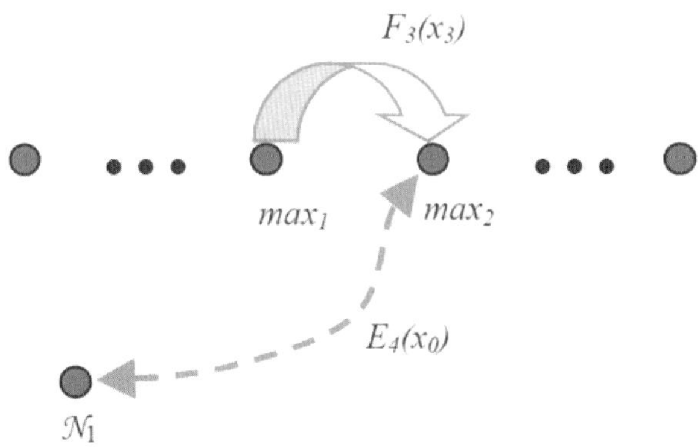

Figure 2.6: An instance of GrC involving two essential components: algorithmic clustering and empirical evaluation of granules.

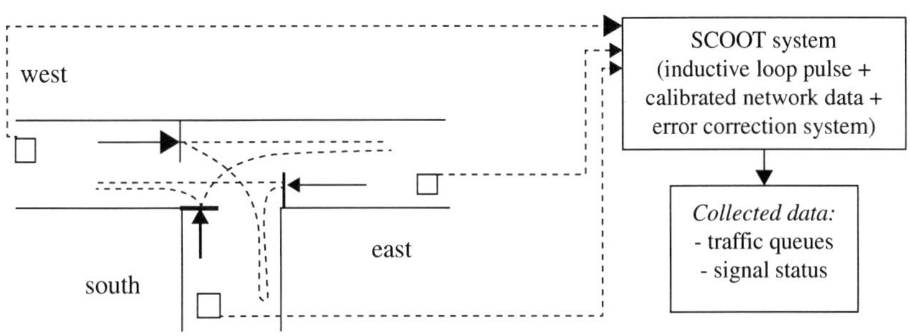

Figure 2.7: A three-way intersection with measured traffic queues.

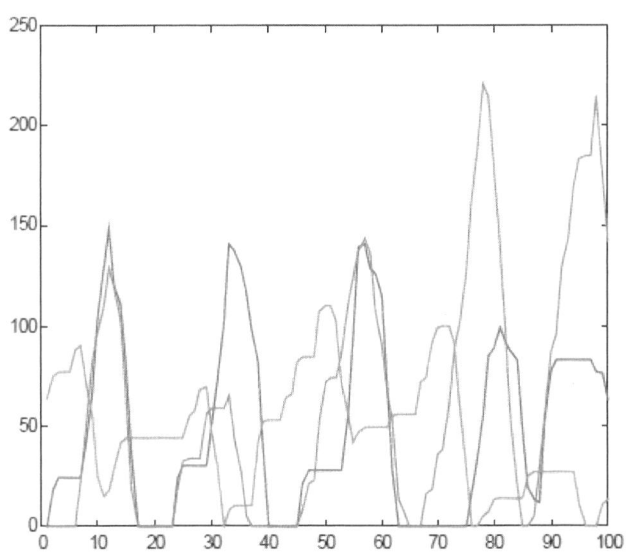

Figure 2.8: A subset of 100 readings from the time series of traffic queues data.

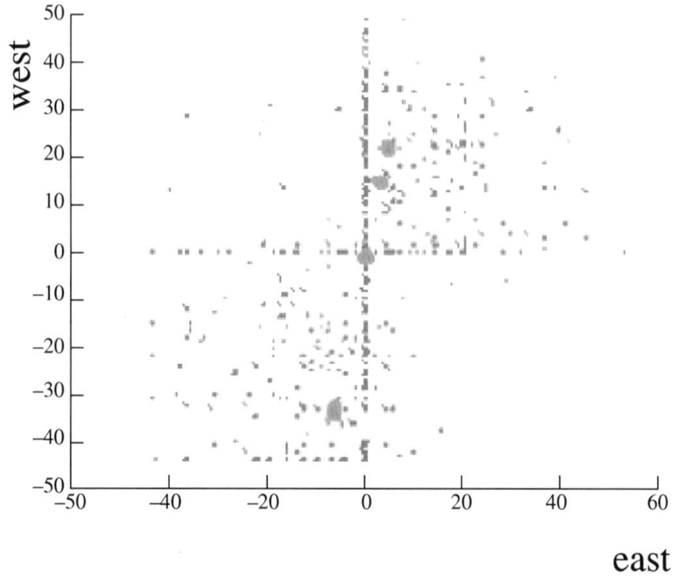

Figure 2.9: FCM prototypes as subset of the original measurements of traffic queues.

It is quite clear that, on its own, data depicted in Figure 2.8 reflects primarily the signaling stages of the junction. This view is reinforced, if we plot the traffic queues on a two-dimensional plane and apply some clustering technique [such as Fuzzy C-Means (FCM)] to identify prototypes that are the best (in terms of the given optimality criterion) representation of data. The prototypes, denoted as small circles in Figure 2.9, indicate that the typical operation of the junction involves simultaneously increasing and decreasing queues on the "east" and "west" junction. This of course corresponds to "red" and "green" signaling stages. It is worth emphasizing here that the above prototypes can be considered as a simple subset of the original numerical data since the nature of the prototypes is entirely consistent with that of the original data.

Unfortunately, within this framework, the interpretation of the prototype indicating "zero" queue in both "east" and "west" direction is not very informative. In order to uncover the meaning of this prototype, we resort to a granulated view of data. Figure 2.10 represents traffic queue data that has been granulated based on maximization of information density measure discussed in Bargiela *et al.* (2006). The semantics of the original readings is now changed from point representation of queues into interval (hyperbox) representation of queues. In terms of set theory, we are dealing here with a class of hyperboxes, which is semantically distinct from point data.

Applying FCM clustering to granular data results in granular prototypes denoted, in Figure 2.10, as rectangles with bold boundaries overlaid on the

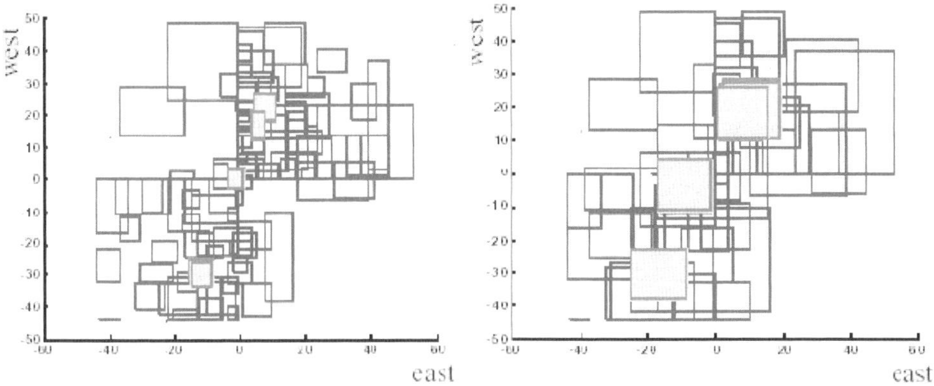

Figure 2.10: Granular FCM prototypes representing a class that is semantically distinct from the original point data.

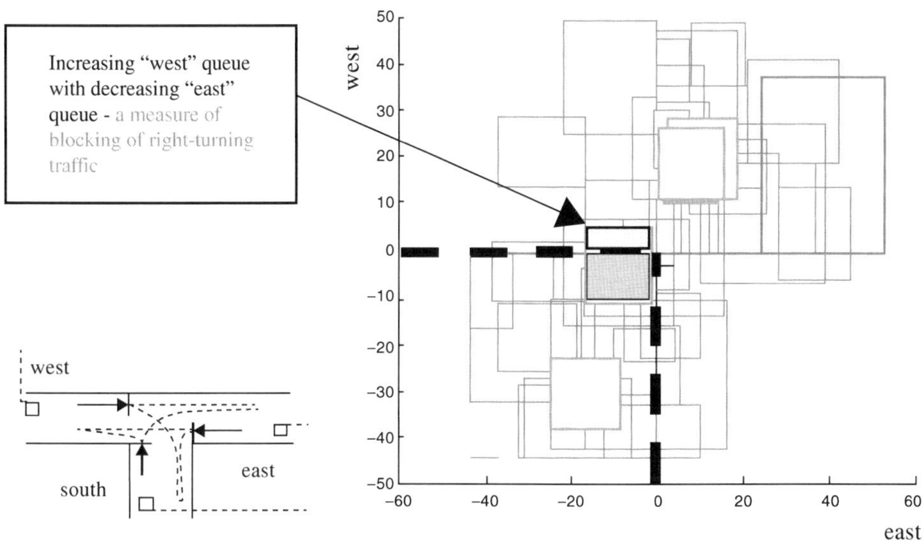

Figure 2.11: Granular prototype capturing traffic delays for "right turning" traffic.

granulated data. In order to ascertain that the granulation does not distort the essential features of the data, different granulation parameters have been investigated and a representative sample of two granulations is depicted in Figure 2.10. The three FCM prototypes lying in the areas of simultaneous increase and decrease of traffic queues have identical interpretation as the corresponding prototypes in Figure 2.9. However, the central prototype highlights a physical property of traffic that was not captured by the numerical prototype.

Figure 2.11 illustrates the richer interpretation of the central prototype. It is clear that the traffic queues on the western approach are increasing while the traffic queues on the eastern approach are decreasing. This is caused by the "right turning" traffic being blocked by the oncoming traffic from the eastern junction. It is worth noting that the prototype is unambiguous about the absence of a symmetrical situation where an increase of traffic queues on the eastern junction would occur simultaneously with the decrease of the queues on the western junction. The fact is that this is a three-way junction with no right turn for the traffic from the eastern junction and has been captured purely from the granular interpretation of data. Note that the same cannot be said about the numerical data illustrated in Figure 2.9.

As we have argued in this chapter, the essential component of GrC is the experimental validation of the semantics of the information granules. We have conducted a planned experiment in which we placed counting devices on the entrance to the "south" link. The proportion of the vehicles entering the "south" junction (during the green stage of the "east–west" junction) to the count of vehicles on the stop line on the "west" approach, represents a measure of the right turning traffic. The ratio of these numerical counts was 0.1428. A similar measurement derived from two different granulations depicted in Figure 2.10 was 0.1437 and 0.1498. We conclude therefore that the granulated data captured the essential characteristics of the right turning traffic and that, in this particular application, the granulation parameters do not affect the result to a significant degree (which is clearly a desirable property).

A more extensive experimentation could involve verification of the granular measurement of right turning traffic for drivers that have different driving styles in terms of acceleration and gap acceptance. Although we do not make any specific claim in this respect, it is possible that the granulation of traffic queue data would need to be parameterized with the dynamic driver behavior data. Such data could be derived by differentiating the traffic queues (measurement of the speed of change of queues) and granulating the resulting six-dimensional data.

References

Bains, S. (2003). Intelligence as physical computation. *AISBJ*, 1(3), 225–240.

Bains, S. (2005). Physical computation and embodied artificial intelligence. Ph.D. thesis. The Open University, January, 1–199.

Bargiela, A. and Pedrycz, W. (2002a). *Granular Computing: An Introduction*. Dordrecht, Netherlands: Kluwer Academic Publishers.

Bargiela, A. and Pedrycz, W. (2002b). From numbers to information granules: a study of unsupervised learning and feature analysis. In Bunke, H. and Kandel, A. (eds.), *Hybrid Methods in Pattern Recognition*. Singapore: World Scientific, pp. 75–112.

Bargiela, A. and Pedrycz, W. (2003). Recursive information granulation: aggregation and interpretation issues. *IEEE Trans. Syst. Man Cybern. SMC-B*, 33(1), pp. 96–112.

Bargiela, A. (2004). Hyper-computational characteristics of granular computing. *First Warsaw Int. Semin. Intell. Syst.-WISIS 2004*, Invited lectures. Warsaw, May, pp. 1–8.

Bargiela, A., Pedrycz, W. and Tanaka, M. (2004a). An inclusion/exclusion fuzzy hyperbox classifier. *Int. J. Knowl.-Based Intell. Eng. Syst.*, 8(2), pp. 91–98.

Bargiela, A., Pedrycz, W. and Hirota, K. (2004b). Granular prototyping in fuzzy clustering. *IEEE Trans. Fuzzy Syst.*, 12(5), pp. 697–709.

Bargiela, A. and Pedrycz, W. (2005a). A model of granular data: a design problem with the Tchebyschev FCM. *Soft Comput.*, 9(3), pp. 155–163.

Bargiela, A. and Pedrycz, W. (2005b). Granular mappings. *IEEE Trans. Syst. Man Cybern. SMC-A*, 35(2), pp. 288–301.

Bargiela, A. and Pedrycz, W. (2006). The roots of granular computing. *Proc. IEEE Granular Comput. Conf.*, Atlanta, pp. 741–744. May.

Bargiela, A., Kosonen, I., Pursula, M. and Peytchev, E. (2006). Granular analysis of traffic data for turning movements estimation. *Int. J. Enterp. Inf. Syst.*, 2(2), pp. 13–27.

Cantor, G. (1879). Über einen satz aus der theorie der stetigen mannigfaltigkeiten. *Göttinger Nachr.*, pp. 127–135.

Dubois, D, Prade, H. and Yager, R. (eds.). (1997). *Fuzzy Information Engineering*. New York: Wiley.

Goedel, K. (1940). *The Consistency of the Axiom of Choice and of the Generalized Continuum Hypothesis with the Axioms of Set Theory.* Princeton, NJ: Princeton University Press.

Husserl, E. (1901). Logische untersuchungen. *Phanomenologie und theorie der erkenntnis*, 2, pp. 1–759.

Inuiguchi, M., Hirano, S. and Tsumoto, S. (eds.). (2003). *Rough Set Theory and Granular Computing*. Berlin: Springer.

Lesniewski, S. (1929a). Uber funktionen, deren felder gruppen mit rucksicht auf diese funktionen sind. *Fundamenta Mathematicae*, 13, pp. 319–332.

Lesniewski, S. (1929b). Grundzuge eines neuen systems der grundlagen der mathematic. *Fundamenta Mathematicae*, 14, pp. 1–81.

Lin, T. Y. (1998). Granular computing on binary relations. In Polkowski, L. and Skowron, A. (eds.). *Rough Sets in Knowledge Discovery: Methodology and Applications*. Heildelberg, Germany: Physica-Verlag, pp. 286–318.

Lin, T. Y., Yao, Y. Y. and Zadeh, L. A. (eds.). (2002). *Data Mining, Rough Sets and Granular Computing*, Heildelberg, Germany: Physica-Verlag.

Pawlak, Z. (1991). *Rough Sets: Theoretical Aspects of Reasoning about Data*. Dordrecht, Netherlands: Kluwer Academic Publishers.

Pawlak, Z. (1999). Granularity of knowledge, indiscernibility and rough sets. *Proc. IEEE Conf. Evolutionary Comput.*, Anchorange, Alaska, pp. 106–110.

Pedrycz, W. (1989). *Fuzzy Control and Fuzzy Systems*. New York: Wiley.

Pedrycz, W. and Gomide, F. (1998). *An Introduction to Fuzzy Sets*. Cambridge, MA: MIT Press.

Pedrycz, W., Smith, M. H. and Bargiela, A. (2000). Granular clustering: a granular signature of data. *Proc. 19th Int. (IEEE) Conf. NAFIPS'2000*. Atlanta, pp. 69–73.

Pedrycz, W. and Bargiela, A. (2002). Granular clustering: a granular signature of data. *IEEE Trans. Syst. Man Cybern.*, 32(2), pp. 212–224.

Pontow, C. and Schubert, R. (2006). A mathematical analysis of parthood. *Data Knowl. Eng.*, 59(1), pp. 107–138.

Russell, B. (1937). New foundations for mathematical logic. *Am. Math. Mon.*, 44(2), pp. 70–80.

Siegelmann, H. (1999). *Neural Network and Analogue Computation: Beyond the Turing limit*. Boston, MA: Birkhauser.

Simons, P. (1987). *Parts: A Study in Ontology*. Oxford, UK: Oxford University Press.

Skowron, A. and Stepaniuk, J. (2001). Information granules: towards foundations of granular computing. *Int. J. Intell. Syst.*, 16, pp. 57–85.

Tarski, A. (1983). Foundations of the geometry of solids. In *Logic, Semantics, Metamathematics*: Indianapolis: Hackett.

Turing, A. (1936). On computable numbers, with an application to the entscheidungs problem. *Proc. London Math. Soc.*, 42, pp. 230–265.

Yao, Y. Y. and Yao, J. T. (2002). Granular computing as a basis for consistent classification problems. *Proc. PAKDD'02 Workshop on Found. Data Min.*, pp. 101–106.

Yao, Y. Y. (2004a). Granular computing. *Proc. Fourth Chin. National Conf. Rough Sets Soft Comput. Sci.*, 31, pp. 1–5.

Yao, Y. Y. (2004b). A partition model of granular computing. *LNCS Trans. Rough Sets*, 1, pp. 232–253.

Yao, Y. Y. (2005). Perspectives on granular computing. *Proc. IEEE Conf. Granular Comput.*, 1, pp. 85–90.

Zadeh, L. A. (1965). Fuzzy sets. *Inf. Control*, 8, pp. 338–353.

Zadeh, L. A. (1979). Fuzzy sets and information granularity. In Gupta, N., Ragade, R. and Yager, R. (eds.), *Advances in Fuzzy Set Theory and Applications*. Amsterdam: North-Holland Publishing Company.

Zadeh, L. A. (1997). Toward a theory of fuzzy information granulation and its centrality in human reasoning and fuzzy logic. *Fuzzy Sets Syst.*, 90, pp. 111–127.

Zadeh, L. A. (2002). From computing with numbers to computing with words — from manipulation of measurements to manipulation of perceptions. *Int. J. Appl. Math Comput. Sci.*, 12(3), pp. 307–324.

Zermelo, E. (1908). Untersuchungen ueber die grundlagen der mengenlehre. *Math. Annalen*, 65, pp. 261–281.

Chapter 3

Evolving Fuzzy Systems — Fundamentals, Reliability, Interpretability, Useability, Applications

Edwin Lughofer

This chapter provides a round picture of the development and advances in the field of *evolving fuzzy systems* (EFS) made during the last decade since their first appearance in 2002. Their basic difference to conventional fuzzy systems (discussed in other chapters in this book) is that they can be learned from data on-the-fly (fast) during online processes in an incremental and mostly single-pass manner. Therefore, they stand for a very emerging topic in the field of soft computing for addressing modeling problems in the quickly increasing complexity of real-world applications, more and more implying a shift from batch offline model design phases (as conducted since the 80s) to permanent online (active) model teaching and adaptation. The focus will be placed on the definition of various model architectures used in the context of EFS, on providing an overview about the basic learning concepts, on listing the most prominent EFS approaches (fundamentals), and on discussing advanced aspects toward an improved stability, reliability and useability (usually must-to-haves to guarantee robustness and user-friendliness) as well as an educated interpretability (usually a nice-to-have to offer insights into the systems' nature). It will be concluded with a list of real-world applications where various EFS approaches have been successfully applied with satisfactory accuracy, robustness and speed.

3.1. Introduction — Motivation

Due to the increasing complexity and permanent growth of data acquisition sites in today's industrial systems, there is an increasing demand of fast modeling algorithms from online data streams (Gama, 2010). Such algorithms are ensuring that models can be quickly adapted to the actual system situation and thus are able to provide reliable outputs at any time during online real-world processes. Their changing operating conditions, environmental influences and new unexplored system states may trigger quite a dynamic behavior, causing previously trained models to become inefficient or even inaccurate (Sayed-Mouchaweh and Lughofer, 2012). In this sense, conventional static models which are trained once in an offline stage and are not able to adapt dynamically to the actual system states are not an adequate alternative for coping with these demands (severe downtrends in accuracy have been examined in previous publications). A list of potential real-world application examples relying on online dynamic aspects and thus demanding flexible modeling techniques can be found in Table 3.3 (Section 3.6.5).

Another challenge which has recently become a very hot topic within the machine learning community and is given specific attention in the new European framework programme Horizon 2020, is the processing and mining of the so-called *Big Data*,[1] usually stemming from very large databases (VLDB).[2] The occurrence of *Big Data* takes place in many areas such as meteorology, genomics, connectomics, complex physics simulations and biological and environmental research (Reichmann *et al.*, 2011). This data is that big (exabytes) such that it cannot be handled in a one-shot experience, such as exceeding virtual memory of nowadays conventional computers. Thus, standard batch modeling techniques are not applicable.

In order to tackle the aforementioned requirements, the field of "evolving intelligent systems (EISs)"[3] or, in a wider machine learning sense, the field of "learning in dynamic environments (LDE)" enjoyed increasing attraction during the last years (Angelov *et al.*, 2010). This even lead to the emergence of their own journal in 2010, termed as "Evolving Systems" at Springer (Heidelberg).[4] Both fields support learning topologies which operate in single-pass manner and are able to update models and surrogate statistics on-the-fly and on demand. Single-pass nature and incrementality of the updates assure online and in most cases even real-time learning and model training capabilities. While EIS focuses mainly on adaptive evolving models within the field of soft computing, LDE goes a step further and also joins incremental machine learning and data mining techniques, originally stemming from the area of "incremental heuristic search".[5] The update in these approaches concerns both parameter adaptation and structural changes depending on the degree of change required. The structural changes are usually enforced by evolution and pruning components, and finally responsible for the terminus *Evolving Systems*. In this context, *Evolving* should be not confused with *Evolutionary* (as sometimes happened in the past, unfortunately). Evolutionary approaches are usually applied in the context of complex optimization problems to learn parameters and structures based on genetic operators, but they do this by using all the data in an iterative optimization procedure rather than integrating new knowledge permanently on-the-fly.

---

[1] http://en.wikipedia.org/wiki/Big_data.

[2] http://en.wikipedia.org/wiki/Very_large_database.

[3] http://en.wikipedia.org/wiki/Evolving_intelligent_system.

[4] http://www.springer.com/physics/complexity/journal/12530.

[5] http://en.wikipedia.org/wiki/Incremental_heuristic_search.

Apart from the requirements and demands in industrial (production and control) systems, another important aspect about evolving models is that they provide the opportunity for self-learning computer systems and machines. In fact, evolving models are permanently updating their knowledge and understanding about diverse complex relationships and dependencies in real-world application scenarios by integrating new system behaviors and environmental influences (which are manifested in the captured data). Their learning follows a life-long learning context and is never really terminated, but lasts as long as new information arrives. Therefore, they can be seen as a valuable contribution within the field of computational intelligence (Angelov and Kasabov, 2005) or even in artificial intelligence (Lughofer, 2011a).

There are several possibilities for using an adequate model architecture within the context of an evolving system. This strongly depends on the learning problem at hand, in particular, whether it is supervised or unsupervised. In case of the later, techniques from the field of clustering, usually termed as *incremental clustering* (Bouchachia, 2011) are a prominent choice. In case of classification and regression models, the architectures should support decision boundaries respectively approximation surfaces with an arbitrary nonlinearity degree. Also, the choice may depend on past experience with some machine learning and data mining tools: for instance, it is well-known that SVMs are usually among the top-10 performers for many classification tasks (Wu *et al.*, 2006), thus are a reasonable choice to be used in an online classification setting as well [in form of incremental SVMs (Diehl and Cauwenberghs, 2003; Shilton *et al.*, 2005)]; whereas in a regression setting they are usually performing much weaker. Soft computing models such as neural networks (Haykin, 1999), fuzzy systems (Pedrycz and Gomide, 2007) or genetic programming (Affenzeller *et al.*, 2009) and any hybrid concepts of these [e.g., neuro-fuzzy systems (Jang, 1993)] are all known to be universal approximators (Balas *et al.*, 2009) and thus able to resolve nonlinearities implicitly contained in the systems' behavior (and thus reflected in the data streams). Neural networks suffer from their black box nature, i.e., not allowing operators and users any insight into the models extracted from the streams. This may be essential in many contexts for the interpretation of model outputs to realize why certain decisions have been made etc. Genetic programming is a more promising choice in this direction, however, it is often expanding unnecessarily complex formulas with many nested functional terms [suffering from the so-called bloating effect (Zavoianu, 2010)], which are again hard to interpret.

Fuzzy systems are specific mathematical models which build upon the concept of fuzzy logic, firstly introduced in 1965 by Lotfi A. Zadeh (Zadeh, 1965), are a very useful alternative, as they contain rules which are linguistically readable and interpretable. This mimicks the human thinking about relationships and structural dependencies being present in a system. This will become more clear in the subsequent section when mathematically defining possible architecture variants within the field of fuzzy systems, which have been also used in the context of data stream mining and evolving systems. Furthermore, the reader may refer to Chapter 1 in this book, where the basic concepts of fuzzy sets and systems are introduced and described in detail.

3.2. Architectures for Evolving Fuzzy Systems (EFSs)

The first five subsections are dedicated to architectures for regression problems, for which EFS have been preliminary used. Then, various variants of fuzzy classification model structures are discussed, as have been recently introduced for representing of decision boundaries in various forms in evolving fuzzy classifiers (EFCs).

3.2.1. *Mamdani*

Mamdani fuzzy systems (Mamdani, 1977) are the most common choice for coding expert knowledge/experience into a rule-based IF-THEN form, examples can be found in Holmblad and Ostergaard (1982); Leondes (1998) or Carr and Tah (2001); Reveiz and Len (2010).

In general, assuming p input variables (features), the definition of the ith rule in a single output Mamdani fuzzy system is as follows:

$$\text{Rule}_i : \text{IF } (x_1 \text{ IS } \mu_{i1}) \text{ AND} \ldots \text{AND } (x_p \text{ IS } \mu_{ip}) \text{ THEN } l_i(\vec{x}) \text{ IS } \Phi_i,$$

with Φ_i the consequent fuzzy set in the fuzzy partition of the output variable used in the consequent $l_i(\vec{x})$ of the ith rule, and $\mu_{i1}, \ldots, \mu_{ip}$ are the fuzzy sets appearing in the rule antecedents. The *rule firing degree* (also called *rule activation level*) for a concrete input vector $\vec{x} = (x_1, \ldots, x_p)$ is then defined by:

$$\mu_i(\vec{x}) = \operatorname*{T}_{j=1}^{p} \mu_{ij}(x_j), \tag{1}$$

with T a specific conjunction operator, denoted as t-norm Klement *et al.* (2000) — most frequently, minimum or product are used, i.e.,

$$\mu_i(\vec{x}) = \min_{j=1}^{p}(\mu_{ij}(x_j)) \quad \mu_i(\vec{x}) = \prod_{j=1}^{p}(\mu_{ij}(x_j)). \tag{2}$$

It may happen that $\Phi_i = \Phi_j$ for some $i \neq j$. Hence, a t-conorm (Klement *et al.*, 2000) is applied which combines the rule firing levels of those rules having the same consequents to one output set. The most common choice for the t-conorm is the maximum operator. In this case, the consequent fuzzy set is cut at the alpha-level:

$$\alpha_i = max_{j_i=1,\dots,C_i}(\mu_{j_i}(\vec{x})), \tag{3}$$

with C_i the number of rules whose consequent fuzzy set is the same as for Rule i, and j_i the indices of these rules. This is done for the whole fuzzy rule-base and the various α-cut output sets are joined to one fuzzy area employing the *supremum operator*. An example of such a fuzzy output area is shown in Figure 3.1.

In order to obtain a crisp output value, a defuzzification method is applied, most commonly used are the mean of maximum (MOM) over the whole area, the center of gravity (COG) or the bisector (Leekwijck and Kerre, 1999) which is the vertical line that will divide the whole area into two sub-regions of equal areas. For concrete formulas of the defuzzification operators, please refer to Piegat (2001) and Nguyen *et al.* (1995). MOM and COG are exemplarily shown in Figure 3.1.

Due to the defuzzification process, it is quite intuitive that the inference in Mamdani fuzzy systems loses some accuracy, as an output fuzzy number is reduced to a crisp number. Therefore, they have been hardly applied within the context of online modeling and data stream mining, where the main purpose is to obtain an accurate evolving fuzzy model in the context of *precise evolving fuzzy modeling* [an exception can be found in Rubio (2009), termed as the SOFMLS approach]. On the other hand, they are able to provide linguistic interpretability on the output level, thus may be preferable in the context of interpretability demands for knowledge gaining and reasoning (see also Section 3.5). The approach in Ho *et al.* (2010), tries

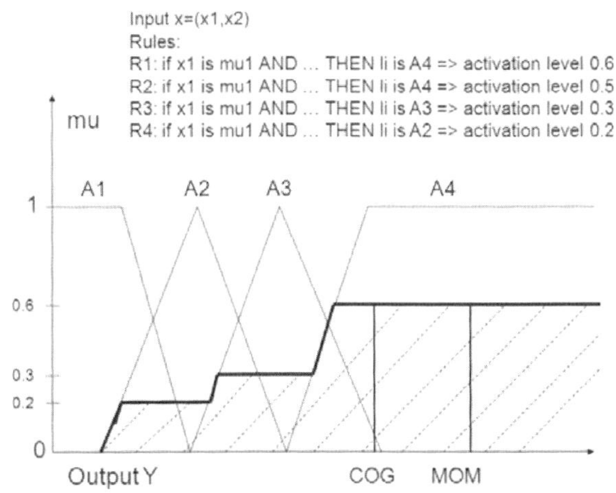

Figure 3.1: MOM and COG defuzzification for a rule consequent partition (fuzzy partition in output variable Y) in a Mamdani fuzzy system, the shaded area indicates the joint consequents (fuzzy sets) in the active rules (applying supremum operator); the cutoff points (alpha cuts) are according to maximal membership degrees obtained from the rule antecedent parts of the active rules.

to benefit from this while keeping the precise modeling spirit by applying a switched architecture, joining Mamdani and Takagi–Sugeno type consequents in form of a convex combination.

3.2.2. *Takagi–Sugeno*

Opposed to Mamdani fuzzy systems, Takagi–Sugeno (TS) fuzzy systems (Takagi and Sugeno, 1985) are the most common architectorial choices in evolving fuzzy systems approaches (Lughofer, 2011b). This has several reasons. First of all, they enjoy a large attraction in many fields of real-world applications and systems engineering (Pedrycz and Gomide, 2007), ranging from process control (Babuska, 1998; Karer and Skrjanc, 2013; Piegat, 2001), system identification (Abonyi, 2003; Nelles, 2001), through condition monitoring (Serdio *et al.*, 2014a, 2014b) and chemometric calibration (Cernuda *et al.*, 2013; Skrjanc, 2009) to machine vision and texture processing approaches (Lughofer, 2011b; Riaz and Ghafoor, 2013). Thus, their robustness and applicability for the standard batch modeling case has been already proven since several decades. Second, they are known to be universal approximators (Castro and Delgado, 1996), i.e., being able to model any implicitly contained nonlinearity with a sufficient degree of accuracy, while their interpretable capabilities are still intact or may offer even advantages: while the antecedent parts remain linguistic, the consequent parts can be interpreted either in a more physical sense (see Bikdash, 1999; Herrera *et al.*, 2005) or as local functional tendencies (Lughofer, 2013) (see also Section 3.5). Finally, parts of their architecture (the consequents) can be updated exactly by recursive procedures, as will be described in Section 3.3.1. This is a strong point as they are converging to the same solution as when (hypothetically) sending all data samples at once into the optimization process (*true optimal incremental solutions*).

3.2.2.1. *Takagi–Sugeno standard*

A single rule in a (single output) standard TS fuzzy system is of the form

$$\text{Rule } i: \text{IF} \quad (x_1 \text{ IS } \mu_{i1}) \quad \text{AND} \ \ldots \ \text{AND} \quad (x_p \text{ IS } \mu_{ip}), \tag{4}$$

$$\text{THEN} \quad l_i(\vec{x}) = w_{i0} + w_{i1}x_1 + w_{i2}x_2 + \cdots + w_{ip}x_p, \tag{5}$$

where $\vec{x} = (x_1, \ldots, x_p)$ is the p-dimensional input vector and μ_{ij} the fuzzy set describing the j-th antecedent of the rule. Typically, these fuzzy sets are associated with a linguistic label. As in case of Mamdani fuzzy systems, the AND connective is modeled in terms of a t-norm, i.e., a generalized logical conjunction (Klement *et al.*, 2000). Again, the output $l_i = l_i(\vec{x})$ is the so-called consequent function of the rule.

The output of a TS system consisting of C rules is a linear combination of the outputs produced by the individual rules (through the l_i's), where the contribution of each rule is given by its normalized degree of activation Ψ_i, thus:

$$\hat{f}(\vec{x}) = \hat{y} = \sum_{i=1}^{C} \Psi_i(\vec{x}) \cdot l_i(\vec{x}) \quad \text{with } \Psi_i(\vec{x}) = \frac{\mu_i(\vec{x})}{\sum_{j=1}^{C} \mu_j(\vec{x})}, \tag{6}$$

with $\mu_i(\vec{x})$ as in Equation (1). From a statistical point of view, a TS fuzzy model can be interpreted as a collection of piecewise local linear predictors by a smooth (normalized) kernel, thus in its local parts (rules) having some synergies with local weighted regression (LWR) (Cleveland and Devlin, 1988). The difference is that in LWR the model is extracted on demand based on the nearest data samples [also termed as the reference base in an instance-based learning context for data streams (Shaker and Hüllermeier, 2012)] while TS fuzzy systems are providing a global model defined over the whole feature space (thus preferable in the context of interpretability issues and online prediction speed).

The most convenient choice for fuzzy sets in EFS and fuzzy systems design in general are Gaussian functions, which lead to the so-called *fuzzy basis function networks* (Wang and Mendel, 1992) and multi-variate kernels following normal distributions are achieved for representing the rules' antecedent parts:

$$\mu_i(\vec{x}) = \prod_{i=1}^{p} exp\left(-\frac{1}{2}\frac{(x_i - c_i)^2}{\sigma_i^2}\right). \tag{7}$$

In this sense, the linear hyper-planes l_i are connected with multi-variate Gaussians to form an overall smooth function. Then, the output form in Equation (6) becomes some synergies with Gaussian mixture models (GMMs) (Day, 1969; Sun and Wang, 2011), often used for clustering and pattern recognition tasks (Bishop, 2007; Duda *et al.*, 2000). The difference is that l_i's are hyper-planes instead of singleton weights and do not reflect the degree of density of the corresponding rules (as *mixing proportion*), but the linear trend of the approximation/regression surface in the corresponding local parts.

3.2.2.2. *Takagi–Sugeno generalized*

Recently, the generalized form of TS fuzzy systems has been offered to the evolving fuzzy systems community, launching its origin in Lemos *et al.* (2011a) and Leite *et al.* (2012a); latter explored and further developed in Pratama *et al.* (2014a) and Pratama *et al.* (2014b). The basic principle is that it employs multi-dimensional normal (Gaussian) distributions in arbitrary position for representing single rules. Thus, it overcomes the deficiency of not being able to model local correlations between input and output variables appropriately, as is the case with the

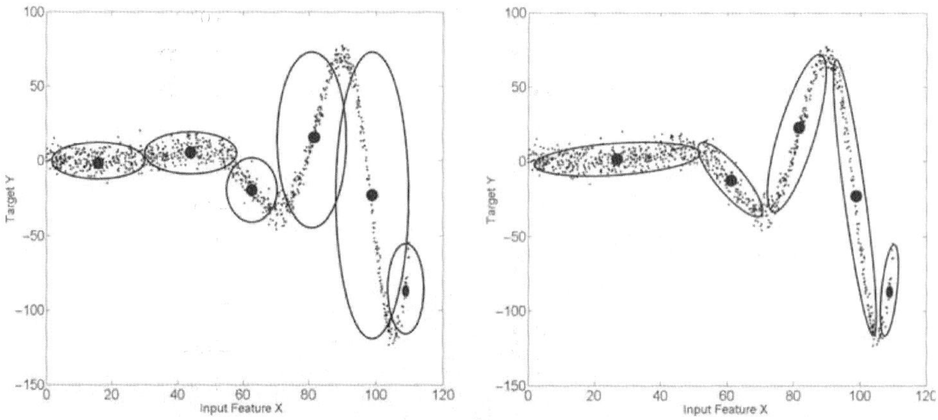

Figure 3.2: Left: Conventional axis parallel rules (represented by ellipsoids) achieve an inaccurate representation of the local trends (correlations) of a nonlinear approximation problem (defined by noisy data samples). Right: Generalized rules (by rotation) achieve a much more accurate representation.

t-norm operator used in standard rules (Klement *et al.*, 2000) — these may represent inexact approximations of the real local trends and finally causing information loss in rules (Abonyi *et al.*, 2002).

An example for visualizing this problematic nature is provided in Figure 3.2: in the left image, axis-parallel rules (represented by ellipsoids) are used for modeling the partial tendencies of the regression curves which are not following the input axis direction, but are rotated to some degree; obviously, the volume of the rules are artificially blown-up and the rules do not represent the real characteristics of the local tendencies well → *information loss*. In the right image, non axis-parallel rules using general multivariate Gaussians are applied for a more accurate representation (rotated ellipsoids).

To avoid such information loss, the generalized fuzzy rules have been defined in Lemos *et al.* (2011a) (there used for evolving stream mining), as

$$\text{IF } \vec{x} \text{ IS (about)} \Psi_i \text{ THEN } l_i(\vec{x}) = w_{i0} + w_{i1}x_1 + w_{i2}x_2 + \cdots + w_{ip}x_p, \quad (8)$$

where Ψ denotes a high-dimensional kernel function, which in accordance to the basis function networks spirit are given by the generalized multivariate Gaussian distribution:

$$\Psi_i(\vec{x}) = exp\left(-\frac{1}{2}(\vec{x} - \vec{c}_i)^T \Sigma_i^{-1}(\vec{x} - \vec{c}_i)\right), \quad (9)$$

with $\vec{c}_i$ the center and Σ_i^{-1} the inverse covariance matrix of the ith rule, allowing any possible rotation and spread of the rule. It is also known in the neural network literature that Gaussian radial basis functions are a nice option to characterize local properties (Lemos *et al.*, 2011a; Lippmann, 1991); especially, someone may inspect the inner core part, i.e., all samples fulfilling $(\vec{x} - \vec{c}_i)^T \Sigma_i^{-1}(\vec{x} - \vec{c}_i) \leq 1$, as the characteristic contour/spread of the rule.

The fuzzy inference then becomes a linear combination of multivariate Gaussian distributions in the form:

$$\hat{y} = \frac{\sum_{i=1}^{C} l_i(\vec{x}) * exp\left(-\frac{1}{2}(\vec{x} - \vec{c}_i)^T \Sigma_i^{-1}(\vec{x} - \vec{c}_i)\right)}{\sum_{i=1}^{C} exp\left(-\frac{1}{2}(\vec{x} - \vec{c}_i)^T \Sigma_i^{-1}(\vec{x} - \vec{c}_i)\right)} = \sum_{i=1}^{C} l_i(\vec{x})\Phi_i(\vec{x}), \tag{10}$$

with C the number of rules, $l_i(\vec{x})$ the consequent hyper-plane of the ith rule and Φ_i the normalized membership degrees, summing up to 1 for each query sample.

In order to maintain (input/output) interpretability of the evolved TS fuzzy models for users/operators (see also Section 3.5), the authors in Lughofer *et al.* (2013) foresee a projection concept to form fuzzy sets and classical rule antecedents. It relies on the angle between the principal components directions and the feature axes, which has the effect that long spread rules are more effectively projected than when using the inner contour spreads (through axis parallel cutting points). The spread σ_i of the projected fuzzy set is set according to:

$$\sigma_i = max_{j=1,\ldots p}\left(\frac{r}{\sqrt{\lambda_j}} cos(\Phi(e_i, a_j))\right), \tag{11}$$

with r the range of influence of one rule, usually set to 1, representing the (inner) characteristic contour/spread of the rule (as mentioned above). The center of the fuzzy set in the ith dimension is set equal to the ith coordinate of the rule center. $\Phi(e_i, a_j)$ denotes the angle between principal component direction (eigenvector a_j) and the ith axis e_i, λ_j the eigenvalue of the jth principal component.

3.2.2.3. *Takagi–Sugeno extended*

An extended version of Takagi–Sugeno fuzzy systems in the context of evolving systems has been applied in Komijani *et al.* (2012). There, instead of a hyper-plane $l_i = w_{i0} + w_{i1}x_1 + w_{i2}x_2 + \cdots + w_{ip}x_p$, the consequent function for the ith rule is defined as LS_SVM model according to Smola and Schölkopf (2004):

$$l_i(\vec{x}) = \sum_{k=1}^{N} \alpha_{ik} K(\vec{x}, \vec{x}_k) + \beta_i, \tag{12}$$

with $K(.,.)$ a kernel function fulfilling the Mercer criterion (Mercer, 1909) for characterizing a symmetric positive semi-definite kernel (Zaanen, 1960), N the number of training samples and α and β the consequent parameters (support vectors and intercept) to learn. The l_i's can be, in principle, combined within in any inference scheme, either with the standard one in Equation (6) or with the generalized one in

Equation (10) [in Komijani *et al.* (2012), they are combined with Equation (6)]. The advantage of these consequents is that they are supposed to provide more accuracy, as a support vector regression modeling (Smola and Schölkopf, 2004) is applied to each local region. Hence, nonlinearities within local regions may be better resolved. On the other hand, the consequents are more difficult to interpret.

3.2.3. *Type-2*

Type-2 fuzzy systems were invented by Lotfi Zadeh in 1975 (Zadeh, 1975) for the purpose of modeling the uncertainty in the membership functions of usual (type-1) fuzzy sets. The distinguishing feature of a type-2 fuzzy set $\tilde{\mu}_{ij}$ versus its type-1 counterpart μ_{ij} is that the membership function values of $\tilde{\mu}_{ij}$ are blurred, i.e., they are no longer a single number in [0, 1], but are instead a continuous range of values between 0 and 1, say $[a, b] \subseteq [0, 1]$. One can either assign the same weighting or a variable weighting to membership function values in $[a, b]$. When the former is done, the resulting type-2 fuzzy set is called an interval type-2 fuzzy set. When the latter is done, the resulting type-2 fuzzy set is called a general type-2 fuzzy set (Mendel and John, 2002).

The ith rule of an interval-based type-2 fuzzy system is defined in the following way (Liang and Mendel, 2000; Mendel, 2001):

$$\text{Rule}_i : \text{IF } x_1 \text{ IS } \tilde{\mu}_{i1} \text{ AND} \ldots \text{AND } x_p \text{ IS } \tilde{\mu}_{ip} \text{ THEN } l_i(\vec{x}) = \tilde{f}_i,$$

with $\tilde{f}_i$ a general type-2 uncertainty function.

In case of a Takagi–Sugeno-based consequent scheme (as e.g., used in Juang and Tsao (2008), the first approach of an evolving type-2 fuzzy system), the consequent function becomes:

$$l_i(\vec{x}) = \tilde{w}_{i0} + \tilde{w}_{i1}x_1 + \tilde{w}_{i2}x_2 + \cdots + \tilde{w}_{ip}x_p, \tag{13}$$

with $\tilde{w}_{ij}$ an interval set (instead of a crisp continuous value), i.e.,

$$\tilde{w}_{ij} = [c_{ij} - s_{ij}, c_{ij} + s_{ij}]. \tag{14}$$

In case of a Mamdani-based consequent scheme (as e.g., used in Tung *et al.* (2013), a recent evolving approach), the consequent function becomes: $l_i = \tilde{\Phi}_i$, with $\tilde{\Phi}_i$ a type two fuzzy set.

An enhanced approach for eliciting the final output is applied, the so-called Karnik–Mendel iterative procedure (Karnik and Mendel, 2001), where a type reduction is performed before the defuzzification process. In this procedure, the consequent values $\bar{l}_i = c_{i0} - s_{i0} + (c_{i1} - s_{i1})x_1 + (c_{i2} - s_{i2})x_2 + \cdots + (c_{ip} - s_{ip})x_p$ and $\underline{l}_i = c_{i0} + s_{i0} + (c_{i1} + s_{i1})x_1 + (c_{i2} + s_{i2})x_2 + \cdots + (c_{ip} + s_{ip})x_p$ are sorted in ascending order denoted as $\bar{y}_i$ and $\underline{y}_i$ for all $i = 1, \ldots, C$. Accordingly, the membership values $\bar{\Psi}_i(\vec{x})$ and $\underline{\Psi}_i(\vec{x})$ are sorted in ascending order denoted as $\bar{\psi}_i(\vec{x})$ and $\underline{\psi}_i(\vec{x})$. Then, the outputs $\bar{y}$ and $\underline{y}$ are computed by:

$$\bar{y} = \frac{\sum_{i=1}^{L} \bar{\psi}_i(\vec{x})\bar{y}_i + \sum_{i=L+1}^{C} \underline{\psi}_i(\vec{x})\bar{y}_i}{\sum_{i=1}^{L} \bar{\psi}_i(\vec{x}) + \sum_{i=L+1}^{C} \underline{\psi}_i(\vec{x})} \quad \underline{y} = \frac{\sum_{i=1}^{R} \underline{\psi}_i(\vec{x})\underline{y}_i + \sum_{i=R+1}^{C} \bar{\psi}_i(\vec{x})\underline{y}_i}{\sum_{i=1}^{R} \underline{\psi}_i(\vec{x}) + \sum_{i=R+1}^{C} \bar{\psi}_i(\vec{x})} \tag{15}$$

with L and R positive numbers, often $L = \frac{C}{2}$ and $R = \frac{C}{2}$. Taking the average of these two yields the final output value y.

3.2.4. *Neuro-Fuzzy*

Most of the neuro-fuzzy systems (Fuller, 1999) available in literature can be interpreted as a layered structural form of Takagi–Sugeno–Kang fuzzy systems. Typically, the fuzzy model is transformed into a neural network structure (by introducing layers, connections and weights between the layers) and learning methods already established in the neural network context are applied to the neuro-fuzzy system. A well-known example for this is the ANFIS approach (Jang, 1993), where the back-propagation algorithm (Werbos, 1974) is applied and the components of the fuzzy model (fuzzification, calculation of rule fulfillment degrees, normalization, defuzzification), represent different layers in the neural network structure. However, the inference scheme finally leads to the same model outputs as for conventional TS fuzzy systems. A visualization example is presented in Figure 3.3. This layered structure will be used by several EFS approaches as can be seen from Tables 3.1 and 3.2.

Recently, a new type of neuro-fuzzy architecture has been proposed by Silva *et al.* (2014), termed as neo-fuzzy neuron network, and applied in evolving context. It relies on the idea to use a set of TS fuzzy rules for each input dimension

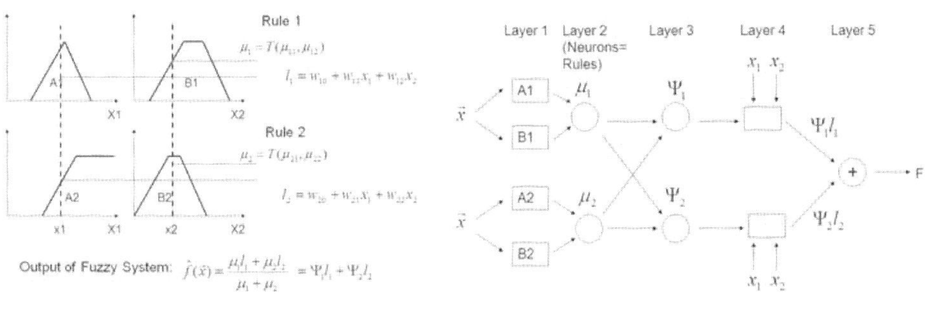

Figure 3.3: (a) Standard Takagi–Sugeno type fuzzy system, (b) Equivalent neural network structure.

independently and then connect these with a conventional sum for obtaining the final model output. The domain of each input i is granulated into m complementary membership functions.

3.2.5. *Hierarchical Structures*

Hierarchical architectures for evolving fuzzy modeling have been recently introduced in Shaker *et al.* (2013) and Lemos *et al.* (2011b). Both architectures have been designed for the purposes to provide a more slim, thus more transparent rule-base by inducing rules with flexible lengths. This is opposed to all the flat model architectures which have been presented above, always using all input features in all rules' antecedent parts.

The first approach is an incremental extension of top-down induction of fuzzy pattern trees (Senge and Huellermeier, 2011) and thus uses a hierarchical tree-like concept to evolve nodes and leaves on demand. Thereby, a collection of fuzzy sets and aggregation operators can be specified by the user as allowed patterns and conjunction operators in the leaf nodes. In particular, a pattern tree has the outlook as shown in the example of Figure 3.4. Thereby, one basic difference to classical fuzzy systems is that the conjunction operator do not necessarily have to be t-norms [can be a more general aggregation operator (Saminger-Platz *et al.*, 2007)] and the type of the fuzzy sets can be different in different tree levels [as indicated in the rectangles in Figure 3.4 (left)], allowing a composition of a mixture of patterns in hierarchical form. Another difference is the possibility to obtain a single compact rule for describing a certain characteristics of the output (a good house price quality with 0.9 in the example in Figure 3.4).

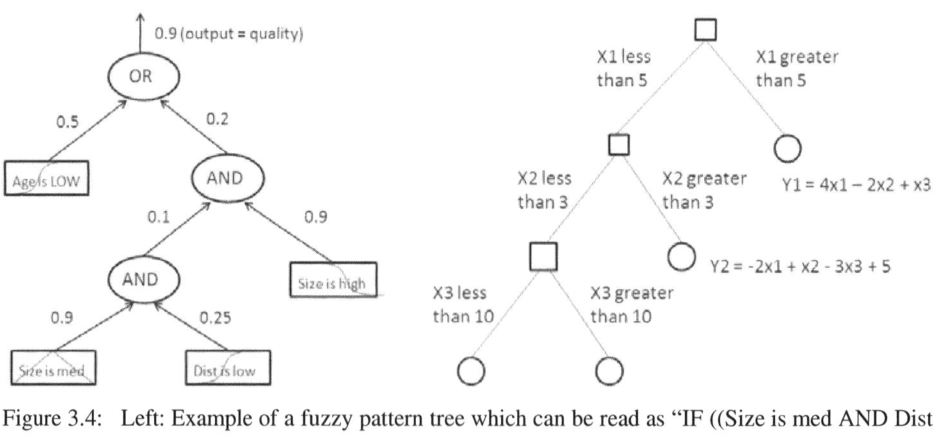

Figure 3.4: Left: Example of a fuzzy pattern tree which can be read as "IF ((Size is med AND Dist is high) AND Size is HIGH) OR Age is LOW THEN Output (Quality) is 0.9". Right: Example of a fuzzy decision tree with four rules, a rule example is "IF x1 is LESS THAN 5 AND x2 is GREATER THAN 3 THEN y2 = −2x1 + x2 − 3x3 + 5".

The second one (Lemos *et al.*, 2011b) has some synergies to classical decision trees for classification tasks [CART (Breiman *et al.*, 1993) and C4.5 (Quinlan, 1994)], where, however, the leafs are not class labels, but linear hyper-planes as used in classical TS fuzzy systems. Thus, as the partitioning may be arbitrarily fine-granuled as is the case for classical TS fuzzy systems, they still enjoy the favorable properties of being universal approximators. A visual example of such a tree is shown in the right image in Figure 3.4. It is notable that the nodes do not contain crisp decision rules, but fuzzy terms "Smaller Than" and "Greater Than", which are represented by sigmoidal fuzzy sets: e.g., "Less Than 5" is a fuzzy set which cuts the fuzzy set "Greater than 5" at $x = 5$ with a membership degree 0.5. One path from the root node to a terminal node represents a rule, which is then similar to a classical TS fuzzy rule, but allowing an arbitrary length.

3.2.6. *Classifiers*

Fuzzy classifiers have been enjoyed a wide attraction in various applications since almost two decades (Eitzinger *et al.*, 2010; Kuncheva, 2000; Nakashima *et al.*, 2006). Their particular strength is the ability to model decision boundaries with arbitrary nonlinearity degree while maintaining interpretability in the sense "which rules on the feature set imply which output class labels (classifier decisions)". In a winner-takes-it-all concept, the decision boundary proceeds between rule pairs having different majority class labels. As rules are usually nonlinear contours in the high-dimensional space, the nonlinearity of the decision boundary is induced — enjoying arbitrary complexity due to a possible arbitrary number of rules. If rules have linear contours, then overall nonlinearity is induced in form of piecewise linear boundaries between rule pairs.

3.2.6.1. *Classical and extended single-model*

The rule in a classical fuzzy classification model architecture with singleton consequent labels is a widely studied architecture in the fuzzy systems community (Ishibuchi and Nakashima, 2001; Kruse *et al.*, 1994; Kuncheva, 2000; Nauck and Kruse, 1998) and is defined by:

$$\text{Rule}_i : \text{IF } x_1 \text{ IS } \mu_{i1} \text{ AND} \ldots \text{AND } x_p \text{ IS } \mu_{ip} \text{ THEN } l_i = L_i, \tag{16}$$

where L_i is the crisp output class label from the set $\{1, \ldots, K\}$ with K the number of classes for the ith rule. This architecture precludes use of confidence labels in the single classes per rule. In case of clean classification rules, when each single rule contains/covers training samples from a single class, this architecture provides adequate resolution of the class distributions. However, in real-world problems, classes usually overlap significantly and therefore often rules are extracted containing samples from more than one class.

Thus, an extended fuzzy classification model that includes the confidence levels $conf_{i1,\dots,K}$ of the ith rule in the single classes has been applied in evolving, adaptive learning context (see e.g., Bouchachia, 2009; Bouchachia and Mittermeir, 2006):

$$\begin{aligned}\text{Rule}_i: \quad & \text{IF } x_1 \text{ IS } \mu_{i1} \text{ AND} \dots \text{AND } x_p \text{ IS } \mu_{ip} \\ & \text{THEN } l_i = [conf_{i1}, conf_{i2}, \dots, conf_{iK}]. \end{aligned} \tag{17}$$

Thus, a local region represented by a rule in the form of Equation (17) can better model class overlaps in the corresponding part of the feature space: for instance, three classes overlap with a support of 200, 100 and 50 samples in one single fuzzy rule; then, the confidence in Class #1 would be intuitively 0.57 according to its relative frequency (200/350), in Class #2 it would be 0.29 (100/350) and in Class #3 it would be 0.14 (50/350). A more enhanced treatment of class confidence levels will be provided in Section 3.4.5 when describing options for representing reliability in class responses.

In a winner-takes-it-all context [the most common choice in fuzzy classifiers (Kuncheva, 2000)], the final classifier output L will be obtained by

$$L = l_{i^*} \text{ with } l_{i^*} = \text{argmax}_{1 \le k \le K}\, conf_{i^*k} \quad i^* = \text{argmax}_{1 \le i \le C}\, \mu_i(\vec{x}) \quad \text{with} \tag{18}$$

In a more enhanced (weighted) classification scheme as recently used for evolving fuzzy classifiers (EFC) in Lughofer (2012a), the *degree of purity* is respected as well and integrated into the calculation of the final classification response L:

$$L = \text{argmax}_{k=m,m*}\left(conf_k = \frac{\mu_1(\vec{x})h*_{1,k} + \mu_2(\vec{x})h*_{2,k}}{\mu_1(\vec{x}) + \mu_2(\vec{x})}\right) \tag{19}$$

with

$$h*_{1,k} = \frac{h_{1,k}}{h_{1,m} + h_{1,m*}} \quad h*_{2,k} = \frac{h_{2,k}}{h_{2,m} + h_{2,m*}} \tag{20}$$

and $h_{i,k}$ the class frequency of class k in rule i, and $\mu_1(\vec{x})$ the membership degree of the nearest rule (with majority class m), and $\mu_2(\vec{x})$ the membership degree of the second nearest rule with a different majority class $m* \neq m$. This difference is important as two nearby lying rules with the same majority class label do not induce a decision boundary in-between them. The nearest rule and second nearest rule are obtained by sorting the membership degrees of the current query point to all rules.

Figure 3.5 shows an example for decision boundaries induced by Equation (18) (left image) and by Equation (19) (right image). Obviously, a more purified rule (i.e., having less overlap in classes, right side) is favored among that with significant

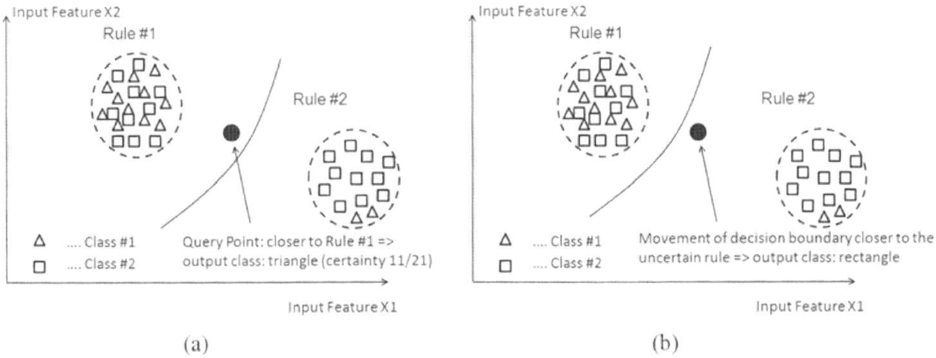

Figure 3.5: (a) Classification according to the winner takes it all concepts using Equation (18); (b) The decision boundary moves towards the more unpurified rule due to the *gravitation concept* applied in Equation (19).

overlap (left side), as the decision boundary moves away → more samples are classified to the majority class in the purified rule, which is intended to obtain a clearer, less uncertain decision boundary. A generalization of Equation (19) would be that k varies over all classes: then, an overwhelmed but significant class in two nearby lying rules may become also the final output class label L, although it has no majority in both rules. On the other hand, this variant would then be able to output a certainty level for each class, an advantage which could be used when calculating a kind of reliability degree overall classes (see Section 3.6.4) respectively when intending to normalize and study class certainty distributions. This variant has not been studied under the scope of EFC so far.

3.2.6.2. *Multi-model one-versus-rest*

The first variant of multi-model architecture leans on the well-known *one-versus-rest* classification scheme from the field of machine learning (Bishop, 2007) and has been introduced in the fuzzy community and especially evolving fuzzy systems community in Angelov *et al.* (2008). It diminishes the problematic of having complex nonlinear multi-decision boundaries in case of multi-class classification problems, which is the case for single model architecture as all classes are coded into one model. This is achieved by representing K binary classifiers for the K different classes, each one for the purpose to discriminate one single class from the others (→ one-versus-rest). Thus, during the training cycle (batch or incremental), for the kth classifier all feature vectors resp. samples belonging to the kth class are assigned a label of 1, and all other samples belonging to other classes are assigned a label of 0.

The nice thing is that a (single model) classification model $D(f) = C$ respectively any regression model $D(f) = R$ (such as Takagi–Sugeno variants discussed in this section) can be applied for one sub-model in the ensemble. Interestingly, in Angelov *et al.* (2008), it has been studied that, when using Takagi–Sugeno architecture for the binary classifiers by regressing on $\{0, 1\}$, the masking problem as occurring in *linear regression by indicator matrix* approach can be avoided (Hastie *et al.*, 2009). This is due to the increased flexibility of TS fuzzy systems, being able to resolve nonlinearities in the class regression surfaces.

At the classification stage for a new query point $\vec{x}$, the model which is producing the maximal model response is used as basis for the final classification label output L, i.e.,

$$\begin{aligned} L &= \text{argmax}_{m=1,\dots,K} \hat{f}_m(\vec{x}) \text{ in case when } D(f) = R, \\ L &= \text{argmax}_{m=1,\dots,K} conf_m(\vec{x}) \text{ in case when } D(f) = C. \end{aligned} \tag{21}$$

Recently, a rule-based one-versus-rest classification scheme was proposed within the context of a MIMO (Multiple Input Multiple Output) fuzzy system and applied in an evolving classification context (Pratama *et al.*, 2014c). There, a rule is defined by:

$$\text{IF } \vec{x} \text{ IS (about) } \Psi_i \text{ THEN } l_i = \vec{x}\Omega_i, \tag{22}$$

where

$$\Omega_i = \begin{bmatrix} w_{i0}^1 & w_{i0}^2 & \dots & w_{i0}^K \\ w_{i1}^1 & w_{i1}^2 & \dots & w_{i1}^K \\ \vdots & \vdots & \vdots & \vdots \\ w_{ip}^1 & w_{ip}^2 & \dots & w_{ip}^K \end{bmatrix}.$$

Thus, a complete hyper-plane for each class per rule is defined. This offers the flexibility to regress on different classes within single rules, thus to resolve class overlaps in a single region by multiple regression surfaces (Pratama *et al.*, 2014c).

3.2.6.3. *Multi-model all-pairs*

The multi-model *all-pairs (aka all-versus-all)* classifier architecture, originally introduced in the machine learning community (Allwein *et al.*, 2001; Fürnkranz, 2002) and firstly introduced for (evolving) fuzzy classifiers design in Lughofer and Buchtala (2013), overcomes the often occurring imbalanced learning problems induced by one-versus-rest classification scheme in case of *multi-class (polychotomous)* problems. On the other hand, it is well known that imbalanced problems cause severe down-trends in classification accuracy (He and Garcia, 2009). Thus, it is beneficial to avoid imbalanced problems while still trying to enforce the decision boundaries as easy as possible to learn. This is achieved by the all-pairs architecture, as for each class pair (k, l) an own classifier is trained, decomposing the whole learning problem into binary less complex sub-problems.

Formally, this can be expressed by a classifier $\mathbb{C}_{k,l}$ which is induced by a training procedure $\mathbb{T}_{k,l}$ when using (only) the class samples belonging to classes k and l:

$$\mathbb{C}_{k,l} \longleftarrow \mathbb{T}_{k,l}(X_{k,l}) \quad X_{k,l} = \{\vec{x} | L(\vec{x}) = k \vee L(\vec{x}) = l\}, \tag{23}$$

with $L(\vec{x})$ the class label associated with feature vector $\vec{x}$. This means that $\mathbb{C}_{k,l}$ is a classifier for separating samples belonging to class k from those belonging to class l. It is notable that any classification architecture as discussed above in Section 3.2.6.1 or any regression-based model as defined in Section 3.2.2 can be used for $\mathbb{C}_{k,l}$.

When classifying a new sample $\vec{x}$, each classifier outputs a confidence level $conf_{k,l}$ which denotes the degree of preference of class k over class l for this sample. This degree lies in $[0, 1]$ where 0 means no preference, i.e., a crisp vote for class l, and 1 means a full preference, i.e., a crisp vote for class k. This is conducted for each pair of classes and stored into a *preference relation matrix* R:

$$R = \begin{bmatrix} 0 & conf_{1,2} & conf_{1,3} & \dots & conf_{1,K} \\ conf_{2,1} & 0 & conf_{2,3} & \dots & conf_{2,K} \\ \vdots & \vdots & \vdots & \vdots & \vdots \\ conf_{K,1} & conf_{K,2} & conf_{K,3} & \dots & 0 \end{bmatrix}. \tag{24}$$

If we assume reciprocal preferences, i.e., $conf_{k,l} = 1 - conf_{l,k}$, then the training of half of the classifiers can be omitted, hence finally $\frac{K(K-1)}{2}$ binary classifiers are obtained. The preference relation matrix in Equation (24) opens another interpretation dimension on output level: considerations may go into partial uncertainty reasoning or preference relational structure in a fuzzy sense (Hüllermeier and Brinker, 2008). In the most convenient way, the final class response is often obtained by:

$$L = argmax_{k=1,\dots,K}(score_k) = argmax_{k=1,\dots,K}\left(\sum_{K \geq i \geq 1} conf_{k,i}\right). \tag{25}$$

i.e., the class with the highest score = highest preference degree summed up over all classes is returned by the classifier.

In Fürnkranz (2002, 2001) it was shown that pairwise classification is not only more accurate than one-versus-rest technique, but also more efficient regarding computation times [see also Lughofer and Buchtala (2013)], which is an important characteristic for fast stream learning problems. The reason for this is basically that binary classification problems contain significantly lower number of samples, as each sub-problem uses only a small subset of samples.

3.3. Fundamentals

Data streams are one of the fundamental reasons for the necessity of applying evolving, adaptive models in general and evolving fuzzy systems in particular. This is simply because streams are theoretically an infinite sequence of samples, which cannot be processed at once within a batch process, even not in modern computers with high virtual memory capacities. Data streams may not necessarily be online based on permanent recordings, measurements or sample gatherings, but can also arise due to a block- or sample-wise loading of batch data sites, e.g., in case of *very large databases (VLDB)*[6] or in case of *big data* problems (White, 2012); in this context, they are also often referred as *pseudo-streams*. In particular, a data stream (or pseudo-stream) is characterized by the following properties (Gama, 2010):

- The data samples or data blocks are continuously arriving online over time. The frequency depends on the frequency of the measurement recording process.
- The data samples are arriving in a specific order, over which the system has no control.
- Data streams are usually not bounded in a size; i.e., a data stream is alive as long as some interfaces, devices or components at the system are switched on and are collecting data.
- Once a data sample/block is processed, it is usually discarded immediately, afterwards.

Changes in the process such as new operation modes, system states, varying environmental influences etc. are usually implicitly also effecting the data stream in way that for instance *drifts* or *shifts* may arise (see Section 3.4.1), or new regions in the feature/system variable space are explored (knowledge expansion).

Formally, a stream can be defined as an infinite sequence of samples $(\vec{x}_1, \vec{y}_1)$, $(\vec{x}_2, \vec{y}_2)$, $(\vec{x}_3, \vec{y}_3)$, ..., where $\vec{x}$ denotes the vector containing all input features (variables) and $\vec{y}$ the output variables which should be predicted. In case of unsupervised learning problems, $\vec{y}$ disappears — note that, however, in the context of fuzzy systems, only supervised regression and classification problems are studied. Often $y = \vec{y}$, i.e., single output systems are encouraged, especially as it is often possible to decast a MIMO (multiple input multiple output problem) system into single independent MISO (multiple input single output problem) systems (e.g., when the outputs are independent).

Handling streams for modeling tasks in an appropriate way requires the usage of *incremental learning* algorithms, which are deduced from the concept of incremental heuristic search (Koenig *et al.*, 2004). These algorithms possess the property to build and learn models in step-wise manner rather than with a whole dataset at once.

[6]http://en.wikipedia.org/wiki/Very_large_database.

From formal mathematical point of view, an incremental model update I of the former model f_N (estimated from the N initial samples) is defined by

$$f_{N+m} = I(f_N, (\vec{x}_{N+1,\ldots,N+m}, \vec{y}_{N+1,\ldots,N+m})). \tag{26}$$

So, the incremental model update is done by just taking the new m samples and the old model, but not using any prior data. Hereby, the whole model may also include some additional statistical help measures, which needs to be updated synchronously to the 'real' model. If $m = 1$, we speak about *incremental learning in sample mode* or *sample-wise incremental learning*, otherwise about *incremental learning in block mode* or *block-wise incremental learning*. If the output vector starts to be missing in the data stream samples, but a supervised model has been trained already before which is then updated with the stream samples either in unsupervised manner or by using its own predictions, then someone speaks about *semi-supervised* (online) learning (Chapelle *et al.*, 2006).

Two update modes in the incremental learning process are distinguished:

(1) Update of the model parameters: In this case, a fixed number of parameters $\Phi_N = \{\phi_1, \ldots, \phi_l\}_N$ of the original model f_N is updated by the incremental learning process and the outcome is a new parameter setting Φ_{N+m} with the same number of parameters, i.e., $|\Phi_{N+m}| = |\Phi_N|$. Here, we also speak about a *model adaptation* respectively a *model refinement* with new data.
(2) Update of the whole model structure: This case leads to the evolving learning concept, as the number of the parameters may change and also the number of structural components may change automatically (e.g., rules are added or pruned in case of fuzzy systems) according to the characteristics of the new data samples $\vec{x}_{N+1,\ldots,N+m}$. This means that usually (but not necessarily) $|\Phi_{N+m}| \neq |\Phi_N|$ and $C_{N+m} \neq C_N$ with C the number of structural components. The update of the whole model structure also may include an update of the input structure, i.e., input variables/features may be exchanged during the incremental learning process — see also Section 3.4.2.

An important aspect in incremental learning algorithms is the so-called *plasticity-stability dilemma* (Abraham and Robins, 2005), which describes the problem of finding an appropriate tradeoff between flexible model updates and structural convergence. This strongly depends on the nature of the stream: in some cases, a more intense update is required than in others (drifting versus life-long concepts in the stream). If an algorithm converges to an optimal solution or at least to the same solution as the hypothetical batch solution (obtained by using all data up to a certain sample at once), it is called a *recursive algorithm*. Such an algorithm is usually beneficial as long as no drifts arise, which make the older learned relations obsolete (see Section 3.4.1).

An *initial batch mode training step* with the first amount of training samples is, whenever possible, usually preferable to *incremental learning from scratch*, i.e., a building up of the model sample per sample from the beginning. This is because within a batch mode phase, it is possible to carry out validation procedures [such as cross-validation (Stone, 1974) or bootstrapping (Efron and Tibshirani, 1993)] in connection with search techniques for finding an optimal set of parameters for the learning algorithm in order to achieve a good generalization quality. The obtained parameters are then usually reliable start parameters for the incremental learning algorithm to evolve the model further. When performing incremental learning from scratch, the parameters have to be set to some blind default values, which may be not necessarily appropriate for the given data stream mining problem.

In a pure online learning setting, however, incremental learning from scratch is indispensable. Then, often start default parameters of the learning engines need to be parameterized. Thus, it is beneficial that the algorithms require as less as possible parameters (see Section 3.3.5). Overcoming unlucky settings of parameters can be sometimes achieved with dynamic structural changes such as component-based split-and-merge techniques (as described in Section 3.6.2).

3.3.1. *Recursive Learning of Linear Parameters*

A lot of the EFS approaches available in literature (see Section 3.3.5) use the TS-type fuzzy systems architecture with linear parameters in the consequents. The reason lies in the highly accurate and precise models which can be achieved with these systems (Lughofer, 2011b), and therefore enjoy a wide attraction in several application fields, see Sections 3.2.2 and 3.6.5. Also, within several classification variants, TS-fuzzy systems may be used as regression-based binary classifiers, e.g., in all-pairs technique (Lughofer and Buchtala, 2013) as well as in one-versus-rest classification schemes (Angelov *et al.*, 2008). Sometimes, singleton numerical values in the consequents (native Sugeno systems) or higher order polynomials (Takagi–Sugeno–Kang) are used in the consequents. These just change the number of parameters to learn but not the way how to learn them.

The currently available EFS techniques rely on the optimization of the least-squares error criterion, which is defined as the squared deviation between observed outputs $y_1, \ldots, y_N$ and predicted outputs $\hat{y}_1, \ldots, \hat{y}_N$; thus:

$$J = \|y - \hat{y}\|_{L_2} = \sum_{k=1}^{N}(y(k) - \sum_{i=1}^{C} l_{i;\vec{w}}(\vec{x}(k))\Psi_i(\vec{x}(k)))^2 \rightarrow \min_{\vec{w}}!. \tag{27}$$

This problem can be written as a classical linear least squares problem with a weighted regression matrix containing the global regressors

$$\vec{r}_i(k) = [\Psi_i(\vec{x}(k)) \quad x_1(k)\Psi_i(\vec{x}(k)) \cdots x_p(k)\Psi_i(\vec{x}(k))], \tag{28}$$

for $i = 1, \ldots, C$, with C the current number of rules and k the kth data sample denoting the kth row. For this problem, it is well known that a recursive solution exists which converges to the optimal one within each incremental learning step, see Ljung (1999) and Lughofer (2011b). Also Chapter 2 for its detailed derivation in the context of evolving TS fuzzy systems.

However, the problem with this *global learning* approach is that it does not offer any flexibility regarding rule evolution and pruning, as these cause a change in the size of the regressors and thus a dynamic change in the dimensionality of the recursive learning problem, which leads to a disturbance of the parameters in the other rules and to the loss of optimality. Therefore, the authors in Angelov *et al.* (2008) emphasize the usage of *local learning* approach which learns and updates the consequent parameters for each rule separately. Adding or deleting a new rule therefore does not affect the convergence of the parameters of all other rules; thus, optimality in least squares sense is preserved. The local learning approach leads to a weighted least squares formulation for each rule given by (without loss of generality the ith):

$$J_i = \sum_{k=1}^{N} \Psi_i(\vec{x}(k))(y(k) - \hat{y}_i(k))^2 \rightarrow \min_{\vec{w}_i} \quad i = 1, \ldots, C, \tag{29}$$

with $\hat{y}_i(k) = l_{i;\vec{w}_i}(\vec{x}(k))$.

This problem can be written as a classical weighted least squares problem, where the weighting matrix is a diagonal matrix containing the basis function values Ψ_i for each input sample. Again, an exact recursive formulation can be derived [see Lughofer (2011b) and Chapter 2], which is termed as *recursive fuzzily weighted least squares* (RFWLS). As RFWLS is so fundamental and used in many EFS approaches, we explicitly deploy the update formulas (from the kth to the $k+1$st cycle):

$$\vec{w}_i(k+1) = \vec{w}_i(k) + \gamma(k)(y(k+1) - \vec{r}^T(k+1)\vec{w}_i(k)), \tag{30}$$

$$\gamma(k) = P_i(k+1)\vec{r}(k+1) = \frac{P_i(k)\vec{r}(k+1)}{\frac{\lambda}{\Psi_i(\vec{x}(k+1))} + \vec{r}^T(k+1)P_i(k)\vec{r}(k+1)}, \tag{31}$$

$$P_i(k+1) = \frac{1}{\lambda}(I - \gamma(k)\vec{r}^T(k+1))P_i(k), \tag{32}$$

with $P_i(k) = (R_i(k)^T Q_i(k) R_i(k))^{-1}$ the inverse weighted Hessian matrix and $\vec{r}(k+1) = [1\ x_1(k+1)\ x_2(k+1)\ \ldots\ x_p(k+1)]^T$ the regressor values of the $k+1$st data sample, which is the same for all i rules, and λ a forgetting factor, with default value equal to 1 (no forgetting) — see Section 3.4.1 for a description and meaning of its usage. Whenever $\lambda < 1$, the following function is minimized: $J_i = \sum_{k=1}^{N} \lambda^{N-k} \Psi_i(\vec{x}(k))(y(k) - \hat{y}_i(k))^2$, instead of Equation (29), thus samples which appeared a long time ago are almost completely out-weighted. Obviously, the actual weight of the sample is Ψ_i (the membership degree to Rule i), thus a sample receives a low weight when it does not fall into rule i: then, the Kalman filter gain $\gamma(k)$ in Equation (31) becomes a value close to 0 and the update of P_i and $\vec{w}_i$ is marginal. Again, Equation (30) converges to the optimal solution within one incremental learning step.

The assurance of convergence to optimality is guaranteed as long as there is not structural change in the rules' antecedents. However, due to rule center movements or resettings in the incremental learning phase (see Section 3.3.4), this is usually not the case. Therefore, a kind of sub-optimality is caused whose deviation degree to the real optimality could have been bounded for some EFS approaches such as FLEXFIS (Lughofer, 2008) and PANFIS (Pratama *et al.*, 2014a).

Whenever a new rule is evolved by a rule evolution criterion, the parameters and inverse weighted Hessian matrix (required for an exact update) have to be initialized. In Ljung (1999), it is emphasized to set $\vec{w}$ to 0 and P_i to αI with α big enough. However, this is for the purpose of a global modeling approach starting with a faded out regression surface over the whole input space. In local learning, the other rules defining other parts of the feature space remain untouched. Thus, setting the hyperplane of the new rule which may appear somewhere inbetween the other rules to 0 would lead to an undesired muting of one local region and to discontinuities in the online predictions (Cernuda *et al.*, 2012). Thus, it is more beneficial to inherit the parameter vector and the inverse weighted Hessian matrix from the most nearby lying rule (Cernuda *et al.*, 2012).

Recent extensions of RFWLS are as follows:

- In PANFIS (Pratama *et al.*, 2014a), an additional constant α is inserted, conferring a noteworthy effect to foster the asymptotic convergence of the system error and weight vector being adapted, which acts like a binary function. In other words, the constant α is in charge to regulate the current belief of the weight vectors $\vec{w}_i$ and depends on the approximation and the estimation errors. It is 1 whenever the approximation error is bigger than the system error, and 0 otherwise. Thus, adaptation takes fully place in the first case and completely not place in the second case (which may have advantages in terms of flexibility and computation time). A similar concept is used in the improved version of SOFNN, see Leng *et al.* (2012).
- Generalized version of RFWLS (termed as *FWGRLS*) as used in GENEFIS (Pratama *et al.*, 2014b): This exploits the generalized RLS as derived in Xu *et al.* (2006) and adopts it to the local learning context in order to favor from its benefits as discussed above. The basic difference to RFWLS is that it adds a weight decay regularization term in the least squares problem formulation in

order to punish more complex models. In a final simplification step, it ends up with similar formulas as in Equations (30)–(32), but with the difference to subtract the term $\alpha P_i(k+1)\nabla\phi(\vec{w}_i(k))$ in Equation (30), with α a regularization parameter and ϕ the weight decay function: one of the most popular ones in literature is the quadratic function defined as $\phi(\vec{w}) = \frac{1}{2}\|\vec{w}\|^2$, thus $\nabla\phi = \vec{w}$).

- In some approaches [e.g., eMG (Lemos *et al.*, 2011a) or rGK (Dovzan and Skrjanc, 2011)], weights Ψ_i of the data samples are integrated in the second term of Equation (30) as well, which however do not exactly follow the original derivation of recursive weighted least-squares (Aström and Wittenmark, 1994; Ljung, 1999), but leads to a similar effect.

Alternatively, Cara *et al.* (2013) proposes a different learning scheme for singleton consequent parameters (in a Sugeno fuzzy system) within an evolving fuzzy controller design, which relies on the prediction error of the current model. The update of the ith rule singleton consequent parameter w_{i0} becomes:

$$w_{i0}(k+1) = w_{i0}(k) + C\mu_i(\vec{x}(k+1))(y(k+1) - \hat{y}(k+1)), \tag{33}$$

with μ_i the activation degree of the ith rule as present in the previous time step k (before being updated with the new sample $\vec{x}(k+1)$), and C a normalization constant. Hence, instead of γ, μ_i is used as update gain which is multiplied with the normalization constant.

3.3.2. *Recursive Learning of Nonlinear Parameters*

Nonlinear parameters occur in every model architecture as defined throughout Section 3.2.2, mainly only in the fuzzy sets included in the rules' antecedent parts — except for the extended version of TS fuzzy systems (Section 3.2.2.3), where they also appear in the consequents. Often, the parameters in the fuzzy sets define their centers c and characteristic spreads σ, but often the parameters may appear in a different form, for instance, in case of sigmoid functions they define the slope and the point of gradient change. Thus, we generally refer to a nonlinear parameter as ϕ and a whole set of nonlinear parameters as Φ. The incremental update of nonlinear parameters is necessary in order to adjust and move the fuzzy sets and rules composed by the sets to the actual distribution of the data in order to achieve always the correct, well-placed positions. An example is provided in Figure 3.6 where the initial data cloud (circles) in the left upper part changes slightly the position due to new data samples (rectangles). Leaving the original rule (marked with an ellipsoid) untouched, would cause a misplacement of the rule. Thus, it is beneficial to adjust the rule center and its spread accordingly to the new samples. This figure also shows the case of a rule evolution in the lower right part (new samples significantly away from the old rule contour) — as will be discussed in the subsequent section.

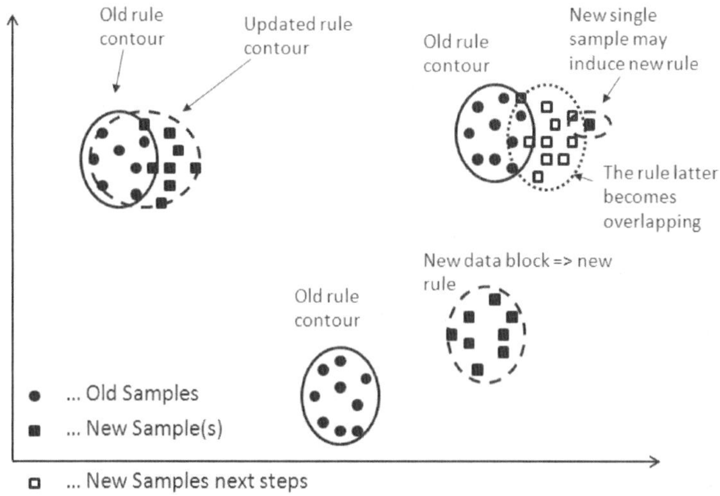

Figure 3.6: Three cases affecting rule contours (antecedents): The left upper part shows a case where a rule movement is demanded to appropriately cover the joint partition (old and new samples), the lower right part shows a case where a new rule should be evolved and the upper right part shows a case where sample-wise incremental learning may trigger a new rule which may turn out to be superfluous later (as future samples are filling up the gap forming one cloud) → (back-)merge requested as discussed in Section 3.3.4.

A possibility to update the nonlinear parameters in EFS is again, similar to the consequent parameters, by applying a numerical incremental optimization procedure. Relying on the least squares optimization problem as in case of recursive linear parameter updates, its formulation in dependency of the nonlinear parameters Φ becomes:

$$J = J(\Phi) = \sum_{k=1}^{N} \|(y_k - \hat{y}(\Phi))\|_{L_2} \rightarrow min_{\Phi;[\vec{w}]}!. \tag{34}$$

In case of TS fuzzy systems, for instance, $\hat{y}(\Phi) = \sum_{i=1}^{C} l_i(\vec{x})\Psi_i(\Phi)(\vec{x})$. Then, the linear consequent parameters $\vec{w}$ needs to be synchronously optimized to the nonlinear parameters (thus, in optional braces), in order to guarantee optimal solution. This can be done either in an alternating nested procedure, i.e., perform an optimization step for nonlinear parameters first, see below, and then optimizing the linear ones, e.g., by Equation (30), or within one joint update formula, e.g., when using one Jacobian matrix on all parameters, see below).

Equation (34) is still a free optimization problem, thus any numerical, gradient-based or Hessian-based technique for which a stable incremental algorithm can be developed is a good choice: this is the case for steepest descent, Gauss–Newton method and Levenberg–Marquardt. Interestingly, a common parameter update formula can be deduced for all three variants (Ngia and Sjöberg, 2000):

$$\Phi(k+1) = \Phi(k) + \mu(k)P(k)^{-1}\psi(\vec{x}(k), \Phi)e(\vec{x}(k), \Phi), \tag{35}$$

where $\psi(\vec{x}(k), \Phi) = \frac{\partial y}{\partial \Phi}(\vec{x}(k))$ the partial derivative of the current model y after each nonlinear parameter evaluated at the current input sample $\vec{x}(k)$, $e(\vec{x}(k), \Phi)$ is the residual in the kth sample: $e(\vec{x}(k), \Phi) = y_k - \hat{y}_k$. and $\mu(k)P(k)^{-1}$ the learning gain with $P(k)$ an approximation of the Hessian matrix, which is substituted in different ways:

- For the steepest descent algorithm, $P(k) = I$, thus the update depends only on first order derivative vectors; furthermore, $\mu(k) = \frac{\mu}{\|\vec{r}(k)\|^2}$ with $\vec{r}(k)$ the current regression vector.
- For Gauss–Newton, $\mu(k) = 1-\lambda$ and $P(k) = (1-\lambda)H(k)$ with $H(k)$ the Hessian matrix which can be approximated by $Jac^T(k)Jac(k)$ with Jac the Jacobian matrix (including the derivatives w.r.t. all parameters in all rules for all samples up to the kth) resp. by $Jac^T(k)diag(\Psi_i(\vec{x}(k)))Jac(k)$ in case of the weighted version for local learning (see also Section 3.3.1) — note that the Jacobian matrix reduces to the regression matrix R in case of linear parameters, as the derivatives are the original input variables (thus, $H = R^T R$ in case of recursive linear parameter learning resulting in the native (slow) recursive least squares without inverse matrix update). Additionally to updating the parameters according to Equation (35), the update of the matrix P is required, which is given by:

$$P(k) = \lambda P(k-1) + (1-\lambda)\psi(\vec{x}(k), \Phi)\psi(\vec{x}(k), \Phi)^T. \tag{36}$$

- For Levenberg–Marquardt, $P(k) = (1-\lambda)H(k) + \alpha I$ with $H(k)$ as in case of Gauss–Newton and again $\mu(k) = 1-\lambda$. The update of the matrix P is done by:

$$P(k) = \lambda P(k-1) + (1-\lambda)\left(\psi(\vec{x}(k), \Phi)\psi(\vec{x}(k), \Phi)^T + \alpha I\right). \tag{37}$$

Using matrix inversion lemma (Sherman and Morrison, 1949) and some reformulation operations to avoid matrix inversion in each step (P^{-1} is required in Equation (35)) leads to the well-known recursive Gauss–Newton approach, which is e.g., used in Komijani *et al.* (2012) for recursively updating the kernel widths in the consequents and also for fine-tuning the regularization parameter. It also results in the recursive least squares approach in case of linear parameters (formulas for the local learning variant in Equation (30)). In case of recursive Levenberg Marquardt (RLM) algorithm, a more complex reformulation option is requested to approximate the update formulas for $P(k)^{-1}$ directly (without intermediate inversion step). This leads to the recursive equations as successfully used in the EFP method by Wang and Vrbanek (2008) for updating centers and spreads in Gaussian fuzzy sets (multivariate Gaussian rules), see also Lughofer (2011b) and Chapter 2.

3.3.3. *Learning of Consequents in EFC*

The most common choice in EFC design for consequent learning is simply to use the class majority voting for each rule separately. This can be achieved by incrementally counting the number of samples falling into each class k and rule i, h_{ik} (the rule which is the nearest one in the current data stream process). The class with majority count $k* = argmax_{k=1}^{K} h_{ik}$ is the consequent class of the corresponding (ith) rule in case of the classical architecture in Equation (16). The confidences in each class per rule can be obtained by the relative frequencies among all classes $conf_{ik} = \frac{h_{ik}}{\sum_{k=1}^{K} h_{ik}}$ in case of extended architecture in Equation (17). For multi-model classifiers, the same strategy can be applied within each single binary classifier. An enhanced confidence calculation scheme will be handled under the scope of *reliability* in Section 3.4.5.

3.3.4. *Incremental Partitioning of the Feature Space* (*Rule Learning*)

A fundamental issue in *evolving systems*, which differs them from *adaptive systems* is that they possess the capability to change their structure during online, incremental learning cycles — adaptive systems are only able to update their parameters as described in the preliminary two sub-sections. The evolving technology addresses the dynamic expansion and contraction of the rule-base. Therefore, almost all of the EFS approaches foresee two fundamental concepts for incremental partitioning of the feature space (only some foresee only the first option):

- *Rule evolution*: It addresses the problem when and how to evolve new rules on-the-fly and on demand → knowledge expansion.
- *Rule pruning*: It addresses the problem when and how to prune rules in the rule-base on-the-fly and on demand → knowledge contraction, rule-base simplification.

The first issue guarantees to include new systems states, operation modes, process characteristics in the models to enrich their knowledge and expand them to so far unexplored regions in the feature space. The second issue guarantees that a rule-base cannot grow forever and become extremely large, hence is responsible for smart computation times and compactness of the rule-base which may be beneficial for interpretability reasons, see Section 3.5. Also, it is a helpful engine for preventing model over-fitting, especially in case when rules are evolved close to each other or are moving together over time, thus turning out to be superfluous at a later stage. Whenever new rules are evolved, the incremental update of their parameters (as described in the preliminary sub-sections) can begin and continue in the subsequent cycles.

The current state-of-the-art in EFS is that both concepts are handled in different ways in different approaches, see Lughofer (2011b) and "*Evolving Systems*" Journal by Springer[7] for recently published approaches. Due to space limitations of this book chapter in the whole encyclopedia, it is not possible to describe the various options for rule evolution and pruning anchored in the various EFS approaches. Therefore, we outline the most important directions, which enjoy some common understanding and usage in various approaches.

One concept which is widely used is the *incremental clustering* technique [see Bouchachia (2011)] for a survey of methods], which searches for an optimal grouping of the data into several clusters, ideally following the natural distribution of data clouds. In particular, the aim is that similar samples contribute to the (formation of the) same cluster while different samples should fall into different clusters (Gan *et al.*, 2007). In case when using clustering techniques emphasizing clusters with *convex shapes* (e.g., ellipsoids), these can then be directly associated with rules. Due to their projection onto the axes, the fuzzy sets appearing in the rule antecedents can be obtained. The similarity concept applied in the various approaches differ: some are using distance-oriented criteria [e.g., DENFIS (Kasabov and Song, 2002), FLEXFIS (Lughofer, 2008) or eFuMo (Zdsar *et al.*, 2014)], some are using density-based criteria [e.g., eTS (Angelov and Filev, 2004) and its extension eTS+ Angelov (2010), or Almaksour and Anquetil (2011)] and some others are using statistical-oriented criteria [e.g., ENFM (Soleimani *et al.*, 2010)]; this also affects the rule evolution criterion, often being a threshold (e.g., a maximal allowed distance) which decides whether a new rule is evolved or not. Distance-based criteria may be more prone to outliers than density-based and statistical-based ones; on the other hand, the latter ones can be quite lazy until new rules are evolved (e.g., a significant new dense area is required such that a new rule is evolved there). A summary of EFS approaches and which one applies which criterion will be given in Section 3.3.5.

Fundamental and quite common to many incremental clustering approaches is the update of the centers $\vec{c}$ defining the cluster prototype given by

$$\vec{c}(N+1) = \frac{N\vec{c}(N) + \vec{x}(N+1)}{N+1}, \tag{38}$$

and the update of the inverse covariance matrix Σ^{-1} defining the shape of clusters given by

$$\Sigma^{-1}(N+1) = \frac{\Sigma^{-1}(N)}{1-\alpha} - \frac{\alpha}{1-\alpha}\frac{(\Sigma^{-1}(N)(\vec{x}-\vec{c}))(\Sigma^{-1}(N)(\vec{x}-\vec{c}))^T}{1+\alpha((\vec{x}-\vec{c})^T\Sigma^{-1}(N)(\vec{x}-\vec{c}))},$$

[7] http://www.springer.com/physics/complexity/journal/12530.

with $\alpha = \frac{1}{N+1}$ and N the number of samples seen so far. Usually, various clusters/rules are updated, each representing an own covariance matrix Σ_i^{-1}, thus the symbol $N = k_i$ then represents the number of samples "seen by the corresponding cluster so far", i.e., falling into the corresponding cluster so far (also denoted as the *support of the cluster*).

Other concepts rely

- On the degree of the coverage of the current input sample, i.e., when the coverage is low, a new rule is evolved [e.g., SOFNN (Leng *et al.*, 2005), the approach in Leng *et al.* (2012)].
- On the system error criteria such as the one-step-ahead prediction, i.e., when this is high, a new rule is evolved (e.g., as in SOFNN (Leng *et al.*, 2005) or the approach in Leng *et al.* (2012)) or even a split is performed as in AHLTNM (Kalhor *et al.*, 2010).
- On the rule significance in terms of (expected) statistical contribution and influence, i.e., when a new rule is expected to significantly influence the output of the system it is actually added to the system [e.g., SAFIS (Rong *et al.*, 2006) and its extensions (Rong *et al.*, 2011; Rong, 2012) PANFIS (Pratama *et al.*, 2014a), GENEFIS (Pratama *et al.*, 2014b)).
- On Yager's participatory learning concept (Yager, 1990), comparing the arousal index and the compatibility measure with thresholds [as in ePL (Lima *et al.*, 2010; Lemos *et al.*, 2013), eMG (Lemos *et al.*, 2011a)].
- On the goodness of fit tests based on statistical criteria (e.g., F-statistics) for candidate splits. The leafs are replaced with a new subtree, inducing an expansion of the hierarchical fuzzy model [e.g., in Lemos *et al.* (2011b) or incremental LOLIMOT (Local Linear Model Tree) (Hametner and Jakubek, 2013)].

Furthermore, most of the approaches which are applying an adaptation of the rule contours, e.g., by recursive adaptation of the nonlinear antecedent parameters, are equipped with a merging strategy for rules. Whenever rules are forced to move together due to the nature of data stream samples falling in-between these, they may become inevitably overlapping, see the upper right case in Figure 3.6 for an example. The rule evolution concepts cannot omit such occasions in advance, as streaming samples are loaded in the same timely order as they are appearing/recorded in the system — sometimes, originally it may seem that two clusters are contained in the data, which may turn out later as erroneous assumption. Various criteria have been suggested to identify such occurrences and to eliminate them, see Lughofer (2013) and Section 3.2 for a recent overview. In Lughofer and Hüllermeier (2011); Lughofer *et al.* (2011a), a generic concept has been defined for recognizing such overlapping situations based on fuzzy set and rule level. It is applicable for most of the conventional EFS techniques as relying on a geometric-based criterion employing a rule inclusion metric. This has been expanded in Lughofer *et al.* (2013) to the case of adjacent rules in the feature space showing the same trend in the antecedents and consequents, thus guaranteeing a kind of joint homogeneity. Generic rule merging formulas have been established in Lughofer *et al.* (2011a) and go hand in hand with consistency assurance, especially when equipped with specific merging operations for rule consequent parts, see also Section 3.5.

3.3.5. *EFS Approaches*

In this section, we provide an overview of most important EFS approaches developed since the invention of evolving fuzzy systems approximately 10 years ago. Due to space limitations and the wide variety and manifold of the approaches, we are not able to give a compact summary about the basic methodological concepts in each of these. Thus, we restrict ourselves to report a rough comparison, which is based on the main characteristics and properties of the EFS approaches. This comparison is provided in Table 3.1. Additionally, we demonstrate a pseudo-code in Algorithm 3.1, which shows more or less a common denominator of which steps are performed within the learning engines of the EFS approaches.

Algorithm 3.1. Key Steps in an Evolving Fuzzy Systems Learning Engine

(1) Load new data sample $\vec{x}$.
(2) Pre-process data sample (e.g., normalization).
(3) **If** rule-base is empty, initialize the first rule with its center to the data sample $\vec{c} = \vec{x}$ and its spread (range of influence) to some small value; go to Step (1).
(4) **Else**, perform the following Steps (5–10):
(5) Check if rule evolution criteria are fulfilled
    (a) If yes, evolve a new rule (Section 3.3.4) and perform body of Step (3) (without if-condition).
    (b) If no, proceed with next step.
(6) Update antecedents parts of (some or all) rules (Sections 3.3.4 and 3.3.2).
(7) Update consequent parameters (of some or all) rules (Sections 3.3.3 and 3.3.1).
(8) Check if the rule pruning/merging criteria are fulfilled
    (a) If yes, prune or merge rules (Section 3.3.4); go to Step (1).
    (b) If no, proceed with next step.
(9) Optional: Perform corrections of parameters towards more optimality.
(10) Go to Step (1).

One comment refers to the update of antecedents and consequents: some approaches may only update those of *some* rules (e.g., the rule corresponding to the

Table 3.1: Comparison of properties and characteristics of important EFS approaches.

Method	Architecture	Ant. Learning	Cons. Learning	Rule Pr.	Forget.	Dim. Red.	# of P.	Note
AHLTNM (Kalhor *et al.*, 2010)	TS fuzzy system	Incremental Split-and-Merge (own)	RFWLS	Yes	Yes, cons. only	No	1–2	
DENFIS (Kasabov and Song, 2002)	Neuro-fuzzy system	Evolving Clustering (ECM)	RFWLS with distance weights	No	No	No	1–2	One of the first approaches
EFC-AP (Lughofer and Buchtala, 2013)	All-pairs classifiers	Evolving Clustering (eVQ)	RFWLS or Consequent labeling	Yes	No	No	1–2	Very high accuracy, first all-pairs EFC
EFP (Wang and Vrbanek, 2008)	Mamdani + TS fuzzy system	Evolving Clustering (own) + RLM	RLM + RLS (global)	Yes	Yes, cons. only	No	1–2	First attempt of recursive learning of nonlinear params
eFPT (Shaker *et al.*, 2013)	Tree-based structure	Dynamic substitution with neighbor tree	None	Yes	No	Yes	3	Good interpretability, exploits architecture from Huang *et al.* (2008)
eFT (Lemos *et al.*, 2011b)	Tree-based structure	Replacement of leaves with subtrees	RFWLS double-weight	No	No	Yes	4	First approach of evolving fuzzy decision tree

(*Continued*)

Table 3.1: (*Continued*)

Method	Architecture	Ant. Learning	Cons. Learning	Rule Pr.	Forget.	Dim. Red.	# of P.	Note
eFuMo (Zdsar *et al.*, 2014)	Dynamic TS fuzzy system (lags)	Evolving Clustering (Gustafson-Kessel)	RFWLS double-weight.	Yes	Yes, cons. + ante.	No	3–5	Capable of splitting of rules
eMG (Lemos *et al.*, 2011a)	Generalized TS fuzzy system	Participatory Learning	RFWLS double-weight	Yes	No	No	4	First approach using generalized rules
ENFM (Soleimani *et al.*, 2010)	Generalized TS fuzzy system	Recursive Clustering (Gath-Geva)	RFWLS	Yes	Yes, cons. only	No	3	
eClass (Angelov *et al.*, 2008)	single model, one-versus-rest classifiers and MIMO	Evolving clustering (eClustering)	RFWLS + or Cons. labeling	No	Yes, cons. only	No	1–2	First one-vs-rest in EFC
ePL (Lima *et al.*, 2010)	TS fuzzy system	Participatory Learning	RLS (global)	Yes	No	No	5	First usage of participatory (Yager, 1990)
eT2FIS (Tung *et al.*, 2013)	Type-2 Mamdani	Native activation levels, parameter updates	same as antecedent learning	Yes	No	No	3	First evolving Type-2 Mamdani system

(*Continued*)

Table 3.1: (*Continued*)

Method	Architecture	Ant. Learning	Cons. Learning	Rule Pr.	Forget.	Dim. Red.	# of P.	Note
eTS(+) (Angelov, 2010; Angelov and Filev, 2004)	TS fuzzy system	Evolving clustering (eClustering)	RFWLS double-weight	Yes	Yes, later in (Lughofer and Angelov, 2011)	Yes	1–2	One of the pioneering methods (2004)
eTS-LS-SVM (Komijani *et al.*, 2012)	Extended TS fuzzy system	Recursive clustering, suitability	Recursive Gauss–Newton	Yes	No	No	6 (2 + 4)	First approach for evolving extended TS fuzzy system

winning cluster), others may always update those of *all* rules. The former may have some advantages regarding the prevention of the *unlearning effect* in parts where actual samples do not fall (Lughofer, 2010a), the latter achieves significance and thus reliability in the rule parameters faster (more samples are used for updating).

Although many of these have different facets with a large variety of pros and cons, which cannot be strictly arranged in an ordered manner to say one method is for sure better than the other, the number of parameters (last but one column) gives somehow a bit clarification about the useability resp. the effort to tune the method and finally, to let it run. Tendentially, the more parameters a method has, the more sensitive it is to a particular result and the higher the effort to get it successfully run in an industrial installation. In case when mentioning "$X - Y$" number of parameters it means that Y parameters are the case when forgetting is parameterized (fixed forgetting factor), which is often an optional choice in many applications.

For further details about the concrete algorithms and concepts of the approaches listed in Tables 3.1 and 3.2, please refer to Lughofer (2011b), describing approaches in a compact detailed form from the origin of EFS up to June 2010 and to recently published ones (since July 2010) in "*Evolving Systems*" Journal by Springer[8] as well as papers in the recent special issues "Evolving Soft Computing Techniques and Applications" (Bouchachia *et al.*, 2014) in *Applied Soft Computing* Journal (Elsevier) and "Online Fuzzy Machine Learning and Data Mining" (Bouchachia *et al.*, 2013) in *Information Sciences* Journal (Elsevier), and also some recent regular contributions in "IEEE Transactions on Fuzzy Systems"[9] and "IEEE Transactions on Neural Networks and Learning Systems"[10] (neuro-fuzzy approaches).

3.4. Stability and Reliability

Two important issues when learning from data streams are the assurance of stability during the incremental learning process and the investigation of reliability of model outputs in terms of predictions, forecasts, quantifications, classification statements etc. These usually leads to an enhanced *robustness* of the evolved models. Stability is usually guaranteed by all the aforementioned approaches listed in Tables 3.1 and 3.2 as long as the data streams from which the models are learnt appear in a quite "smooth, expected" fashion. However, specific occasions such as *drifts* and *shifts* (Klinkenberg, 2004) or high noise levels may appear in these, which require a specific handling within the learning engine of the EFS approaches. Another problem

[8] http://www.springer.com/physics/complexity/journal/12530.
[9] http://ieeexplore.ieee.org/xpl/RecentIssue.jsp?punumber=91.
[10] http://ieeexplore.ieee.org/xpl/RecentIssue.jsp?punumber=5962385.

Table 3.2: Comparison of properties and characteristics of important EFS approaches.

Method	Architecture	Ant. Learning	Cons. Learning	Rule Pr.	Forget.	Dim. Red.	# of P.	Note
FLEXFIS (++) (Lughofer, 2008, 2012b)	TS fuzzy system	Evolving clustering (eVQ)	RFWLS	Yes	Yes, cons. + ante.	No	1–2	First approach forgetting in ante, enhanced robustness
FLEXFIS-Class (Angelov *et al.*, 2008; Lughofer, 2011c)	Single model, one-vs-rest classifiers	Evolving clustering (eVQ)	RFWLS	No	Yes, cons. only	Yes (smooth)	1–2	First one-versus-rest in EFC
FPA (Wang *et al.*, 2013)	Single model classifiers	Incremental con.-based optimization	Weight vector update	No	No	No	2	
Gen-Smart-EFS (GS-EFS) (Lughofer *et al.*, 2013)	Generalized TS fuzzy system	Evolving clustering (extended eVQ)	RFWLS	Yes	Yes, cons. only	Yes (smooth)	1–2	First joint concept dim. red. for gen. rules + pruning
GENEFIS (Pratama *et al.*, 2014b)	Generalized TS fuzzy system	Gen. adaptive resonance theory + stat. influence	FWGRLS	Yes	No	Yes (crisp)	3–4	Gen. rules + online dim. red.

(*Continued*)

Table 3.2: (*Continued*)

Method	Architecture	Ant. Learning	Cons. Learning	Rule Pr.	Forget.	Dim. Red.	# of P.	Note
HAW-NFS (Bodyanskiy and Vynokurova, 2013)	Neuro-fuzzy system	inc opt. [mod. of (Kaczmarz, 1993)]	RLS (global)	No	No	No	3	First wavelet-based neuro-fuzzy
LOLIMOT inc. (Hametner and Jakubek, 2013)	Tree-based structure	Node replacement (recursive split)	Recursive nonlinear least squares	No	No	No	1–2	First approach for an incremental LOLIMOT (Nelles, 2001)
PANFIS (Pratama *et al.*, 2014a)	Generalized TS fuzzy system	Extended Self-Organizing Map, statistical influence	FWGRLS	Yes	No	No	2	First proj. concept of gen. rules, stability proofs
rGK (Dovzan and Skrjanc, 2011)	TS fuzzy system	Recursive clustering (GK)	RLS (global), RFWLS (local)	No	Yes, cons. only	No	3–6	No rule evolution
(E)SAFIS (Rong *et al.*, 2014, 2006)	TS fuzzy system (MIMO)	Statistical influence, distance criterion	RLS (global), inc. stability with Lyapunov	Yes	No	No	3	One of the pioneering methods (2005–2006)

(*Continued*)

Table 3.2: (*Continued*)

Method	Architecture	Ant. Learning	Cons. Learning	Rule Pr.	Forget.	Dim. Red.	# of P.	Note
SAFIS-Class (Rong *et al.*, 2011)	Single model using TS fuzzy system	Statistical influence, distance criterion	RLS (global)	Yes	No	No	6	
SEIT2FNN (Juang and Tsao, 2008)	Type-2 TS fuzzy system	Incremental steepest descent	RLS (global)	No	Yes, cons. only	No	3	First evolving type-2 fuzzy system
SOFMLS (Rubio, 2009)	Mamdani	Evolving clustering (nearest neighborhood)	Modified RLS with increased stability	Yes	No	No	4	First approach of an evolving Mamdani fuzzy system
SOFNN (imp) (Leng *et al.*, 2005, 2012)	Neuro-fuzzy system	Coverage and system error criteria, rule enlargement	Modified RLS (global) with weights	Yes	No	No	2	One of the pioneering methods (2005)

is dedicated to high-dimensional streams, usually stemming from large-scale time-series (Morreale *et al.*, 2013) embedded in the data, and mostly causing a *curse of dimensionality* effect, which leads to over-fitting and downtrends in model accuracy. As can be realized from Column #7 in Tables 3.1 and 3.2, only a few approaches embed any online dimensionality reduction procedure so far in order to diminish this effect. Although high noise levels can be automatically handled by RFWLS, its spin-offs and modifications as well as by the antecedent learning engines discussed in Sections 3.3.2 and 3.3.4, reliability aspects in terms of increasing the certainty in model outputs respecting the noise are weakly discussed. Drift handling is included in some of the methods by forgetting strategies, but these are basically only applied for consequent learning in Takagi–Sugeno type fuzzy models (see Column 6 in Tables 3.1 and 3.2).

This section is dedicated to a summary of recent developments in stability, reliability and robustness of EFS which can be generically used in combination with most of the approaches listed in Tables 3.1 and 3.2.

3.4.1. *Drift Handling in Streams*

Drifts in data streams refer to a gradual evolution of the underlying data distribution and therefore of the learning concept over time (Tsymbal, 2004; Widmer and Kubat, 1996) and are frequent occurrences in nowadays non-stationary environments (Sayed-Mouchaweh and Lughofer, 2012). Drifts can happen because the system behavior, environmental conditions or target concepts dynamically change during the online learning process, which makes the relations, concepts contained in the old data samples obsolete. Such situations are in contrary to new operation modes or system states which should be integrated into the models with the same weight as the older ones in order to extend the models, but keeping the relations in states seen before untouched (still valid for future predictions). Drifts, however, usually mean that the older learned relations (as parts of a model) are not valid any longer and thus should be incrementally out-weighted, ideally in a smooth manner to avoid catastrophic forgetting (French, 1999; Moe-Helgesen and Stranden, 2005).

A smooth forgetting concept for consequent learning employing the idea of exponential forgetting (Aström and Wittenmark, 1994), is used in approximately half of the EFS approaches listed in Tables 3.1 and 3.2 (refer to Column #6). The strategy in all of these is to integrate a forgetting factor $\lambda \in [0, 1[$ for strengthening the influence of newer samples in the Kalman gain γ — see Equation (31). Figure 3.7 shows the weight impact of samples obtained for different forgetting factor values. This is also compared to a standard sliding window technique, which weighs all samples up to a certain point of time in the past equally, but forgets all others before completely $\rightarrow$ non-smooth forgetting. This variant is also termed as decremental

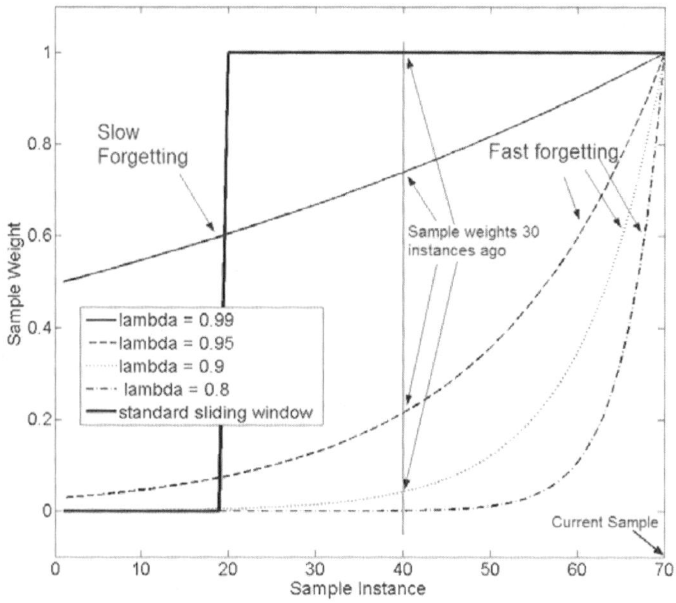

Figure 3.7: Smooth forgetting strategies achieving different weights for past samples; compared to a sliding window with fixed width → complete forgetting of older samples (decremental learning).

learning (Bouillon *et al.*, 2013; Cernuda *et al.*, 2014), as the information contained in older samples falling out of the sliding window is fully unlearned (= decremented) from the model. The effect of this forgetting factor integration is that changes of the target concept in regression problems can be tracked appropriately, i.e., a movement and shaping of the current regression surface towards the new output behavior is enforced, see Lughofer and Angelov (2011). Decremental learning may allow more flexibility (only the latest N samples are really used for model shaping), but increases the likelihood of catastrophic forgetting.

Regarding a drift handling in the antecedent part, several techniques may be used such as a reactivation of rule centers and spreads from a converged situation by an increase of the learning gain: this is conducted in Lughofer and Angelov (2011) for the two EFS approaches eTS and FLEXFIS and has the effect that rules are helped out from their stucked, converged positions to cover the new data cloud appearance of the drifted situation. In eFuMo, the forgetting in antecedent learning is integrated as the degree of the weighted movement of the rule centers $\vec{c}_.$ towards a new data sample $\vec{x}_{N+1}$:

$$\vec{c}_i(N+1) = \vec{c}_i(N) + \Delta\vec{c}_i(N+1) \quad \text{with } \Delta\vec{c}_i(N+1) = \frac{\mu_i(\vec{x}_{N+1})^{\eta}(\vec{x}_{N+1} - \vec{c}_i(N))}{s_i(N+1)}, \tag{39}$$

with $s_i(N+1) = \lambda s_i(N) + \mu_i(\vec{x}_{N+1})^\eta$ the sum of the past memberships $\mu_i(\vec{x}_j)$, $j = 1, \ldots, N$, η the fuzziness degree also used as parameters in fuzzy c-means, and λ the forgetting factor. Forgetting is also integrated in the inverse covariance matrix and determinant update defining the shape of the clusters. All other EFS techniques in Tables 3.1 and 3.2 do not embed an antecedent forgetting.

An important investigation is the question when to trigger forgetting and when to apply the conventional life-long learning concept (all samples equally weighted) (Hamker, 2001). In Shaker and Lughofer (2014), it could be analyzed that when using a permanent (fixed) forgetting factor respectively an increased model flexibility in case when no drift happens, the accuracy of the evolved models may decrease over time. Thus, it is necessary to install a drift indication concept, which is able to detect drifts and in ideal cases also to quantify their intensity levels; based on these, it is possible to increase or decrease the degree of forgetting, also termed as *adaptive forgetting*. A recent approach for EFS which performs this by using an extended version of Page–Hinkley test (Mouss *et al.*, 2004), (a widely known and respected test in the field of drift handling in streams (Gama, 2010; Sebastiao *et al.*, 2013) is demonstrated in Shaker and Lughofer (2014). It is also the first attempt to localize the drift intensity by quantifying drift effects in different local parts of the features space with different intensities and smoothly: EFS is a perfect model architecture to support such a local smooth handling (fuzzy rules with certain overlaps).

3.4.2. *Online Curse of Dimensionality Reduction*

For models including localization components as is the case of evolving fuzzy systems (in terms of rules), it is well known that *curse of dimensionality* is very severe in case when a high number of variables are used as model inputs (Pedrycz and Gomide, 2007), e.g., in large-scale time-series, recorded in multi-sensor networks (Chong and Kumar, 2003). This is basically because in high-dimensional spaces, someone cannot speak about locality any longer (on which these types of models rely), as all samples are moving to the edges of the joint feature space — see Hastie *et al.* (2009) and Chapter 1 for a detailed analysis of this problem.

Therefore, the reduction of the dimensionality of the learning problem is highly desired. In data stream sense, to ensure an appropriate reaction onto the system dynamics, the feature reduction should be conducted online and be open for *anytime changes*. A possibility is to track the importance levels of features over time and to cut out that ones which become unnecessary — as has been used in connection with EFS for regression problems in Angelov (2010); Pratama *et al.* (2014b) and for classification problems in a first attempt in Bouchachia and Mittermeir (2006). However, features which are unimportant at an earlier point of time may become important at a later stage (*feature reactivation*). This means that crisply cutting out some features with the usage of online feature selection and ranking approaches such as Li (2004); Ye *et al.* (2005) can fail to represent the recent feature dynamics appropriately. Without a re-training cycle, which, however slows down the process and causes additional sliding window parameters, this would lead to discontinuities in the learning process (Lughofer, 2011b), as parameters and rule structures have been learnt on different feature spaces before.

An approach which is addressing input structure changes incrementally on-the-fly is presented in Lughofer (2011c) for classification problems using classical single model and one-versus-rest based multi-model architectures (in connection with FLEXFIS-Class learning engine). It operates on a global basis, hence features are either seen as important or unimportant for the whole model. The basic idea is that feature weighs $\lambda_1, \ldots, \lambda_p \in [0, 1]$ for the p features included in the learning problem are calculated based on a stable separability criterion (Dy and Brodley, 2004):

$$J = trace(S_w^{-1} S_b), \tag{40}$$

with S_w the within scatter matrix modeled by the sum of the covariance matrices for each class, and S_b the between scatter matrix, modeled by the sum of the degree of mean shift between classes. The criterion in Equation (40) is applied (1). Dimension-wise to see the impact of each feature separately — note that in this case it reduces to a ratio of two variances — and (2). For the remaining $p - 1$ feature subspace in order to gain the quality of separation when excluding each feature. In both cases, p criteria $J_1, \ldots, J_p$ according to Equation (40) are obtained. For normalization purposes to [0, 1], finally the feature weighs are defined by:

$$\lambda_j = 1 - \frac{J_j - min_{j=1,\ldots,p}(J_j)}{max_{j=1,\ldots,p}(J_j) - min_{j=1,\ldots,p}(J_j)}. \tag{41}$$

To be applicable in online learning environments, updating the weighs in incremental mode is achieved by updating the within-scatter and between-scatter matrices using the recursive covariance matrix formula (Hisada *et al.*, 2010). This achieves a smooth change of feature weighs = feature importance levels over time with new incoming samples. Features may become out-weighted (close to 0) and reactivated (weighs significantly larger than 0) at a later stage without "disturbing" the parameter and rule structure learning process. Hence, this approach is also denoted as *smooth and soft online dimension reduction* — the term *softness* comes from the decreased weighs instead of a crisp deletion. Down-weighted features then play a marginal role during the learning process, e.g., the rule evolution criterion relies more on the highly weighted features.

The feature weighs concept has been recently employed in Lughofer *et al.* (2014), in the context of data stream regression problems, there with the usage of generalized rules as defined in Section 3.2.2.2, instead of axis-parallel ones as used in Lughofer (2011c). The features weights are calculated by a combination of future-based expected statistical contributions of the features in all rules and their influences in the rules' hyper-planes (measured in terms of gradients), see Lughofer *et al.* (2014).

3.4.3. *Incremental Smoothing*

Recently, a concept for incremental smoothing of consequent parameters has been introduced in Rosemann *et al.* (2009), where a kind of *incremental regularization* is conducted after each learning step. This has the effect to decrease the level of over-fitting whenever the noise level in the data is high. Indeed, when applying the local recursive least squares estimator as in Equations (30)–(32) and some of its modifications, the likelihood of over-fitting is small due to the enforcement of the local approximation and interpretation property [as analyzed in Angelov *et al.* (2008)], but still may be present. The approach in Rosemann *et al.* (2009) accomplishes the smoothing by correcting the consequent functions of the updated rule(s) by a template T measuring the violation degree subject to a meta-level property on the neighboring rules.

Finally, it should be highlighted that this strategy assures smoother consequent hyper-planes over nearby lying or even touching rules, thus increases the likelihood of further rule reduction through extended simplicity assurance concepts (adjacency, homogeneuity, trend-continuation criteria) as discussed in Lughofer (2013) and successfully applied to obtain compact rule bases in data stream regression problems in Lughofer *et al.* (2013), employing generalized fuzzy rules, defined in Section 3.2.2.2.

3.4.4. *Convergence Analysis/Ensurance*

Another important criterion when applying EFS is some sort of convergence of the parameters included in the fuzzy systems over time (in case of a regular stream without a drift etc.) — this accounts for the stability aspect in the stability-plasticity dilemma (Hamker, 2001), which is important in the life-long learning context. This is for instance accomplished in the FLEXFIS approach, which, however only guarantees a sub-optimality subject to a constant (thus guaranteeing finite solutions) due to a quasi-monotonic decreasing intensity of parameter updates, but is not able to provide a concrete level of this sub-optimality, see Lughofer (2008) and Lughofer (2011b) and Chapter 3. In the approach by Rubio (2010), a concrete upper bound on the identification error is achieved by the modified least squares algorithm to train both, parameters and structures, is achieved with the support of Lyapunov function. The upper bound depends on the actual certainty of the model output. Another approach which is handling the problem of constraining the model error while assuring parameter convergence simultaneously is applied within the PANFIS learning engine (Pratama *et al.*, 2014a): This is achieved with the usage of an extended recursive least squares approach.

3.4.5. *Reliability*

Reliability deals with the *interpretation of the model predictions* in terms of classification statements, quantification outputs or forecasted values in time series. Reliability points to the trustworthiness of the predictions of current query points which may be basically influenced by two factors:

- The quality of the training data w.r.t data stream samples seen so far.
- The nature and localization of the current query point for which a prediction should be obtained.

The trustworthiness/certainty of the predictions may support/influence the users/operators during a final decision finding — for instance, a query assigned to a class may cause a different user's reaction when the trustworthiness about this decision is low, compared to when it is high. In this sense, it is an essential add-on to the actual model predictions which may also influence its further processing.

The first factor basically concerns the noise level in measurement data. This also may cover aspects in the direction of uncertainties in users' annotations in classification problems: a user with lower experience level may cause more inconsistencies in the class labels, causing overlapping classes, finally increasing conflict cases (see below); similar occasions may happen in case when several users annotate samples on the same systems, but have different opinions in borderline cases.

The second factor concerns the position of the current query point with respect to the definition space of the model. A model can show a perfect trend with little uncertainty, but a new query point appears far away from all training samples seen so far, yielding a severe degree of extrapolation when conducting the model inference process. In a classification context, a query point may also fall close in a highly overlapped region or close to the decision boundary between two classes. The first problem is denoted as *ignorance*, the second as *conflict* (Hüllermeier and Brinker, 2008; Lughofer, 2012a). A visualization of these two occasions is shown in Figure 3.8(a) (for conflict) and 3.8(b) (for ignorance). The conflict case is due to a sample falling in-between two classes and the ignorance case due to a query point falling outside the range of training samples, which is indeed linearly separable, but by several possible decision boundaries [also termed as the *variability of the version space* (Hüllermeier and Brinker, 2008)].

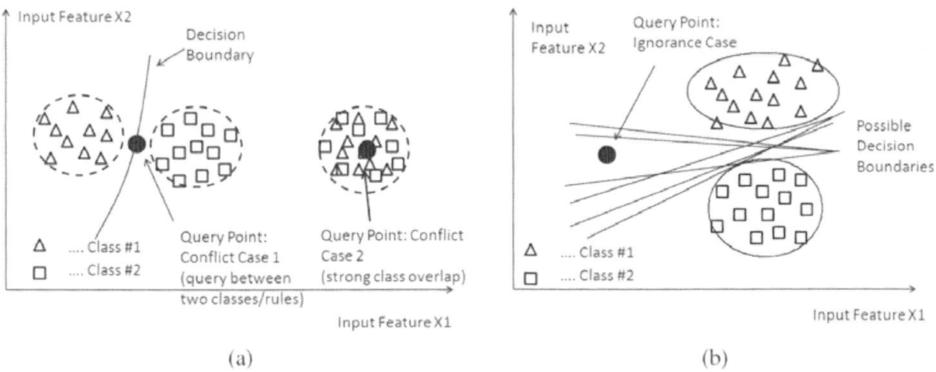

Figure 3.8: (a) Two conflict cases: query point falls inbetween two distinct classes and within the overlap region of two classes; (b) Ignorance case as query point lies significantly away from the training samples, thus increasing the *variability of the version space* (Hüllermeier and Brinker, 2008); in both figures, rules modeling the two separate classes are shown by an ellipsoid, the decision boundaries indicated by solid lines.

In the regression context, the estimation of parameters through RWFLS and modifications usually can deal with high noise levels in order to find a non-overfitting trend of the approximation surface. However, it is not possible to represent uncertainty levels of the model predictions later on. These can be modeled by the so-called error bars or confidence intervals (Smithson, 2003). In EFS, they have been developed based on parameter uncertainty in Lughofer and Guardiola (2008a) [applied to online fault detection in Serdio *et al.* (2014a)] and in an extended scheme in Skrjanc (2009) (for chemometric calibration purposes). The latter is based on a funded deduction from statistical noise and quantile estimation theory (Tschumitschew and Klawonn, 2012). Both are applicable in connection with local (LS) learning of TS consequent parameters.

In the classification context, conflict and ignorance can be reflected and represented by means of fuzzy classifiers in a quite natural way (Hühn and Hüllermeier, 2009). These concepts have been only recently tackled once in the field of evolving fuzzy classifiers (EFC), see Lughofer and Buchtala (2013), where multiple binary classifiers are trained in an all-pairs context for obtaining simper decision boundaries in multi-class classification problems (see Section 3.2.6.3). On a single rule level, the confidence in a prediction can be obtained by the confidence in the different classes coded into the consequents of the rules having the form of Equation (17). This provides a perfect conflict level (close to 0.5 $\rightarrow$ high conflict, close to 1 $\rightarrow$ low conflict) in case of overlapping classes within a single rule. If a query point $\vec{x}$ falls in-between rules with different majority classes (different maximal confidence levels), then the extended weighted classification scheme in Equation (19) is requested to represent a conflict level. If the confidence in the final output class L, $conf_L$, is close to 0.5, conflict is high, when it is close to 1, conflict is low. In case of all-pairs architecture, Equation (19) can be used to represent conflict levels in the binary classifiers. Furthermore, an overall conflict level on the final classifier output is obtained by Lughofer and Buchtala (2013):

$$conflict_{deg} = \frac{score_k}{score_k + score_l}, \tag{42}$$

with k and l the classes with the highest scores.

The ignorance criterion can be resolved in a quite natural way, represented by a degree of extrapolation, thus:

$$Ign_{deg} = 1 - \max_{i=1}^{C} \mu_i(\vec{x}), \tag{43}$$

with C the number of rules currently contained in the evolved fuzzy classifier. In fact, the degree of extrapolation is a good indicator of the degree of ignorance, but not necessarily sufficient, see Lughofer (2012a), for an extended analysis and further concepts. However, integrating the ignorance levels into the preference relation scheme of all-pairs evolving fuzzy classifiers according to Equation (24) for obtaining the final classification statement, helped to boost the accuracies of the classifier significantly, as then classifiers which show a strongly extrapolated situation in the current query are down-weighted towards 0, thus masked-out, in the scoring process. This leads to an out-performance of incremental machine learning classifiers from MOA framework[11] (Bifet *et al.*, 2010) on several large-scale problems, see Lughofer and Buchtala (2013). The overall ignorance level of an all-pairs classifier is the minimal ignorance degree calculated by Equation (43) over all binary classifiers.

3.5. Interpretability

Improved transparency and interpretability of the evolved models may be useful in several real-world applications where the operators and experts intend to gain a deeper understanding of the interrelations and dependencies in the system. This may enrich their knowledge and enable them to interpret the characteristics of the system on a deeper level. Concrete examples are decision support systems or classification systems, which sometimes require the knowledge why certain decisions have been made, e.g., see Wetter (2000): Insights into these models may provide answers to important questions (e.g., providing the health state of a patient) and support the user in taking appropriate actions. Another example is the substitution of expensive hardware with *soft sensors*, referred to as *eSensors* in an evolving context (Angelov

[11] http://moa.cms.waikato.ac.nz/.

and Kordon, 2010a; Macias-Hernandez and Angelov, 2010): The model has to be linguistically or physically understandable, reliable, and plausible to an expert, before it can be substituted for the hardware. In often cases, it is beneficial to provide further insights into the control behavior (Nelles, 2001).

Interpretability, apart from pure complexity reduction, has been addressed very little in the evolving systems community so far (under the scope of data stream mining). A recent position paper published in *Information Sciences* journal Lughofer (2013) summarizes the achievements in EFS, provides avenues for new concepts as well as concrete new formulas and algorithms and points out open issues as important future challenges. The basic common understanding is that complexity reduction as a key prerequisite for compact and therefore transparent models is handled in most of the EFS approaches, which can be found nowadays in literature (please also refer to Column "Rule pruning" in Tables 3.1 and 3.2), whereas other important criteria [known to be important from conventional batch offline design of fuzzy systems (Casillas *et al.*, 2003; Gacto *et al.*, 2011)], are more or less loosely handled in EFS. These criteria include:

- Distinguishability and Simplicity
- Consistency
- Coverage and Completeness
- Local Property and Addition-to-One-Unity
- Feature Importance Levels
- Rule Importance Levels
- Interpretation of Consequents
- Interpretability of Input–Output Behavior
- Knowledge Expansion

Distinguishability and *simplicity* are handled under the scope of complexity reduction, where the difference between these two lies in the occurrence of the degree of overlap of rules and fuzzy sets: Redundant rules and fuzzy sets are highly overlapping and therefore indistinguishable, thus should be merged, whereas obsolete rules or close rules showing similar approximation/classification trends belong to an unnecessary complexity which can be simplified (due to pruning). Figure 3.9 visualizes an example of a fuzzy partition extracted in the context of house price estimation (Lughofer *et al.*, 2011b), when conducting native precise modeling (left) and when conducting some simplification steps according to merging, pruning and constrained-based learning (right). Only in the right case, it is possible to assign linguistic labels to the fuzzy sets and hence to achieve interpretation quality.

Consistency addresses the problem of assuring that no contradictory rules, i.e., rules which possess similar antecedents but dissimilar consequents, are present in the system. This can be achieved by merging redundant rules, i.e., those one which

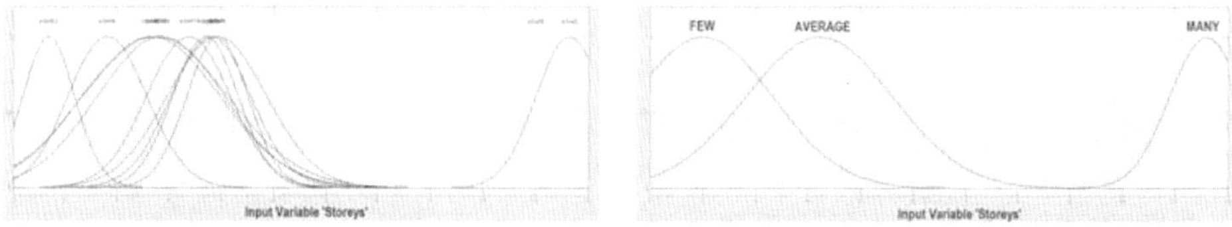

Figure 3.9: (a) Weird un-interpretable fuzzy partition for an input variable in house pricing; (b) The same partition achieved when conducting merging, pruning options of rules and sets during the incremental learning phase → assignments of linguistic labels possible.

are similar in their antecedents, with the usage of the participatory learning concept introduced by Yager (1990). An appropriate merging of the linear parameter vectors $\vec{w}$ is given by Lughofer and Hüllermeier (2011):

$$\vec{w}_{\text{new}} = \vec{w}_{R_1} + \alpha \cdot Cons(R_1, R_2) \cdot (\vec{w}_{R_2} - \vec{w}_{R_1}), \tag{44}$$

where $\alpha = k_{R_2}/(k_{R_1} + k_{R_2})$ represents the *basic learning rate* with k_{R_1} the support of the more supported rule R_1 and $Cons(R_1, R_2)$ the *compatibility measure* between the two rules within the participatory learning context. The latter is measured by a consistency degree between antecedent and consequents of the two rules. It relies on the exponential proportion between rule antecedent similarity degree (overlap) and rule consequent similarity degree.

Coverage and *completeness* refer to the problem of a well-defined coverage of the input space by the rule-base. Formally, ϵ-completeness requires that for each new incoming data sample there exists at least one rule to which this sample has a membership degree of at least ϵ. A specific re-adjustment concept of fuzzy sets and thus rules is presented in Lughofer (2013), which restricts the re-adjustment level in order to keep the accuracy high. An alternative, more profound option for data stream regression problems, is offered as well in Lughofer (2013), which integrates a punishment term for ϵ-completeness into the least squares optimization problem. Incremental optimization techniques based on gradients of the extended optimization function may be applied in order to approach but not necessarily fully assure ϵ-completeness. On the other hand, the joint optimization guarantees a reasonable tradeoff between model accuracy and model coverage of the feature space.

Local property and *addition-to-one-unity* have been not considered so far, but will go a step further by ensuring fuzzy systems where only maximal 2^p rules fire at the same time (Bikdash, 1999), with p the input dimensionality. From our point of experience, this cannot be enforced by significantly loosing some model accuracy, as it requires significant shifts of rules away from the real position of the data clouds/density swarms.

Feature importance levels are an outcome of the online dimensionality reduction concept discussed in Section 3.4.2. With their usage, it is possible to obtain an interpretation on input structure level which features are more important and which ones are less important. Furthermore, they may also lead to a reduction of the rule lengths thus increasing rule transparency and readability, as features with weights smaller than ϵ have a very low impact on the final model output and therefore can be eliminated from the rule antecedent and consequent parts when showing the rule-base to experts/operators.

Rule importance levels could serve as essential interpretation component as they tend to show the importance of each rule in the rule-base. Furthermore, rule weights may be used for a smooth rule reduction during learning procedures, as rules with low weights can be seen as unimportant and may be pruned or even re-activated at a later stage in an online learning process (*soft rule pruning mechanism*). This strategy may be beneficial when starting with an expert-based system, where originally all rules are fully interpretable (as designed by experts/users), however, some may turn out to be superfluous over time for the modeling problem at hand (Lughofer, 2013). Furthermore, rule weights can be used to handle inconsistent rules in a rule-base, see e.g., Pal and Pal (1999); Cho and Park (2000), thus serving for another possibility to tackle the problem of consistency (see above). The usage of rule weights and their updates during incremental learning phases, was, to our best knowledge, not studied so far in the evolving fuzzy community. In Lughofer (2013), a first concept was suggested to adapt the rule weights, integrated as nonlinear parameters in the fuzzy systems architecture, based on incremental optimization procedures, see also Section 3.3.2.

Interpretation of consequents is assured by nature in case of classifiers with consequent class labels plus confidence levels; in case of TS fuzzy systems, it is assured as soon as local learning of rule consequents is used (Angelov *et al.*, 2008; Lughofer, 2011b) Chapter 2 and Lughofer (2013). Please also refer to Section 3.3.1: Then, a snuggling of the partial linear trends along the real approximation surface is guaranteed, thus giving rise in which parts of the feature space the model will react in which way and intensity (gradients of features).

Interpretability of Input–Output Behavior refers to the understanding which output(s) will be produced when showing the system concrete input queries. For instance, a model with constant output has a maximal input–output interpretability (as being very predictable what outcome will be produced for different input values), however, usually suffers from predictive accuracy (as long as the behavior of the system to be modeled is non-constant). Most actively firing rules can be used as basis for this analysis.

Knowledge expansion refers to the automatic integration of new knowledge arising during the online process on demand and on-the-fly, also in order to expand the interpretation range of the models, and is handled by all conventional EFS approaches through rule evolution and/or splitting, see Tables 3.1 and 3.2.

3.5.1. *Visual Interpretability*

Visual interpretability refers to an interesting alternative to *linguistic interpretability* (as discussed above), namely, to the representation of a model in a graphical form. In our context, this approach could be especially useful if models evolve quickly, since monitoring a visual representation might then be easier than following a frequently changing linguistic description. Under this scope, alternative "interpretability criteria" may then become interesting which are more dedicated to the timely development of the evolving fuzzy model — for instance, a trajectory of rule centers showing their movement over time, or trace paths showing birth, growth, pruning and merging of rules; first attempts in this direction have been conducted in Henzgen *et al.* (2013), employing the concept of *rule chains*. These have been significantly extended in Hentzgen *et al.* (2014) by setting up a visualization framework with a grown-up user front-end (GUI), integrating various similarity, coverage and overlap measures as well as specific techniques for an appropriate catchy representation of high-dimensional rule antecedents and consequents. Internally, it uses the FLEXFIS++ approach (Lughofer, 2012b) as incremental learning engine.

3.6. Useability and Applications

In order to increase the useability of evolving fuzzy systems, several issues are discussed in this section, ranging from the reduction of annotation efforts in classification settings through a higher plug-and-play capability (more automatization, less tuning) to the decrease of computational resources and as well as to online evaluation measures for supervising modeling performance. At the end of this section, a list of real-world applications making use of evolving fuzzy systems will be discussed.

Finally, the increase of the useability together with the assurance of interpretability serves as basis for a successful future development of the *human-inspired evolving machines (HIEM)* concept as discussed in Lughofer (2011a), which is expected to be the *next generation of evolving intelligent systems*[12] — the aim is to enrich the pure machine learning systems with human knowledge and feelings, and to form a joint concept of *active learning and teaching* in terms of a higher-educated computational intelligence useable in artificial intelligence.

[12]http://en.wikipedia.org/wiki/Evolving_intelligent_system.

3.6.1. *Single-Pass Active Learning*

3.6.1.1. *For classification problems*

In online classification tasks, all evolving and incremental classifier variants require provision of the *ground truth* in form of *true class labels* for incoming samples to guarantee smooth and well-defined updates for increased classifiers' performance. Otherwise, classifiers' false predictions self-reinforce and are back-propagated into their structure and parameters, leading to a deteriorization of their performance over time (Gama, 2010; Sayed-Mouchaweh and Lughofer, 2012). The problem, however, is that the true class labels of new incoming samples are usually not included in the stream neither provided automatically by the system. Mostly, operators or experts have to provide the ground truth which requires considerable manpower and fast manual responses in case of online processes. Therefore, in order to attract the operators and users to work and communicate with the system, thus to assure classifier useability in online mode, decreasing the number of required samples for evolving and improving a classifier over time is essential.

This task can be addressed by *active learning* (Settles, 2010), a technique where the learner itself has control over which samples are used to update the classifiers (Cohn *et al.*, 1994). Conventional active learning approaches operate fully in batch mode: (1) New samples are selected iteratively and sequentially from a pool of training data; (2) The true class labels of the selected samples are queried from an expert; and (3) Finally, the classifier is re-trained based on the new samples together with those previously selected. In an online setting, such iteration phases over a pool of data samples are not practicable. Thus, a requirement is that the sample selection process operates autonomously in a single-pass manner, omitting time-intensive re-training phases.

Several first attempts have been made in connection with linear classifiers (Chu *et al.*, 2011; Sculley, 2007). A nonlinear approach which employs both, single fuzzy model architecture with extended confidence levels in the rule consequents [as defined in Equation (17)] and the all-pairs concept as defined in Section 3.2.6.3, is demonstrated in Lughofer (2012a). There, the actual evolved fuzzy classifier itself decides for each sample whether it helps to improve the performance and, when indicated, requests the true class label for updating its parameters and structure. In order to obtain the certainty level for each new incoming data sample (query point), two reliability concepts are explored: *conflict* and *ignorance*, both motivated and explained in detail in Section 3.4.5: when one of the two cases arises for a new data stream sample, a class label is requested from operators. A common understanding based on several results on high-dimensional classification streams (binary and multi-class problems) was that a very similar tendency of accuracy trend lines over time can be achieved when using only 20–25% of the data samples in the stream for classifier updates, which are selected based on the single-pass active learning policy. Upon random selection, the performance deteriorates significantly. Furthermore, a batch active learning scheme based on re-training cycles using SVMs classifiers (Schölkopf and Smola, 2002) (lib-SVM implementation[13]) could be significantly out-performed in terms of accumulated one-step-ahead accuracy (see Section 3.6.4 for its definition).

3.6.1.2. *For regression problems*

Online active learning may be also important in case of regression problems whenever for instance the measurements of a supervised target are quite costly to obtain. An example is the gathering of titration values within a spin-bath analytics at a viscose production process (courtesy to Lenzing GmbH), which are for the purpose to supervise the regulation of the substances H_2SO_4, Na_2SO_4, and Z_nSO_4 (Cernuda *et al.*, 2014). There, active learning is conducted in *incremental and decremental stages* with the help of a sliding window-based approach (sample selection for incoming as well as outgoing points) and using TS fuzzy models connected with PLS. It indeed exceeds the performance of conventional equidistant and costly model updates, but is not fully operating in a single-pass manner (a window of samples is required for re-estimation of statistics, etc.) . Single-pass strategies have been, to our best knowledge, not handled in data stream regression problems, neither in connection with evolving fuzzy systems.

3.6.2. *Toward a Full Plug-and-Play Functionality*

The *plug-and-play functionality* of online incremental learning methods is one of the most important properties in order to prevent time-intensive pre-training cycles in batch mode and to support an easy useability for experts and operators. The situation in the EFS community is that all EFS approaches as listed in Tables 3.1 and 3.2 allow the possibility to incrementally learn the models from scratch. However, all of these require at least one or a few learning parameters guiding the engines to correct, stable models — see Column #8 in these tables. Sometimes, a default parametrization exists, but is sub-optimal for upcoming new future learning tasks, as having been optimized based on streams from past processes and application scenarios. Cross-validation (Stone, 1974) or boot-strapping (Efron and Tibshirani, 1993) may help to guide the parameters to good values during the start of the learning phase (carried out on some initial collected samples), but, apart that these iterative batch methods are eventually too slow (especially when more than two parameters need to be adjusted), a stream may turn out to change its characteristics later on (e.g., due

[13]http://www.csie.ntu.edu.tw/ cjlin/libsvm/.

to a drift, see Section 3.4.1). This usually would require a dynamic update of the learning parameters, which is not supported by any EFS approach so far and has to be specifically developed in connection with the concrete learning engine.

An attempt to overcome such an unlucky or undesired parameter setting is presented in Lughofer and Sayed-Mouchaweh (2015) for evolving cluster models, which, however, may be easily adopted to EFS approaches, especially to those ones performing an incremental clustering process for rule extraction. Furthermore, the prototype-based clusters in Lughofer and Sayed-Mouchaweh (2015) are axis-parallel defining local multivariate Gaussian distributions in the feature space. Thus, when using Gaussian fuzzy sets in connection with product t-norm, the same rule shapes are induced. The idea in Lughofer and Sayed-Mouchaweh (2015) is based on dynamic split-and-merge concepts for clusters (rules) which are either moving together forming a homogenous joint region ($\rightarrow$ merge requested) or are internally containing two or more distinct data clouds, thus already housing some internal heterogeneity ($\rightarrow$ split requested), see Figure 3.10 (Cluster #4) for an example, also showing the internal structure of Cluster #4 in the right image. Both occurrences may arise either due to the nature of the stream or often due to a wrong parametrization of the learning engine (e.g., a too low threshold such that new rules are evolved too early). The main difficulty lies on the identification of when to merge and when to split: parameter-free options are discussed in Lughofer and Sayed-Mouchaweh (2015). Opposed to other *joint* merging and splitting concepts in some EFS approaches, one strength of the approach in Lughofer and Sayed-Mouchaweh (2015) is that it can be used independently from the concrete learning engine. The application of the unsupervised automatic splitting and merging concepts

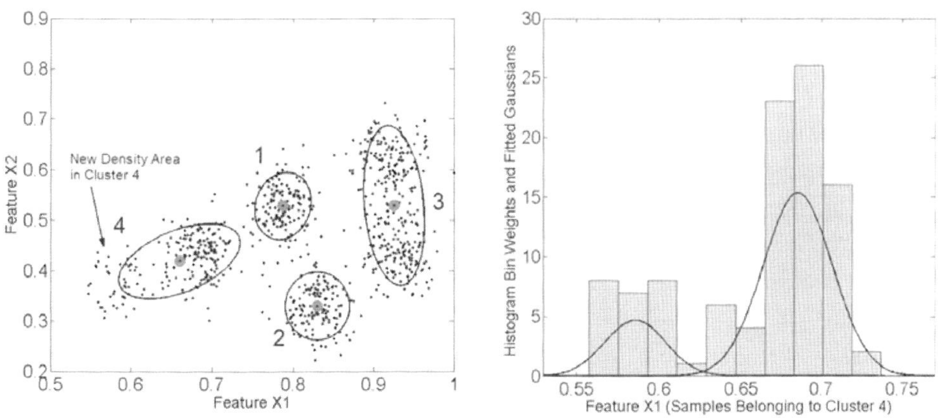

(a) (b)

Figure 3.10: (a) The cluster structure after 800 samples, Cluster #4 containing already a more distinct density area; (b) Its corresponding histogram along Feature X1, showing the clear implicit heterogenous nature.

to supervised streaming problems under the scope of EFS/EFC may thus be an interesting and fruitful future challenge.

3.6.3. *On Improving Computational Demands*

When dealing with online data stream processing problems, usually the computational demands required for updating the fuzzy systems are an essential criteria whether to install and use the component or not. It can be a kick-off criterion, especially in real-time systems, where the update is expected to terminate in real-time, i.e., before the next sample is loaded, the update cycle should be finished. Also, the model predictions should be in-line the real-time demands, but these are known to be very fast in case of fuzzy inference scheme (significantly below milliseconds) (Kruse *et al.*, 1994; Pedrycz and Gomide, 2007; Piegat, 2001). An extensive evaluation and especially a comparison of computational demands for a large variety of EFS approaches over a large variety of learning problems with different number of classes, different dimensionality etc. is unrealistic, also because most of the EFS approaches are hardly downloadable or to obtain from the authors. A loose attempt in this direction has been made by Komijani *et al.* (2012), where they classify various EFS approaches in terms of computation speed into three categories: *low, medium, high*.

Interestingly, the consequent update is more or less following the complexity of $O(Cp^2)$ with p the dimensionality of the feature space and C the number of rules, when local learning is used (as for most EFS approaches, compare in Tables 3.1 and 3.2), and following the complexity of $O((Cp)^2)$ when global learning is applied. The quadratic terms p^2 resp. $(Cp)^2$ are due to the multiplication of the inverse Hessian with the actual regressor vector in Equation (31), and because their sizes are $(p+1)\times(p+1)$ and $p+1$ in case of local learning (storing the consequent parameters of one rule) resp. $(C(p+1))\times(C(p+1))$ and $C(p+1)$ in case of global learning (storing the consequent parameters of all rules). Regarding antecedent learning, rule evolution and pruning, most of the EFS approaches try to be restricted to have at most cubic complexity in terms of the number of rules plus the number of inputs. This may guarantee some sort of smooth termination in an online process, but it is not a necessary prerequisite and has to be inspected for the particular learning problem at hand.

However, some general remarks on the improvement of computational demands can be given: first of all, the reduction of *unnecessary complexity* such as merging of redundant overlapping rules and pruning of obsolete rules (as discussed in Section 3.3.4) is always beneficial for speeding up the learning process. This also ensures that fuzzy systems are not growing forever, thus restricted in their expansion and virtual memory requests. Second, some fast version of incremental optimization techniques could be adopted to fuzzy systems estimation, for instance, there exists a fast RLS algorithm for recursively estimating linear parameters in near linear time ($O(nlog(n))$), but with the costs of some stability and convergence, see Douglas (1996); Gay (1996) or Merched and Sayed (1999). Another possibility for decreasing the computation time for learning is the application of active learning for exquisitely selecting only a subset of samples, based on which the model will be updated, please also refer to Section 3.6.1.

3.6.4. *Evaluation Measures*

Evaluation measures may serve as indicators about the actual state of the evolved fuzzy systems, pointing to its accuracy and trustworthiness in predictions. In a data streaming context, the temporal behavior of such measures plays an essential role in order to track the model development over time resp. to realize down-trends in accuracy at an early stage (e.g., caused by drifts), and to react appropriately (e.g., conducting a re-modeling phase, changes at the system setup, etc.). Furthermore, the evaluation measures are indispensable during the development phase of EFS approaches. In literature dealing with incremental and data-stream problems (Bifet and Kirkby, 2011), basically three variants of measuring the (progress of) model performance are suggested:

- Interleaved-test-and-then-train.
- Periodic hold out test.
- Fully-train-and-then-test.

Interleaved-test-and-then-train, also termed as *accumulated one-step ahead error/accuracy*, is based on the idea to measure model performance in one-step ahead cycles, i.e., based on one newly loaded sample only. In particular, the following steps are carried out:

(1) Load a new sample (the Nth).
(2) Predict its target $\hat{y}$ using the current evolved fuzzy systems.
(3) Compare the prediction $\hat{y}$ with the true target value y and update the performance measure pm:

$$pm(y, \hat{y})(N) \leftarrow upd(pm(y, \hat{y})(N-1)). \quad (45)$$

(4) Update the evolved fuzzy system (arbitrary approach).
(5) Erase sample and go to Step (1).

This is a rather optimistic approach, assuming that the target response is immediately available for each new sample after its prediction. Often, it may be delayed (Marrs *et al.*, 2012; Subramanian *et al.*, 2013), postponing the update of the model performance to a later stage. Furthermore, in case of single sample updates its prediction horizon is minimal that makes it difficult to really provide a clear distinction between training and test data, hence weakening their independence. In this sense, this variant is sometimes too optimistic, under-estimating the true model error. On the other hand, all training samples are also used for testing, thus it is quite practicable for small streams.

The periodic holdout procedure can "look ahead" to collect a batch of examples from the stream for use as test examples. In particular, it uses each odd data block for learning and updating the model and each even data block for eliciting the model performance on this latest block; thereby, the data block sizes may be different for training and testing and may vary in dependence of the actual stream characteristics. In this sense, a lower number of samples is used for model updating/tuning than in case of *interleaved-test-and-then-train* procedure. In experimental test designs, where the streams are finite, it is thus more practicable for longer streams. On the other hand, this method would be preferable in scenarios with concept drift, as it would measure a model's ability to adapt to the *latest trends* in the data — whereas in *interleaved-test-and-then-train* procedure all the data seen so far is reflected in the current accuracy/error, becoming less flexible over time. Forgetting may be integrated into Equation (45), but this requires an additional tuning parameter (e.g., a window size in case of sliding windows). The following steps are carried out in a periodic holdout process:

(1) Load a new data block $X_N = \vec{x}_{N*m+1}, \ldots, \vec{x}_{N*m+m}$ containing m samples.
(2) If N is odd:
   (a) Predict the target values $\hat{y}_1, \ldots, \hat{y}_m$ using the current evolved fuzzy systems.
   (b) Compare the predictions $\hat{y}_{N*m+1}, \ldots, \hat{y}_{N*m+m}$ with the true target values $y_{N*m+m}, \ldots, y_{N*m+m}$ and calculate the performance measure (one or more of Equation (46) to Equation (51)) using $\vec{y}$ and $\vec{\hat{y}}$.
   (c) Erase block and go to Step (1).
(3) Else (N is even):
   (a) Update the evolved fuzzy system (arbitrary approach) with all samples in the buffer using the real target values.
   (b) Erase block and go to Step (1).

Last but not least, an alternative to the online evaluation procedure is to evolve the model an a certain training set and then evaluate it on an independent test set, termed as *fully-train-and-then-test*. This procedure is most heavily used in many applications of EFS, especially in nonlinear system identification and forecasting problems, as summarized in Table 3.3. It extends the prediction horizon of *interleaved-test-and-then-train* procedure with the size of the test set, but only does this in one occasion (at the end of learning). Therefore, it is not useable in drift cases or severe changes during online incremental learning processes and should be only used during development and experimental phases.

Regarding appropriate performance measures, the most convenient choice in classification problems is the number of correctly classified samples (accuracy). In the time instance N (processing the Nth sample), the update of the performance measure as in Equation (45) is then conducted by

$$Acc(N) = \frac{Acc(N-1) * (N-1) + I(\hat{y}, y)}{N}, \tag{46}$$

with $Acc(0) = 0$ and I the indicator function, i.e., $I(a, b) = 1$ whenever $a = b$, otherwise $I(a, b) = 0$, $\hat{y}$ the predicted class label and y the real one. It can be used in the same manner for eliciting the accuracy on whole data blocks as in the periodic hold out case. Another important measure is the so-called *confusion matrix* (Stehman, 1997), which is defined as:

$$C = \begin{bmatrix} N_{11} & N_{12} & \dots & N_{1K} \\ N_{21} & N_{22} & \dots & N_{2K} \\ \vdots & \vdots & \vdots & \vdots \\ N_{K1} & N_{K2} & \dots & N_{KK} \end{bmatrix}, \tag{47}$$

with K the current number of classes, where the diagonal elements denote the number of class j samples which have been correctly classified as class j samples and the element N_{ij} denotes the number of class i samples which are wrongly classified to class j. These can be simply updated by counting.

Furthermore, often someone may be not only interested how strong the samples are miss-classified, but also how certain they are classified (either correctly or wrongly). For instance, a high classification accuracy with a lot of certain classifier outputs may have a higher value than with a lot of uncertain outputs. Furthermore, a high uncertainty degree in the statements point to a lot of conflict cases (compare with Equation (19) and Figure 3.5), i.e., a lot of samples falling into class overlap regions. Therefore, a measure telling the uncertainty degree over samples seen so far is of great interest — a widely used measure is provided in (Amor *et al.*, 2004):

$$Rel_N = 1 - \frac{1}{K} \sum_{k=1}^{K} |conf_k(N) - y_k(N)|, \tag{48}$$

where $y_k(i) = 1$ if k is the class the current sample N belongs to, and $y_k(i) = 0$ otherwise, and $conf_k$ the certainty level in class k, which can be calculated by Equation (19), for instance. It can be accumulated in the same manner as the accuracy above.

In case of regression problems, the most common choices are the root mean squared error (RMSE), the mean absolute error (MAE) or the average percentual deviation (APE). Their updates are achieved by:

$$\text{RMSE}(N) = \sqrt{\frac{1}{N} * \left((N-1) * (\text{RMSE}(N-1)^2) + (y - \hat{y})^2\right)}, \tag{49}$$

$$\text{MAE}(N) = \frac{1}{N} * \left((N-1) * \text{MAE}(N-1) + |y - \hat{y}|\right), \tag{50}$$

$$\text{APE}(N) = \frac{1}{N} * \left((N-1) * \text{APE}(N-1) + \frac{|y - \hat{y}|}{\text{range}(y)}\right). \tag{51}$$

Their batch calculation for even blocks in periodic hold out test is following the standard procedure and thus can be realized from Wikipedia. Instead of calculating the concrete error values, often the observed versus predicted curves over time and their correlation plots are shown. This gives an even better impression under which circumstances and at which points of time the model behaves in which way. A systematic error shift can be also realized.

Apart from accuracy criteria, other measures rely on the complexity of the models. In most EFS application cases (refer to Table 3.3), the development of the number of rules over time is plotted as a two-dimensional function. Sometimes, also the number of fuzzy sets are reported as additionally criteria which depend on the rule lengths. These mostly depend on the dimensionality of the learning problem. In case of embedded feature selection, there may be a big drop in the number of fuzzy sets once some features are discarded resp. out-weighted (compare with Section 3.4.2). Figure 3.11 shows a typical accumulated accuracy curve over time in the left image

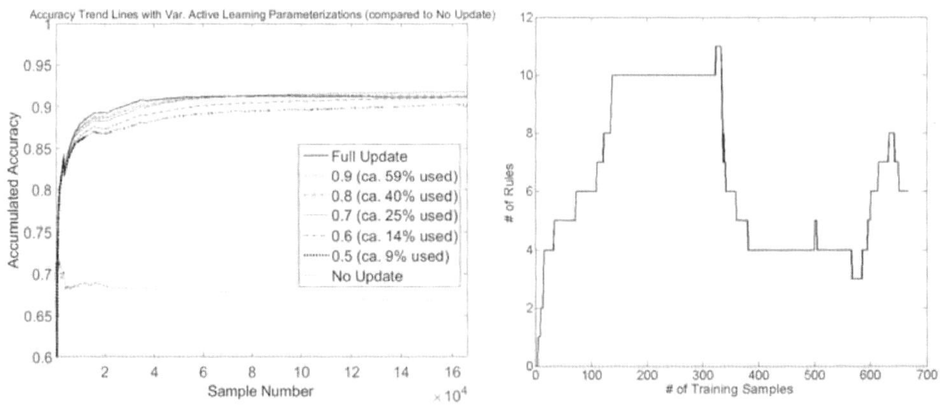

(a) (b)

Figure 3.11: (a) Typical accumulated accuracy increasing over time in case of full update and active learning variants (reducing the number of samples used for updating while still maintaining high accuracy); (b) Typical evolution of the number of rules over time.

(using an all-pairs EFC including active learning option with different amount of samples for updating) and a typical development of the number of rules in the right one: At the start, rules are evolved and accumulated, later some rules turned out to be superfluous and hence are back-pruned and merged. This guarantees an anytime flexibility.

3.6.5. *Real-World Applications of EFS — Overview*

Due to space restrictions, a complete description of application scenarios in which EFSs have been successfully implemented and used so far is simply impossible. Thus, we restrict ourselves to a compact summary within Table 3.3 showing application types and classes and indicating which EFS approaches have been used

Table 3.3: Application classes in which EFS approaches have been successfully applied so far.

Application Type/Class (alphabetically)	EFS approaches (+ refs)	Comment
Active learning / human–machine interaction	FLEXFIS-Class (Lughofer *et al.*, 2009; Lughofer, 2012d), EFC-AP (Lughofer, 2012a), FLEXFIS-PLS (Cernuda *et al.*, 2014)	Reducing the annotation effort and measurement costs in industrial processes
Adaptive online control	evolving PID and MRC controllers in (Angelov and Skrjanc, 2013), eFuMo (Zdsar *et al.*, 2014), rGK (Dovzan *et al.*, 2012), self-evolving NFC (Cara *et al.*, 2013), adaptive controller in (Rong *et al.*, 2014).	Design of fuzzy controllers which can be updated and evolved on-the-fly
Bioinformatics	EFuNN (Kasabov, 2002)	Specific applications such as ribosome binding site (RBS) identification, gene profiling
Chemometric Modeling and Process Control	FLEXFIS++ (Cernuda *et al.*, 2013, 2012); the approach in Bodyanskiy and Vynokurova (2013)	The application of EFS onto processes in chemical industry (high-dim. NIR spectra)
EEG signals classification and processing	eTS (Xydeas *et al.*, 2006), epSNNr (Nuntalid *et al.*, 2011)	Time-series modeling with the inclusion of time delays
Evolving Smart Sensors (eSensors)	eTS+ (Macias-Hernandez and Angelov, 2010) (gas industry), (Angelov and Kordon, 2010a, 2010b) (chemical process industry), FLEXFIS (Lughofer *et al.*, 2011c) and PANFIS (Pratama *et al.*, 2014a) (NOx emissions)	Evolving predictive and forecasting models in order to substitute cost-intensive hardware sensors

(*Continued*)

Table 3.3: (*Continued*)

Application Type/Class (alphabetically)	EFS approaches (+ refs)	Comment
Forecasting and prediction (general)	AHLTNM (Kalhor *et al.*, 2010) (daily temp.), eT2FIS (Tung *et al.*, 2013) (traffic flow), eFPT (Shaker *et al.*, 2013) (Statlog from UCI), eFT (Lemos *et al.*, 2011b) and eMG (Lemos *et al.*, 2011a) (short-term electricity load), FLEXFIS+ (Lughofer *et al.*, 2011b) and GENEFIS (Pratama *et al.*, 2014b) (house prices), LOLIMOT inc. (Hametner and Jakubek, 2013) (maximum cylinder pressure), rGK (Dovzan *et al.*, 2012) (sales prediction) and others	Various successful implementations of EFS
Financial domains	eT2FIS (Tung *et al.*, 2013), evolving granular systems (Leite *et al.*, 2012b), ePL (Maciel *et al.*, 2012), PANFIS (Pratama *et al.*, 2014a), SOFNN (Prasad *et al.*, 2010)	Time-series modeling with the inclusion of time delays
Identification of dynamic benchmark problems	DENFIS (Kasabov and Song, 2002), eT2FIS (Tung *et al.*, 2013), eTS+ (Angelov, 2010), FLEXFIS (Lughofer, 2008), SAFIS (Rong, 2012), SEIT2FNN (Juang and Tsao, 2008), SOFNN (Prasad *et al.*, 2010)	Mackey-Glass, Box-Jenkins, etc.
Online fault detection and condition monitoring	eMG for classification (Lemos *et al.*, 2013), FLEXFIS++ (Lughofer and Guardiola, 2008b; Serdio *et al.*, 2014a), rGK (Dovzan *et al.*, 2012)	EFS applied as SysID models for extracting residuals
Online monitoring	eTS+ (Macias-Hernandez and Angelov, 2010) (gas industry)	Supervision of system behaviors
Robotics	eTS+ (Zhou and Angelov, 2007)	In the area of self-localization
Time-series modeling	DENFIS (Widiputra *et al.*, 2012), ENFM (Soleimani *et al.*, 2010) and eTS-LS-SVM (Komijani *et al.*, 2012) (sun spot)	Local modeling of multiple time-series versus instance-based learning
User behavior identification	eClass and eTS (Angelov *et al.*, 2012; Iglesias *et al.*, 2010), eTS+ (Andreu and Angelov, 2013), FPA (Wang *et al.*, 2013)	Analysis of the user's behaviors in multi-agent systems, on computers, indoor environments etc.
Video processing	eTS, eTS+ (Angelov *et al.*, 2011; Zhou and Angelov, 2006)	Including real-time object id., obstacles tracking and novelty detection
Visual quality control	EFC-AP (Lughofer and Buchtala, 2013), FLEXFIS-Class (Eitzinger *et al.*, 2010; Lughofer, 2010b), pClass (Pratama *et al.*, 2014c)	Image classification tasks based on feature vectors

in the circumstance of which application type. In all of these cases, EFS(C) helped to increase automatization capability, improving performance of the models and finally increasing the useability of the whole systems; in some cases, no modeling has been (could be) applied before at all.

Acknowledgments

This work was funded by the research programme at the LCM GmbH as part of a K2 project. K2 projects are financed using funding from the Austrian COMET-K2 programme. The COMET K2 projects at LCM are supported by the Austrian federal government, the federal state of Upper Austria, the Johannes Kepler University and all of the scientific partners which form part of the K2-COMET Consortium. This publication reflects only the author's views.

References

Abonyi, J., Babuska, R. and Szeifert, F. (2002). Modified Gath–Geva fuzzy clustering for identification of Takagi–Sugeno fuzzy models. *IEEE Trans. Syst., Man Cybern. Part B*, 32(5), pp. 612–621.

Abonyi, J. (2003). *Fuzzy Model Identification for Control*. Boston, U.S.A.: Birkhäuser.

Abraham, W. and Robins, A. (2005). Memory retention: The synaptic stability versus plasticity dilemma. *Trends Neurosci.*, 28(2), pp. 73–78.

Affenzeller, M., Winkler, S., Wagner, S. and Beham, A. (2009). *Genetic Algorithms and Genetic Programming: Modern Concepts and Practical Applications*. Boca Raton, Florida: Chapman & Hall.

Allwein, E., Schapire, R. and Singer, Y. (2001). Reducing multiclass to binary: a unifying approach for margin classifiers. *J. Mach. Learn. Res.*, 1, pp. 113–141.

Almaksour, A. and Anquetil, E. (2011). Improving premise structure in evolving Takagi–Sugeno neuro-fuzzy classifiers. *Evolving Syst.*, 2, pp. 25–33.

Amor, N., Benferhat, S. and Elouedi, Z. (2004). Qualitative classification and evaluation in possibilistic decision trees. In *Proc. FUZZ-IEEE Conf.*, Budapest, Hungary, pp. 653–657.

Andreu, J. and Angelov, P. (2013). Towards generic human activity recognition for ubiquitous applications. *J. Ambient Intell. Human Comput.*, 4, pp. 155–156.

Angelov, P. (2010). Evolving Takagi–Sugeno fuzzy systems from streaming data, eTS+. In Angelov, P., Filev, D. and Kasabov, N. (eds.), *Evolving Intelligent Systems: Methodology and Applications*. New York: John Wiley & Sons, pp. 21–50.

Angelov, P. and Filev, D. (2004). An approach to online identification of Takagi–Sugeno fuzzy models. *IEEE Trans. Syst. Man Cybern., Part B: Cybern.*, 34(1), pp. 484–498.

Angelov, P. and Kasabov, N. (2005). Evolving computational intelligence systems. In *Proc. 1st Int. Workshop on Genet. Fuzzy Syst.*, Granada, Spain, pp. 76–82.

Angelov, P. and Kordon, A. (2010a). Evolving inferential sensors in the chemical process industry. In Angelov, P., Filev, D. and Kasabov, N. (eds.), *Evolving Intelligent Systems: Methodology and Applications*. New York: John Wiley & Sons, pp. 313–336.

Angelov, P. and Kordon, A. (2010b). Adaptive inferential sensors based on evolving fuzzy models: An industrial case study. *IEEE Trans. Syst., Man Cybern., Part B: Cybern.*, 40(2), pp. 529–539.

Angelov, P. and Skrjanc, I. (2013). Robust evolving cloud-based controller for a hydraulic plant. In *Proc. 2013 IEEE Conf. Evolving Adapt. Intell. Syst. (EAIS)*. Singapore, pp. 1–8.

Angelov, P., Filev, D. and Kasabov, N. (2010). *Evolving Intelligent Systems — Methodology and Applications*. New York: John Wiley & Sons.

Angelov, P., Ledezma, A. and Sanchis, A. (2012). Creating evolving user behavior profiles automatically. *IEEE Trans. Knowl. Data Eng.*, 24(5), pp. 854–867.

Angelov, P., Lughofer, E. and Zhou, X. (2008). Evolving fuzzy classifiers using different model architectures. *Fuzzy Sets Syst.*, 159(23), pp. 3160–3182.

Angelov, P., Sadeghi-Tehran, P. and Ramezani, R. (2011). An approach to automatic real-time novelty detection, object identification, and tracking in video streams based on recursive density estimation and evolving Takagi–Sugeno fuzzy systems. *Int. J. Intell. Syst.*, 26(3), pp. 189–205.

Aström, K. and Wittenmark, B. (1994). *Adaptive Control Second Edition*. Boston, MA, USA: Addison-Wesley Longman Publishing Co. Inc.

Babuska, R. (1998). *Fuzzy Modeling for Control*. Norwell, Massachusetts: Kluwer Academic Publishers.

Balas, V., Fodor, J. and Varkonyi-Koczy, A. (2009). *Soft Computing based Modeling in Intelligent Systems*. Berlin, Heidelberg: Springer.

Bifet, A., Holmes, G., Kirkby, R. and Pfahringer, B. (2010). MOA: Massive online analysis. *J. Mach. Learn. Res.*, 11, pp. 1601–1604.

Bifet, A. and Kirkby, R. (2011). Data stream mining — a practical approach. Technical report, University of Waikato, Japan, Department of Computer Sciences.

Bikdash, M. (1999). A highly interpretable form of sugeno inference systems. *IEEE Trans. Fuzzy Syst.*, 7(6), pp. 686–696.

Bishop, C. (2007). *Pattern Recognition and Machine Learning*. New York: Springer.

Bodyanskiy, Y. and Vynokurova, O. (2013). Hybrid adaptive wavelet-neuro-fuzzy system for chaotic time series identification, *Inf. Sci.*, 220, pp. 170–179.

Bouchachia, A. (2009). Incremental induction of classification fuzzy rules. In *IEEE Workshop Evolving Self-Dev. Intell. Syst. (ESDIS) 2009*. Nashville, U.S.A., pp. 32–39.

Bouchachia, A. (2011). Evolving clustering: An asset for evolving systems. *IEEE SMC Newsl.*, 36.

Bouchachia, A. and Mittermeir, R. (2006). Towards incremental fuzzy classifiers. *Soft Comput.*, 11(2), pp. 193–207.

Bouchachia, A., Lughofer, E. and Mouchaweh, M. (2014). Editorial to the special issue: Evolving soft computing techniques and applications. *Appl. Soft Comput.*, 14, pp. 141–143.

Bouchachia, A., Lughofer, E. and Sanchez, D. (2013). Editorial to the special issue: Online fuzzy machine learning and data mining. *Inf. Sci.*, 220, pp. 1–4.

Bouillon, M., Anquetil, E. and Almaksour, A. (2013). Decremental learning of evolving fuzzy inference systems: Application to handwritten gesture recognition. In Perner, P. (ed.), *Machine Learning and Data Mining in Pattern Recognition*, 7988, *Lecture Notes in Computer Science*. New York: Springer, pp. 115–129.

Breiman, L., Friedman, J., Stone, C. and Olshen, R. (1993). *Classification and Regression Trees*. Boca Raton: Chapman and Hall.

Cara, A., Herrera, L., Pomares, H. and Rojas, I. (2013). New online self-evolving neuro fuzzy controller based on the tase-nf model. *Inf. Sci.*, 220, pp. 226–243.

Carr, V. and Tah, J. (2001). A fuzzy approach to construction project risk assessment and analysis: construction project risk management system. *Adv. Eng. Softw.*, 32(10–11), pp. 847–857.

Casillas, J., Cordon, O., Herrera, F. and Magdalena, L. (2003). *Interpretability Issues in Fuzzy Modeling*. Berlin, Heidelberg: Springer Verlag.

Castro, J. and Delgado, M. (1996). Fuzzy systems with defuzzification are universal approximators. *IEEE Trans. Syst. Man Cybern. Part B: Cybern.*, 26(1), pp. 149–152.

Cernuda, C., Lughofer, E., Hintenaus, P., Märzinger, W., Reischer, T., Pawlicek, M. and Kasberger, J. (2013). Hybrid adaptive calibration methods and ensemble strategy for prediction of cloud point in melamine resin production. *Chemometr. Intell. Lab. Syst.*, 126, pp. 60–75.

Cernuda, C., Lughofer, E., Mayr, G., Röder, T., Hintenaus, P., Märzinger, W. and Kasberger, J. (2014). Incremental and decremental active learning for optimized self-adaptive calibration in viscose production. *Chemometr. Intell. Lab. Syst.*, 138, pp. 14–29.

Cernuda, C., Lughofer, E., Suppan, L., Röder, T., Schmuck, R., Hintenaus, P., Märzinger, W. and Kasberger, J. (2012). Evolving chemometric models for predicting dynamic process parameters in viscose production. *Anal. Chim. Acta*, 725, pp. 22–38.

Chapelle, O., Schoelkopf, B. and Zien, A. (2006). *Semi-Supervised Learning*. Cambridge, MA: MIT Press.

Cho, J. and Park, D. (2000). Novel fuzzy logic control based on weighting of partially inconsistent rules using neural network. *J. Intell. Fuzzy Syst.*, 8(2), pp. 99–110.

Chong, C.-Y. and Kumar, S. (2003). Sensor networks: Evolution, opportunities, and challenges. *Proc. IEEE*, 91(8), pp. 1247–1256.

Chu, W., Zinkevich, M., Li, L., Thomas, A. and Zheng, B. (2011). Unbiased online active learning in data streams. In *Proc. KDD 2011*. San Diego, California.

Cleveland, W. and Devlin, S. (1988). Locally weighted regression: An approach to regression analysis by local fitting. *J. Am. Stat. Assoc.*, 84(403), pp. 596–610.

Cohn, D., Atlas, L. and Ladner, R. (1994). Improving generalization with active learning. *Mach. Learn.*, 15(2), pp. 201–221.

Day, N. E. (1969). Estimating the components of a mixture of normal distributions. *Biometrika*, 56(463–474).

Diehl, C. and Cauwenberghs, G. (2003). SVM incremental learning, adaptation and optimization. In *Proc. Int. Joint Conf. Neural Netw.*, Boston, 4, pp. 2685–2690.

Douglas, S. (1996). Efficient approximate implementations of the fast affine projection algorithm using orthogonal transforms. In *Proc. IEEE Int. Conf. Acoust., Speech Signal Process.*, Atlanta, Georgia, pp. 1656–1659.

Dovzan, D. and Skrjanc, I. (2011). Recursive clustering based on a Gustafson–Kessel algorithm. *Evolving Syst.*, 2(1), pp. 15–24.

Dovzan, D., Logar, V. and Skrjanc, I. (2012). Solving the sales prediction problem with fuzzy evolving methods. In *WCCI 2012 IEEE World Congr. Comput. Intell.*, Brisbane, Australia.

Duda, R., Hart, P. and Stork, D. (2000). *Pattern Classification, Second Edition*. Southern Gate, Chichester, West Sussex, England: Wiley-Interscience.

Dy, J. and Brodley, C. (2004). Feature selection for unsupervised learning. *J. Mach. Learn. Res.*, 5, pp. 845–889.

Efron, B. and Tibshirani, R. (1993). *An Introduction to the Bootstrap*. Boca Raton, Florida: Chapman & Hall/CRC.

Eitzinger, C., Heidl, W., Lughofer, E., Raiser, S., Smith, J., Tahir, M., Sannen, D. and van Brussel, H. (2010). Assessment of the influence of adaptive components in trainable surface inspection systems. *Mach. Vis. Appl.*, 21(5), pp. 613–626.

Fürnkranz, J. (2001). Round robin rule learning. In *Proc. Int. Conf. Mach. Learn. (ICML 2011)*, Williamstown, MA, pp. 146–153.

Fürnkranz, J. (2002). Round robin classification. *J. Mach. Learn. Res.*, 2, pp. 721–747.

French, R. M. (1999). Catastrophic forgetting in connectionist networks. *Trends Cogn. Sci.*, 3(4), pp. 128–135.

Fuller, R. (1999). *Introduction to Neuro-Fuzzy Systems*. Heidelberg, Germany: Physica-Verlag.

Gacto, M., Alcala, R. and Herrera, F. (2011). Interpretability of linguistic fuzzy rule-based systems: An overview of interpretability measures. *Inf. Sci.*, 181(20), pp. 4340–4360.

Gama, J. (2010). *Knowledge Discovery from Data Streams*. Boca Raton, Florida: Chapman & Hall/CRC.

Gan, G., Ma, C. and Wu, J. (2007). *Data Clustering: Theory, Algorithms, and Applications (Asa-Siam Series on Statistics and Applied Probability)*. U.S.A.: Society for Industrial & Applied Mathematics.

Gay, S. L. (1996). Dynamically regularized fast recursive least squares with application to echo cancellation. In *Proc. IEEE Int. Conf. Acoust., Speech Signal Process.*, Atalanta, Georgia, pp. 957–960.

Hametner, C. and Jakubek, S. (2013). Local model network identification for online engine modelling. *Inf. Sci.*, 220, pp. 210–225.

Hamker, F. (2001). RBF learning in a non-stationary environment: the stability-plasticity dilemma. In Howlett, R. and Jain, L. (eds.), *Radial Basis Function Networks* 1*: Recent Developments in Theory and Applications*, Heidelberg, New York: Physica Verlag, pp. 219–251.

Hastie, T., Tibshirani, R. and Friedman, J. (2009). *The Elements of Statistical Learning: Data Mining, Inference and Prediction, Second Edition*. New York Berlin Heidelberg: Springer.

Haykin, S. (1999). *Neural Networks: A Comprehensive Foundation, 2nd Edition*. Upper Saddle River, New Jersey: Prentice Hall Inc.

He, H. and Garcia, E. (2009). Learning from imbalanced data. *IEEE Trans. Knowl. Data Eng.*, 21(9), pp. 1263–1284.

Hentzgen, S., Strickert, M. and Huellermeier, E. (2014). Visualization of evolving fuzzy rule-based systems. *Evolving Syst.*, DOI: 10.1007/s12530-014-9110-4, on-line and in press.

Henzgen, S., Strickert, M. and Hüllermeier, E. (2013). Rule chains for visualizing evolving fuzzy rule-based systems. In *Advances in Intelligent Systems and Computing*, 226, *Proc. Eighth Int. Conf. Comput. Recognit. Syst. CORES 2013*. Cambridge, MA: Springer, pp. 279–288.

Herrera, L., Pomares, H., Rojas, I., Valenzuela, O. and Prieto, A. (2005). TaSe, a taylor series-based fuzzy system model that combines interpretability and accuracy. *Fuzzy Sets Syst.*, 153(3), pp. 403–427.

Hisada, M., Ozawa, S., Zhang, K. and Kasabov, N. (2010). Incremental linear discriminant analysis for evolving feature spaces in multitask pattern recognition problems. *Evolving Syst.*, 1(1), pp. 17–27.

Ho, W., Tung, W. and Quek, C. (2010). An evolving Mamdani–Takagi–Sugeno based neural-fuzzy inference system with improved interpretability–accuracy. In *Proc. WCCI 2010 IEEE World Congr. Comput. Intell.*, Barcelona, pp. 682–689.

Holmblad, L. and Ostergaard, J. (1982). Control of a cement kiln by fuzzy logic. *Fuzzy Inf. Decis. Process.*, pp. 398–409.

Huang, Z., Gedeon, T. D. and Nikravesh, M. (2008). Pattern trees induction: A new machine learning method. *IEEE Trans. Fuzzy Syst.*, 16(4), pp. 958–970.

Hüllermeier, E. and Brinker, K. (2008). Learning valued preference structures for solving classification problems. *Fuzzy Sets Syst.*, 159(18), pp. 2337–2352.

Hühn, J. and Hüllermeier, E. (2009). FR3: A fuzzy rule learner for inducing reliable classifiers, *IEEE Trans. Fuzzy Syst.*, 17(1), pp. 138–149.

Iglesias, J., Angelov, P., Ledezma, A. and Sanchis, A. (2010). Evolving classification of agent's behaviors: a general approach. *Evolving Syst.*, 1(3), pp. 161–172.

Ishibuchi, H. and Nakashima, T. (2001). Effect of rule weights in fuzzy rule-based classification systems. *IEEE Trans. Fuzzy Syst.*, 9(4), pp. 506–515.

Jang, J.-S. (1993). ANFIS: Adaptive-network-based fuzzy inference systems. *IEEE Trans. Syst. Man Cybern.*, 23(3), pp. 665–685.

Juang, C. and Tsao, Y. (2008). A self-evolving interval type-2 fuzzy neural network with on-line structure and parameter learning. *IEEE Trans. Fuzzy Syst.*, 16(6), pp. 1411–1424.

Kaczmarz, S. (1993). Approximate solution of systems of linear equations. *Int. J. Control*, 53, pp. 1269–1271.

Kalhor, A., Araabi, B. and Lucas, C. (2010). An online predictor model as adaptive habitually linear and transiently nonlinear model. *Evolving Syst.*, 1(1), pp. 29–41.

Karer, G. and Skrjanc, I. (2013). *Predictive Approaches to Control of Complex Systems*. Berlin, Heidelberg: Springer Verlag.

Karnik, N. and Mendel, J. (2001). Centroid of a type-2 fuzzy set. *Inf. Sci.*, 132(1–4), pp. 195–220.

Kasabov, N. (2002). *Evolving Connectionist Systems — Methods and Applications in Bioinformatics, Brain Study and Intelligent Machines*. London: Springer Verlag.

Kasabov, N. K. and Song, Q. (2002). DENFIS: Dynamic evolving neural-fuzzy inference system and its application for time-series prediction. *IEEE Trans. Fuzzy Syst.*, 10(2), pp. 144–154.

Klement, E., Mesiar, R. and Pap, E. (2000). *Triangular Norms*. New York: Kluwer Academic Publishers.

Klinkenberg, R. (2004). Learning drifting concepts: example selection vs. example weighting, *Intell. Data Anal.*, 8(3), pp. 281–300.

Koenig, S., Likhachev, M., Liu, Y. and Furcy, D. (2004). Incremental heuristic search in artificial intelligence. *Artif. Intell. Mag.*, 25(2), pp. 99–112.

Komijani, M., Lucas, C., Araabi, B. and Kalhor, A. (2012). Introducing evolving Takagi–Sugeno method based on local least squares support vector machine models. *Evolving Syst.* 3(2), pp. 81–93.

Kruse, R., Gebhardt, J. and Palm, R. (1994). *Fuzzy Systems in Computer Science*. Wiesbaden: Verlag Vieweg.

Kuncheva, L. (2000). *Fuzzy Classifier Design*. Heidelberg: Physica-Verlag.

Leekwijck, W. and Kerre, E. (1999). Defuzzification: criteria and classification. *Fuzzy Sets Syst.* 108(2), pp. 159–178.

Leite, D., Ballini, R., Costa, P. and Gomide, F. (2012a). Evolving fuzzy granular modeling from nonstationary fuzzy data streams. *Evolving Syst.* 3(2), pp. 65–79.

Leite, D., Costa, P. and Gomide, F. (2012b). Interval approach for evolving granular system modeling. In Sayed-Mouchaweh, M. and Lughofer, E. (eds.), *Learning in Non-Stationary Environments: Methods and Applications*. New York: Springer, pp. 271–300.

Lemos, A., Caminhas, W. and Gomide, F. (2011a). Multivariable gaussian evolving fuzzy modeling system. *IEEE Trans. Fuzzy Syst.*, 19(1), pp. 91–104.

Lemos, A., Caminhas, W. and Gomide, F. (2011b). Fuzzy evolving linear regression trees. *Evolving Syst.*, 2(1), pp. 1–14.

Lemos, A., Caminhas, W. and Gomide, F. (2013). Adaptive fault detection and diagnosis using an evolving fuzzy classifier. *Inf. Sci.*, 220, pp. 64–85.

Leng, G., McGinnity, T. and Prasad, G. (2005). An approach for on-line extraction of fuzzy rules using a self-organising fuzzy neural network. *Fuzzy Sets Syst.*, 150(2), pp. 211–243.

Leng, G., Zeng, X.-J. and Keane, J. (2012). An improved approach of self-organising fuzzy neural network based on similarity measures. *Evolving Syst.*, 3(1), pp. 19–30.

Leondes, C. (1998). *Fuzzy Logic and Expert Systems Applications (Neural Network Systems Techniques and Applications)*. San Diego, California: Academic Press.

Li, Y. (2004). On incremental and robust subspace learning. *Pattern Recognit.*, 37(7), pp. 1509–1518.

Liang, Q. and Mendel, J. (2000). Interval type-2 fuzzy logic systems: Theory and design. *IEEE Trans. Fuzzy Syst.*, 8(5), pp. 535–550.

Lima, E., Hell, M., Ballini, R. and Gomide, F. (2010). Evolving fuzzy modeling using participatory learning. In Angelov, P., Filev, D. and Kasabov, N. (eds.), *Evolving Intelligent Systems: Methodology and Applications*. New York: John Wiley & Sons, pp. 67–86.

Lippmann, R. (1991). A critical overview of neural network pattern classifiers. In *Proc. IEEE Workshop Neural Netw. Signal Process.*, pp. 266–275.

Ljung, L. (1999). *System Identification: Theory for the User*. Upper Saddle River, New Jersey: Prentice Hall PTR, Prentic Hall Inc.

Lughofer, E., Smith, J. E., Caleb-Solly, P., Tahir, M., Eitzinger, C., Sannen, D. and Nuttin, M. (2009). Human-machine interaction issues in quality control based on on-line image classification. *IEEE Trans. Syst., Man Cybern., Part A: Syst. Humans*, 39(5), pp. 960–971.

Lughofer, E. (2008). FLEXFIS: A robust incremental learning approach for evolving TS fuzzy models. *IEEE Trans. Fuzzy Syst.*, 16(6), pp. 1393–1410.

Lughofer, E. (2010a). Towards robust evolving fuzzy systems. In Angelov, P., Filev, D. and Kasabov, N. (eds.), *Evolving Intelligent Systems: Methodology and Applications*. New York: John Wiley & Sons, pp. 87–126.

Lughofer, E. (2010b). On-line evolving image classifiers and their application to surface inspection. *Image Vis. Comput.*, 28(7), 1065–1079.

Lughofer, E. (2011a). Human-inspired evolving machines — the next generation of evolving intelligent systems? *SMC Newsl.*, 36.

Lughofer, E. (2011b). *Evolving Fuzzy Systems — Methodologies, Advanced Concepts and Applications*. Berlin, Heidelberg: Springer.

Lughofer, E. (2011c). On-line incremental feature weighting in evolving fuzzy classifiers. *Fuzzy Sets Syst.*, 163(1), pp. 1–23.

Lughofer, E. (2012a). Single-pass active learning with conflict and ignorance. *Evolving Syst.*, 3(4), pp. 251–271.

Lughofer, E. (2012b). Flexible evolving fuzzy inference systems from data streams (FLEXFIS++). In Sayed-Mouchaweh, M. and Lughofer, E. (eds.), *Learning in Non-Stationary Environments: Methods and Applications*. New York: Springer, pp. 205–246.

Lughofer, E. and Sayed-Mouchaweh, M. (2015). Autonomous data stream clustering implementing incremental split-and-merge techniques — Towards a plug-and-play approach. *Inf. Sci.*, 204, pp. 54–79.

Lughofer, E. (2012d). Hybrid active learning (HAL) for reducing the annotation efforts of operators in classification systems, *Pattern Recognit.*, 45(2), pp. 884–896.

Lughofer, E. (2013). On-line assurance of interpretability criteria in evolving fuzzy systems — achievements, new concepts and open issues. *Inf. Sci.*, 251, pp. 22–46.

Lughofer, E. and Angelov, P. (2011). Handling drifts and shifts in on-line data streams with evolving fuzzy systems. *Appl. Soft Comput.*, 11(2), pp. 2057–2068.

Lughofer, E. and Buchtala, O. (2013). Reliable all-pairs evolving fuzzy classifiers. *IEEE Trans. Fuzzy Syst.*, 21(4), pp. 625–641.

Lughofer, E. and Guardiola, C. (2008a). Applying evolving fuzzy models with adaptive local error bars to on-line fault detection. In *Proc. Genet. Evolving Fuzzy Syst., 2008*. Witten-Bommerholz, Germany, pp. 35–40.

Lughofer, E. and Guardiola, C. (2008b). On-line fault detection with data-driven evolving fuzzy models. *J. Control Intell. Syst.*, 36(4), pp. 307–317.

Lughofer, E. and Hüllermeier, E. (2011). On-line redundancy elimination in evolving fuzzy regression models using a fuzzy inclusion measure. In *Proc. EUSFLAT 2011 Conf.*, Aix-Les-Bains, France: Elsevier, pp. 380–387.

Lughofer, E., Bouchot, J.-L. and Shaker, A. (2011a). On-line elimination of local redundancies in evolving fuzzy systems. *Evolving Syst.*, 2(3), pp. 165–187.

Lughofer, E., Trawinski, B., Trawinski, K., Kempa, O. and Lasota, T. (2011b). On employing fuzzy modeling algorithms for the valuation of residential premises. *Inf. Sci.*, 181(23), pp. 5123–5142.

Lughofer, E., Macian, V., Guardiola, C. and Klement, E. (2011c). Identifying static and dynamic prediction models for NOx emissions with evolving fuzzy systems. *Appl. Soft Comput.*, 11(2), pp. 2487–2500.

Lughofer, E., Cernuda, C. and Pratama, M. (2013). Generalized flexible fuzzy inference systems. In *Proc. ICMLA 2013 Conf.*, Miami, Florida, pp. 1–7.

Lughofer, E., Cernuda, C., Kindermann, S. and Pratama, M. (2014). Generalized smart evolving fuzzy systems. *Evolving Syst.*, online and in press, doi: 10.1007/s12530–015–9132–6

Macias-Hernandez, J. and Angelov, P. (2010). Applications of evolving intelligent systems to the oil and gas industry. In Angelov, P., Filev, D. and Kasabov, N. (eds.), *Evolving Intelligent Systems: Methodology and Applications*. New York: John Wiley & Sons, pp. 401–421.

Maciel, L., Lemos, A., Gomide, F. and Ballini, R. (2012). Evolving fuzzy systems for pricing fixed income options. *Evolving Syst.*, 3(1), pp. 5–18.

Mamdani, E. (1977). Application of fuzzy logic to approximate reasoning using linguistic systems. *Fuzzy Sets Syst.* 26(12), pp. 1182–1191.

Marrs, G., Black, M. and Hickey, R. (2012). The use of time stamps in handling latency and concept drift in online learning. *Evolving Syst.*, 3(2), pp. 203–220.

Mendel, J. (2001). *Uncertain Rule-Based Fuzzy Logic Systems: Introduction and New Directions*. Upper Saddle River: Prentice Hall.

Mendel, J. and John, R. (2002). Type-2 fuzzy sets made simple. *IEEE Trans. Fuzzy Syst.*, 10(2), pp. 117–127.

Mercer, J. (1909). Functions of positive and negative type and their connection with the theory of integral equations. *Philos. Trans. R. Soc. A*, 209, pp. 441–458.

Merched, R. and Sayed, A. (1999). Fast RLS laguerre adaptive filtering. In *Proc. Allerton Conf. Commun., Control Comput.*, Allerton, IL, pp. 338–347.

Moe-Helgesen, O.-M. and Stranden, H. (2005). Catastophic forgetting in neural networks. Technical report. Trondheim, Norway: Norwegian University of Science and Technology.

Morreale, P., Holtz, S. and Goncalves, A. (2013). Data mining and analysis of large scale time series network data. In *Proc. 27th Int. Conf. Adv. Inf. Netw. Appl. Workshops (WAINA)*. Barcelona, Spain, pp. 39–43.

Mouss, H., Mouss, D., Mouss, N. and Sefouhi, L. (2004). Test of Page–Hinkley, an approach for fault detection in an agro-alimentary production system. In *Proc. Asian Control Conf.*, 2, pp. 815–818.

Nakashima, Y. Y. T., Schaefer, G. and Ishibuchi, H. (2006). A weighted fuzzy classifier and its application to image processing tasks. *Fuzzy Sets Syst.*, 158(3), pp. 284–294.

Nauck, D. and Kruse, R. (1998). NEFCLASS-X — a soft computing tool to build readable fuzzy classifiers. *BT Technol. J.*, 16(3), pp. 180–190.

Nelles, O. (2001). *Nonlinear System Identification*. Berlin: Springer.

Ngia, L. and Sjöberg, J. (2000). Efficient training of neural nets for nonlinear adaptive filtering using a recursive Levenberg–Marquardt algorithm. *IEEE Trans. Signal Process*, 48(7), pp. 1915–1926.

Nguyen, H., Sugeno, M., Tong, R. and Yager, R. (1995). *Theoretical Aspects of Fuzzy Control*. New York: John Wiley & Sons.

Nuntalid, N., Dhoble, K. and Kasabov, N. (2011). EEG classification with BSA spike encoding algorithm and evolving probabilistic spiking neural network. In *Neural Inf. Process., LNCS 7062*. Berlin Heidelberg: Springer Verlag, pp. 451–460.

Pal, N. and Pal, K. (1999). Handling of inconsistent rules with an extended model of fuzzy reasoning. *J. Intell. Fuzzy Syst.*, 7, pp. 55–73.

Pedrycz, W. and Gomide, F. (2007). *Fuzzy Systems Engineering: Toward Human-Centric Computing*. Hoboken, New Jersey: John Wiley & Sons.

Piegat, A. (2001). *Fuzzy Modeling and Control*. Heidelberg, New York: Physica Verlag, Springer Verlag Company.

Prasad, G., Leng, G., McGuinnity, T. and Coyle, D. (2010). Online identification of self-organizing fuzzy neural networks for modeling time-varying complex systems. In Angelov, P., Filev, D. and Kasabov, N. (eds.), *Evolving Intelligent Systems: Methodology and Applications*. New York: John Wiley & Sons, pp. 201–228.

Pratama, M., Anavatti, S., Angelov, P. and Lughofer, E. (2014a). PANFIS: A novel incremental learning machine. *IEEE Trans. Neural Netw. Learn. Syst.*, 25(1), pp. 55–68.

Pratama, M., Anavatti, S. and Lughofer, E. (2014b). GENEFIS: Towards an effective localist network. *IEEE Trans. Fuzzy Syst.*, 22(3), pp. 547–562.

Pratama, M., Anavatti, S. and Lughofer, E. (2014c). pClass: An effective classifier to streaming examples. *IEEE Transactions on Fuzzy Systems*, 23(2), pp. 369–386.

Quinlan, J. R. (1994). *C4.5: Programs for Machine Learning*. San Francisco, CA: Morgan Kaufmann Publishers.

Reichmann, O., Jones, M. and Schildhauer, M. (2011). Challenges and opportunities of open data in ecology. *Science*, 331(6018), pp. 703–705.

Reveiz, A. and Len, C. (2010). Operational risk management using a fuzzy logic inference system. *J. Financ. Transf.*, 30, pp. 141–153.

Riaz, M. and Ghafoor, A. (2013). Spectral and textural weighting using Takagi–Sugeno fuzzy system for through wall image enhancement. *Prog. Electromagn. Res. B.*, 48, pp. 115–130.

Rong, H.-J. (2012). Sequential adaptive fuzzy inference system for function approximation problems. In Sayed-Mouchaweh, M. and Lughofer, E. (eds.), *Learning in Non-Stationary Environments: Methods and Applications*. New York: Springer.

Rong, H.-J., Han, S. and Zhao, G.-S. (2014). Adaptive fuzzy control of aircraft wing-rock motion. *Appl. Soft Comput.*, 14, pp. 181–193.

Rong, H.-J., Sundararajan, N., Huang, G.-B. and Saratchandran, P. (2006). Sequential adaptive fuzzy inference system (SAFIS) for nonlinear system identification and prediction. *Fuzzy Sets Syst.*, 157(9), pp. 1260–1275.

Rong, H.-J., Sundararajan, N., Huang, G.-B. and Zhao, G.-S. (2011). Extended sequential adaptive fuzzy inference system for classification problems. *Evolving Syst.*, 2(2), pp. 71–82.

Rosemann, N., Brockmann, W. and Neumann, B. (2009). Enforcing local properties in online learning first order TS fuzzy systems by incremental regularization. In *Proc. IFSA-EUSFLAT 2009*. Lisbon, Portugal, pp. 466–471.

Rubio, J. (2009). SOFMLS: Online self-organizing fuzzy modified least square network. *IEEE Trans. Fuzzy Syst.*, 17(6), pp. 1296–1309.

Rubio, J. (2010). Stability analysis for an on-line evolving neuro-fuzzy recurrent network. In Angelov, P., Filev, D. and Kasabov, N. (eds.), *Evolving Intelligent Systems: Methodology and Applications*. New York: John Wiley & Sons, pp. 173–199.

Saminger-Platz, S., Mesiar, R. and Dubois, D. (2007). Aggregation operators and commuting. *IEEE Trans. Fuzzy Syst.*, 15(6), pp. 1032–1045.

Sayed-Mouchaweh, M. and Lughofer, E. (2012). *Learning in Non-Stationary Environments: Methods and Applications*. New York: Springer.

Schölkopf, B. and Smola, A. (2002). *Learning with Kernels — Support Vector Machines, Regularization, Optimization and Beyond*. London, England: MIT Press.

Sculley, D. (2007). Online active learning methods for fast label efficient spam filtering. In *Proc. Fourth Conf. Email AntiSpam*. Mountain View, California.

Sebastiao, R., Silva, M., Rabico, R., Gama, J. and Mendonca, T. (2013). Real-time algorithm for changes detection in depth of anesthesia signals. *Evolving Syst.*, 4(1), pp. 3–12.

Senge, R. and Huellermeier, E. (2011). Top–down induction of fuzzy pattern trees. *IEEE Trans. Fuzzy Syst.*, 19(2), pp. 241–252.

Serdio, F., Lughofer, E., Pichler, K., Buchegger, T. and Efendic, H. (2014a). Residual-based fault detection using soft computing techniques for condition monitoring at rolling mills. *Inf. Sci.*, 259, pp. 304–320.

Serdio, F., Lughofer, E., Pichler, K., Pichler, M., Buchegger, T. and Efendic, H. (2014b). Fault detection in multi-sensor networks based on multivariate time-series models and orthogonal transformations. *Inf. Fusion*, 20, pp. 272–291.

Settles, B. (2010). Active learning literature survey. Technical report, Computer Sciences Technical Report 1648. Madison: University of Wisconsin.

Shaker, A. and Hüllermeier, E. (2012). IBLStreams: a system for instance-based classification and regression on data streams. *Evolving Syst.*, 3, pp. 239–249.

Shaker, A. and Lughofer, E. (2014). Self-adaptive and local strategies for a smooth treament of drifts in data streams. *Evolving Syst.*, 5(4), pp. 239–257.

Shaker, A., Senge, R. and Hüllermeier, E. (2013). Evolving fuzzy patterns trees for binary classification on data streams. *Inf. Sci.*, 220, pp. 34–45.

Sherman, J. and Morrison, W. (1949). Adjustment of an inverse matrix corresponding to changes in the elements of a given column or a given row of the original matrix. *Ann. Math. Stat.*, 20, p. 621.

Shilton, A., Palaniswami, M., Ralph, D. and Tsoi, A. (2005). Incremental training of support vector machines. *IEEE Trans. Neural Netw.*, 16(1), pp. 114–131,

Silva, A. M., Caminhas, W., Lemos, A. and Gomide, F. (2014). A fast learning algorithm for evolving neo-fuzzy neuron. *Appl. Soft Comput.*, 14(B), pp. 194–209.

Skrjanc, I. (2009). Confidence interval of fuzzy models: An example using a waste-water treatment plant. *Chemometri. Intell. Lab. Syst.*, 96, pp. 182–187.

Smithson, M. (2003). *Confidence Intervals*. SAGE University Paper, Series: Quantitative Applications in the Social Sciences. Thousand Oaks, California.

Smola, A. and Schölkopf, B. (2004). A tutorial on support vector regression. *Stat. Comput.*, 14, pp. 199–222.

Soleimani, H., Lucas, K. and Araabi, B. (2010). Recursive Gath-Geva clustering as a basis for evolving neuro-fuzzy modeling. *Evolving Syst.*, 1(1), pp. 59–71.

Stehman, V. (1997). Selecting and interpreting measures of thematic classification accuracy. *Remote Sens. Environ.*, 62(1), pp. 77–89.

Stone, M. (1974). Cross-validatory choice and assessment of statistical predictions. *J. R. Stat. Soc.*, 36(1), pp. 111–147.

Subramanian, K., Savita, R. and Suresh, S. (2013). A meta-cognitive interval type-2 fuzzy inference system classifier and its projection based learning algorithm. In *Proc. IEEE EAIS 2013 Workshop (SSCI 2013 Conf.)*, Singapore, pp. 48–55.

Sun, H. and Wang, S. (2011). Measuring the component overlapping in the gaussian mixture model. *Data Min. Knowl. Discov.*, 23, pp. 479–502.

Takagi, T. and Sugeno, M. (1985). Fuzzy identification of systems and its applications to modeling and control. *IEEE Trans. Syst., Man Cybern.*, 15(1), pp. 116–132.

Tschumitschew, K. and Klawonn, F. (2012). Incremental statistical measures. In Sayed-Mouchaweh, M. and Lughofer, E. (eds.), *Learning in Non-Stationary Environments: Methods and Applications*. New York: Springer, pp. 21–55.

Tsymbal, A. (2004). The problem of concept drift: definitions and related work. Technical Report TCD-CS-2004-15. Trinity College Dublin, Ireland, Department of Computer Science.

Tung, S., Quek, C. and Guan, C. (2013). eT2FIS: An evolving type-2 neural fuzzy inference system. *Inf. Sci.*, 220, pp. 124–148.

Wang, L. and Mendel, J. (1992). Fuzzy basis functions, universal approximation and orthogonal least-squares learning. *IEEE Trans. Neural Netw.*, 3(5), pp. 807–814.

Wang, L., Ji, H.-B. and Jin, Y. (2013). Fuzzy passive-aggressive classification: A robust and efficient algorithm for online classification problems, *Inf. Sci.*, 220, pp. 46–63.

Wang, W. and Vrbanek, J. (2008). An evolving fuzzy predictor for industrial applications. *IEEE Trans. Fuzzy Syst.*, 16(6), pp. 1439–1449.

Werbos, P. (1974). *Beyond Regression: New Tools for Prediction and Analysis in the Behavioral Sciences*. PhD thesis. Harvard University, USA: Appl. Math.

Wetter, T. (2000). Medical decision support systems. In *Medical Data Analysis*. Berlin/Heidelberg: Springer, pp. 458–466.

White, T. (2012). *Hadoop: The Definitive Guide*. O'Reilly Media.

Widiputra, H., Pears, R. and Kasabov, N. (2012). Dynamic learning of multiple time series in a nonstationary environment. In Sayed-Mouchaweh, M. and Lughofer, E. (eds.), *Learning in Non-Stationary Environments: Methods and Applications*. New York: Springer, pp. 303–348.

Widmer, G. and Kubat, M. (1996). Learning in the presence of concept drift and hidden contexts, *Mach. Learn.*, 23(1), pp. 69–101.

Wu, X., Kumar, V., Quinlan, J., Gosh, J., Yang, Q., Motoda, H., MacLachlan, G., Ng, A., Liu, B., Yu, P., Zhou, Z.-H. Steinbach, M., Hand, D. and Steinberg, D. (2006). Top 10 algorithms in data mining. *Knowl. Inf. Syst.* 14(1), pp. 1–37.

Xu, Y., Wong, K. and Leung, C. (2006). Generalized recursive least square to the training of neural network. *IEEE Trans. Neural Netw.*, 17(1), pp. 19–34.

Xydeas, C., Angelov, P., Chiao, S. and Reoulas, M. (2006). Advances in eeg signals classification via dependant hmm models and evolving fuzzy classifiers. *Int. J. Comput. Biol. Med., special issue on Intell. Technol. Bio-inf. Med.*, 36(10), pp. 1064–1083.

Yager, R. R. (1990). A model of participatory learning. *IEEE Trans. Syst., Man Cybern.*, 20(5), pp. 1229–1234.

Ye, J., Li, Q., Xiong, H., Park, H., Janardan, R. and Kumar, V. (2005). IDR, QR: An incremental dimension reduction algorithms via QR decomposition. *IEEE Trans. Knowl. Data Eng.*, 17(9), pp. 1208–1222.

Zaanen, A. (1960). *Linear Analysis*. Amsterdam: North Holland Publishing Co.

Zadeh, L. (1965). Fuzzy sets. *Inf. Control*, 8(3), pp. 338–353.

Zadeh, L. (1975). The concept of a linguistic variable and its application to approximate reasoning. *Inf. Sci.*, 8(3), pp. 199–249.

Zavoianu, A. (2010). *Towards Solution Parsimony in an Enhanced Genetic Programming Process*. PhD thesis. Linz, Austria: Johannes Kepler University Linz.

Zdsar, A., Dovzan, D. and Skrjanc, I. (2014). Self-tuning of 2 DOF control based on evolving fuzzy model. *Appl. Soft Comput.*, 19, pp. 403–418.

Zhou, X. and Angelov, P. (2006). Real-time joint landmark recognition and classifier generation by an evolving fuzzy system. In *Proc. FUZZ-IEEE 2006*. Vancouver, Canada, pp. 1205–1212.

Zhou, X. and Angelov, P. (2007). Autonomous visual self-localization in completely unknown environment using evolving fuzzy rule-based classifier. In *2007 IEEE Int. Conf. Comput. Intell. Appl. Def. Secur.*, Honolulu, Hawaii, USA, pp. 131–138.

Chapter 4

Modeling Fuzzy Rule-Based Systems

Rashmi Dutta Baruah and Diganta Baruah

The objective of this chapter is to familiarize the reader with various approaches used for fuzzy modeling. It is expected that the discussion presented in the chapter would enable the reader to understand, compare, and choose between the different fuzzy modeling alternatives, both in knowledge-based and automated approaches, so as to apply it to model real-world systems. It is assumed that the reader has a basic knowledge of fuzzy set theory and linear algebra. However, illustrative examples are provided throughout the text to comprehend the basic concepts. The chapter is organized in five sections. In the first section, fuzzy systems are introduced very briefly as a foundation to start the discussion on the fuzzy modeling techniques. Next, an overview of design issues is presented in the same section. Section 4.2 describes the knowledge-based methods and Section 4.3 discusses the automated methods. The automated methods include template-based method, neuro-fuzzy approaches, genetic-fuzzy approaches, and clustering-based approaches. Section 4.4 presents a brief description on another automated approach, viz., online approach that has recently grabbed a lot of attention from the researchers. Finally, in Section 4.5, a short summary of the chapter is presented.

4.1. Introduction

In simple terms, a system that uses fuzzy sets and fuzzy logic in some form can be considered as a fuzzy system. For example, the system's input and output can be represented using fuzzy sets or the system itself can be defined in terms of fuzzy *if-then* rules. In this chapter, the focus is on fuzzy systems that are based on fuzzy *if-then* rules which use fuzzy set theory to make decisions or draw conclusions. Such systems are often referred to as *fuzzy rule-based* (FRB) systems. For simplicity, here we will be referring to a FRB system as fuzzy system. Fuzzy systems can be broadly classified into two families: Mamdani-type (Mamdani, 1997) and Takagi–Sugeno-type (Takagi and Sugeno, 1985). In the Mamdani-type, also called linguistic systems, rules are represented as:

$$\textbf{\textit{if}}\ x_1\ \textit{is}\ A_1\ \textbf{\textit{and}}\ x_2\ \textit{is}\ A_2\ \textbf{\textit{and}}\ \ldots \textbf{\textit{and}}\ x_n\ \textit{is}\ A_n\ \textbf{\textit{then}}\ y\ \textit{is}\ B, \tag{1}$$

where $x_i, i = 1, 2, \ldots, n$, is the ith input variable, and A_i and B are the linguistic terms (e.g., Small, Large, High, Low, etc.) defined by fuzzy sets, and y is the output associated with the given rule.

The rule structure of the Takagi–Sugeno-type (TSK), also called functional type, is usually given as:

$$\textbf{\textit{if}}\ x_1\ \textit{is}\ A_1\ \textbf{\textit{and}}\ x_2\ \textit{is}\ A_2\ \textbf{\textit{and}} \ldots \textbf{\textit{and}}\ x_n\ \textit{is}\ A_n\ \textbf{\textit{then}}\ y = f(x_1, x_2, \ldots, x_n), \quad (2)$$

where $x_i, i = 1, 2, \ldots, n$, is the ith input variable, A_i is the antecedent fuzzy set, y is the output of the rule, and f is a real valued function. If f is a constant then the rule is of zero-order type and the corresponding system is called zero-order TSK system, and if f is first order polynomial then the rule is of first-order type and the resulting system is called first-order system as given below:

- Zero-order TSK rule

$$\textbf{\textit{if}}\ x_1\ \textit{is}\ A_1\ \textbf{\textit{and}}\ x_2\ \textit{is}\ A_2\ \textbf{\textit{and}}\ \ldots \textbf{\textit{and}}\ x_n\ \textit{is}\ A_n\ \textbf{\textit{then}}\ y = a, \quad (3)$$

  where a is a real number.
- First-order TSK rule

$$\begin{aligned}&\textbf{\textit{if}}\ x_1\ \textit{is}\ A_1\ \textbf{\textit{and}}\ x_2\ \textit{is}\ A_2\ \textbf{\textit{and}} \ldots \textbf{\textit{and}}\ x_n\ \textit{is}\ A_n\ \textbf{\textit{then}}\ y\\ &= a_0 + a_1x_1 + a_2x_2 + \cdots + a_nx_n, \quad (4)\end{aligned}$$

  where a_i is the ith consequence parameter.

Thus, in the Mamdani-type, the consequent of each rule is a fuzzy set whereas in the Sugeno-type the consequent is a function of input variables. Due to this difference, the inference mechanism of determining the output of the system in both the categories somewhat varies.

The early approaches to FRB system design involve representing the knowledge and experience of a human expert, associated with a particular system, in terms of *if-then* rules. To avoid the difficult task of knowledge acquisition and to improve the system performance another alternative is to use expert knowledge as well as system generated input-output data. This fusion of expert knowledge and data can be done in many ways. For example, one way is to combine linguistic rules from human expert and rules learnt by numerical data, and another way is to derive the initial structure and parameters from expert knowledge and optimize the parameters using input-output data by applying machine learning techniques. The common approaches used for learning and adjusting the parameters from the training data are neural networks and genetic algorithms (GAs). These approaches are often referred to as *automated methods* or *data-driven methods*. Due to the complexity of systems and availability of huge data, presently the automated approaches are commonly used for fuzzy modeling.

The majority of applications of fuzzy systems are in the area of process control (Fuzzy Logic Control- FLC), decision-making (Fuzzy Expert Systems), estimation (prediction, forecasting), and pattern recognition (classification). Regardless of the type of application most systems are based on simple fuzzy *if-then* rules, and so have a common structure. Thus, the basic design steps are same for all such FRB systems. In general, the design of a fuzzy system or fuzzy system modeling is a multi-step process that involves the following:

- Formulation of the problem.
- Specification of the fuzzy sets.
- Generation of rule set.
- Selection of fuzzy inference and defuzzification mechanism.

In the knowledge-based approach, all the steps are completed based on intuition and experience. The automated methods usually require designer's involvement only in problem formulation and selection of fuzzy inference and defuzzification mechanism. In the following sections, we describe all the design steps by considering a simple control application.

4.2. Knowledge-Based Approach

The knowledge-based approach can be applied to linguistic fuzzy models. We illustrate the steps to obtain a linguistic fuzzy model for a simple cooling fan system. The problem is to control the regulator knob of a cooling fan inside a room based on two inputs temperature and humidity. The speed of fan increases as the knob is turned right and decreases when it is turned left. The scenario is depicted in Figure 4.1.

4.2.1. *Formulation of the Problem*

In problem formulation step, the problem is defined in terms of the system input, the required output, and the objectives. For example, to model a fuzzy control system typically one needs to state: What is to be controlled? What are the input variables? What kind of response is expected from the control system? What are the possible system failure states? The selection of input and output variables and the range of the variables are mainly dependent on the problem at hand and the designer sensibility.

For example, consider the cooling fan system problem given in Figure 4.1. For this problem, the inputs are temperature and humidity measures and the output is the action in terms of turning the knob right or left in small or big steps.

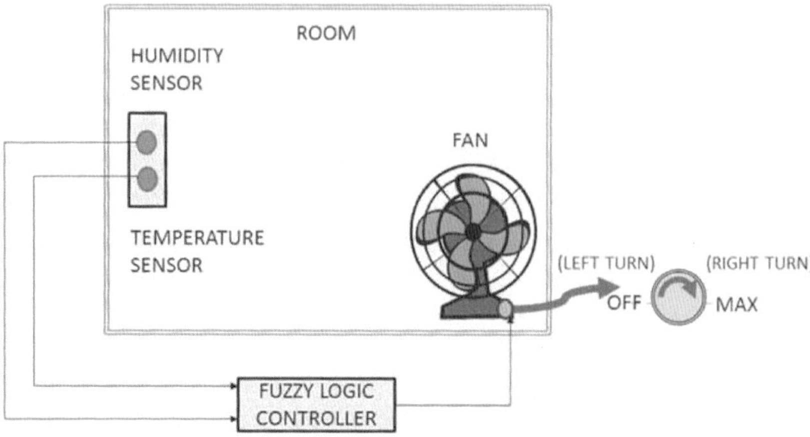

Figure 4.1: Cooling fan system.

Table 4.1: Temperature ranges and linguistic values.

Temperature range (°C)	Linguistic values
15–19	Low
18–25	Normal
24–30	High

4.2.2. *Specification of Fuzzy Sets*

The fuzzy sets are specified in terms of membership functions. For each input and output variable, the linguistic values (or fuzzy terms or labels) are specified before defining the membership functions. For the system depicted in Figure 4.1, if the range of the input variable temperature is 15–30°C, then the linguistic values, *Low, Normal*, and *High* can be associated with it (see Table 4.1). Now, the membership functions for temperature can be defined as shown in Figure 4.2. Similarly, the membership functions for the input humidity and the output action is shown in Figures 4.3 and 4.4. It is assumed that the range of relative *humidity* is 20–70% and the knob can be rotated in degrees from −3 to 3.

The number and shape of the membership functions depend on application domain, experts' knowledge and are chosen subjectively or (and) are generated automatically. An important observation is that usually three to seven membership functions are used. As the number grows, it becomes difficult to manage especially in case of manual design. Many fuzzy logic control problems assume linear membership functions usually Triangular in shape, the other commonly used membership functions are Trapezoidal and Gaussian. The other modeling issues can

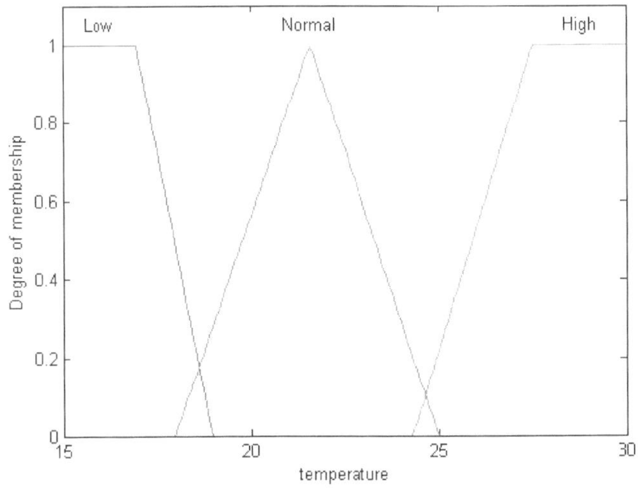

Figure 4.2: Fuzzy membership functions for input variable temperature.

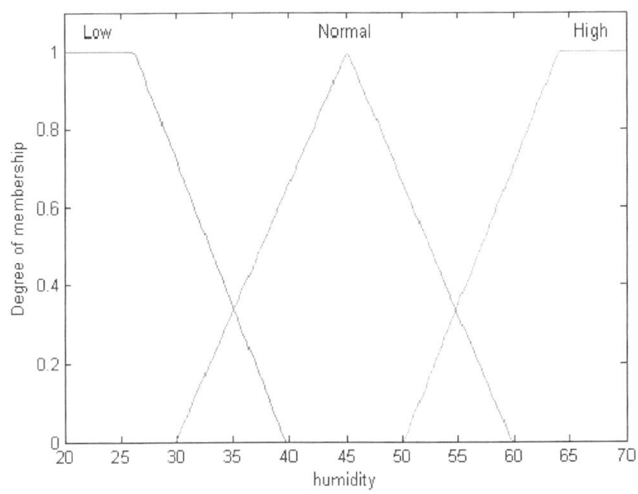

Figure 4.3: Fuzzy membership functions for input variable humidity.

be the amount of overlapping between the membership functions and the distribution of membership functions (even or uneven distribution) (Figures 4.5a and 4.5b). Also, any point in the range of the input variables has to be covered by at least one fuzzy set participating to at least one rule (Figure 4.5c). It is recommended that each membership function overlaps only with the closest neighboring membership function (Figure 4.5d). In uneven distribution some of the membership functions can cover smaller range to achieve precision (Figure 4.5b). Currently, more focus

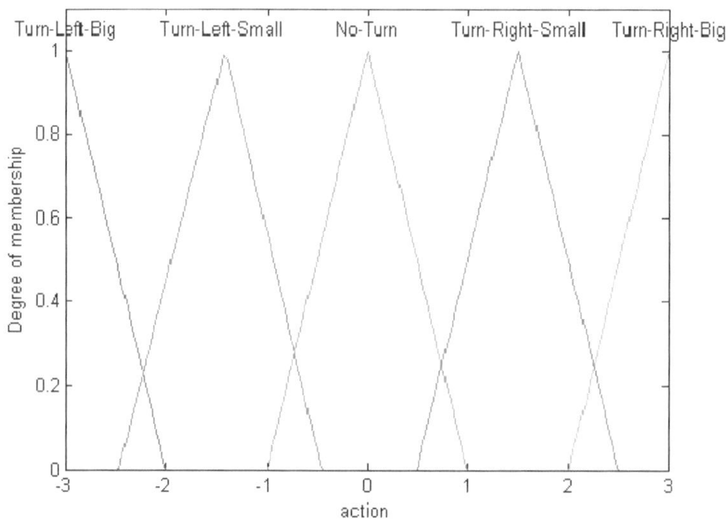

Figure 4.4: Fuzzy membership functions for output variable action.

is towards identification of these parameters automatically using machine learning techniques.

4.2.3. *Generation of Rule Set*

A rule maps the input to output and the set of rules mainly defines the fuzzy model. For a simple system with two inputs and single output, the rules can be enumerated with the help of a matrix. For example, for the system shown in Figure 4.1, the matrix is given in Table 4.2 and the corresponding rules are given in Figure 4.6. For a system with more than two inputs and outputs the rules can be presented in a tabular form. For example, Table 4.3 gives the partial rule-set of the fan control system when another input *rate-of-change of temperature* (ΔT) is added.

4.2.4. *Selection of Fuzzy Inference and Defuzzification Mechanism*

After generating the rule-set, it is required to specify how the system would calculate the final output for a given input. This can be specified in terms of inference and defuzzification mechanism. The designer needs to specify how to infer or compute the fuzzy operator in the antecedent part, how to get the fuzzy output from each rule, and finally how to aggregate these outputs to get a single crisp output.

Usually the fuzzy rules involve more than one fuzzy set connected with fuzzy operators (AND, OR, NOT). The inference mechanism depends on the fuzzy combination operators used in the rules. These fuzzy combination operators are also referred to as *T-norms*. There are many ways to compute these operators. A designer

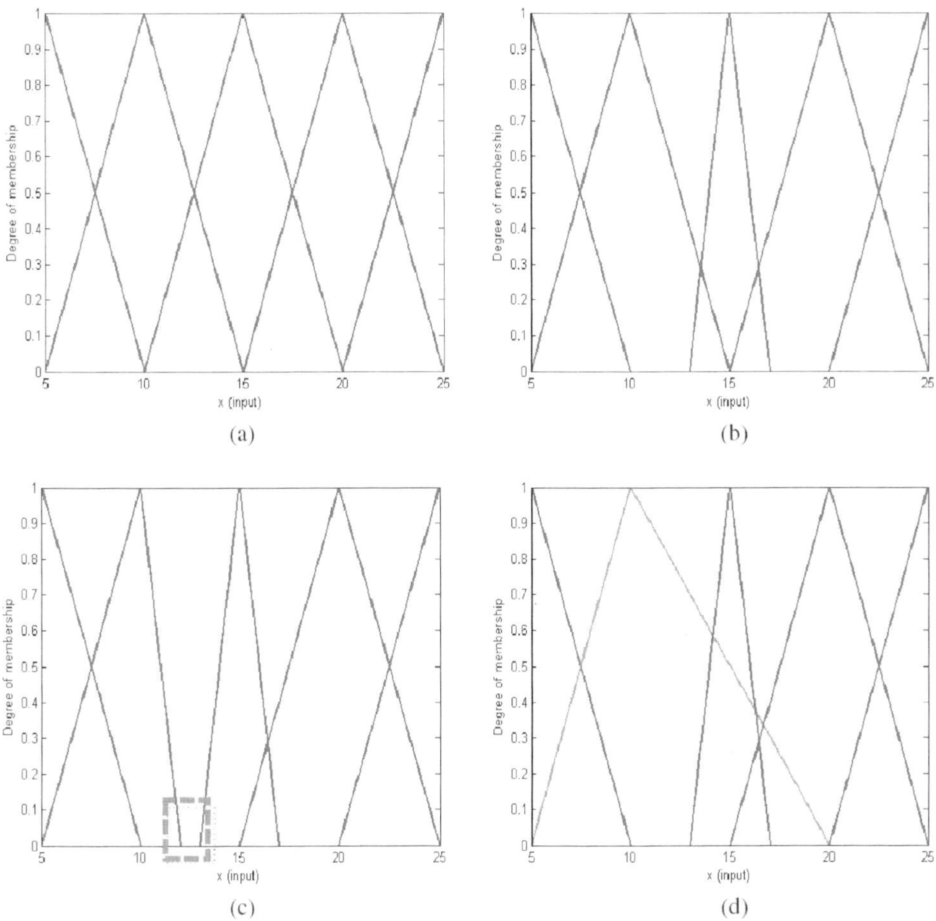

Figure 4.5: (a) MFs evenly distributed, (b) MFs unevenly distributed, (c) MFs not covering all the input points, (d) MFs overlapping with more than one neighbor.

Table 4.2: Rule matrix for cooling fan system.

Temperature(T)/ humidity (H)	Low	Normal	High
Low	Turn left big	No turn	Turn right small
Normal	Turn left small	No turn	Turn right small
High	Turn right small	Turn right small	Turn right big

Rule1: ***if*** T is low ***and*** H is low ***then*** turn the knob left big.

Rule2: ***if*** T is low ***and*** H is normal ***then*** no need to turn the knob.

Rule3: ***if*** T is low ***and*** H is high ***then*** turn the knob right small.

Rule4: ***if*** T is normal ***and*** H is low ***then*** no need to turn the knob.

Rule5: ***if*** T is normal ***and*** H is normal ***then*** no need to turn the knob.

Rule6: ***if*** T is normal ***and*** H is high ***then*** turn the knob right small.

Rule7: ***if*** T is high ***and*** H is low ***then*** turn the knob right small.

Rule8: ***if*** T is high ***and*** H is normal ***then*** turn the knob right small.

Rule9: ***if*** T is high ***and*** H is high ***then*** turn the knob right big.

Figure 4.6: Rule set for fan speed control.

Table 4.3: Rule table for cooling fan system considering three inputs.

Input 1 temperature	Input 2 humidity	Input 3 ΔT	Output action
Low	Low	Decreasing	Turn left big
Low	Low	Steady	Turn left big
Low	Low	Increasing	Turn right small

needs to specify which one to apply to the specific system. For example, the AND operator is expressed as,

$\mu_{A \cap B} = T(\mu_A(x), \ \mu_B(x)), \ \mu_A(x)$ is membership of x in fuzzy set A and $\mu_B(x)$ is membership of x in fuzzy set B.

The two most commonly used methods to compute AND are:

- $T(\mu_A(x), \mu_B(x)) = \min(\mu_A(x), \mu_B(x))$, this method is widely known as Zadeh method.
- $T(\mu_A(x), \mu_B(x)) = \mu_A(x) \cdot \mu_B(x)$ this method is Product method that computes the fuzzy AND by simply multiplying the two membership values.

Example 2.1. Consider the scenario presented in Figure 4.1 and assume that the present room temperature is 18.5°C and humidity is 36.5%. Also, consider that the Zadeh (or minimum) method is used as fuzzy combination operator.

For a given input, first its degree of membership to each of the input fuzzy sets is determined; this step is often referred to as fuzzification. After fuzzification, the firing strength of each rule can be determined in the following way:

$$\begin{aligned}
\text{Rule 1: } & T(\mu_{\text{Low}}(18.5), \mu_{\text{Low}}(36.5)) \\
& = \min(\mu_{\text{Low}}(18.5), \mu_{\text{Low}}(36.5)) = \min(0.5, 0.25) = 0.25, \\
\text{Rule 2: } & T(\mu_{\text{Low}}(18.5), \mu_{\text{Normal}}(36.5)) \\
& = \min(\mu_{\text{Low}}(18.5), \mu_{\text{Normal}}(36.5)) = \min(0.5, 0.43) = 0.43, \\
\text{Rule 3: } & T(\mu_{\text{Low}}(18.5), \mu_{\text{High}}(36.5)) \\
& = \min(\mu_{\text{Low}}(18.5), \mu_{\text{High}}(36.5)) = \min(0.5, 0) = 0.
\end{aligned}$$

Thus, for the given input, Rule 1 applies (or triggers or fires) at 25%, Rule 2 applies at 43%, and Rule 3 at 0%, i.e., it does not apply at all. This means the *then* part or the action of Rule 1, Rule 2 fires at strength of 0.25 and 0.43 respectively. The firing strengths of the remaining rules are determined in a similar way, and the value is 0 for Rule 4 to Rule 9.

After determining the firing strength of each rule, the consequent of the rule is obtained or the rule conclusion is inferred. The commonly used method to obtain the rule consequent is by clipping the output membership function at the rule strength. Figure 4.7 shows the degree of membership of input to each of the input fuzzy sets and the inferred conclusions using the clipping method.

There are number of defuzzification techniques such as centroid method which is also known as center of area or center of gravity (COG) method, weighted average method, Maximum membership method (or height method), Mean (first or last) of maxima method, etc. Each method has its own advantages and disadvantages. For example, both the maximum membership method and weighted average method are computationally faster and simpler. However, in terms of accuracy, weighted average is better as maximum membership accounts only for rules, which are triggered at the maximum membership level. The COG method is most widely used and provides better results, however computational overhead is more and it has disadvantage of not allowing control actions towards the extremes of the action (output) range (Ross, 2010).

Example 2.2. Consider the aggregated output shown in Figures 4.8 and 4.9. Application of COG method results in crisp output of −0.6, i.e., the knob is required to be turned 0.6 degrees to the left.

The COG method is given by $z^* = \frac{\int \mu_{\text{output}}(z).z\,dz}{\int \mu_{\text{output}}(z)dz}$, where z^* is the defuzzified or crisp output, μ_{output} is the aggregated resultant membership function of the two output fuzzy sets, and z is the universe of discourse. For this example, the

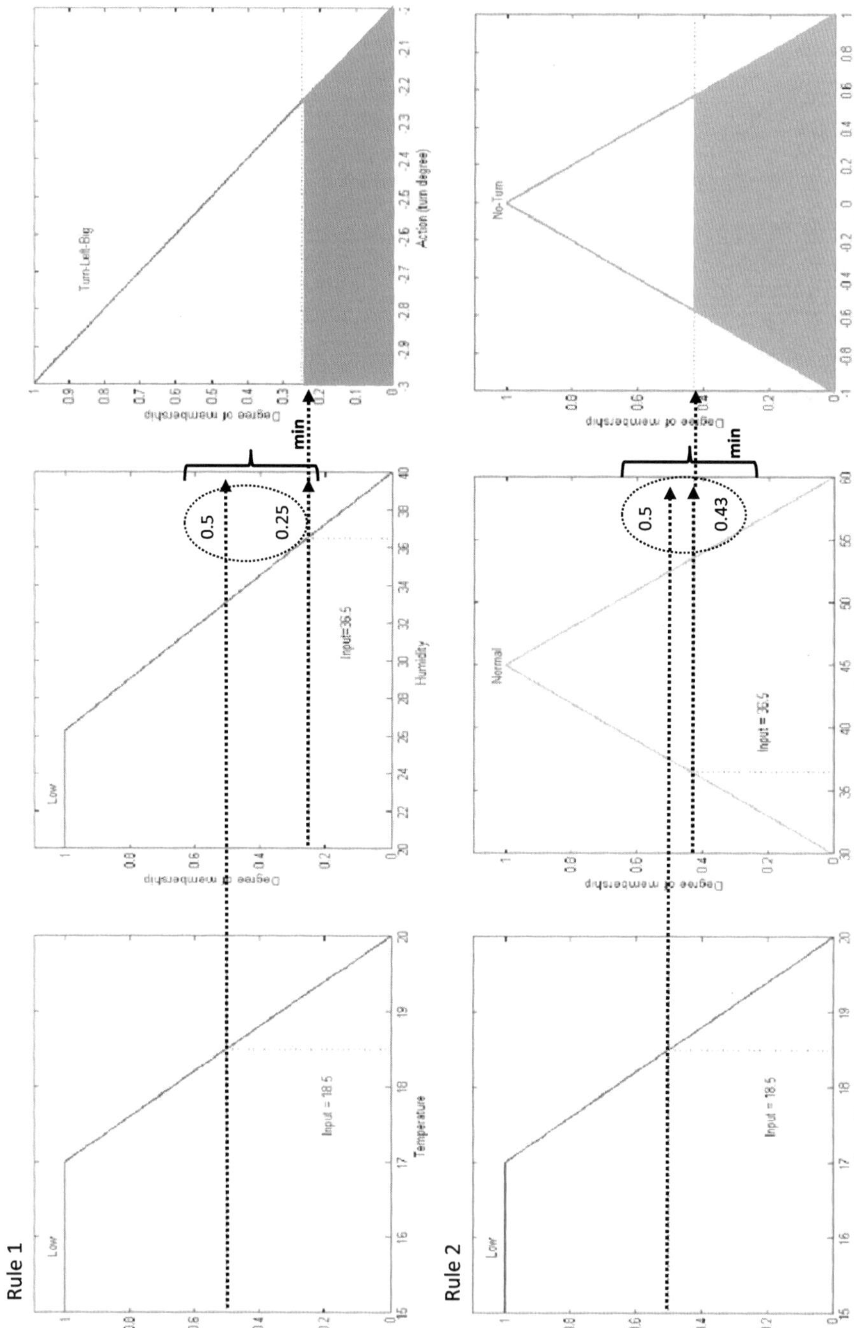

Figure 4.7: Membership degrees and inferred conclusions (Example 2.1).

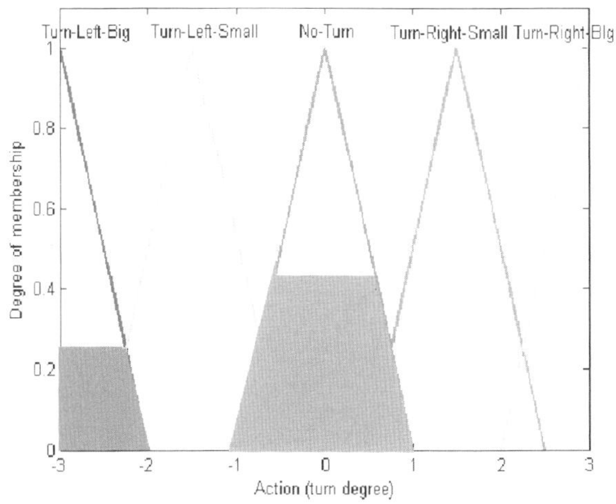

Figure 4.8: Rule consequents from Mamdani inference system (Example 2.2).

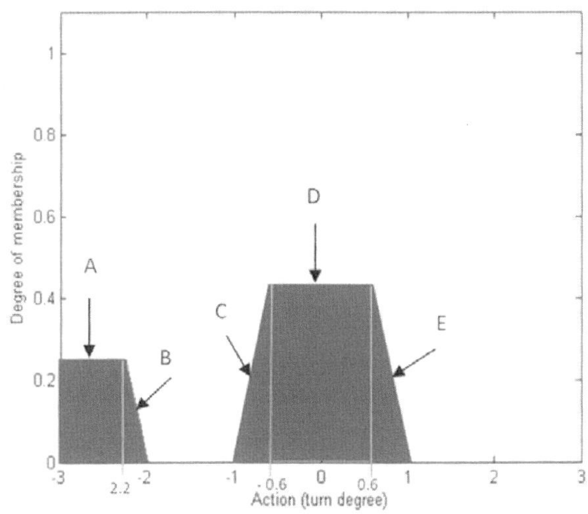

Figure 4.9: Result of aggregation (Example 2.2).

COG method requires calculation of the blue shaded area in the graph shown in Figure 4.9. This area can be determined by adding the area A, B, C, D, and E. The detailed calculations involved in the COG method are provided on page 148 based on Figures 4.8 and 4.9.

Considering Figure 4.9 and Example 2.2, the COG defuzzification can be given as:

$$z^* = \frac{\int \mu_{\text{output}}(z).z\,dz}{\int \mu_{\text{output}}(z)dz}$$

$$= \frac{\int_{-3}^{-2.2} (0.25)z\,dz + \int_{-2.2}^{-2} (-1.25z - 2.5)z\,dz + \int_{-1}^{-0.6} (1.075z + 1.075)z\,dz + \int_{-0.6}^{0.6} (0.43)z\,dz + \int_{0.6}^{1} (-1.075z + 1.075)z\,dz}{\int_{-3.0}^{-2.2} (0.25)dz + \int_{-2.2}^{-2.0} (-1.25z - 2.5)dz + \int_{-1}^{-0.6} (1.075z + 1.075)dz + \int_{-0.6}^{0.6} (0.43)dz + \int_{0.6}^{1} (-1.075z + 1.075)dz}$$

$$= \frac{(-0.52) + (-0.053) + (-0.063) + 0.063}{0.2 + 0.025 + 0.086 + 0.516 + 0.086} = -0.627 \approx -0.6.$$

The first three modeling steps are common to both Mamdani systems and Sugeno systems. The primary difference is that in Sugeno systems, the output consequence is not computed by clipping an output membership function at the rule strength. The reason is that in Sugeno systems there is no output membership function at all. Instead the output is a crisp number which is either a constant or computed by multiplying each input by a constant and then adding up the results. In the latter case, the output is a linear function of inputs.

Example 2.3. Consider the same system depicted in Figure 4.1 and the inputs as 18.5°C temperature and 36.5% humidity. As shown in Example 2.2, only the first three rules will be fired for the given inputs. Let us assume that the system is Sugeno type (zero-order) and the first three rules are given as:

Rule 1: ***If*** T is low ***and*** H is low ***then*** −2.5

Rule 2: ***If*** T is low ***and*** H is normal ***then*** 0

Rule 3: ***If*** T is low ***and*** H is high ***then*** 1.5

The firing strength of a rule is computed using product method as shown below:

$$\begin{aligned}
\text{Rule 1: } & T(\mu_{\text{Low}}(18.5), \mu_{\text{Low}}(36.5)) \\
& = \mu_{\text{Low}}(18.5) \cdot \mu_{\text{Low}}(36.5) = 0.5 \cdot 0.25 = 0.125, \\
\text{Rule 2: } & T(\mu_{\text{Low}}(18.5), \mu_{\text{Normal}}(36.5)) \\
& = \mu_{\text{Low}}(18.5) \cdot \mu_{\text{Normal}}(36.5) = 0.5 \cdot 0.43 = 0.215,
\end{aligned}$$

$$\text{Rule 3: } T(\mu_{\text{Low}}(18.5), \mu_{High}(36.5)) = \mu_{\text{Low}}(18.5) \cdot \mu_{High}(36.5) = 0.5 \cdot 0 = 0.$$

The final output of the system is the weighted average of all the rule outputs, computed as

$$\hat{y} = \frac{\sum_{i=1}^{N} w_i y_i}{\sum_{i=1}^{N} w_i},$$

w_i is the weight and is same as the firing strength of rule i, y_i is the output of rule i, $\hat{y}$ is the final output, and N is the number of rules.

$$\hat{y} = \frac{0.125 \times (-2.5) + 0.215 \times 0 + 0 \times 1.5}{0.125 + 0.215 + 0} = -0.92,$$

which indicates the knob is required to be turned 0.9° to the left.

Selection of defuzzification method is context or problem dependent. However, Hellendroon and Thomas (1993) have provided five criteria against which the defuzzification methods can be measured. The first criterion is *continuity*; a small variation in input should not lead to large output variation. The second criterion is *disambiguity* that requires the output from the defuzzification method to be always unique. The third criterion called *plausibility* requires the output to lie approximately in the middle of the support region and have high degree of membership. *Computational simplicity* is the fourth criterion. Finally, the fifth one is *weighting method* that weights the output method. This criterion is problem dependent as judging the weighting methods do not have any straightforward rules. One can compare the computational simplicity of the weighting methods but this is already taken into account by the fourth criterion. However, it is interesting to note that the defuzzification methods that are commonly used do not comply with all the given criteria. Although time consuming, another method is to use simulation tool like MATLAB to compare the results with various defuzzification methods and make the selection based on the obtained results.

4.3. Automated Modeling Approaches

Let us consider the system depicted in Figure 4.1 and assume that there are two persons in the room Alex and Baker. Alex turns the knob to the right or left depending on his comfort level, for example, he turns the knob to the right when he feels hot and humid. Baker is taking note of Alex's actions on particular temperature and humidity (readings from the sensors) in a log book. The recordings in Baker's book constitute the input–output data. The inputs are the temperature and humidity readings and the corresponding outputs are Alex's actions on those temperature and humidity readings. Such input–output data for a (manual or existing) system can be

Table 4.4: Example input–output data for cooling fan system.

x_1 (Temperature)	16	18	20	20	25	25	28	26	26	23
x_2 (Humidity)	25	25	20	40	50	60	65	55	50	55
y (Action)	−3	−3	−2	0	0	2	3	1	1	1

collected through various means. Table 4.4 represents a small set of input–output data with 10 data samples for this cooling fan system. Automated methods make use of such input–output data for fuzzy system modeling, in this case the modeling of an automatic fuzzy cooling fan control.

As discussed in the previous section, the modeling process mainly requires specification of two main components of a fuzzy system: inference mechanism and rule-base. The fuzzy inference needs specification of the implication, aggregation, and defuzzification mechanism, which can be resolved by the designer subjectively. In this section, we will discuss automated methods that can be used to construct the rule-base. However, it should be noted that these automated methods do not completely eliminate the involvement of a designer.

Rules constitutes a rule-base and if we look at a rule closely (Figure 4.10), then we need to address the following issues:

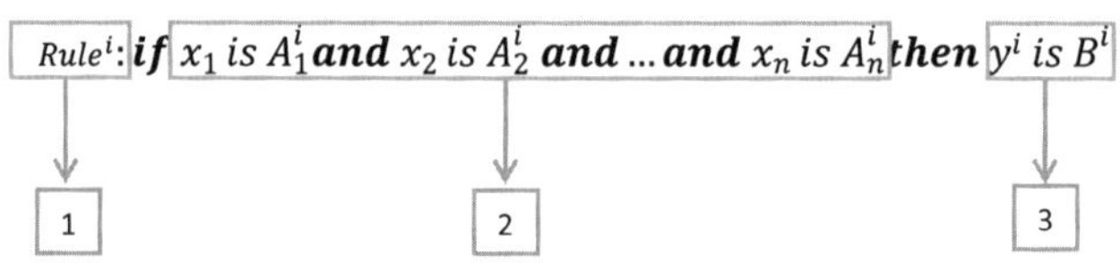

Figure 4.10: A fuzzy linguistic rule.

1. How many rules?
2. Antecedent part:
   a. What are the antecedent fuzzy sets and corresponding membership functions (antecedent parameters)?
   b. What is the type of membership function (Triangular, Trapezoidal, Gaussian etc.)?
   c. How many membership functions?
   d. Which operator (Fuzzy OR, AND or NOT) to use for connecting the rule antecedents?
3. Consequent part:
   a. What are the consequent fuzzy sets and corresponding membership functions? If the rule is of TSK type then the issue is determining each consequent parameter.
   b. What is the type and number of each membership function?
   c. How many membership functions?

If sufficient input–output data from the system are available then issue 1 can be solved with automated methods. The remaining issues can be solved only partially through automated methods. The type of membership function (issue 2b, 3b) and the fuzzy connectives (issue 2d) still require designer involvement. As mentioned in the previous section, these issues can be resolved subjectively. Further, there are several comparative studies available in literature that can also guide the designer in selecting best possible fuzzy operator for a particular application (Beliakov and Warren, 2001; Cordon *et al.*, 1997).

There are two ways in which the automated methods can aid the fuzzy system modeling process. In some fuzzy systems, the rules and the membership functions and associated parameters, e.g., the center and spread of a Gaussian function, are defined by the designer (not necessarily taking into account the input–output data). The automated methods are then used to find better set of parameters using the input–output data. This process is commonly referred to as *tuning* the fuzzy system. On the other hand, the automated methods can be used to determine the rules and the membership functions along with parameters using the input–output data and without designer intervention. This process is referred to as *learning* the rule-base of the fuzzy system, and the input–output data used in the learning process is often referred to as *training data.*

4.3.1. *Template-Based Approach*

This approach combines the expert knowledge and input–output data. In this approach, the domains of the antecedent variable are simply partitioned into a specified number of membership functions. We explain the rule generation process considering the method developed by Wang and Mendel (1992).

The rules are generated by following steps:

(i) *Partition the input and output spaces into fuzzy regions*: First, the domain intervals for the input and output variables, within which the values of the variable are expected to lie, are defined as:

$$X_1 = [x_1^-, x_1^+], \quad X_2 = [x_2^-, x_2^+], \quad Y = [y^-, y^+],$$

where x_i^-, x_i^+, $i = 1, 2$ and y^-, y^+ are the upper and lower limits of the intervals for input and output variables respectively. Each domain interval is divided into $2P+1$ number of equal or unequal fuzzy partitions; P is an integer that can be different for different variables. Next, a type of membership function (triangular, trapezoidal, Gaussian) is selected and a fuzzy set is assigned to each partition.

(ii) *Generate a preliminary rule set*: First, we determine the degree of each of the input and output data in all the partitions. A data is assigned to a partition and corresponding fuzzy set where it has maximum degree. Finally, one rule is formed for each input–output pair of data.

(iii) *Assign degrees to each rule*: The step (ii) generates as many rules as the number of training data points. In such a scenario, the chance of getting conflicting rules is very high. The conflicting rules have same antecedent but different consequents. In this step such rules are removed by assigning degrees, and in the process the number of rules is also reduced. Suppose the following rule is extracted from the ith training example $[x_1^i, x_2^i, \ldots, x_n^i, y^i]$.

$$\textbf{\textit{Rule}}^i\textbf{: \textit{if}}\ x_1\ \textit{is}\ A_1\ \textbf{\textit{and}}\ x_2\ \textit{is}\ A_2\ \textbf{\textit{and}} \ldots \textbf{\textit{and}}\ x_n\ \textit{is}\ A_n\ \textbf{\textit{then}}\ y\ \textit{is}\ B,$$

then the degree of this rule is given as,

$$\deg(Rule^i) = \mu_{A_1}(x_1^i) \cdot \mu_{A_2}(x_2^i) \cdot \cdots \cdot \mu_{A_n}(x_n^i) \cdot \mu_B(y^i).$$

Also, the degree of a rule can be represented as a product of the degree of its components and the degree of the training example that has generated this rule and can be given as,

$$\deg(Rule^i) = \mu_{A_1}(x_1^i) \cdot \mu_{A_2}(x_2^i) \cdots \mu_{A_n}(x_n^i) \cdot \mu_B(y^i) \cdot \mu^i,$$

where μ^i is the degree of the training example.

The degree of the training example is provided by the human expert based on its usefulness. For example, if the expert believes that a particular data sample is useful and crucial then a higher degree is assigned to it, and a lower degree is assigned for bad data sample that may be a measurement error.

(iv) *Obtain the final set of rules from the preliminary set*: In this step the rules with high degrees are selected for each combination of antecedents.

Example 3.1. Let us consider the data in Table 4.4 as the training data and the shape of the membership function to be triangular (other shapes for membership functions are also possible).

For the given training data and cooling fan system, the domain intervals are given as:

$$x_1 = [x_1^-, x_1^+] = [15, 30], \quad x_2 = [x_2^-, x_2^+] = [20, 70], \quad y = [y^-, y^+] = [-3, 3].$$

Next, the domain intervals are divided into equal size partitions as shown in Figure 4.11.

Also from Figure 4.11a, it can be observed that $x_1^1 = 16$ has maximum degree in the fuzzy set A1 and therefore it is assigned that fuzzy set. Similarly, $x_2^1 = 25$ is assigned to fuzzy set B2 (Figure 4.11b) and $y^1 = -3$ is assigned to C1 (Figure 4.12). Therefore, the rule corresponding to the first training data point $[16, 25, -3]$ can be

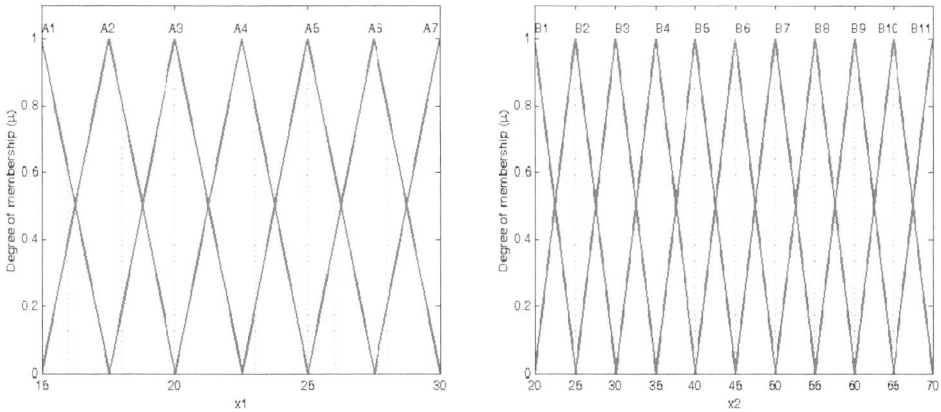

(a) Input x_1 (b) Input x_2

Figure 4.11: Partitions of input domain interval and corresponding fuzzy sets.

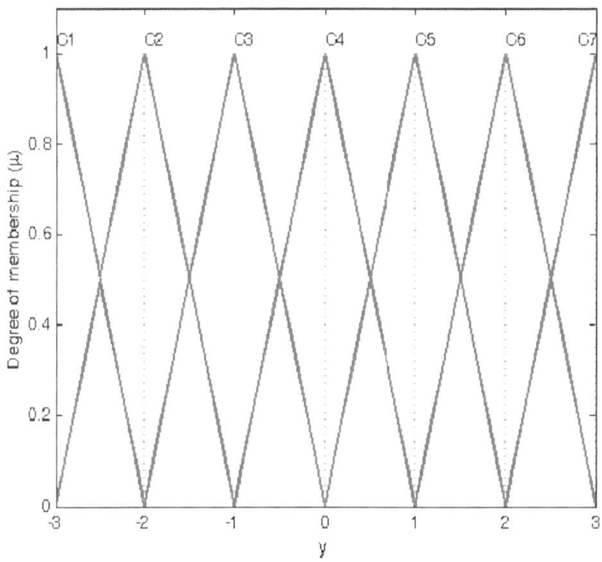

Figure 4.12: Output domain interval partitions and corresponding fuzzy sets.

given as:

$$\textbf{\textit{if}}\ x_1\ is\ A1\ \textbf{\textit{and}}\ x_2\ is\ B2\ \textbf{\textit{then}}\ y\ is\ C1.$$

The remaining rules are generated in the similar fashion and the preliminary set of rules is given as:

Rule 1: ***if*** x_1 *is* $A1$ ***and*** x_2 *is* $B2$ ***then*** y *is* $C1$.

Rule 2: ***if*** x_1 *is* $A2$ ***and*** x_2 *is* $B2$ ***then*** y *is* $C1$.

Rule 3: ***if*** x_1 *is* $A3$ ***and*** x_2 *is* $B1$ ***then*** y *is* $C2$.

Rule 4: ***if*** x_1 *is* $A3$ ***and*** x_2 *is* $B5$ ***then*** y *is* $C4$.

Rule 5: ***if*** x_1 *is* $A5$ ***and*** x_2 *is* $B7$ ***then*** y *is* $C4$.

Rule 6: ***if*** x_1 *is* $A5$ ***and*** x_2 *is* $B9$ ***then*** y *is* $C6$.

Rule 7: ***if*** x_1 *is* $A6$ ***and*** x_2 *is* $B10$ ***then*** y *is* $C7$.

Rule 8: ***if*** x_1 *is* $A5$ ***and*** x_2 *is* $B8$ ***then*** y *is* $C5$.

Rule 9: ***if*** x_1 *is* $A5$ ***and*** x_2 *is* $B7$ ***then*** y *is* $C5$.

Rule 10: ***if*** x_1 *is* $A4$ ***and*** x_2 *is* $B8$ ***then*** y *is* $C5$.

For this problem, Rule 5 and Rule 9 are conflicting, therefore we determine the degree of Rule 5 and Rule 9. The degree of rule Rule 5 is 1 and that of Rule 9 is 0.6 [step (iii)]. Therefore, Rule 9 is removed and the final set of rules consists of Rule 1 to Rule 8, and Rule 10. Note that here the degree of all the data samples is considered to be 1, i.e., all are believed to be useful.

4.3.2. *Neuro-Fuzzy Approach*

A fuzzy system that employs neuro-fuzzy approach is commonly referred to as neuro-fuzzy system. Such a system is trained by a learning algorithm usually derived from neural network theory (Mitra and Hayashi, 2000). Neuro-fuzzy approaches are motivated by the fact that at the computational level, a fuzzy model can be seen as a layered structure (network), similar to artificial neural networks. A widely known neuro-fuzzy system is ANFIS (adaptive network-based fuzzy inference System) (Jang, 1993). ANFIS is an adaptive network consisting of nodes connected with directional links. It is called adaptive because some, or all, of the nodes have parameters which affect the output of the node and these parameters change to minimize the error. The ANFIS structure consists of TSK type of rules. However, the author suggests that it is possible to develop Mamdani system as well. ANFIS consists of nodes with variable parameters (square nodes) that represent membership functions of the antecedents, and membership functions of Mamdani-type consequent or the linear functions of the TSK-type consequent. The parameters of the nodes in the intermediate layers that connect the antecedents with the consequents are fixed (circular nodes). It is worth to note that in ANFIS the structure (nodes and layers) remains static, only the parameters of the nodes are adapted. This is the key distinction between 'adaptive' and 'evolving' fuzzy systems, in the latter both the structure and parameters are adapted (evolving fuzzy systems will be discussed in Section 4.4).

Figure 4.13 shows the ANFIS structure for a rule-base consisting of following two TSK type rules.

Rule 1 : ***if*** x_1 *is* A_1 ***and*** x_2 *is* B_1 ***then*** $y_1 = a_{10} + a_{11}x_1 + a_{12}x_2$.

Rule 2 : ***if*** x_1 *is* A_2 ***and*** x_2 *is* B_2 ***then*** $y_2 = a_{20} + a_{21}x_1 + a_{23}x_2$.

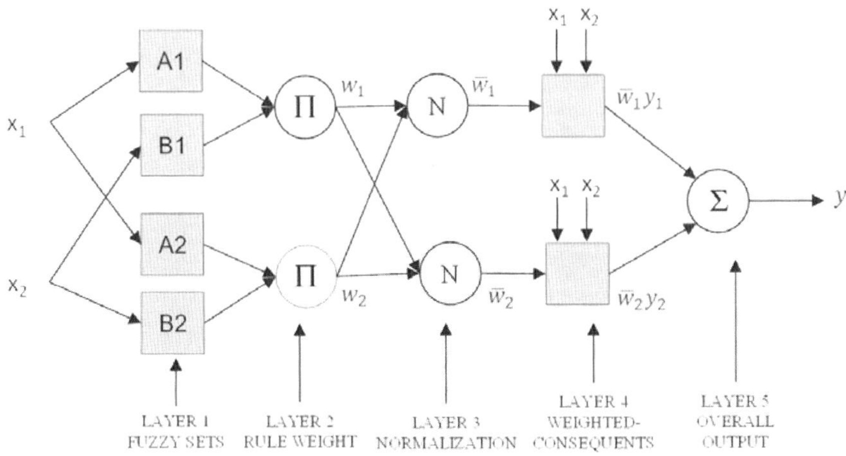

Figure 4.13: ANFIS structure.

In Layer 1, each node defines the fuzzy set in terms of bell-shaped membership function. The output from a node in this layer is the degree of membership of a given input given as

$$O_i^1 = \mu_{A_i}(x) = \exp\left\{-\left[\left(\frac{x-c_i}{\sigma_i}\right)^2\right]^{b_i}\right\}, \tag{5}$$

where $\{\sigma_i, b_i, c_i\}$ are antecedent parameter set. The bell shape function changes with the change in the values of these parameters.

Every node in Layer 2 determines the firing strength of a rule and the output of a node i can be given as

$$O_i^2 = w_i = \mu_{A_i}(x_1) \cdot \mu_{B_i}(x_2), \quad i = 1, 2. \tag{6}$$

In Layer 3, the nodes normalizes the firing strength of a rule, and the output of a node i is given as

$$O_i^3 = \bar{w}_i = \frac{w_i}{w_1 + w_2}, \quad i = 1, 2. \tag{7}$$

In Layer 4, the nodes calculate the weighted output from each rule:

$$O_i^4 = \bar{w}_i y_i = \bar{w}_i(a_{i0} + a_{i1}x_1 + a_{i2}x_2), \tag{8}$$

where $\{a_{i0}, a_{i1}, a_{i2}\}$ is the consequent parameter set.

Finally, the single node in Layer 5 computes the overall output:

$$O_i^5 = \sum_i \bar{w}_i y_i. \tag{9}$$

For the given network in Figure 4.13, the final output can be rewritten as

$$\begin{aligned} y &= \frac{w_1}{w_1 + w_2} y_1 + \frac{w_2}{w_1 + w_2} y_2 \\ &= \bar{w}_1 y_1 + \bar{w}_2 y_2 \\ &= (\bar{w}_1) a_{10} + (\bar{w}_1 x_1) a_{11} + (\bar{w}_1 x_2) a_{12} + (\bar{w}_2) a_{20} \\ &\quad + (\bar{w}_2 x_1) a_{21} + (\bar{w}_2 x_2) a_{22} \end{aligned} \tag{10}$$

which is a linear combination of consequent parameters.

Therefore, we have two sets of parameters, antecedent and consequent parameters. Initially, these parameters are set through partitioning of input data space. After the network parameters are set with their initial values, they are tuned using training data and hybrid learning algorithm. In the forward pass, the antecedent parameters are fixed, the functional signals go forward in the network till Layer 4, and finally the consequent parameters are determined using the method of least squares or recursive least squares. In the backward pass the consequent parameters are fixed, the error rates propagates back and the antecedent parameters are updated using gradient descent method. The combination of gradient descent and least squares method forms the hybrid learning algorithm.

Example 3.2. Consider the data in Table 4.4 as training data. For this example, the input–output data given in Table 4.4 are normalized as shown in Table 4.5. Data normalization is performed as subtractive clustering (discussed later in Section 4.3.4) is used here to determine the initial set of antecedent parameters.

Let $[x_1^k, x_2^k, \ldots, x_n^k, y^k]$ be the kth training example. Also, let r represent the number of rules and n represent the number of input variables.

Table 4.5: Training data (Example 3.2).

Input variable 1 (x_1)	Input variable 2 (x_2)	Output (y)
0	0.11	0
0.17	0.11	0
0.33	0	0.17
0.33	0.44	0.50
0.75	0.67	0.50
0.75	0.89	0.83
1.00	1.00	1.00
0.83	0.78	0.67
0.83	0.67	0.50
0.58	0.78	0.67

Table 4.6: Initial antecedent parameters.

—	—	c	σ
Rule 1	A1	0.75	0.18
—	B1	0.67	0.18
Rule 2	A2	0.17	0.18
—	B2	0.11	0.18

Considering Gaussian membership functions, the initial set of antecedent parameters are given in Table 4.6. These initial parameters can be obtained using any data partitioning method, for example, clustering. Let us assume that all the consequent parameters are initialized to 0.

To tune the antecedent and the consequent parameters we use the hybrid learning algorithm. We take the first data point $[x_1^1 = 0,\ x_2^1 = 0.11]$ as the input to the network shown in Figure 4.13 and determine the output from Layer 1 to Layer 3.

Layer 1 output:

$$O_1^1 = \mu_{A_1}\left(x_1^1\right) = e^{\frac{-(0-0.75)^2}{2*0.18^2}} = 0.0002,$$

$$O_2^1 = \mu_{B_1}\left(x_2^1\right) = e^{\frac{-(0.11-0.67)^2}{2*0.18^2}} = 0.0079,$$

$$O_3^1 = \mu_{A_2}\left(x_1^1\right) = e^{\frac{-(0-0.17)^2}{2*0.18^2}} = 0.6402,$$

$$O_4^1 = \mu_{B_2}\left(x_2^1\right) = e^{\frac{-(0.11-0.11)^2}{2*0.18^2}} = 1.$$

Layer 2 output:

$$O_1^2 = w_1 = \mu_{A_1}\left(x_1^1\right) \cdot \mu_{B_1}\left(x_2^1\right) = 0.000004,$$

$$O_2^2 = w_2 = \mu_{A_2}\left(x_1^1\right) \cdot \mu_{B_2}\left(x_2^1\right) = 0.00003.$$

Layer 3 output:

$$O_1^3 = \bar{w}_1 = \frac{w_1}{w_1 + w_2} = 0.000002,$$

$$O_2^3 = \bar{w}_2 = \frac{w_2}{w_1 + w_2} = 1.$$

Now, the consequent parameter can be determined using the Recursive Least Square (RLS) method. In the RLS method, the consequent parameters of r rules are represented in a matrix form $A = [a_{10}, a_{11}, \ldots, a_{1n}, \ldots, a_{r1}, \ldots, a_{rn}]^T$ and the estimate of A at k^{th} iteration (based on k data points) is given as:

$$A_k = A_{k-1} + C_k X_{ek}\left(Y_k - X_{ek}^T A_{k-1}\right), \tag{11}$$

$$C_k = C_{k-1} - \frac{C_{k-1} X_{ek} X_{ek}^T C_{k-1}}{1 + X_{ek}^T C_{k-1} X_{ek}}, \tag{12}$$

where $X_{ek} = [\bar{w}_1, \bar{w}_1 x_1^k, \ldots, \bar{w}_1 x_n^k, \bar{w}_2, \bar{w}_2 x_1^k, \ldots, \bar{w}_1 x_n^k, \bar{w}_r, \bar{w}_r x_1^k, \ldots, \bar{w}_r x_n^k]^T$, $Y_k = y^k$, C_k is $r(n+1) \times r(n+1)$ covariance matrix, and the initial conditions are $A_0 = 0$, $C_0 = \Omega I$, where Ω is a large positive integer.

For our example, with $k = 1$

$$\begin{aligned} X_{e1} &= [\bar{w}_1, \quad \bar{w}_1 * 0, \quad \bar{w}_{1.} * 0.11, \quad \bar{w}_2, \quad \bar{w}_2 * 0, \quad \bar{w}_2 * 0.11]^T \\ &= [0.000002 \quad 0 \quad 0.00000022 \quad 1 \quad 0 \quad 0.11]^T, \\ Y_k &= 1.0 \\ C_0 &= \begin{bmatrix} 1000 & 0 & 0 & 0 & 0 & 0 \\ 0 & 1000 & 0 & 0 & 0 & 0 \\ 0 & 0 & 1000 & 0 & 0 & 0 \\ 0 & 0 & 0 & 1000 & 0 & 0 \\ 0 & 0 & 0 & 0 & 1000 & 0 \\ 0 & 0 & 0 & 0 & 0 & 1000 \end{bmatrix}. \\ C_1 &= C_0 - \frac{C_0 X_{e1} X_{e1}^T C_0}{1 + X_{e1}^T C_0 X_{e1}} \\ &= \begin{bmatrix} 1000 & 0 & 0 & 0 & 0 & 0 \\ 0 & 1000.0 & 0 & 0 & 0 & 0 \\ 0 & 0 & 1000 & 0 & 0 & 0 \\ 0 & 0 & 0 & 500.2 & 0 & -499.8 \\ 0 & 0 & 0 & 0 & 1000.0 & 0 \\ 0 & 0 & 0 & -499.8 & 0 & 500.2 \end{bmatrix}, \\ A_0 &= [000000]^T, \\ A_1 &= A_0 + C_1 X_{e1}\left(Y_1 - X_{e1}^T A_0\right) = \begin{bmatrix} 0 \\ 0 \\ 0 \\ 0.4998 \\ 0 \\ 0.4998 \end{bmatrix}. \end{aligned}$$

After $k = 1$ iteration of RLS method, we get the following consequent parameters:

$$a_{10} = 0, \;\; a_{11} = 0, \;\; a_{12} = 0, \;\; a_{20} = 0.4998, \;\; a_{21} = 0, \;\; a_{22} = 0.4998.$$

This process is continued for all the data points, i.e., for $k = 2, \ldots, 10$. After getting the final set of consequent parameters (i.e., after $k = 10$), now the antecedent parameters are updated in the backward pass using gradient descent method. The aim of gradient descent is to minimize the error between the neural net's output and actual observed outputs.

The instantaneous error between the output y and the current reading y_k can be given as:

$$E_k = \frac{1}{2}(y - y_k)^2 = e, \quad k = 1, 2, \ldots, 10. \tag{13}$$

By applying the chain rule, we obtain from Equation (13) the following equations for updating the antecedent parameters:

$$\begin{aligned} c_{ij}(k) &= c_{ij}(k-1) - \alpha \frac{\partial E_k}{\partial c_{ij}}, \\ &= c_{ij}(k-1) - \alpha \bar{w}_i (a_{i0} + a_{i1}x_1 + \cdots + a_{in}x_n - y) e \frac{x_j - c_{ij}(k-1)}{\sigma_{ij}^2(k-1)}, \end{aligned} \tag{14}$$

$$\begin{aligned} \sigma_{ij}(k) &= \sigma_{ij}(k-1) - \alpha \frac{\partial E_k}{\partial \sigma_{ij}} \\ &= \sigma_{ij}(k-1) - \alpha \bar{w}_i (a_{i0} + a_{i1}x_1 + \cdots + a_{in}x_n - y) e \frac{(x_j - c_{ij}(k-1))^2}{\sigma_{ij}^3(k-1)}, \end{aligned} \tag{15}$$

where $i = 1, 2, \ldots, r$ and $j = 1, 2, \ldots, n$.

So, the antecedent parameters for every rule can be updated considering each of the data points at a time. One such cycle of update of antecedent and consequent parameters is referred to as epoch and many such epochs can be performed until the errors are within acceptable limits. Further, a separate set of input–output data (validation data or test data) can be used to validate the performance of the model by checking how closely it can predict the actual observed values.

4.3.3. *Genetic-Fuzzy Approach*

Fuzzy rule-based systems that involve GAs in the design process are commonly referred to *as genetic fuzzy rule-based systems* or *genetic fuzzy systems*, in general. When GA is used in the process of determining the membership functions with a fixed set of rules is often referred to as genetic tuning or optimizing parameters, and the process of determining rules is commonly known as genetic learning. During the genetic learning process, the rules can be determined at two levels. In the first level, the rules are determined with known membership functions, and in the second level both membership functions and fuzzy rules are determined using GA (Cordon *et al.*, 2004). In this section, first a brief overview of GAs is presented and then genetic tuning of membership functions and genetic learning of rules are described.

4.3.3.1. *GAs*

GAs are search algorithms that are inspired by the principles of natural evolution. A GA starts with a set of different possible solutions to the problem (population), then the performance of these solutions are evaluated based on a *fitness* or *evaluation function* (i.e., how good a solution is to the given problem). From these solutions only a fraction of good solutions is selected and the rest are eliminated (survival of the fittest). Finally, in the search for better solutions, the selected solutions undergo the process of reproduction, crossover, and mutation to create a new set of possible solutions (evolved population). This process of production of a new generation and its evaluation is repeated until convergence is reached (Goldberg, 1989). This entire GA process is represented in Figure 4.14.

There are primarily two representations of GAs, binary-coded GA (BCGA) and real-coded GA (RCGA). In BCGA, the possible solutions (or chromosomes or individuals in a population) are represented as strings of binary digits. In RCGAs, each chromosome is represented as a vector of floating-point numbers. Each gene represents a variable of the problem, and the size of the chromosome is kept the same as the length of the solution to the problem. Therefore, the RCGA can be considered to be directly operating on the optimization parameters whereas BCGA operates on an encoded (discretized) representation of these parameters.

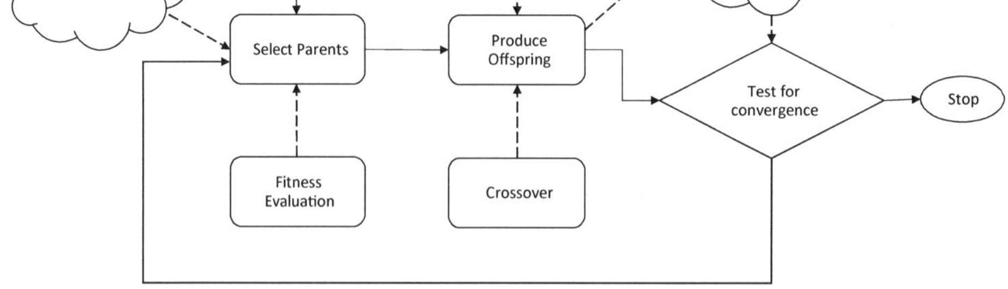

Figure 4.14: Diagrammatic representation of GA.

To apply GAs to solve a problem one needs to take into account the following issues:

(i) Encoding scheme or genetic representation of solution to the problem: The choice of encoding scheme is one of the important design decisions. The bit string representation is the most commonly used encoding technique.
(ii) Fitness evaluation function: Choosing and formulating an appropriate evaluation function is crucial to the efficient solution of any given genetic algorithm problem. One approach is to define a function that determines the error between the actual output (from training data) and the output returned by the model.
(iii) Genetic operators: The genetic operators are used to create the next generation individuals by altering the genetic composition of an individual (from previous generation) during reproduction. The fundamental genetic operators are: selection, crossover, and mutation.
(iv) Selection of input parameters: GAs requires some user-defined input parameters, for example, selection probability, mutation and crossover probability, and population size.

Selection: The aim of the selection operator is to allow better individuals (those that are close to the solution) to pass on their genes to the next generation. In other words, they are the fittest individuals in the population and so are given the chance to become parents or to reproduce. The commonly known selection mechanisms are: proportionate selection method (e.g., Roulette wheel selection), ranking selection (e.g., linear ranking selection), and tournament selection (e.g., binary tournament selection).

Crossover: The purpose of the crossover operator is to produce new chromosomes that are distinctly different from their parents, yet retain some of their parent characteristics. It combines the features of two parent chromosomes to form two offspring with the possibility that the offspring generated through recombination are better adapted than their parents. A random choice is made, where the likelihood of crossover being applied depends on probability defined by a crossover rate, the crossover probability. Definitions for this operator are highly dependent on the particular representation chosen. Two widely known techniques for binary encoding are: one-point crossover and two-point crossover. In one-point crossover, two parent chromosomes are interchanged at a randomly selected point thus creating two children (Figure 4.15). In two-point crossover, two points are selected instead of just one crossover point. (Figure 4.16).

Mutation: The structure of some of the individuals in the new generation produced by selection and crossover is modified further by using the mutation operator. The most common form of mutation is to alter bits from a chromosome with some

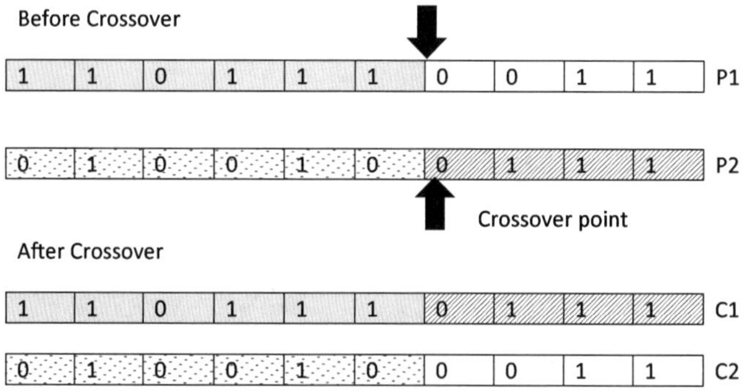

Figure 4.15: One-point crossover.

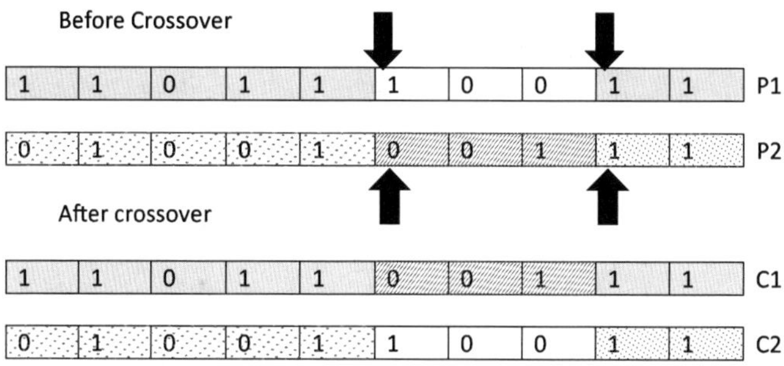

Figure 4.16: Two-point crossover.

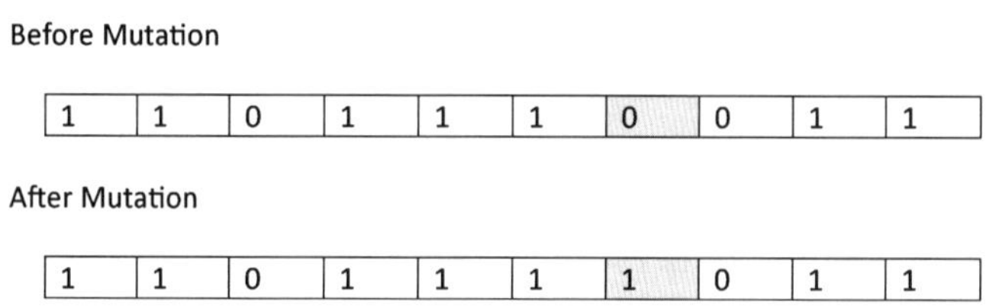

Figure 4.17: Mutation.

predetermined probability (mutation probability) (Figure 4.17). Generally, in BCGA the mutation probability is set to very low value.

There is an additional policy, called elitist policy, that can be applied after crossover and mutation to retain some number of the best individuals at each generation. This is required because in the process of crossover and mutation the fittest individual may disappear.

4.3.3.2. *Genetic tuning*

In case of genetic tuning, the rules, the number of membership functions (fuzzy sets), and the type of each membership function are assumed to be available. The most common membership functions for which GAs are used to tune the parameters are triangular, trapezoidal, or Gaussian functions. Depending on the type of membership function the number of parameters per membership function ranges from one to four and each parameter is binary or real coded. In the following example, we demonstrate the genetic tuning of membership function parameter, given the fuzzy rules of the system.

Example 3.3. Consider a system with single input (x) and single output (y) with input–output values as shown in Table 4.7 and the rules are represented in Table 4.8 (For simplicity, we are not using the input–output data of the cooling fan system (Table 4.4), with two input and single output).

The range of x is [0, 10] and the range of y is [0, 100]. The shape of both input and output membership functions is assumed to be triangular.

Figure 4.18 shows the five parameters ($P1, P2, \ldots, P5$) that are required to be optimized by the GA.

Based on the range of input and output variables, and the required precision, first the length of the bit string required to encode each parameter is determined. The

Table 4.7: Input–output data (Example 3.3).

Input (x)	1	2	3	4	5	6	7	8	9	10
Output (y)	2	5	10	17	26	37	50	65	80	100

Table 4.8: Rules (Example 3.3).

x	y
Low	Small
Medium	Big
High	Big

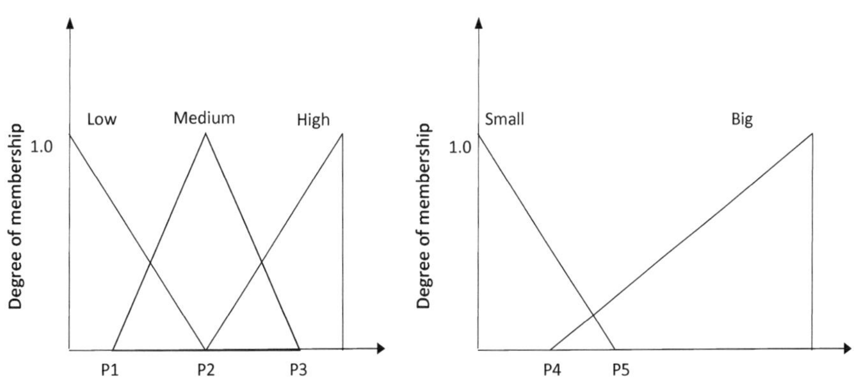

Figure 4.18: Membership functions and parameters for input and output variables.

range of input is 10 and let us assume that the required precision is one digit after the decimal point, so each of the input parameter will require 7 bits ($\log_2 (10 \times 10)$). Similarly, 10 bits will be used to encode each of the output parameters. So an individual or a chromosome will have a total of 41 bits (3×7 bits for $P1$, $P2$, $P3$ plus 2×10 bits for $P4$ and $P5$).

Next, we need a mapping function to map the bit string to the value of a parameter. This can be done using the following mapping function (Goldberg, 1989):

$$d(UB, LB, L, bs) = LB + \frac{B}{2^L - 1}(UB - LB), \tag{16}$$

where bs is the bit string to be mapped to a parameter value, B is the number in decimal form that is being represented in binary form by the given bit string, UB is upper bound, LB is lower bound, L is the length of the bit string.

Finally, we need a fitness function to evaluate the chromosomes. The fitness function for this problem is given as:

$$f(I) = \frac{1}{1 + \text{RMSE}}, \tag{17}$$

where I is the individual for which the fitness is evaluated and RMSE is the root mean squared error.

Table 4.9 shows the first iteration of genetic algorithm with an initial population size of four. The bit strings are first decoded into binary values (column 2) and then mapped to decimal values (column 3) using Equation (16). For parameters $P1$, $P2$, $P3$ the value of LB is set to 0, UB is 10 and L is 7 and for parameters $P4$, $P5$, the value of LB is 0, UB 100, and L is 10. Figure 4.19 shows the membership functions of the system with values $P1 = 4.0$, $P2 = 7.3$, $P3 = 8.7$, and $P5 = 57.2$ (Individual 2 from Table 4.9).

After the decimal values of the string are determined, the estimated output is computed using the parameter values represented by each individual. To evaluate the fitness of each individual the RMSE is calculated as shown in Table 4.10. Using the RMSE values from Table 4.10 and Equation (17), the fitness of each individual is determined. From the initial population and based on the fitness values, some parents are selected for reproduction or to generate a new set of solutions. In this example, *roulette wheel* method is used for parent selection. In roulette wheel method first the fitness values are normalized so that the range of fitness values becomes [0, 1]. Then the normalized values are sorted in descending order. A random number is generated between 0 and 1. The first individual is selected whose fitness added to the preceding individual is greater than or equal to the generated random number. As shown in Table 4.11, the individual 2 is selected two times out of four times and individual 3 and 4 are selected once, and individual 1 did not get a chance to

Table 4.9: First iteration of genetic algorithm.

String number (Individual)	(1) Bit string	(2) Decimal value					(3) Mapped value				
		P1	P2	P3	P4	P5	P1	P2	P3	P4	P5
1	0101100 1101010 1110000 0000001001 1010010001	44	106	112	9	657	3.5	8.3	8.8	0.9	64.2
2	0110011 1011101 1101111 0111000011 1001001001	51	93	111	451	585	4.0	7.3	8.7	44.1	57.2
3	1001011 1001101 1011100 1000011100 1100110011	75	77	92	540	819	5.9	6.1	7.2	52.8	80.1
4	0101000 1001110 1100101 0111000101 1110001110	40	78	101	453	910	3.1	6.1	8.0	44.3	89

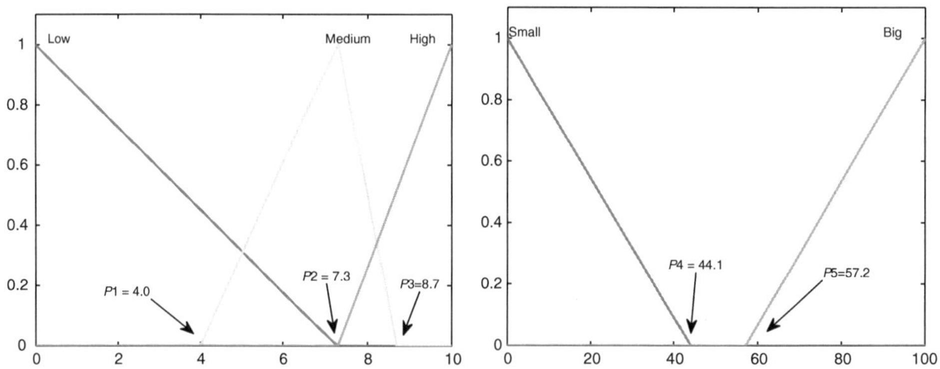

Figure 4.19: Input and output membership functions.

reproduce as it has the lowest fitness value. After the parents are selected the next generation of population is generated by applying crossover and mutation as shown in columns (1) and (2) of Table 4.12. In this example, the crossover is applied to all the individuals (crossover probability is 1.0), and mutation is applied to two randomly selected individuals, where 1 out of 41 bit is flipped. The locations of crossover and mutation are indicated in column (1) and the individuals generated after these operations are shown in column (2) of Table 4.12. These bit strings also undergo the same process of decoding and fitness evaluation as shown in Table 4.12 (columns 3 and 4) and Table 4.13. The final fitness values for the individuals in this new generation are indicated in Table 4.14. It is clear from Tables 4.11 and 4.14 that in the new generation none of the individuals have fitness value lower than 0.4, whereas the fitness value in the previous generation was 0.3. Also, if we compare the two best strings from the first generation and the second generation, then the former string has lower fitness value than the latter.

This process of generation and evaluation of the strings continues till convergence to the solution is arrived.

4.3.3.3. *Genetic learning of rules*

Many researchers have investigated the automatic generation of fuzzy rules using GAs. Their work in this direction can be broadly grouped into following categories:

- Genetic learning of rules with fixed membership functions.
- Learning both fuzzy rules and membership functions but serially, for example, first good membership functions are determined and then they are used to determine the set of rules.
- Simultaneous learning of both fuzzy membership functions and rules.

While learning rules, GAs can be applied to obtain a suitable rule-base using chromosomes that code single rules or a complete rule-base. On the

Table 4.10: RMSE values.

	Individual 1		Individual 2		Individual 3		Individual 4	
Actual output	Estimated output	Squared-error	Estimated output	Squared-error	Estimated output	Squared-error	Estimated output	Squared-error
2	0	4	14.6	158.76	17.7	246.49	14.8	163.84
5	0	25	15.3	106.09	18.8	190.44	15.7	114.49
10	0	100	16.2	38.44	20.2	104.04	16.9	47.61
17	72.8	3113.64	17.3	0.09	21.9	24.01	32.8	249.64
26	81.6	3091.36	49.2	538.24	23.8	4.84	51.1	630.01
37	84.8	2284.84	66.2	852.64	85.8	2381.44	88.5	2652.25
50	86.9	1361.61	81	961	91.4	1713.96	96	2116
65	88.2	538.24	83.6	345.96	92.5	756.25	96	961
80	85.7	32.49	84.6	21.16	93.3	176.89	96.4	268.96
100	88.4	134.56	86.1	193.21	93.7	39.69	96.7	10.89
MSE	1068.57		321.56		568.8		721.47	
RMSE	32.69		17.93		23.84		26.86	

Table 4.11: Fitness values for initial population.

String number (Individual)	Bit string	Fitness (f)	Normalized fitness (f/f_{tot})	Selection
1	0101100 1101010 1110000 0000001001 1010010001	0.03	0.19	0
2	0110011 1011101 1101111 0111000011 1001001001	0.05	0.31	2
3	1001011 1001101 1011100 1000011100 1100110011	0.04	0.25	1
4	0101000 1001110 1100101 0111000101 1110001110	0.04	0.25	1
		Sum (f_{tot}) = 0.16	Sum = 1.00	

Table 4.12: Crossover and mutation operation.

String number (Old individual)	String number (New individual)	(1) Selected individuals (Bit string)	(2) New individuals (Bit string)	(3) Decimal value					(4) Mapped value				
				P1	P2	P3	P4	P5	P1	P2	P3	P4	P5
2	1	0110011 101|1101 1101111 0111000011 1001001001	0110011 1011101 1**1**11100 1000011100 1100110011	51	93	124	540	819	4.0	7.3	9.7	52.8	80.1
3	2	1001011 100|1101 1**0**11100 1000011100 1100110011	1001011 1001101 1101111 0111000011 1001001001	75	77	111	451	585	5.9	6.1	8.7	44.1	57.2
2	3	0110011 101|1101 1101111 0111000011 1001001001	0110011 1011110 11**1**0101 0111000101 1110001110	51	94	117	453	910	4.0	7.4	9.2	44.3	89
4	4	0101000 100|1110 11**0**0101 0111000101 1110001110	0101000 1001101 1101111 0111000011 1001001001	40	77	111	451	585	3.1	6.1	8.7	44.1	57.2

Table 4.13: RMSE values for individuals of second generation.

	Individual 1		Individual 2		Individual 3		Individual 4	
Actual output	Estimated output	Squared-error	Estimated output	Squared-error	Estimated output	Squared-error	Estimated output	Squared-error
2	17.6	243.36	14.5	156.25	14.7	161.29	14.7	161.29
5	18.4	179.56	15.3	106.09	15.3	106.09	15.6	112.36
10	19.4	88.36	16.5	42.25	16.2	38.44	16.8	46.24
17	20.8	14.44	17.9	0.81	17.3	0.09	47.8	948.64
26	41.1	228.01	19.5	42.25	33.3	53.29	66.5	1640.25
37	58.5	462.25	85.5	2352.25	49.4	153.76	84	2209
50	81.9	1017.61	96.3	2143.69	75	625	84.7	1204.09
65	93.2	795.24	96	961	96.3	979.69	83.5	342.25
80	93	169	96.4	268.96	96.2	262.44	85.3	28.09
100	93.7	39.69	96.7	10.89	96.7	10.89	86.1	193.21
MSE	323.75		608.44		239.09		688.54	
RMSE	17.99		24.66		15.46		26.24	

Table 4.14: Fitness values for individuals of second generation.

String number (Individual)	Bit string	Fitness (f)
1	0110011 1011101 1111100 1000011100 1100110011	0.05
2	1001011 1001101 1101111 0111000011 1001001001	0.04
3	0110011 1011110 1110101 0111000101 1110001110	0.06
4	0101000 1001101 1101111 0111000011 1001001001	0.04

basis of chromosome as a single or complete rule-base, there are three widely known approaches in which GAs have been applied, the Michigan (Holland and Reitman, 1978), the Pittsburgh (Smith, 1980), and the Iterative Rule Learning (IRL) (Venturini, 1993) approaches. In Michigan approach, the chromosome correspond to rules and a rule set is represented by entire population with genetic operators applied at the level of rules, whereas in the Pittsburgh approach, each chromosome encodes a complete set of rules. In the IRL approach, each chromosome represents only one rule, but contrary to the first approach, only the best individual is considered as the solution, discarding the remaining chromosomes in the population.

Thrift (1991) described a method for genetic learning of rules with fixed membership functions based on encoding of complete set of rules (Pittsburg approach). Using genetic algorithm a two-input, one-output fuzzy controller was designed for centering a cart on a frictionless one-dimensional track. Considering triangular membership functions, for each input variable and output variable the fuzzy sets, Negative-Medium (NM), Negative-Small (NS), Zero (ZE), Positive-Small (PS) and Positive-Medium (PM), were defined. The control logic was presented in the form of a 5×5 decision table with each entry encoding an output fuzzy set taken from {NM, NS, ZE, PS, PM, _} where the symbol "_" indicated absence of a fuzzy set. A chromosome is formed from the decision table by going row-wise and producing a string of numbers from the given code set $\{0, 1, 2, 3, 4, 5\}$ corresponding to {NM, NS, ZE, PS, PM, _} respectively. For example, consider the following decision table (Table 4.15), the corresponding chromosome for the given table (rule set) is: '0321041425023413205110134'.

Thrift's method of designing the control employed elitist selection scheme with standard two-point crossover operator. The GA mutation operator changes a code from the given code set either up or down a level, or to a blank code. After a simulation of 100 generations and using a population size of 31, Thrift's system was able to evolve a good fuzzy control strategy.

Kinzel *et al.* (1994) described an evolutionary approach for learning both rules and membership functions in three stages. The design process involves the following three phases: (i) determine a good initial rule-base and fuzzy sets, (ii) apply GA to

Table 4.15: Example decision table considering five membership functions.

	NM	NS	ZE	PS	PM
NM	0	3	2	1	0
NS	4	1	4	2	5
ZE	0	2	3	4	1
PS	3	2	0	5	1
PM	1	0	1	3	4

(before Mutation)

NM	NB	ZE	NM	PM
NB	NM	NM	ZE	PM
NM	NM	ZE	PM	PM
NB	NM	ZE	PM	PB
PB	PM	PB	PB	PM

(ZE replace by PM)

(after Mutation)

NM	NB	PM	NM	PM
NB	NM	NM	ZE	PM
NM	NM	ZE	PM	PM
NB	NM	ZE	PM	PB
PB	PM	PB	PB	PM

Figure 4.20: Mutation of rule-base.

the rules by keeping the membership functions fixed, (iii) tune the fuzzy sets using GA to get optimal performance. In this approach also, the rule-base is represented in the form of a table and each chromosome encodes such a table. Firstly, the population is generated by applying the mutation operator on all genes of the initial rule-base. Figure 4.20 shows mutation of rule-base considering cart-pole problem. During Mutation one fuzzy set (gene) is replaced by randomly chosen but similar fuzzy set. For example, the fuzzy set 'ZE' could be mutated to 'NM' or 'PM'. After calculating the fitness of the population, the genetic operations selection, crossover and mutation are used to generate the next population. This process is continued until a good rule-base is found.

After a rule-base is found, in the next stage the fuzzy sets are tuned. The authors argue against the use of bit string encoded genomes, due to the destructive action of crossover. The fuzzy sets are encoded by representing each domain by a string of genes. Each gene represents the membership values of the fuzzy sets of domain d at a certain x-value. Thus, a fuzzy partition is described by discrete membership values. The standard two-point crossover operator is used and the mutation is done by randomly choosing a membership value $\mu_i(x)$ in a chromosome and changing it to a value in [0, 1]. For the cart-pole problem, Kinzel *et al.*'s (1994) method discovers good fuzzy rules after 33 generations using a population size of 200.

The learning method described by Liska and Melsheimer (1994) simultaneously learns the rules and membership function parameters. The design process tries to optimize, the number of rules, the structure of rules, and the membership function parameters simultaneously by using RCGA with one-at-time reproduction. In this type of GA, two offspring are produced by selecting and combining two parents. One of the offspring is randomly discarded, the other replaces the poorest performance string in the population. During each reproduction step only one operator is employed.

For simultaneous optimization, the chromosome is composed of three substrings: the first substring of real numbers encodes membership functions of input and output variables. Each membership function is represented by the two parameters (center and width). The second substring of integer numbers encodes the structure of each rule in the rule-base such that one integer number represents one membership in the space of an input variable. The membership functions are numbered in ascending order according to their centers. For example, a number "1" refers to the MF with the lowest value of the MF center in a particular input variable. The value "0" in the second substring indicates the "null" MF, i.e., the input variable is not involved in the rule. The third substring of integer numbers encodes MFs in rule consequents. A value "0" in the third substring means that the rule is deleted from the FLS rule-base. For example, in a system with n input variables and one output variable, p_i membership functions in ith input variable, q membership functions in the output variable, and N rules, the three substrings can be represented as shown in Figure 4.21.

The inclusion of "0" in the second substring allows the number of input variables involved in each rule to change dynamically during the GA search. Similarly, '0' in the third substring allows the number of rules to vary dynamically. The number of rules in FLS rule-base is constrained by the upper limit specified by a designer. The evolution process used a set of ordered genetic operators such that the relative order of MFs in each variable is preserved. The ordered operators are used only for the first substring, for the second and third substring ordinary genetic operators are used, viz., uniform crossover, mutation, and creep. Uniform crossover creates two offspring from two parents by deciding randomly which offspring receives the gene from which parent. Mutation replaces randomly selected gene in a parent by a random value between the minimum and maximum allowed values. Creep

	Width	Center	Width	Center	...	Width	Center
x_i	0.15	0.20	0.19	0.50	...	0.22	0.75
	MF_1		MF_2			MF_{p_i}	

	Width	Center	Width	Center	...	Width	Center
$y(\boldsymbol{x})$	0.20	0.10	0.32	0.45	...	0.38	0.52
	MF_1		MF_2			MF_q	

(a) Membership function substring for all input and output variables.

	x_1	x_2	...	x_n
$rule_k$	1	3	...	0

(b) Rule-base substring

	$rule_1$	$rule_2$	...	$rule_N$
$y(\boldsymbol{x})$	1	0	...	2

(c) Rule consequents substring

Figure 4.21: The three substrings of a chromosome.

creates one offspring from one parent by altering randomly its gene within a specified range.

An exponential ranking technique based on error function is used to evaluate the performance of each chromosome. This technique assigns the highest fitness to the string with the lowest value of the error function (e.g., $\mathit{fitness}(1) = 1000$). If $\mathit{fitness}(i)$ is the fitness value for the ith lowest value of the error then the fitness value of the next lowest value is set to $\mathit{fitness}(i + 1) = \alpha * \mathit{fitness}(i), \alpha \in [0, 1]$, except that no string is given a fitness lesser than 1. Liska and Melsheimer (1994) obtained the best results with α value set to 0.96. In their GA implementation, no duplicates were allowed, i.e., a new offspring is allowed to be the member of the current population if it differs from every existing member at least in one gene.

Liska and Melsheimer (1994) applied their genetic learning approach to learn a dynamic model of a plant using input–output data. After the genetic learning process, they further applied another technique to fine tune the membership function parameters. The obtained results are comparable to those achieved using a three-layer feed-forward neural network.

4.3.4. *Clustering-Based Approach*

The aim of clustering is to partition a given dataset into different groups (clusters) so that the members in the same group are of similar nature, whereas members of different groups are dissimilar. While clustering, various similarity measures can be considered, one of the most commonly used measure is distance between data samples. Clustering can be either *hard* (or *crisp*) clustering technique, e.g., k-means (Hastie *et al.*, 2009), where a data sample is assigned only to one cluster or *fuzzy* clustering where a data sample can belong to all the clusters with certain degree of membership (de Oliveira and Pedrycz, 2007).

In the domain of fuzzy system design, a clustering algorithm is applied to structure identification by partitioning the input–output data in to clusters. Each cluster corresponds to a rule in the rule-base. The cluster centers can be considered as focal points for rules in the rule-base. Different clustering methods can be used for the purpose of data partitioning and rule generation, however, fuzzy clustering is being used extensively either independently or combined with other techniques. Methods based on fuzzy clustering are appealing as there is a close connection between fuzzy clusters and fuzzy rules (Klawonn, 1994; Kruse *et al.*, 1994). Some of the clustering algorithms that are commonly used for structure identification are, fuzzy c-means (Dunn, 1974; Bezdek, 1981), Gustafsson–Kessel algorithm (Gustafsson and Kessel, 1979), mountain clustering (Yager and Filev, 1993, 1994), and subtractive clustering (Chiu, 1997).

To get the fuzzy rules, clustering can be applied separately to input and/or output data or jointly to the input–output data. Sugeno and Yasukawa (1993) and

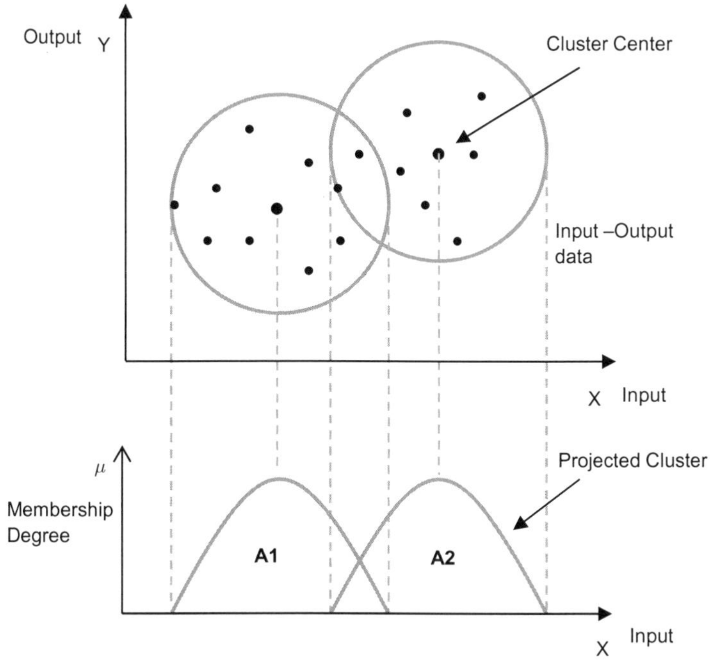

Figure 4.22: Fuzzy clusters and their interpretation as membership functions.

Emami *et al.* (1998) used fuzzy clustering to cluster the output data and then these clusters are projected on to the input coordinate axes in order to generate linguistic fuzzy rules. For fuzzy system with TSK type rules, the common approach is to apply clustering in the input–output data and projecting the clusters on to the input variables coordinate to determine the premise part of the rule in terms of input fuzzy sets (Babuška and Verbruggen, 1996; Zhao *et al.*, 1994; Chiu, 1994) (Figure 4.22). Each of the clusters give rise to local regression models and the overall model is then structured into a set of *if-then* rules. The consequent parameters of such rules may be estimated separately by using methods like least squares method. Some authors have used clustering only on the input data and combined the results with a TSK-like consequent (Wang and Langari, 1994). While others have applied clustering separately to each input and output data for fuzzy modeling in terms of fuzzy relational equations (Pedrycz, 1984).

In the following example, we demonstrate the generation of rules using subtractive clustering method. Subtractive clustering is an improved version of mountain method for cluster estimation. One of the advantages of mountain method and subtractive clustering method over fuzzy *c*-means is that the former methods do not require specification of number of clusters (or number rules) by the user before the clustering process begins. In subtractive clustering data points are considered as potential clusters. The method assumes normalized data points bounded by a hypercube. For every data point, a *potential* value is calculated as given in Equation (18), and the point with the highest potential value is selected as the first cluster center.

$$P(\mathbf{x}_k) = \sum_{i=1}^{N} e^{-\alpha \|\mathbf{x}_k - \mathbf{x}_i\|^2}, \tag{18}$$

where $\mathbf{x}_k$ is the kth data point, $k = 1, 2, 3, \ldots, N$, and $\alpha = \frac{4}{r_a^2}$, r_a is a positive constant.

The potential value is dependent on the distance of the data point to all other data points, i.e., the larger the number of neighboring data points the higher is the potential. The constant r_a defines the neighborhood of a data point and the data points outside the neighborhood do not have significant influence on the potential value. After the first cluster center is identified, in the next step the potential of all data points is reduced by an amount that is dependent on their distance to the cluster center. The revised potential of each data point is given by Equation (19). So, the points closer to the cluster center have less chance to be selected as next cluster center. Now, the next cluster center is the point with the remaining maximum potential.

$$P(\mathbf{x}_k) = P(\mathbf{x}_k) - P_1^* e^{-\beta \|\mathbf{x}_k - \mathbf{x}_1^*\|^2}, \tag{19}$$

where $\mathbf{x}_1^*$ is the first cluster center and P_1^* is its potential value, and $\beta = \frac{4}{r_b^2}$, r_b is a positive constant.

The constant r_b is the radius defining the neighborhood that will have measureable reductions in potential. To obtain cluster centers that are not too close to each other, r_b is set to a value greater than r_a.

The process of selection of cluster centers based on the potential values and subsequent reduction of potential values of each of the data points continues till the following conditions are satisfied:

if $P_k^* > uP_1^*$ ***then*** *accept* x_k^* *as a cluster center and continue,*
    else if $P_k^* < vP_1^*$ ***then*** *reject* x_k^* *and end the clustering process,*
  else *let* d_{min} *be the minimum distance between* x_k^* *and all existing cluster centers.*
      if $\frac{d_{min}}{r_a} + \frac{P_k^*}{P_1^*} \geq 1$ ***then*** *accept* x_k^* *as a cluster center and continue,*
        else *reject* x_k^* *and set the potential at* x_k^* *to* 0,
        select the data point with the next highest potential as the new x_k^*
          and retest.
      end if
    end if
end if

Here, u is a threshold potential value above which the data point is definitely accepted as a cluster center, and a data point is rejected if the potential is lower than the threshold v. If the potential falls within u and v, then it is checked if the data point provides a good trade-off between having a sufficient potential and is not close to any existing cluster centers.

Example 4.1. Let us consider the input–output data from the cooling fan system provided in Table 4.4. Subtractive clustering assumes normalized data for clustering, which is given in Table 4.5. We assume Gaussian membership functions and TSK-type fuzzy rules.

The antecedent parameters of Gaussian membership function (c, σ) are identified by subtractive clustering and the consequent parameters are determined using RLS approach. First, subtractive clustering is applied to input–output data with the value of radius parameter set to $r_a = 0.5$. The rest of the user-defined input parameters are set to their default values, $r_b = 1.5r_a$, $u = 0.5$, and $v = 0.15$ (Chiu, 1997). The σ value is determined as, $\sigma^2 = 1/(2\alpha)$. The clustering resulted in six clusters with cluster centers and the range of influence as shown in Table 4.16. Figure 4.23 shows the cluster centers and the range of influence considering the two input variables. The number of clusters corresponds to number of fuzzy rules. As we have initialized the neighborhood parameter with same values for each of the data dimension so subtractive clustering returns same sigma values (radius) in each of the data dimensions. In Table 4.16, the sigma value is represented with a scalar. Also note that it returns same sigma values for each of the clusters. While

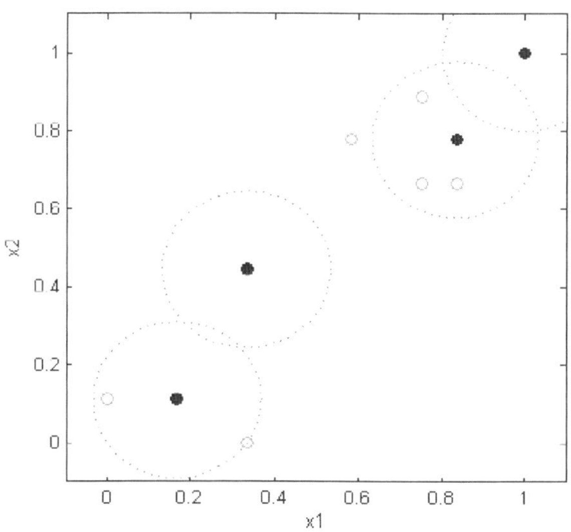

Figure 4.23: Cluster centers obtained by subtractive clustering (black dots indicate cluster centers).

Table 4.16: Cluster centers and corresponding radii.

x_1	x_2	y	*radius*
0.83	0.78	0.67	0.18
0.17	0.11	0	0.18
0.33	0.44	0.5	0.18
1.0	1.0	1.0	0.18

considering the antecedent parameters we neglect the cluster output dimension, i.e., only the values in the columns 1, 2, and 4 of Table 4.16 are considered as c and σ respectively. The input fuzzy sets based on the cluster centers and respective range of influences are shown in Figure 4.24.

In the next step, the consequent parameters are determined using the least square estimate method. The resulting parameters are shown in Table 4.17.

Therefore, the rules generated using the subtractive clustering method can be given as:

$$\textbf{\textit{Rule 1}} : \textbf{\textit{if}}\ x_1\ is\ A_1\ \textbf{\textit{and}}\ x_2\ is\ B_1\ \textbf{\textit{then}}\ y_1 = -3.39 + 5.37x_1 - 0.35x_2.$$

$$\textbf{\textit{Rule 2}} : \textbf{\textit{if}}\ x_1\ is\ A_2\ \textbf{\textit{and}}\ x_2\ is\ B_2\ \textbf{\textit{then}}\ y_2 = 0.06 + 2.39x_1 + 1.93x_2.$$

$$\textbf{\textit{Rule 3}} : \textbf{\textit{if}}\ x_1\ is\ A_3\ \textbf{\textit{and}}\ x_2\ is\ B_3\ \textbf{\textit{then}}\ y_3 = -8.45 + 19.85x_2.$$

$$\textbf{\textit{Rule 4}} : \textbf{\textit{if}}\ x_1\ is\ A_4\ \textbf{\textit{and}}\ x_2\ is\ B_4\ \textbf{\textit{then}}\ y_4 = -9.25x_1 + 10.07x_2.$$

It should be noted that the antecedent parameter obtained using clustering can further be tuned using neural networks or GAs as discussed in previous sections.

4.4. Online Approaches

Online approaches can also be categorized under automated modeling approaches, however the FRB systems that are developed using these approaches have some interesting characteristics as discussed here. So far we have discussed the modeling of fuzzy systems that have fixed structure. Though we have mentioned the design of adaptive systems like ANFIS, such systems are adaptive in terms of parameters and not the structure. By fixed structure, we mean the number of rules in the rule-base and the number of fuzzy membership functions are fixed during the design process. The clustering methods like mountain clustering and subtractive clustering when applied to the design process do not require to specify the number of clusters (i.e., number of rules) beforehand. They assume that the entire data is present in the memory and iteratively delineates the clusters. The manner in which the rules are learnt is often referred to as *offline* or *batch* mode where the learning algorithm performs multiple iterations over the data to finally determine a fixed set of rules. However, due to

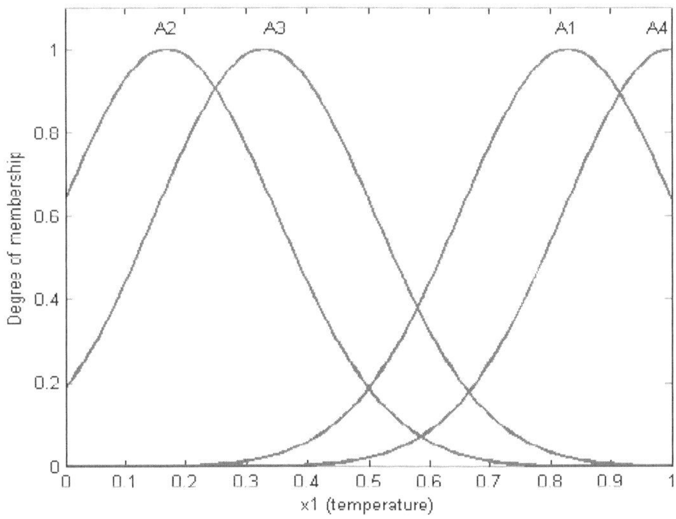

(a) Input fuzzy sets (x_1)

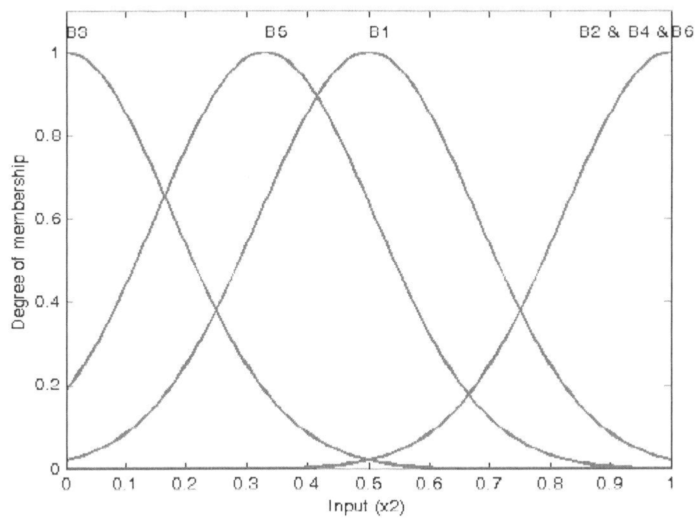

(b) Input fuzzy sets (x_2)

Figure 4.24: Input fuzzy sets formed from the cluster centers and radii obtained from subtractive clustering.

Table 4.17: Consequent parameters.

a_0	a_1	a_2
−3.39	5.37	−0.35
0.06	2.39	1.93
−8.45	0	19.85
0	−9.25	10.07

the static nature of the rule-base, the resulting system cannot handle any deviations in the input data which may be due to changes in the operating environment over time. Such changes cannot be incorporated in the rule-base or existing model unless the entire design process is repeated with the new data and the whole system is re-modeled.

In the present scenario, the overabundance of data due to the technological advancement poses new challenges for the fuzzy system design. The application such as packet monitoring in the IP network, monitoring chemical process, real time surveillance systems and sensor networks, etc. generate data continuously at high speed that often evolve with time, commonly referred to as *data streams*, inhibit the application of conventional approaches to fuzzy system design. Learning rules from such type of data require the method to be fast and memory efficient. To attain real-time or online response, the processing time per data sample should be a small constant amount of time to keep up with their speed of arrival, and the memory requirements should not increase appreciably with the progress of the data stream. Another requirement for a data stream learning approach is to be adaptive and robust to noise. The approach should be able to adapt the model structure and parameters in the presence of deviation so as to give an up-to-date model. In a streaming environment, it is difficult to distinguish noise from data shift. Noisy data can interfere with the learning process, for example, a greedy learning approach that adapts itself as soon as it sees a change in the data pattern may over-fit noise by mistakenly interpreting it as new data. On the other hand, if it is too conservative and slow to adapt, it may fail to incorporate important changes.

To meet such requirements, the area of *evolving fuzzy systems* (EFSs) emerged that focuses on *online* learning of fuzzy models that are capable of adapting autonomously to changes in the data pattern (Angelov, 1999, 2000, 2002; Angelov and Buswell, 2001, 2002; Kasabov, 1998a, 1998b). Typically, an EFS learns autonomously without much user intervention in an online mode by analyzing each incoming sample, and adjusting both model structure and parameters. The online working mode of EFS involves a sequence of 'predict' and 'update' phases. In the prediction phase, when an input sample is received, it is fuzzified using the membership function and the output is estimated using the existing fuzzy rules and inference mechanism. Finally, the output is determined and defuzzified. The update (or learning) phase occurs when the actual output for the given input is received. During the update phase, the rule-base is updated through the learning module using the actual output and the previously estimated output. In the update phase usually an online clustering is applied on a per sample basis (or sometimes on a chunk of data). Upon receiving the output for the current input data sample, the online clustering process determines if a new cluster is required to be formed (with the current data sample as the cluster center) or an existing cluster is required to be modified in terms of shift of the existing cluster center or change in the range of influence of the existing cluster center. If a new cluster is generated then it in turn generates a new rule corresponding to that or if an existing cluster is updated then fuzzy sets of the corresponding rule get updated. After the update of antecedent parameters, the consequent parameters are updated using recursive least square method. Some of the online structure identification techniques that have been successfully applied to EFS design are evolving Clustering (eClustering) (Angelov and Filev, 2004), evolving Vector Quantization (eVQ) (Lughofer, 2008), Evolving Clustering Method (ECM) (Kasabov and Song, 2002), online Gustafsson–Kessel algorithm (Georgieva and Filev, 2009), evolving Participatory Learning (ePL) (Lima *et al.*, 2006), and Dynamically Evolving Clustering (DEC) (Baruah and Angelov, 2014).

4.5. Summary

In this chapter, we presented various approaches to fuzzy system modeling. The early design approaches were solely based on expert knowledge. The knowledge-based approach is easy to implement for simple systems. The chapter has described the knowledge-based method for fuzzy modeling with illustrative examples and guidelines. Though the knowledge-based method is simple, it is not suitable for complex systems and has several limitations. For example, one expert may not have the complete knowledge or understanding of a particular system, in such a scenario multiple experts are consulted. Finally, integrating the views of all the experts into a single system can be difficult, particularly when the views are conflicting. Also, if the expert knowledge about the system is faulty then the resulting model will be incorrect leading to undesirable results. Due to such reasons and availability of input–output data, automated methods are more preferred over knowledge-based methods. However, automated methods do not completely eliminate expert's involvement. When sufficient input–output data are available, the automated methods can be applied in three levels: (i) only to tune the antecedent and consequent parameters with fixed rules, (ii) to learn the rules with predefined membership functions and fuzzy sets, (iii) to learn both rules and parameters. The chapter has described various automated methods that have been applied at all the three levels. First, it described the template-based methods that works at level (ii), then it presented the neuro-fuzzy approach and described its application at level (i). The chapter discussed application of GAs to fuzzy system design at all the three levels. Finally, clustering-based approach has been explained that is applied at level (iii). The chapter has also provided a brief discussion on online modeling approaches. Over the past decade this area has received enormous attention from the researchers due to its applicability to various application domains that include robotics, process control, image processing, speech processing, bioinformatics, and finance. Readers interested in this area are encouraged to refer (Angelov *et al.*, 2010; Angelov, 2012; Lughofer, 2011).

References

Angelov, P. (1999). Evolving fuzzy rule-based models. In *Proc. Eighth Int. Fuzzy Syst. Assoc. World Congr.* Taipei, Taiwan, 1, pp. 19–23.

Angelov, P. (2000). Evolving fuzzy rule-based models. *J. Chin. Inst. Ind. Eng.*, 17, pp. 459–468.

Angelov, P. (2002). *Evolving Rule-Based Models: A Tool for Design of Flexible Adaptive Systems.* Heidelberg: Physica-Verlag.

Angelov, P. (2012). *Autonomous Learning Systems: From Data Streams to Knowledge in Real-time.* Chichester, UK: John Wiley & Sons.

Angelov, P. and Buswell, R. (2001). Evolving rule-based models: a tool for intelligent adaptation. In Smith, M. H., Gruver, W. A. and Hall, L. O. (eds.), *Proc. Ninth Int. Fuzzy Syst. Assoc. World Congr.* Vancouver, Canada, 1–5, pp. 1062–1067.

Angelov, P. and Buswell, R. (2002). Identification of evolving fuzzy rule-based models. *IEEE Trans. Fuzzy Syst.*, 10(5), pp. 667–677.

Angelov, P. and Filev, D. P. (2004). An approach to online identification of Takagi–Sugeno fuzzy models. *IEEE Trans. Syst., Man, Cybern., Part B-Cybern.*, 34(1), pp. 484–498.

Angelov, P., Filev, D. and Kasabov, N. (eds.). (2010). *Evolving Intelligent Systems: Methodology and Applications. IEEE Press Series on Computational Intelligence.* Hoboken, NJ: John Wiley & Sons.

Babuška, R. and Verbruggen, H. B. (1996). An overview of fuzzy modeling for control. *Control Eng. Pract.*, 4(11), 1593–1606.

Baruah, R. D. and Angelov, P. (2014). DEC: Dynamically evolving clustering and its application to structure identification of evolving fuzzy models. *IEEE Trans. Cybern.*, 44(9), pp. 1619–1631.

Beliakov, G. and Warren, J. (2001). Appropriate choice of aggregation operators in fuzzy decision support systems. *IEEE Trans. Fuzzy Syst.*, 9(6), pp. 773–784.

Bezdek, J. (1981). *Pattern Recognition with Fuzzy Objective Function Algorithms.* New York: Plenum Press.

Chiu, S. L. (1994). Fuzzy model identification based on cluster estimation. *J. Intell. Fuzzy Syst.*, 2, pp. 267–278.

Chiu, S. L. (1997). Extracting fuzzy rules from data for function approximation and pattern classification. In Dubois, D., Prade, H. and Yager, R. (eds.), *Fuzzy Information Engineering: A Guided Tour of Applications.* Hoboken, NJ: John Wiley & Sons.

Cordon, O., Herrera, F. and Peregrin, A. (1997). Applicability of the fuzzy operators in the design of fuzzy logic controllers. *Fuzzy Sets Syst.*, 86(1), pp. 15–41.

Cordón, O., Gomide, F., Herrera, F., Hoffmann, F. and Magdalena, L. (2004). Ten years of genetic fuzzy systems: current framework and new trends. *Fuzzy Sets Syst.*, 141(1), pp. 5–31.

de Oliveira, J. V. and Pedrycz, W. (eds.). (2007). *Advances in Fuzzy Clustering and its Applications.* Hoboken, NJ: Wiley.

Dunn, J. C. (1974). A fuzzy relative of the ISODATA process and its use in detecting compact, well-separated clusters. *J. Cybern.*, 3, pp. 32–57.

Emami, M. R., Turksen, I. B. and Goldenberg, A. A. (1998). Development of a systematic methodology of fuzzy logic modeling. *IEEE Trans. Fuzzy Syst.*, 6, pp. 346–361.

Georgieva, O. and Filev, D. (2009). Gustafsson–Kessel algorithm for evolving data stream clustering. In *Proc. Int. Conf. Comput. Syst. Technol.*, 3B, pp. 14–16.

Goldberg, D. E. (1989). *Genetic Algorithms in Search, Optimization and Machine Learning*. Boston, MA, USA: Addison-Wesley Longman Publishing Co., Inc.

Gustafsson, D. and Kessel, W. (1979). Fuzzy clustering with a fuzzy covariance matrix. In *Proc. IEEE CDC*, San Diego, California. Piscataway, New Jersey: IEEE Press, pp. 761–766.

Hastie, T., Tibshirani, R. and Friedman, J. (2009). *The Elements of Statistical Learning Data Mining, Inference, and Prediction, Second Edition*. Heidelberg: Springer.

Hellendoorn, H. and Thomas, C. (1993). Defuzzification in fuzzy controllers. *J. Intell. Fuzzy Syst.*, 1, pp. 109–123.

Holland, J. H. and Reitman, J. S. (1978). Cognitive systems based on adaptive algorithms. In Waterman, D. A. and Roth, F. H. (eds.), *Pattern-Directed Inference Systems*. Waltham, MA: Academic Press.

Jang, J.-S. R. (1993). ANFIS: adaptive-network-based fuzzy inference system. *IEEE Trans. Syst., Man, Cybern.*, 23(3), pp. 665–685.

Kasabov, N. (1998a). ECOS: A framework for evolving connectionist systems and the ECO learning paradigm. In Usui, S. and Omori, T. (eds.), *Proc. Fifth Int. Conf. Neural Inf. Process.*, Kitakyushu, Japan: IOS Press, 1–3, pp. 1232–1235.

Kasabov, N. (1998b). The ECOS framework and the ECO learning method for evolving connectionist system. *J. Adv. Comput. Intell.*, 2(6), pp. 195–202.

Kasabov, N. and Song, Q. (2002). DENFIS: dynamic evolving neural-fuzzy inference system and its application for time-series prediction. *IEEE Trans. Fuzzy Syst.*, 10(2), pp. 144–154.

Kinzel, J., Klawonn, F. and Kruse, R. (1994). Modifications of genetic algorithms for designing and optimizing fuzzy controllers. In *Proc. First IEEE Conf., IEEE World Congr. Comput. Intell., Evol. Comput.*, 1, pp. 28–33.

Klawonn, F. (1994). Fuzzy sets and vague environments. *Fuzzy Sets Syst.*, 66, pp. 207–221.

Kruse, R., Gebhardt, J. and Klawonn, F. (1994). *Foundations of Fuzzy Systems*. Chichester: Wiley.

Lima, E., Gomide, F. and Ballini, R. (2006). Participatory evolving fuzzy modeling. In Angelov, P., Filev, D., Kasabov, N. and Cordon, O. (eds.), *Proc. Int. Symp. Evolving Fuzzy Syst.* Ambleside, Lake District, U.K.: IEEE Press, pp. 36–41.

Liska, J. and Melsheimer, S. S. (1994). Complete design of fuzzy logic systems using genetic algorithms. In *Proc. Third IEEE Conf., IEEE World Congr. Comput. Intell., Fuzzy Syst.*, 2, pp. 1377–1382.

Lughofer, E. D. (2008). Extensions of vector quantization for incremental clustering. *Pattern Recognit.*, 41(3), pp. 995–1011.

Lughofer, E. (2011). *Evolving Fuzzy Systems: Methodologies, Advanced Concepts and Applications*. Berlin Heidelberg: Springer Verlag.

Mamdani, E. H. (1997). Application of fuzzy logic to approximate reasoning using linguistic systems. *Fuzzy Sets Syst.*, 26, pp. 1182–1191.

Mitra, S. and Hayashi, Y. (2000). Neuro-fuzzy rule generation: survey in soft computing framework. *IEEE Trans. Neural Netw.*, 11(3), pp. 748, 768.

Pedrycz, W. (1984). An identification algorithm in fuzzy relational systems. *Fuzzy Sets Syst.*, 13(2), pp. 153–167.

Ross, T. (2010). *Fuzzy Logic with Engineering Applications*. New York: McGraw-Hill.

Smith, S. F. (1980). *A Learning System Based Genetic Adaptive Algorithms*. Doctoral dissertation. University of Pittsburgh, PA, USA: Department of Computer Science.

Sugeno, M. and Yasukawa, T. (1993). A fuzzy-logic based approach to qualitative modeling. *IEEE Trans. Fuzzy Syst.*, 1, pp. 7–31.

Takagi, T. and Sugeno, M. (1985). Fuzzy identification of systems and its application to modeling and control. *IEEE Trans. Syst., Man, Cybern*, 15(1), pp. 116–132.

Thrift, P. (1991). Fuzzy logic synthesis with genetic algorithms. In Rechard, K. B. and Lashon, B. B. (eds.), *Proc. Fourth Int. Conf. Genet. Algorithms*. San Diego, USA: Morgan Kaufman, pp. 509–513.

Venturini, G. (1993). SIA: A supervised inductive algorithm with genetic search for learning attributes based concepts. In Pavel, B. B. (ed.), *Proc. Eur. Conf. Mach. Learn.* London, UK: Springer, pp. 280–296.

Wang, L.-X. and Mendel, J. M. (1992). Generating fuzzy rules by learning from examples. *IEEE Trans. Syst. Man Cybern.*, 22(6), pp. 1414–1427.

Wang, L. and Langari, R. (1994). Complex systems modeling via fuzzy logic. In *Proc. 33rd IEEE Conf. Decis. Control,* 4, Florida, USA, pp. 4136–4141.

Yager, R. R. and Filev, D. P. (1993). Learning of fuzzy rules by mountain clustering. In Bruno, B. and James C. B. (eds.), *Proc. SPIE Conf. Appl. Fuzzy Log. Technol.* Boston, MA, pp. 246–254.

Yager, R. R. and Filev, D. P. (1994). Approximate cluster via the mountain method. *IEEE Trans. Syst., Man, Cybern.*, 24(8), pp. 1279–1284.

Zhao, J., Wertz, V. and Gorez, R. (1994). A fuzzy clustering method for the identification of fuzzy models for dynamical systems. In *Proc. Ninth IEEE Int. Symp. Intell. Control*, Columbus, Ohio, USA: IEEE, pp. 172–177.

Chapter 5

Fuzzy Classifiers

Abdelhamid Bouchachia

Fuzzy classifiers as a class of classification systems have witnessed a lot of developments over many years now by various communities. Their main strengths stem from their transparency to human users and their capabilities to handle uncertainty often present in real-world data. Like with other classification systems, the construction of fuzzy classifiers follows the same development lifecycle. During training, in particular fuzzy classification rules are developed and undergo an optimization process before the classifier is tested and deployed. The first part of the present chapter overviews this process in detail and highlights the various optimization techniques dedicated to fuzzy rule-based systems. The second part of the chapter discusses a particular facet of research, that is, online learning of fuzzy classification systems. Throughout the chapter, a good review of the related literature is covered to highlight the various research directions of fuzzy classifiers.

5.1. Introduction

Over the recent years, fuzzy rule-based classification systems have emerged as a new class of attractive classifiers due to their transparency and interpretability characteristics. Motivated by such characteristics, fuzzy classifiers have been used in various applications such as smart homes (Bouchachia, 2011; Bouchachia and Vanaret, 2013), image classification (Thiruvenkadam *et al.*, 2006), medical applications (Tan *et al.*, 2007), pattern recognition (Toscano and Lyonnet, 2003), etc.

Classification rules are simple consisting of two parts: the premises (conditions) and consequents that correspond to class labels as shown in the following:

$$\text{Rule 1} := \text{If } x_l \text{ is small then Class 1}$$
$$\text{Rule 2} := \text{If } x_l \text{ is large then Class 2}$$
$$\text{Rule 3} := \text{If } x_l \text{ is medium and } x_2 \text{ is very small then Class 1}$$
$$\text{Rule 4} := \text{If } x_2 \text{ is very large then Class 2}$$

Rules may be associated with degrees of confidence that explains how good the rule covers a particular input region:

$$\text{Rule 5} := \text{If } x_1 \text{ is small then Class 1 with confidence 0.8}$$

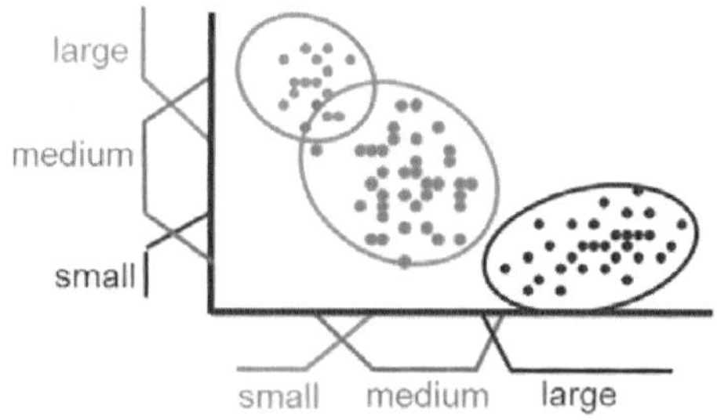

Figure 5.1: Two-dimensional illustrative example of specifying the antecedent part of a fuzzy if-then rule.

Graphically, the rules partition the space into regions. Ideally, each region is covered by one rule as shown in Figure 5.1. Basically, there are two main approaches for designing fuzzy rule-based classifiers:

- Human expertise: The rules are explicitly proposed by the human expert. Usually, no tuning is required and the rules are used for predicting the classes of the input using certain inference steps (see Section 5.3).
- Machine generated: The standard way of building rule-based classifiers is to apply an automatic process which consists of certain steps: partitioning of the input space, finding the fuzzy sets of the rules' premisses and associating class labels as consequents. To predict the label of an input, an inference process is applied. Usually additional steps are involved, especially for optimizing the rule base (Fazzolari *et al.*, 2013).

Fuzzy classifiers come in the form of explicit if-then classification rules as illustrated earlier. However, rules can also be encoded in neural networks resulting in neuro-fuzzy architectures (Kasabov, 1996). Moreover, different computational intelligence techniques have been used to develop fuzzy classifiers: evolutionary algorithms (Fazzolari *et al.*, 2013), rough sets (Shen and Chouchoulas, 2002), ant colony systems (Ganji and Abadeh, 2011), immune systems (Alatas and Akin, 2005), particle swarm optimization (Rani and Deepa, 2010), petri nets (Chen *et al.*, 2002), etc. These computational approaches are used for both design and optimizations of the classifier's rules.

5.2. Pattern Classification

The problem of pattern classification can be formally defined as follows. Let $T = \{(\boldsymbol{x}_i, y_i)_{i=i,\ldots,N}\}$ be a set of training patterns. Each $\boldsymbol{x}_i = (x_{i1}, \ldots, x_{id}) \in X$ is a d-dimensional vector and $y_i \in Y = \{y_1, \ldots, y_C\}$, where Y denotes a discrete set of classes (i.e., labels). A classifier is inherently characterized by a decision function $f \colon X \to Y$ that is used to predict the class label y_i for each pattern $\boldsymbol{x}_i$. The decision function is learned from the training data patterns T drawn i.i.d. at random according to an unknown distribution from the space $X \times Y$. An accurate classifier has very small generalization error (i.e., it generalizes well to unseen patterns). In general, a loss (cost) is associated with errors, meaning that some misclassification errors are "worst" than others. Such a loss is expressed formally as a function $\ell(\boldsymbol{x}_i, y_i, f(\boldsymbol{x}_i))$ which can take different forms (e.g., 0–1, hinge, squared hinge, etc.) (Duda *et al.*, 2001). Ideally the classifier (i.e., decision function) should minimize the expected error $E(f)$ (known as the empirical risk)$= (1/N)\sum_{i=1}^{N} \ell(\boldsymbol{x}_i, y_i, f(\boldsymbol{x}_i))$. Hence, the aim is to learn a function f among a set of all functions that minimizes the error $E(f)$. The empirical risk may be regularized by putting additional constraints (terms) to restrain the function space, penalize the number of parameters and model complexity and avoid overfitting (which occurs when the classifier does not generalize well on unseen data). The regularized risk is then: $R(f) = E(f) + \lambda\Omega(f)$.

Classifiers can be either linear or nonlinear. A linear classifier (i.e., the decision function is linear and the classes are linearly separable) has the form: $y_i = g(\boldsymbol{w}\cdot\boldsymbol{x}_i) = g(\sum_j w_j x_{ij})$ where $\boldsymbol{w}$ is a weight vector computed by learning from the training patterns. The function g outputs discrete values $\{1, -1\}$ or $\{0, 1\}$ which indicate the classes. Clearly the argument of decision function, $f = \sum_j w_j x_{ij}$, is a linear combination of the input and the weight vectors.

Linear classifiers are of types: discriminative or generative. The discriminative linear classifiers try to minimize R (or its simplest version E) without necessarily caring about the way the (training) patterns are generated. Examples of discriminative linear classifiers are: perceptron, support vector machines (SVM) and logistic regression and linear discriminant analysis (LDA).

Generative classifiers aim at learning a model of the joint probability $p(\boldsymbol{x}, y)$ over the data X and the labels Y. They aim at inferring class-conditional densities $p(\boldsymbol{x}|y)$ and priors $p(y)$. The prediction decision is made by exploiting the Bayes' rule to compute $p(y|\boldsymbol{x})$ and then by selecting the label with the higher probability. The discriminative classifiers on the other hand aim at computing $p(y|\boldsymbol{x})$ directly from the pairs $(x_i, y_i)_{i=1\ldots N}$. Examples of generative linear classifiers are: probabilistic linear discriminant analysis (LDA) and the naive Bayes classifier.

Nonlinear classifiers (i.e., the decision function is not linear and can be quadratic, exponential, etc.). The straitforward formulation of nonlinear classifiers is the generalized linear classifier which tries to nonlinearly map the input space onto another space ($X \subset \mathbb{R}^d \to Z \subset \mathbb{R}^K$), where the patterns are separable. Thus, $\boldsymbol{x} \in \mathbb{R}^d \mapsto \boldsymbol{x} \in \mathbb{R}^K$, $z = [f_1(\boldsymbol{x}), \ldots, f_K(\boldsymbol{x})]^T$ where f_k is a nonlinear function (e.g., log-sigmoid, tan-sigmoid, etc.). The decision function is then of the form: $y_i = g(\sum_k w_k f_k(x_i))$.

There are many nonlinear classification algorithms of different types such as generalized linear classifiers, multilayer perceptron, polynomial classifiers, radial basis function networks, etc., nonlinear SVM (kernels), k-nearest neighbor, rule-based classifiers (e.g., decision trees, fuzzy rule-based classifiers, different hybrid neuro-genetic-fuzzy classifiers), etc. (Duda *et al.*, 2001).

We can also distinguish between two classes of classifiers: symbolic and sub-symbolic classifiers. The symbolic classifiers are those that learn the decision function in the form of rules:

$$\textbf{If } x_{i1} \text{ is } A \text{ and } x_{i2} \text{ is } B \text{ and } \cdots \; x_{id} \text{ is } Z \quad \textbf{then} \text{ class is } C. \tag{1}$$

The advantage of this class of classifiers is their transparency and interpretability of their behavior. The sub-symbolic classifiers are those that do not operate on symbols and could be seen as black box.

5.3. Fuzzy Rule-Based Classification Systems

Fuzzy rule-based systems represent knowledge in the form of fuzzy "IF-THEN" rules. These rules can be either encoded by human experts or extracted from raw data by an inductive learning process. Generically, a fuzzy rule has the form:

$$R_r \equiv \text{If } x_1 \textit{ is } A_{r,1} \wedge \cdots \wedge x_d \textit{ is } A_{r,d} \quad \text{then } y_r \tag{2}$$

where $\{x_i\}_{i=1\cdots d}$ are fuzzy linguistic input variables, $A_{r,i}$ are antecedent linguistic terms in the form of fuzzy sets that characterize x_i and y_r is the output. This form can take different variations. However, the most known ones are: Mamdani-type, Takagi–Sugeno type and classification type. The former two ones have been introduced in the context of fuzzy control. Specifically, a rule of *Mamdani-type* has the following structure:

$$\text{If } x_1 \textit{ is } A_{r,1} \wedge \cdots \wedge x_d \textit{ is } A_{r,d} \quad \text{then } y_1 \textit{ is } B_{r,1} \wedge \cdots \wedge y_m \textit{ is } B_{r,m}, \tag{3}$$

where x_i are fuzzy linguistic input variables, y_j are fuzzy linguistic output variables, and $A_{r,i}$ and $B_{r,j}$ are linguistic terms in the form of fuzzy sets that characterize x_i and y_j. The Mamdani's model is known for its transparency since all of the rule's terms are linguistic terms.

The *Takagi–Sugeno type* (T–S) differs from the Mamdani-type model at the rule consequent level. In a T–S rule type, the consequent is a combination of the inputs as shown in Equation (4):

$$\text{If } x_1 \text{ is } A_{r,1} \wedge \cdots \wedge x_d \text{ is } A_{r,d} \quad \text{then} \begin{cases} y_{r,1} = f_{r,1}(x) \\ \cdots \\ y_{r,m} = f_{r,m}(x) \end{cases}. \tag{4}$$

A rule consists of d input fuzzy variables $(x_1, x_2, \ldots, x_d)$ and m output variables $(y_1, y_2, \ldots, y_m)$ such that $y_{r,j} = f_{r,j}(\boldsymbol{x})$. The most popular form of f is the polynomial form: $y_{r,j} = f_{r,j}(\boldsymbol{x}) = b^1_{r,j}x_1 + \cdots + b^d_{r,j}x_d + b^0_{r,j}$, where $b^i_{.,j}$'s denote the system's $m+1$ output parameters. These parameters are usually determined using iterative optimization methods. T–S-type FRS are used to approximate nonlinear systems by a set of linear systems.

In this chapter, we focus on classification systems where a rule looks as follows:

$$\text{If } x_1 \text{ is } A_{r,1}, \wedge \cdots \wedge x_d \text{ is } A_{r,d} \quad \text{then } y_r \text{ is } C_r[\tau_r], \tag{5}$$

where C_r, τ_r indicate respectively the class label and the certainty factor associated with the rule r. A certainty factor represents the confidence degree of assigning the input to a class C_r, i.e., how good the rule covers the space of a class C_r. For a rule r, it is expressed as follows (Ishibuchi and Yamamoto, 2005):

$$\tau_r = \frac{\sum_{x_i \in C_r} \mu_{A_r}(\boldsymbol{x}_i)}{\sum_{i=1}^{N} \mu_{A_r}(\boldsymbol{x}_i)}, \tag{6}$$

where $\mu_{A_r}(\boldsymbol{x}_i)$ is obtained as follows:

$$\mu_{A_r}(\boldsymbol{x}_i) = \prod_{p=1}^{d} \mu A_{r,p}(x_{ip}). \tag{7}$$

Equation (7) uses the product, but can also use any t-norm: $\mu_{A_r}(\boldsymbol{x}_i) = T(\mu_{A_{r,1}}(x_{i1}), \ldots, \mu_{A_{r,d}}(x_{id}))$. Moreover, the rule in Equation (5) could be generalized to multi-classes consequent to account for class distribution and in particular overlap

$$\text{If } x_1 \text{ is } A_{r,1} \wedge \cdots \wedge x_d \text{ is } A_{r,d} \quad \text{then } y_r \text{ is } C_1[\tau_1], \ldots, C_\kappa[\tau_\kappa]. \tag{8}$$

This formulation was adopted in particular in (Bouchachia and Mittermeir, 2007), where τ_j's correspond to the proportion of patterns of each class in the region covered by the rule j.

Note also that the rule's form in Equation (5) could be seen as a special case of the Sugueno-type fuzzy rule model, in particular the zero-order model, where the consequent is a singleton.

Furthermore, there exists another type of fuzzy classification systems based on multidimensional fuzzy sets, where rules are expressed in the form (Bouchachia, 2011):

$$R_r \equiv \text{If } \boldsymbol{x} \text{ is } K_i \text{ then } y_r \text{ is } C_j, \tag{9}$$

where K_i is a cluster. The rule means that if the sample x is CLOSE to K_j then the label of x should be that of class C_j.

Classes in the consequent part of the rules can be determined following two options:

- The generation of the fuzzy sets (partitions) is done using supervised clustering. That is, each partition will be labeled and will emanate from one class. In this case, certainty factors associated with the rules will be needless (Bouchachia and Mittermeir, 2007; Bouchachia, 2011; Bouchachia and Vanaret, 2013).
- The generation of the fuzzy sets is done using clustering, so that partitions can contain patterns from different classes at the same time. In this case, a special process is required to determine the rule consequents. Following the procedure described in (Ishibuchi and Nojima, 2007), the consequent is found as follows

$$y_r = \arg\max_{j=1\cdots C}\{v_j\}, \tag{10}$$

where v_j is given as:

$$v_j = \sum_{x_k \in C_r} \mu_r(\boldsymbol{x}_k) = \sum_{x_k \in C_r} \left(\prod_{p=1}^{d} \mu_{A_{r,p}}(x_{ip}) \right). \tag{11}$$

Given a test pattern, $\boldsymbol{x}_k$, entering the system, the output of the fuzzy classifier with respect to this pattern is the winner class, w, referred in the consequent of the rule with the highest activation degree. The winning class is computed as follows:

$$y(\boldsymbol{x}_k) = \arg\max_{j=1\cdots C}\{w_j(\boldsymbol{x}_k)\}, \tag{12}$$

where w_j is given as:

$$w_j(\boldsymbol{x}_k) = \max\left\{\mu_r(\boldsymbol{x}_k) * \tau_r | y_r = j\right\}. \tag{13}$$

If there is more than one winner (taking the same maximum value w_j), then the pattern is considered unclassifiable.

A general fuzzy rule-based system consists mainly of four components: the knowledge base, the inference engine, the fuzzifier and the defuzzifier as shown in Figure 5.2 and briefly described below. Note that generally fuzzy classifiers do not include the defuzzification step, since a fuzzy output is already indicative.

1. The knowledge base consists of a rule-base that holds a collection of fuzzy IF-THEN rules and a database that includes the membership functions defining the fuzzy sets used by the fuzzy rule system.
2. The inference engine maps the input to the rules and computes an aggregated fuzzy output of the system according to an inference method. The common

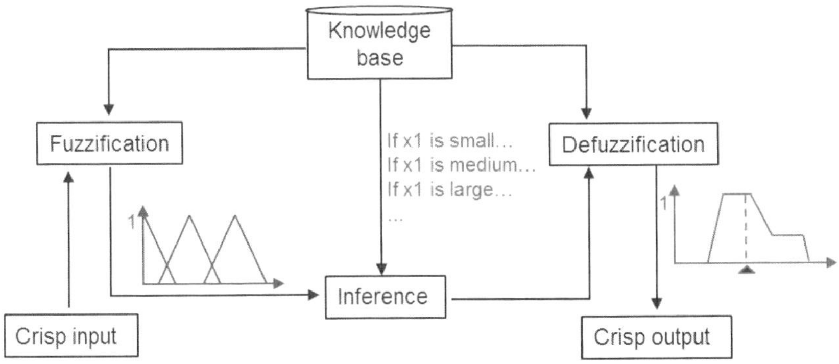

Figure 5.2: Structure of the adaptive fuzzy classifier.

inference method is the Max–Min composition, where rules are first combined with the input before aggregating using some operator (Mamdani, Gödel, etc.) to produce a final output or rules are combined first before acting on the input vector. Typical inference in classification systems is rather simple as explained earlier. It consists of sequentially computing the following degrees: activation [i.e., the product/t-norm of the antecedent part, see Equation (7)], association [i.e., combine the confidence factors with the activation degree to determine association degree of the input with the classes, see Equation (13)], and classification [i.e., choose the class with the highest association degree, see Equation (12)].

3. Fuzzification transforms the crisp input into fuzzy input, by matching the input to the linguistic values in the rules' antecedents. Such values are represented as membership functions (e.g., triangular, trapezoidal and Gaussian) and stored in the database. These functions specify a partitioning of the input and eventually the output space. The number of fuzzy partitions determines that of the rules. There are three types of partitioning: grid, tree, and scatter. The latter is the most common one, since it finds the regions covering the data using clustering. Different clustering algorithms have been used (Vernieuwe *et al.*, 2006). Known algorithms are Gustafson–Kessel and Gath–Geva (Abonyi *et al.*, 2002), mountain (Yager and Filev, 1994), subtractive (Angelov, 2004), fuzzy hierarchical clustering (Tsekouras *et al.*, 2005), and FCM (Bouchachia, 2004).
4. The defuzzifier transforms the aggregated fuzzy output generated by the inference engine into a crisp output because very often a crisp output of the system is required for facilitating decision-making. The known defuzzification methods are: center of area, height-center of area, max criterion, first of maxima, and middle of maxima. However, the most popular method is center of area (Saade and Diab, 2000). Recall that fuzzy classification systems do not necessarily involve defuzzification.

5.4. Quality Issues of Fuzzy Rule-Based Systems

In general, knowledge maintenance entails the activities of knowledge validation, optimization, and evolution. The validation process aims at checking the consistency of knowledge by repairing/removing contradictions. Optimization seeks the compactness of knowledge by alleviating all types of redundancy and rendering the knowledge base transparent. Finally, evolution of knowledge is about incremental learning of knowledge without jeopardizing the old one allowing a continuous and incremental update of the knowledge.

This section aims at discussing the optimization issues of rule-based systems. Optimization in this context deals primarily with the transparency of the rule-base. Given the symbolic representation of rules, the goal is to describe the classifier with a small number of concise rules relying on transparent and inter-pretable fuzzy sets intelligible by human experts. Using data to automatically build the classifier is a process that does not always result in a transparent rule-base (Kuncheva, 2000). Hence, there is a need to optimize the number and the structure of the rules while keeping the classifier accuracy as high as possible (more on this tradeoff will follow in section). Note that beyond classification, the Mamdani model is geared towards more interpretability, hence the name of linguistic fuzzy modeling. Takagi–Sugeno model is geared towards accuracy, hence the name precise fuzzy modeling (Gacto *et al.*, 2011).

Overall, the quality of the rule-base (knowledge) can be evaluated using various criteria: performance, comprehensibility, and completeness which are explained in the following sections.

5.4.1. *Performance*

A classifier, independent of its computational model, is judged on its performance. That is, how well does the classifier perform on unseen novel data? Measuring the performance is about assessing the quality of decision-making.

Accuracy is one of the mostly used measures. It quantifies to which extent the system meets the human being decision. Thus, accuracy measures the ratio of correct decisions. Expressively, $Accuracy = Correct/Test$, where *correct* and *test* indicate respectively the number of patterns well classified (corresponding to true positives + true negatives decisions), while Test is the total number of patterns presented to the classifier). But accuracy as a sole measure for evaluating the performance of the classifier might be misleading in some situations like in the case of imbalanced classes. Obviously, different measures can be used, like precision (positive predictive value), false positive rate (false alarm rate), true positive rate (sensitivity), ROC curves (Fawcett, 2006). It is therefore recommended to use multiple performance measures to objectively evaluate the classifier.

5.4.2. *Completeness*

Knowledge is complete if for making a decision all needed knowledge elements are available. Following the architecture presented in Figure 5.2, the system should have all ingredients needed to classify a pattern. The other aspect of completeness is the coverage of the discourse representation space. That is, all input variables (dimensions) to be considered should be fully covered by the fuzzy sets using *the frame of cognition* (FOC) (Pedrycz and Gomide, 1998), which stipulates that a fuzzy set (patch) along a dimension must satisfy: normality, typicality, full membership, convexity, and overlap.

5.4.3. *Consistency*

Consistency is a key issue in knowledge engineering and is considered as one important aspect of the rule-base comprehensibility assessment. In the absence of consistency, the knowledge is without value and its use leads to contradictory decisions. Inconsistency results from conflicting knowledge elements. For instance, two rules are in conflict if they have identical antecedents but different consequents. In the case of fuzzy rule-based classification, there is no risk to have inconsistency, since each rule corresponds to a given region of the data space. Moreover, even if an overlap between antecedents of various rules exists, the output for a given data point is unambiguously computed using the confidence factors related to each rule in the knowledge base.

5.4.4. *Compactness*

Compactness is about the conciseness and the ease of understanding and reasoning about the knowledge. Systems built on a symbolic ground, like rule-based systems, are easy to understand and to track how and why they reach a particular decision. To reinforce this characteristic, the goal of system design is to reduce, as much as possible, the number of rules to make the system's behavior more transparent. Thus, small number of rules and small number of conditions in the antecedent of rules ensures high compactness of the system's rule-base.

To reduce the complexity of the rule-base and consequently to get rid of redundancy and to strengthen compactness, the optimization procedure can consist of a certain number of steps (Bouchachia and Mittermeir, 2007). All these steps are based on similarity measures.

There are a number of measures based on set-theoretic, proximity, interval, logic, linguistic approximation and fuzzy-valued (Wu and Mendel, 2008). In the following, the optimization steps are described.

- Redundant partitions: They are discovered by computing the similarity of the fuzzy sets describing these partitions to the universe. A fuzzy set $A^r_{i,j}$ is removed if:

$$Sim(A^r_{ij}, U) > \epsilon, \tag{14}$$

where $\epsilon \in (0, 1)$ and indicates a threshold (a required level of similarity), U indicates the universe that is defined as follows:

$$\forall \boldsymbol{x}_k, \mu_U(x_{ki}) = 1.$$

Any pattern has a full membership in the universe of discourse.
- Merge of fuzzy partitions: Two fuzzy partition are merged if their similarity exceeds a certain threshold:

$$Sim(A^r_{ij}, A^r_{ik}) > \tau, \tag{15}$$

where A^r_{ij}, A^r_{ik} are the jth and kth partitions of the feature i in the rule r.
- Removal of weakly firing rules: This consists of identifying rules whose output is always close to 0.

$$\mu^r_i < \beta. \tag{16}$$

β is a threshold close to 0.
- Removal of redundant rules: There is redundancy if the similarity (e.g., overlap) between the antecedents of the rules is high exceeding some threshold δ. The similarity of the antecedents of two rules r and p is given as:

$$sim(A^r, A^p) = \min_{i,i=1,d} \{Sim(A^r_i, A^p_i)\}, \tag{17}$$

where the antecedents A^r and A^p are given by the set of fuzzy partitions representing the d features $A^r = \langle A^r_1, \ldots, A^p_d \rangle$ and $A^r = \langle A^r_1, \ldots, A^r_d \rangle$. That is, similar rules (i.e., having similar antecedents and same consequent) are merged. In doing so, if some rules have the same consequent, the antecedents of those rules can be connected. However, this may result in a conflict if the antecedents are not the same. One can however rely on the following rules of thumb:

  — If, for some set of rules with the same consequent, a variable takes all forms (it belongs to all forms of fuzzy set, e.g., small, medium, large), then such a variable can be removed from the antecedent of that set of rules. In other words, this set of rules is independent of the variable that takes all possible values. This variable corresponds then to "*don't care*". For instance, if we consider Figure 5.3, the rules 1, 3, and 4 are about class C_1 and the input variable x_2 takes all possible linguistic variable. The optimization will replace these rules with a generic rule as shown in Figure 5.4.

	x_1	x_2	x_3	x_4	$Class$
1	S	S	S	S	1
2	M	S	M	M	2
3	S	M	S	S	1
4	S	L	S	S	1
5	M	S	L	M	2

Figure 5.3: Rules in the system's rule-base.

	x_1	x_2	x_3	x_4	$Class$
1	S	S	S	S	1
3	S	M	S	S	1
4	S	L	S	S	1
1'	S	—	S	S	1

Figure 5.4: Combining rules 1, 3 and 4.

	x_1	x_2	x_3	x_4	$Class$
2	M	S	M	M	2
5	M	S	L	M	2
2'	M	S	(M $\vee$ L)	M	2

Figure 5.5: Combining rules 2 and 5.

— If, for some set of rules with the same consequent, a variable takes a subset of all possible forms (e.g., small and medium), then the antecedents of such rules can be combined by or(ing) the values corresponding to that variable. For instance, if we consider Figure 5.3, the rules 2 and 5 are about class C_2 such that the variable x_3 takes the linguistic values: medium and large, while the other variables take the same values. The two rules can be replaced with one generic rule as shown in Figure 5.5.

5.4.4.1. *Feature selection*

To enhance the transparency and the compactness of the rules, it is important that the if-part of the rules does not involve many features. Low classification performance generally results from non-informative features. The very conventional way to get rid of these features is to apply feature selection methods. Basically, there exist three classes of feature selection methods (Guyon and Elisseeff, 2003):

1. Filters: The idea is to filter out features that have small potential to predict the outputs. The selection is done as a pre-processing step ahead of the classification task. Filters are preprocessing techniques and refer to statistical selection methods

such as principal components analysis, LDA, and single value decomposition. For instance, Tikk *et al.* (2003) described a feature ranking algorithm for fuzzy modeling aiming at higher transparency of the rule-based. Relying on interclass separability as in LDA and using the backward selection method, the features are sequentially selected. Vanhoucke and Silipo (2003) used a number of measures that rely on mutual information to design a highly transparent classifier and particularly to select the features deemed to be the most informative. Similar approach has been taken in (Sanchez *et al.*, 2008) using a mutual information-based feature selection for optimizing a fuzzy rule-based system. Lee *et al.* (2001) applied fuzzy entropy (FE) in the context of fuzzy classification to achieve low complexity and high classification efficiency. First, FE was used to partition the pattern space into non-overlapping regions. Then, it was applied to select relevant features using the standard forward selection or backward elimination.
2. Wrappers: Select features that optimize the accuracy of a chosen classifier. Wrappers largely depend on the classifier to judge how well feature subsets are at classifying the training samples. For instance, in Cintra and Camargo (2010), the authors use a fuzzy wrapper and a fuzzy C4.5 decision tree to identify discriminative features. Wrappers are not very popular in the area of fuzzy rule-based systems. But many references claimed their methods to be wrappers, while actually they are embedded.
3. Embedded: Embedded methods perform variable selection in the process of training and are usually specific to given learning machines. In del Jesus *et al.* (2003), to design a fuzzy rule-based classifier while selecting the relevant features, multi-objective genetic algorithms are used. The aim is to optimize the precision of the classifier. Similar approach is suggested in Chen *et al.* (2012), where the T–S model is considered. In the same vein, in Schmitt *et al.* (2008), the selection of features is done while a fuzzy rule classifier is being optimized using the Choquet Integral. The embedded methods dominate the other two categories due to the natural process of optimization rule-based system to obtain high interpretable rules.

5.5. Unified View of Rule-Based Optimization

Different taxonomies related to interpretability of fuzzy systems in general have been suggested:

- Corrado-Mencar and Fanelli (2008) proposed a taxonomy in terms of interpretability constraints to the following levels: the fuzzy sets, the universe of discourse, the fuzzy granules, the rules, the fuzzy models the learning algorithms.
- Zhou and Gan (2008) proposed a taxonomy in terms of low-level inter pretability and high-level interpretability. Low-level interpretability is associated with the

fuzzy set level to capture the semantics, while high-level interpretability is associated with the rule level.

- Gacto *et al.* (2011) proposed a taxonomy inspired from the second one and distinguished between complexity-based interpretability equivalent to the high-level interpretability and semantics-based interpretability equivalent to low-level interpretability associated with the previous taxonomy.

A straight way to deal with interpretability issues in a unified way, by considering both transparency and performance at the same time, is to use optimization methods. We can use either meta-heuristics (evolutionary methods) or special-purpose designed methods. In the following, some studies are briefly reported on.

Ishibuchi *et al.* (1997) proposed a genetic algorithm for rule selection in classification problems, considering the following two objectives: to maximize the number of correctly classified training patterns and minimize the number of selected rules. This improves the complexity of the model, thanks to the reduction in the number of rules and the use of dont care conditions in the antecedent part of the rule. Ishibuchi and Yamamoto (2004); Ishibuchi and Nojima (2007) present a multi-objective evolutionary algorithm (MOEA) for classification problems with three objectives: Maximizing the number of correctly classified patterns, minimizing the number of rules and minimizing the number of antecedent conditions. Narukawa *et al.* (2005) rely on NSGA-II to optimize the rule-base by eliminating redundant rules using a multi-objective optimization that aims at increasing the accuracy while minimizing the number of rules and the premises.

Additional studies using evolutionary algorithms, in particular multi-objective evolutionary algorithms, can be found in a recent survey by Fazzolari *et al.* (2013).

Different from the previously mentioned studies, others have used special purpose optimization methods. For instance, Mikut *et al.* (2005) used decision trees to generate rules before an optimization process is applied. This latter consists of feature selection using an entropy-based method and applying iteratively a search-based formula that combines accuracy and transparency to find the best configuration of the rule-base.

Nauck (2003) introduced a formula that combines by product three components: complexity (expressed as the proportion of the number of classes to the total number of variables used in the rules), coverage (the average extent to which the domain of each variable is covered by the actual partitions of the variable), and partition complexity (quantified for each variable as inversely proportional to the number of partitions associated with that variable).

Guillaume and Charnomordic (2003) devised a distance-based formula to decide whether two partitions can be merged. The formula relies on the intra-distance (called internal distance) of a fuzzy set for a given variable and the inter-distance (called external distance) of fuzzy sets for a variable, similar to that used for computing clusters. Any pairs of fuzzy sets that minimize the combination of these two measures over the set of data points will be merged.

de Oliveira (1999a, 1999b) used backpropagation to optimize a performance index that consists of three constraining terms: accuracy, coverage and distinguishability of fuzzy sets.

5.6. Incremental and Online Fuzzy Rule-Based Classification Systems

Traditional fuzzy classification systems are designed in batch (offline) mode, that is, by using the complete training data at once. Thus, offline development of fuzzy classification systems assumes that the process of rule induction is done in a one-shot experiment, such that the learning phase and the deployment phase are two sequential and independent stages. For stationary processes this is sufficient, but if, for instance, the rule system's performance deteriorates due to a change of the data distribution or a change of the operating conditions, the system needs to be re-designed from scratch. Many offline approaches do simply perform "adaptive tuning", that is, they permanently re-estimate the parameters of the computed model. However, it is quite often necessary to adapt the structure of the rule-base. In general, for time-dependent and complex non-stationary processes, efficient techniques for updating the induced models are needed. Such techniques must be able to adapt the current model using only the new data. They have to be equipped with mechanisms to react to gradual changes or abrupt ones. The adaptation of the model (i.e., rules) should accommodate any information brought in by the new data and reconcile this with the existing rules.

Online development of fuzzy classification systems (Bouchachia and Vanaret, 2013), on the other hand, enables both learning and deployment to happen concurrently. In this context, rule learning takes place over long periods of time, and is inherently open-ended (Bouchachia and Mittermeir, 2007). The aim is to ensure that the system remains amenable to refinement as long as data continues to arrive. Moreover, online systems can also deal with both applications starving of data (e.g., experiments that are expensive and slow to produce data as in some chemical and biological applications) as well as applications that are data intensive (Arandjelovic and Cipolla, 2005; Bouchachia, 2011).

Generally, online systems face the challenge of accurately estimating the statistical characteristics of data in the future. In non-stationary environments, the challenge becomes even more important, since the FRS's behavior may need to change drastically over time due to concept drift (Bouchachia, 2011; Gama *et al.*, 2013). The aim of online learning is to ensure continuous adaptation. Ideally, only the learning model (e.g., only rules) and uses that model as basis in the future learning steps. As new data arrive, new rules may be created and existing ones may be modified allowing the system to evolve over time.

Online and incremental fuzzy rule systems have been recently introduced in a number of studies involving control (Angelov, 2004), diagnostic (Lughofer, 2011), and pattern classification (Angelov and Zhou, 2008; Bouchachia and Mittermeir, 2007; Lughofer, 2011). Type-1 fuzzy systems are currently quite established, since they do not only operate online, but also consider related advanced concepts such as concept drift and online feature selection.

For instance in Bouchachia and Mittermeir (2007), an integrated approach called FRCS was proposed. To accommodate incremental rule learning, appropriate mechanisms are applied at all steps: (1) *Incremental supervised clustering* to generate the rule antecedents in a progressive manner, (2) *Online and systematic* update of fuzzy partitions, (3) *Incremental feature selection* using an *incremental version* of the Fisher's interclass separability criterion to dynamically select features in an online manner.

In Bouchachia (2011), a fuzzy rule-based system for online classification is proposed. Relying on fuzzy minmax neural networks, the paper explains how fuzzy rules can be continuously online generated to meet the requirements of non-stationary dynamic environments, where data arrives over long periods of time. The classifier is sensitive to drift. It is able to detect data drift (Gama *et al.*, 2013) using different measures and react to it. An outline of the algorithm proposed is described in Algorithm 1. Actually, IFCS consists of three steps:

Algorithm 1: Steps of the incremental fuzzy classification system (IFCS)

```
if Initial=true then
M ← Train_Classifier(<TrainingData, Labels>)
E ← Test_Classifier(<TestingData, Labels>, M)
        // Just for the sake of observation
end if
i ← 0
while true do
  i ← i + 1
  Read <Input, Label>
  if IsLabeled(Label)=true then
    if Saturation_Training(i)=false then
      M ← Train_Classifier(<Input, Label>, M)
      If Input falls in a hyperbox with Flabel, then Flabel ← Label
```

Algorithm 1: (*Continued*)

```
else
  Err ← Test_Classifier(<Input,Label>, M)
  Cumulated_Err ← Cumulated_Err + Err
  if Detect_Drift(Cumulated_Err)=true then
    M ← Reset(Cumulated_Err, M)
  else
    M ← Update_Classifier(<Input,Label>, M)
    If Input falls in a hyperbox with Flabel, then Flabel ← Label
  end if
end if
else
  Flabel ← Predict_Label(Input, M)
  M ← Update_Classifier(<Input,Flabel>, M)
end if
end while
```

(a) Initial one-shot experiment training: Available data is used to obtain an initial model of the IFCS.
(b) Training over time before saturation: Given a saturation training level, incoming data is used to further adjust the model.
(c) Correction after training saturation: Beyond the saturation level, incoming data is used to observe the evolution of classification performance which allow to correct the classifier if necessary.

In Bouchachia and Vanaret (2013), a growing type-2 fuzzy classifier (GT2FC) for online fuzzy rule learning from real-time data streams is presented. To accommodate dynamic change, GT2FC relies on a new semi-supervised online learning algorithm called 2G2M (Growing Gaussian Mixture Model). In particular, 2G2M is used to generate the type-2 fuzzy membership functions to build the type-2 fuzzy rules. GT2FC is designed to accommodate data online and to reconcile labeled and unlabeled data using self-learning. Moreover, GT2FC maintains low complexity of the rule-base using online optimization and feature selection mechanisms. Type-2 fuzzy classification is very suitable for dealing with applications where input is prone to faults and noise. Thus, GT2FC offers the advantage of dealing with uncertainty in addition to self-adaptation in an online manner.

Note that at the operational level, T2 FRS differ from T1 FRS in the type of fuzzy sets and the operations applied on these sets. T2 fuzzy sets are equipped mainly with two newly introduced operators called the *meet*, $\sqcap$ and join, $\sqcup$ which correspond to the fuzzy intersection and fuzzy union. As shown in Figure 5.7, T2

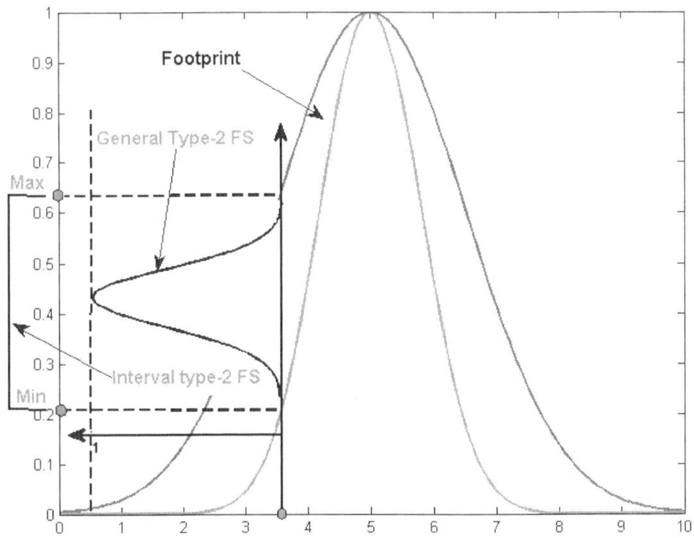

Figure 5.6: Type-2 fuzzy sets.

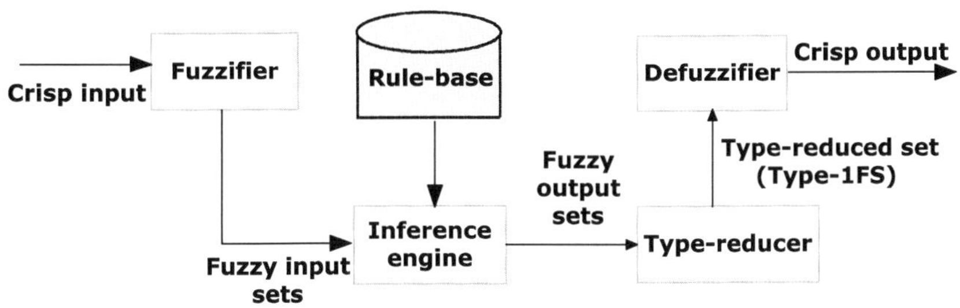

Figure 5.7: Type-2 fuzzy logic system.

FRS at the structural level is similar to T1 FRS but contains an additional module, the *type-reducer*. In a classification type-2 fuzzy rule system, the fuzzy rules for a C-class pattern classification problem with n-input variable can be formulated as:

$$R_j \equiv \text{if } x_1 \text{ is } \tilde{A}_{j,1} \wedge \cdots \wedge x_n \text{ is } \tilde{A}_{j,n} \text{ then } C_i, \tag{18}$$

where $\mathbf{x} = [x_1, \ldots, x_n]^t$ such that each x_i is a an input variable and $\tilde{A}_{r,i}$ the corresponding fuzzy terms in the form of type-2 fuzzy sets. We may associate these fuzzy sets with linguistic labels to enhance interpretability. C_i is a consequent class, and $j = 1, \ldots, N$ is the number of fuzzy rules. The inference engine computes the output of type-2 fuzzy sets by combining the rules. Specifically, the meet operator is used to connect the type-2 fuzzy propositions in the antecedent. The degree of activation of the jth rule using the n input variables is computed as:

$$\tilde{\beta}_j(x) = \sqcap_{q=1}^{n} \mu_{\tilde{A}_{j,q}}, (x_q), \; j = 1, \ldots, N. \tag{19}$$

The meet operation that replaces the fuzzy 'and' in T1 FRS is given as follows:

$$\tilde{A} \sqcap \tilde{B} = \sum_{u \in J_x} \sum_{w \in J_x} f_x(u) * g_x(w)/(u \wedge w), x \in X. \tag{20}$$

If we use the interval Singleton T2 FRS, the meet is given for input $x = x'$ by the firing set, i.e.,

$$\begin{aligned} \tilde{\beta}_j(x) &= \left[\underline{\beta}_j(x), \bar{\beta}_j(x)\right], \\ &= \left[\underline{\mu}_{A_{j,1}}(x_1) * \cdots * \underline{\mu}_{A_{j,n}}(x_n), \bar{\mu}_{A_{j,1}}(x_1) * \cdots * \bar{\mu}_{A_{j,n}}(x_n)\right]. \end{aligned} \tag{21}$$

In (Bouchachia and Vanaret, 2013), the Gaussian membership function is adopted and it is given as follows:

$$\mu_A(x) = \exp\left\{-\frac{(\mathbf{x} - m)^2}{2\sigma^2}\right\} = \mathcal{N}(m, \sigma; x), \tag{22}$$

where m and σ are the mean and the standard deviation of the function. To generate the lower and upper membership functions, the authors used concentration and dilation hedges to generate the footprint of Gaussians with uncertain deviation as shown in Figure 5.8. These are given as follows:

$$\bar{\mu}_{\tilde{A}}(x) = \mu_{DIL(A)}(x) = [\mu_A(x)]^{1/2}. \tag{23}$$

$$\bar{\mu}_{\tilde{A}}(x) = \mu_{CON(A)}(x) = [\mu_A(x)]^2. \tag{24}$$

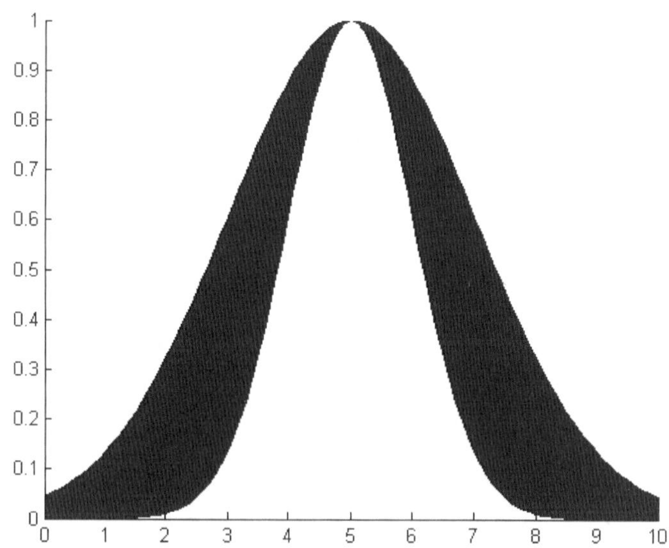

Figure 5.8: Uncertain deviation.

According to Equation (22), we obtain the following expressions:

$$\bar{\mu}_{\tilde{A}}(x) = \mathcal{N}(m, \sqrt{2}\sigma x). \tag{25}$$

$$\underline{\mu}_{\tilde{A}}(x) = \mathcal{N}\left(m, \frac{\sigma}{\sqrt{2}}; x\right). \tag{26}$$

Type-reducer is responsible for converting T2 FSs obtained as output of the inference engine into T1 FSs. Type-reduction for FRS (Mamdani and Sugeno models) was proposed by Karnik and Mendel (2001); Mendel (2013). This will not be adopted in our case, since the rules' consequent represents the label of a class. Traditionally in Type-1 fuzzy classification systems, the output of the classifier is determined by the rule that has the highest degree of activation:

$$\text{Winner} = C_{j*},\ j* = \underset{1\le j\le N}{\arg\max}\, \beta_j, \tag{27}$$

where β_j is the firing degree of the j rule. In type-2 fuzzy classification systems, we have an interval $\tilde{\beta}_j = [\underline{\beta}_j, \bar{\beta}_j]$ as defined in Equation (21). Therefore, we compute the winning class by considering the center of the interval $[\underline{\beta}_j(x), \bar{\beta}_j(x)]$, that is:

$$\text{Winner} = C_{j*}, \tag{28}$$

where

$$j* = \underset{1\le j\le N}{\arg\max}\, \frac{1}{2}(\underline{\beta}_j(x) + \bar{\beta}_j(x)). \tag{29}$$

For the sake of illustration, an excerpt of rules generated is shown in Table 5.1.

Table 5.1: Fuzzy rules for D2.

Rule	Antecedent	C
1	x_1 IN N(−17.60, [0.968, 1.93]) ∧ x_2 IN N(−2.31, [1.42, 2.85] ∨ (x_2 IN N(−9.45, [2.04, 4.08]))	2
2	x_1 IN N(−5.27, [2.62, 5.24]) ∨ x_1 IN N(−13.10, [1.44, 2.89]) ∨ x_2 IN N(1.61, [1.01, 2.02])	2
3	x_1 IN N(−13.10, [1.44, 2.89]) ∧ x_2 IN N(1.61, [1.01, 2.02]) ∨ x_2 IN N(−15.12, [0.98, 1.96]))	2
4	x_1 IN N(5.47, [1.28, 2.56]) ∧ x_2 IN N(7.78, [1.19, 2.39]) ∨ x_2 IN N(−6.10, [0.97,1.94]))	1
5	x_1 IN N(−5.27, [2.62, 5.24]) ∨ x_1 IN N(5.470, [1.28, 2.56]) ∨ x_1 IN N(9.79, [1.89, 3.78]) ∧ x_2 IN N(−5.30, [1.91, 3.83])	1
6	x_1 IN N(2.69, [0.93, 1.87]) ∧ x_2 IN N(−9.45, [2.04, 4.08])	1
7	x_1 IN N(0.28, [0.97, 1.93]) ∨ x_1 IN N(−17.60, [0.96, 1.93]) ∧ x_2 IN N(−2.31, [1.42, 2.85])	2

5.7. Conclusion

This chapter briefly presents fuzzy rule-based classifiers. The working cycle for both type-1 and type-2 fuzzy classification systems has been described. Because the primary requirement of such systems is interpretability, quality issues have been lengthily discussed including various approaches with some illustrative studies. Towards the end, the chapter also introduces incremental and online learning of fuzzy classifiers.

While type-1 fuzzy classifiers have been extensively studied over the past in different contexts, type-2 fuzzy classifiers are still emerging and are not as popular as their predecessors. It is expected that this category of fuzzy classifiers will continue to be the focus of future studies, especially with regard to transparency, interpretability and online generation and deployment.

References

Abonyi, J., Babuska, R. and Szeifert, F. (2002). Modified Gath–Geva fuzzy clustering for identification of Takagi–Sugeno fuzzy models. *IEEE Trans. Syst. Man Cybern. Part B*, 32(5), pp. 612–621.

Alatas, B. and Akin, E. (2005). Mining fuzzy classification rules using an artificial immune system with boosting. In *ADBIS*, pp. 283–293.

Angelov, P. (2004). An approach for fuzzy rule-base adaptation using on-line clustering. *Int. J. Approx. Reason.*, 35(3), pp. 275–289.

Angelov, P. and Zhou, X. (2008). Evolving fuzzy rule-based classifiers from data streams. *IEEE Trans. Fuzzy Systems*, 16(6), pp. 1462–1475.

Arandjelovic, O. and Cipolla, R. (2005). Incremental learning of temporally coherent Gaussian mixture models. In *Proc. 16th Br. Mach. Vis. Conf.*, pp. 759–768.

Bouchachia, A. (2004). Incremental rule learning using incremental clustering. In *Proc. 10th Conf. Inf. Process. Manag. Uncertain. Knowl.-Based Syst.*, 3, pp. 2085–2092.

Bouchachia, A. and Mittermeir, R. (2007). Towards incremental fuzzy classifiers. *Soft Comput.*, 11(2), pp. 193–207.

Bouchachia, A. (2011). Fuzzy classification in dynamic environments. *Soft Comput.*, 15(5), pp. 1009–1022.

Bouchachia, A. and Vanaret, C. (2013). Gt2fc: An online growing interval type-2 self-learning fuzzy classifier. *IEEE Trans. Fuzzy Syst.*, In press.

Chen, X., Jin, D. and Li, Z. (2002). Fuzzy petri nets for rule-based pattern classification. In *Commun., Circuits Syst. West Sino Expositions, IEEE 2002 Int. Conf.*, June, 2, pp. 1218–1222.

Chen, Y.-C., Pal, N. R. and Chung, I.-F. (2012). An integrated mechanism for feature selection and fuzzy rule extraction for classification. *IEEE Trans. Fuzzy Syst.*, 20(4), pp. 683–698.

Cintra, M. and Camargo, H. (2010). Feature subset selection for fuzzy classification methods. In *Inf. Process. Manag. Uncertain Knowl.-Based Syst. Theory and Methods. Commun. Comput. Inf. Sci.*, 80, pp. 318–327.

Corrado-Mencar, C. and Fanelli, A. (2008). Interpretability constraints for fuzzy information granulation. *Inf. Sci.*, 178(24), pp. 4585–4618.

del Jesus, M., Herrera, F., Magdalena, L., Cordn, O. and Villar, P. (2003). *Interpretability Issues in Fuzzy Modeling*. A multiobjective genetic learning process for joint feature selection and granularity and context learning in fuzzy rule-based classification systems. Springer-Verlag, pp. 79–99.

de Oliveira, J. (1999a). Semantic constraints for membership function optimization. *IEEE Trans. Syst. Man Cybern. Part A: Syst. Humans*, 29(1), pp. 128–138.

de Oliveira, J. (1999b). Towards neuro-linguistic modeling: constraints for optimization of membership functions. *Fuzzy Sets Syst.*, 106, pp. 357–380.

Duda, P., Hart, E. and Stork, D. (2001). *Pattern Classification.* New York: Willey.

Fawcett, T. (2006). An introduction to roc analysis. *Pattern Recogn. Lett.*, 27(8), pp. 861–874.

Fazzolari, M., Alcalá, R., Nojima, Y., Ishibuchi, H. and Herrera, F. (2013). A review of the application of multiobjective evolutionary fuzzy systems: Current status and further directions. *IEEE Trans. Fuzzy Syst.*, 21(1), pp. 45–65.

Gacto, M., Alcalá, R. and Herrera, F. (2011). Interpretability of linguistic fuzzy rule-based systems: An overview of interpretability measures. *Inf. Sci.*, 181(20), pp. 4340–4360.

Gama, J., Zliobaite, I., Bifet, A., Pechenizkiy, M. and Bouchachia, A. (2013). A survey on concept drift adaptation. *IEEE Trans. Fuzzy Syst.*, In press.

Ganji, M. and Abadeh, M. (2011). A fuzzy classification system based on ant colony optimization for diabetes disease diagnosis. *Expert Syst. Appl.*, 38(12), pp. 14650–14659.

Guillaume, S. and Charnomordic, B. (2003). *Interpretability Issues in Fuzzy Modeling*. A new method for inducing a set of interpretable fuzzy partitions and fuzzy inference systems from data. Springer-Verlag, p. 148175.

Guyon, I. and Elisseeff, A. (2003). An introduction to variable and feature selection. *J. Mach. Learn. Res.*, 3, pp. 1157–1182.

Ishibuchi, H., Murata, T. and Türkşen, I. (1997). Single-objective and two-objective genetic algorithms for selecting linguistic rules for pattern classification problems. *Fuzzy Sets Syst.*, 89(2), pp. 135–150.

Ishibuchi, H. and Yamamoto, T. (2004). Fuzzy rule selection by multi-objective genetic local search algorithms and rule evaluation measures in data mining. *Fuzzy Sets Syst.*, 141(1), pp. 59–88.

Ishibuchi, H. and Nojima, Y. (2007). Analysis of interpretability-accuracy tradeoff of fuzzy systems by multiobjective fuzzy genetics-based machine learning. *Int. J. Approx. Reason.*, 44(1), pp. 4–31.

Ishibuchi, H. and Yamamoto, T. (2005). Rule weight specification in fuzzy rule-based classification systems. *IEEE Trans. Fuzzy Syst.*, 13(4), pp. 428–435.

Karnik, N. and Mendel, J. (2001). Operations on type-2 fuzzy sets. *Fuzzy Sets Syst.*, 122(2), pp. 327–348.

Kasabov, N. (1996). *Foundations of Neural Networks, Fuzzy Systems and Knowledge Engineering.* MIT Press.

Kuncheva, L. (2000). How good are fuzzy if-then classifiers? *IEEE Trans. Syst. Man Cybern. Part B*, 30(4), pp. 501–509.

Lee, H.-M., Chen, C.-M., Chen, J.-M. and Jou, Y.-L. (2001). An efficient fuzzy classifier with feature selection based on fuzzy entropy. *IEEE Trans. Syst. Man Cybern.*, 31, pp. 426–432.

Lughofer, E. (2011). *Evolving Fuzzy Systems — Methodologies, Advanced Concepts and Applications. Studies in Fuzziness and Soft Computing*. Springer.

Mendel, J. M. (2013). On km algorithms for solving type-2 fuzzy set problems. *IEEE Trans. Fuzzy Syst.*, 21(3), pp. 426–446.

Mikut, R., Jäkel, J. and Gröll, L. (2005). Interpretability issues in data-based learning of fuzzy systems. *Fuzzy Sets Syst.*, 150(2), pp. 179–197.

Narukawa, K., Nojima, Y. and Ishibuchi, H. (2005). Modification of evolutionary multi-objective optimization algorithms for multiobjective design of fuzzy rule-based classification systems. In *14th IEEE Int. Conf. Fuzzy Syst.*, pp. 809–814.

Nauck, D. (2003). Measuring interpretability in rule-based classification systems. In *12th IEEE Int. Conf. Fuzzy Syst.*, 1, pp. 196–201.

Pedrycz, W. and Gomide, F. (1998) *Introduction to Fuzzy Sets: Analysis and Design.* MIT Press.

Rani, C. and Deepa, S. N. (2010). Design of optimal fuzzy classifier system using particle swarm optimization. In *Innov. Comput. Technol. (ICICT), 2010 Int. Conf.*, pp. 1–6.

Saade, J. and Diab, H. (2000). Defuzzification techniques for fuzzy controllers. *IEEE Trans. Syst. Man Cybern. Part B: Cybern.*, 30(1), pp. 223–229.

Schmitt, E., Bombardier, V. and Wendling, L. (2008). Improving fuzzy rule classifier by extracting suitable features from capacities with respect to the choquet integral. *IEEE Trans. Syst. Man Cybern. Part B: Cybern.*, 38(5), pp. 1195–1206.

Shen, Q. and Chouchoulas, A. (2002). A rough-fuzzy approach for generating classification rules. *Pattern Recognit.*, 35(11), pp. 2425–2438.

Sanchez, L., Surez, M. R., Villar, J. R. and Couso, I. (2008). Mutual information-based feature selection and partition design in fuzzy rule-based classifiers from vague data. *Int. J. Approx. Reason.*, 49(3), pp. 607–622.

Tan, W., Foo, C. and Chua, T. (2007). Type-2 fuzzy system for ecg arrhythmic classification. In *FUZZ-IEEE*, pp. 1–6.

Thiruvenkadam, S. R., Arcot, S. and Chen, Y. (2006). A pde based method for fuzzy classification of medical images. In *2006 IEEE Int. Conf. Image Process.*, pp. 1805–1808.

Tikk, D., Gedeon, T. and Wong, K. (2003). *Interpretability Issues in Fuzzy Modeling.* A feature ranking algorithm for fuzzy modelling problems. Springer-Verlag, p. 176192.

Toscano, R. and Lyonnet, P. (2003). Diagnosis of the industrial systems by fuzzy classification. *ISA Trans.*, 42(2), pp. 327–335.

Tsekouras, G., Sarimveis, H., Kavakli, E. and Bafas, G. (2005). A hierarchical fuzzy-clustering approach to fuzzy modeling. *Fuzzy Sets Syst.*, 150(2), pp. 245–266.

Vanhoucke, V. and Silipo, R. (2003). *Interpretability Issues in Fuzzy Modeling.* Interpretability in multidimensional classification. Springer-Verlag, p. 193217.

Vernieuwe, H., De Baets, B. and Verhoest, N. (2006). Comparison of clustering algorithms in the identification of Takagi–Sugeno models: A hydrological case study. *Fuzzy Sets Syst.*, 157(21), pp. 2876–2896.

Wu, D. and Mendel, J. (2008). A vector similarity measure for linguistic approximation: Interval type-2 and type-1 fuzzy sets. *Inf. Sci.*, 178(2), pp. 381–402.

Yager, R. R. and Filev, D. P. (1994). Approximate clustering via the mountain method. *IEEE Trans. Syst. Man Cybern.*, 24(8), pp. 1279–1284.

Zhou, S. and Gan, J. (2008). Low-level interpretability and high-level interpretability: A unified view of data-driven interpretable fuzzy system modelling. *Fuzzy Sets Syst.*, 159(23), pp. 3091–3131.

Chapter 6

Fuzzy Model-Based Control — Predictive and Adaptive Approaches

Igor Škrjanc and Sašo Blažič

This chapter deals with fuzzy model-based control and focuses on approaches that meet the following criteria: (1) The possibility of controlling nonlinear plants, (2) Simplicity in terms of implementation and computational complexity, (3) Stability and robust stability are ensured under some *a priori* known limitations. Two approaches are presented and discussed, namely, a predictive and an adaptive one. Both are based on Takagi–Sugeno model form, which posseses the property of universal approximation of an arbitrary smooth nonlinear function and can be therefore used as a proper model to predict the future behavior of the plant. In spite of many successful implementations of Mamdani fuzzy model-based approaches, it soon became clear that this approach lack the systematic ways to analyze the control systems stability, performance, robustness and the systematic way of tuning the controller parameters to adjust the performance. On the other hand, Takagi–Sugeno fuzzy models enable more compact description of nonlinear system, rigorous treatment of stability and robustness. But the most important feature of Takagi–Sugeno models is the ability that they can be easily adapted to the different linear control algorithms to cope with the demanding nonlinear control problems.

6.1. Introduction

In this chapter, we face the problem of controlling a nonlinear plant. Classical linear approaches try to treat a plant as linear and a linear controller is designed to meet the control objectives. Unfortunately, such an approach results in an acceptable control performance only if the nonlinearity is not too strong. The previous statement is far from being rigorous in the definitions of "acceptable" and "strong". But the fact is that by increasing the control performance requirements, the problems with the nonlinearity also become much more apparent. So, there is a clear need to cope with the control of nonlinear plants.

The problem of control of nonlinear plants has received a great deal of attention in the past. A natural solution is to use a nonlinear controller that tries to "cancel" the nonlinearity in some sense or at least it increases the performance of the controlled system over a wide operating range with respect to the performance of an "optimal" linear controller. Since a controller is just a nonlinear dynamic system that maps controller inputs to controller actions, we need to somehow describe this nonlinear mapping and implement it into the controlled system. In the case of a finite-dimensional system, one possibility is to represent a controller in the state-space form where four nonlinear mappings are needed: state-to-state mapping, input-to-state mapping, state-to-output mapping, and direct input-to-output mapping. The Stone–Weierstrass theorem guarantees that all these mappings can be approximated by basis functions arbitrary well. Immense approximators of nonlinear functions have been proposed in the literature to solve the problem of nonlinear-system control. Some of the most popular ones are: piecewise linear functions, fuzzy models, artificial neural networks, splines, wavelets, etc.

In this chapter, we put our focus on fuzzy controllers. Several excellent books and papers exist that cover various aspects of fuzzy control (Babuska, 1998; Passino and Yurkovich, 1998; Pedrycz, 1993; Precup and Hellendoorn, 2011; Tanaka and Wang, 2002). Following a seminal paper of Zadeh (1973) that introduced fuzzy set theory, the fuzzy logic approach was soon introduced into controllers (Mamdani, 1974). In these early ages of fuzzy control, the controller was usually designed using Zadeh's notion of linguistic variables and fuzzy algorithms. It was often claimed that the approach with linguistic variables, linguistic values and linguistic rules is "parameterless" and therefore the controllers are extremely easy to tune based on the expert knowledge that is easily transformable into the rule database. Many successful applications of fuzzy controllers have shown their ability to control nonlinear plants. But it soon became clear that the Mamdani fuzzy model control approach lacks systematic ways to analyze control system stability, control system performance, and control system robustness.

Takagi–Sugeno fuzzy model (Takagi and Sugeno, 1985) enables more compact description of the fuzzy system. Moreover, it enables rigorous treating of stability and robustness in the form of linear matrix inequalities (Tanaka and Wang, 2002). Several control algorithms originally developed for linear systems can be adapted in a way that it is possible to combine them with the Takagi–Sugeno fuzzy models. Thus, the number of control approaches based on a Takagi–Sugeno model proposed in the literature in the past three decades is huge. In this chapter, we will show how to design predictive and adaptive controllers for certain classes of nonlinear systems where the plant model is given in the form of a Takagi–Sugeno fuzzy model. The proposed algorithms are not developed in an *ad hoc* manner, but having the stability of the over-all system in mind. This is why the stability analysis of the algorithms complements the algorithms themselves.

6.2. Takagi–Sugeno Fuzzy Model

Typical fuzzy model (Takagi and Sugeno, 1985) is given in the form of rules

$$\mathbf{R}_j\text{: } \textbf{if } x_{p1} \textbf{ is } \mathbf{A}_{1,k_1} \textbf{ and } x_{p2} \textbf{ is } \mathbf{A}_{2,k_2} \textbf{ and } \ldots \textbf{ and } x_{pq} \textbf{ is } \mathbf{A}_{q,k_q} \textbf{ then } y = \phi_j(\mathbf{x})$$
$$j = 1, \ldots, m$$
$$k_1 = 1, \ldots, f_1, \quad k_2 = 1, \ldots, f_2 \quad \ldots \quad k_q = 1, \ldots, f_q. \tag{1}$$

The q-element vector $\mathbf{x}_p^T = [x_{p1}, \ldots, x_{pq}]$ denotes the input or variables in premise, and variable y is the output of the model. With each variable in premise x_{pi} ($i = 1, \ldots, q$), f_i fuzzy sets ($\mathbf{A}_{i,1}, \ldots, \mathbf{A}_{i,f_i}$) are connected, and each fuzzy set $\mathbf{A}_{i,k_i}$ ($k_i = 1, \ldots, f_i$) is associated with a real-valued function $\mu_{A_{i,k_i}}(x_{pi}) : \mathbb{R} \to [0, 1]$, that produces membership grade of the variable x_{pi} with respect to the fuzzy set $\mathbf{A}_{i,k_i}$. To make the list of fuzzy rules complete, all possible variations of fuzzy sets are given in Equation (1), yielding the number of fuzzy rules $m = f_1 \times f_2 \times \cdots \times f_q$. The variables x_{pi} are not the only inputs of the fuzzy system. Implicitly, the n-element vector $\mathbf{x}^T = [x_1, \ldots, x_n]$ also represents the input to the system. It is usually referred to as the consequence vector. The functions $\phi_j(\cdot)$ can be arbitrary smooth functions in general, although linear or affine functions are usually used.

The system in Equation (1) can be described in closed form if the intersection of fuzzy sets and the defuzzification method are previously defined. The generalized form of the intersection is the so-called *triangular norm* (T-norm). In our case, the latter was chosen as algebraic product while weighted average method was employed as a method of defuzzification yielding the following output of the fuzzy system

$$\hat{y} = \frac{\sum_{k_1=1}^{f_1} \sum_{k_2=1}^{f_2} \cdots \sum_{k_q=1}^{f_q} \mu_{A_{1,k_1}}(x_{p1})\, \mu_{A_{2,k_2}}(x_{p2}) \ldots \mu_{A_{q,k_q}}(x_{pq})\, \phi_j(\mathbf{x})}{\sum_{k_1=1}^{f_1} \sum_{k_2=1}^{f_2} \cdots \sum_{k_q=1}^{f_q} \mu_{A_{1,k_1}}(x_{p1})\, \mu_{A_{2,k_2}}(x_{p2}) \ldots \mu_{A_{q,k_q}}(x_{pq})}. \tag{2}$$

It has to be noted that a slight abuse of notation is used in Equation (2) since j is not explicitly defined as running index. From Equation (1) is evident that each j corresponds to the specific variation of indexes k_i, $i = 1, \ldots, q$.

To simplify Equation (2), a partition of unity is considered where functions $\beta_j(\mathbf{x}_p)$ defined by

$$\beta_j(\mathbf{x}_p) = \frac{\mu_{A_{1,k_1}}(x_{p1})\, \mu_{A_{2,k_2}}(x_{p2}) \ldots \mu_{A_{q,k_q}}(x_{pq})}{\sum_{k_1=1}^{f_1} \sum_{k_2=1}^{f_2} \cdots \sum_{k_q=1}^{f_q} \mu_{A_{1,k_1}}(x_{p1})\, \mu_{A_{2,k_2}}(x_{p2}) \cdots \mu_{A_{q,k_q}}(x_{pq})},$$
$$j = 1, \ldots, m \tag{3}$$

give information about the fulfilment of the respective fuzzy rule in the normalized form. It is obvious that $\sum_{j=1}^{m} \beta_j(\mathbf{x}_p) = 1$ irrespective of $\mathbf{x}_p$ as long as the denominator of $\beta_j(\mathbf{x}_p)$ is not equal to zero (that can be easily prevented by stretching the membership functions over the whole potential area of $\mathbf{x}_p$). Combining Equations (2) and (3) and changing summation over k_i by summation over j, we arrive to the following equation:

$$\hat{y} = \sum_{j=1}^{m} \beta_j(\mathbf{x}_p)\phi_j(\mathbf{x}). \tag{4}$$

The class of fuzzy models has the form of linear models, this refers to $\{\beta^j\}$ as a set of basis functions. The use of membership functions in input space with overlapping receptive fields provides interpolation and extrapolation.

Very often, the output value is defined as a linear combination of signals in a consequence vector

$$\phi_j(\mathbf{x}) = \boldsymbol{\theta}_j^T \mathbf{x}, \quad j = 1, \ldots, m, \quad \boldsymbol{\theta}_j^T = [\theta_{j1}, \ldots, \theta_{jn}]. \tag{5}$$

If Takagi–Sugeno model of the zeroth order is chosen, $\phi_j(\mathbf{x}) = \theta_{j0}$, and in the case of the first-order model, the consequent is $\phi_j(\mathbf{x}) = \theta_{j0} + \boldsymbol{\theta}_j^T \mathbf{x}$. Both cases can be treated by the model Equation (5) by adding 1 to the vector $\mathbf{x}$ and augmenting vector $\boldsymbol{\theta}$ with θ_{j0}. To simplify the notation, only the model in Equation (5) will be treated in the rest of the chapter. If the matrix of the coefficients for the whole set of rules is written as $\boldsymbol{\Theta}^T = [\boldsymbol{\theta}_1, \ldots, \boldsymbol{\theta}_m]$ and the vector of membership values as $\boldsymbol{\beta}^T(\mathbf{x}_p) = [\beta^1(\mathbf{x}_p), \ldots, \beta^m(\mathbf{x}_p)]$, then Equation (4) can be rewritten in the matrix form

$$\hat{y} = \boldsymbol{\beta}^T(\mathbf{x}_p)\boldsymbol{\Theta}\mathbf{x}. \tag{6}$$

The fuzzy model in the form given in Equation (6) is referred to as affine Takagi–Sugeno model and can be used to approximate any arbitrary function that maps the compact set $\mathbf{C} \subset \mathbb{R}^d$ (d is the dimension of the input space) to $\mathbb{R}$ with any desired degree of accuracy (Kosko, 1994; Wang and Mendel, 1992; Ying, 1997). The generality can be proven by Stone–Weierstrass theorem (Goldberg, 1976) which indicates that any continuous function can be approximated by fuzzy basis function expansion (Lin, 1997).

When identifying the fuzzy model, there are several parameters that can be tuned. One possibility is to only identify the parameters in the rule consequents and let the antecedent-part parameters untouched. If the position of the membership functions is good (the input space of interest is completely covered and the density of membership functions is higher where nonlinearity is stronger), then a good model can be obtained by only identifying the consequents. The price for this is to introduce any existing prior knowledge in the design of the membership functions.

If, however, we do not know anything about the controlled system, we can use some evolving system techniques where the process of identification changes not only the consequent parameters but also the antecedent parameters (Angelov *et al.*, 2001; Angelov and Filev, 2004; Angelov *et al.*, 2011; Cara *et al.*, 2010; Johanyák and Papp, 2012; Sadeghi–Tehran *et al.*, 2012; Vaščák, 2012).

6.3. Fuzzy Model-Based Predictive Control

The fundamental methods which are essentially based on the principle of predictive control are Generalized Predictive Control (Clarke *et al.*, 1987), Model Algorithmic Control (Richalet *et al.*, 1978) and Predictive Functional Control (Richalet, 1993), Dynamic Matrix Control (Cutler and Ramaker, 1980), Extended Prediction Self-Adaptive Control (De Keyser *et al.*, 1988) and Extended Horizon Adaptive Control (Ydstie, 1984). All these methods are developed for linear process models. The principle is based on the process model output prediction and calculation of control signal which brings the output of the process to the reference trajectory in a way to minimize the difference between the reference and the output signal in a certain interval, between two prediction horizons, or to minimize the difference in a certain horizon, called coincidence horizon. The control signal can be found by means of optimization or it can be calculated using the explicit control law formula (Bequette, 1991; Henson, 1998).

The nature of processes is inherently nonlinear and this implies the use of nonlinear approaches in predictive control schemes. Here, we can distinguish between two main group of approaches: the first group is based on the nonlinear mathematical models of the process in any form and convex optimization (Figueroa, 2001), while the second group relies on approximation of nonlinear process dynamics with nonlinear approximators such as neural networks (Wang *et al.*, 1996; Wang and Mendel, 1992), piecewise-linear models (Padin and Figueroa, 2000), Volterra and Wiener models (Doyle *et al.*, 1995), multi-models and multi-variables (Li *et al.*, 2004; Roubos *et al.*, 1999), and fuzzy models (Abonyi *et al.*, 2001; Škrjanc and Matko, 2000). The advantage of the latter approaches is the possibility of stating the control law in the explicit analytical form.

In some highly nonlinear cases the use of nonlinear model-based predictive control can be easily justified. By introducing the nonlinear model into predictive control problem, the complexity increases significantly. In Bequette (1991); Henson (1998), an overview of different nonlinear predictive control approaches is given.

When applying the model-based predictive control with Takagi–Sugeno fuzzy model, it is always important how to choose fuzzy sets and corresponding membership functions. Many existing clustering techniques can be used in the identification phase to make this task easier. There exist many fuzzy model, based predictive algorithms (Andone and Hossu, 2004; Kim and Huh, 1998; Sun *et al.*, 2004) that put significant stress on the algorithm that properly arranges membership functions. An alternative approach is to introduce uncertainty to membership functions which results in the so-called type-2 fuzzy sets. Obviously, control algorithms exist based on type-2 fuzzy logic (Cervantes *et al.*, 2011).

The basic idea of model-based predictive control is to predict the future behavior of the process over a certain horizon using the dynamic model and obtaining the control actions to minimize a certain criterion. Traditionally, the control problem is formally stated as an optimization problem where the goal is to obtain control actions on a relatively short control horizon by optimising the behavior of the controlled system in a larger prediction horizon. One of the main properties of most predictive controllers is that they utilize a so-called receding horizon approach. This means that even though the control signal is obtained on a larger interval in the current point of time, only the first sample is used while the whole optimization routine is repeated in each sampling instant.

The model-based predictive control relies heavily on the prediction model quality. When the plant is nonlinear, the model is also nonlinear. As it is very well-known, fuzzy model possesses the property of universal approximation of an arbitrary smooth nonlinear function and can be used as a prediction model of a nonlinear plant. Many approaches originally developed for the control of linear systems can be adapted to include a fuzzy model-based predictor. In this chapter fuzzy model is incorporated into the Predictive Functional Control (PFC) approach. This combination provides the means of controlling nonlinear systems. Since no explicit optimization is used, the approach is very suitable for the implementation on an industrial hardware. The fuzzy model-based predictive control (FMBPC) algorithm is presented in the state-space form (Blažič and Škrjanc, 2007). The approach is an extension of predictive functional algorithm (Richalet, 1993) to the nonlinear systems. The proposed algorithm easily copes with phase non-minimal and time-delayed dynamics. The approach can be combined by a clustering technique to obtain the FMBPC algorithm where membership functions are not fixed *a priori* but this is not intention of this work.

6.3.1. *The Development of the Control Algorithm*

In the case of FMBPC, the prediction of the plant output is given by its fuzzy model in the state-space domain. This is why the approach in the proposed form is limited to the open-loop stable plants. By introducing some modifications, the algorithm can be made applicable also for the unstable plants.

The problem of delays in the plant is circumvented by constructing an auxiliary variable that serves as the output of the plant if there were no delay present. The so-called "undelayed" model of the plant will be introduced for that purpose. It is obtained by "removing" delays from the original ("delayed") model and converting it to the state space description:

$$\begin{aligned} \mathbf{x}_m^0(k+1) &= \bar{\mathbf{A}}_m \mathbf{x}_m^0(k) + \bar{\mathbf{B}}_m \mathbf{u}(k) + \bar{\mathbf{R}}_m, \\ y_m^0(k) &= \bar{\mathbf{C}}_m \mathbf{x}_m^0(k), \end{aligned} \tag{7}$$

where $y_m^0(k)$ models the "undelayed" output of the plant.

The behavior of the closed-loop system is defined by the reference trajectory which is given in the form of the reference model. The control goal is to determine the future control action so that the predicted output value coincides with the reference trajectory. The time difference between the coincidence point and the current time is called a coincidence horizon. It is denoted by H. The prediction is calculated under the assumption of constant future manipulated variables ($u(k) = u(k+1) = \cdots = u(k+H-1)$), i.e., the mean level control assumption is used. The H-step ahead prediction of the "undelayed" plant output is then obtained from Equation (7):

$$y_m^0(k+H) = \bar{\mathbf{C}}_m \left(\bar{\mathbf{A}}_m^H \mathbf{x}_m^0(k) + \left(\bar{\mathbf{A}}_m^H - \mathbf{I}\right) \left(\bar{\mathbf{A}}_m - \mathbf{I}\right)^{-1} \left(\bar{\mathbf{B}}_m u(k) + \bar{\mathbf{R}}_m\right) \right). \tag{8}$$

The reference model is given by the first-order difference equation

$$y_r(k+1) = a_r y_r(k) + b_r w(k), \tag{9}$$

where w stands for the reference signal. The reference model parameters should be chosen so that the reference model gain is unity. This is accomplished by fulfilling the following equation

$$(1 - a_r)^{-1} b_r = 1. \tag{10}$$

The main goal of the proposed algorithm is to find the control law which enables the reference trajectory tracking of the "undelayed" plant output $y_p^0(k)$. In each time instant, the control signal is calculated so that the output is forced to reach the reference trajectory after H time samples ($y_p^0(k+H) = y_r(k+H)$). The idea of FMBPC is introduced through the equivalence of the objective increment Δ_p and the model output increment Δ_m. The former is defined as a difference between the predicted reference signal $y_r(k+H)$ and the actual output of the "undelayed" plant $y_p^0(k)$

$$\Delta_p = y_r(k+H) - y_p^0(k). \tag{11}$$

Since the variable $y_p^0(k)$ cannot be measured directly, it will be estimated by using the available signals:

$$y_p^0(k) = y_p(k) - y_m(k) + y_m^0(k). \tag{12}$$

It can be seen that the delay in the plant is compensated by the difference between the outputs of the "undelayed" and the "delayed" model. When the perfect model of the plant is available, the first two terms on the right-hand side of Equation (12) cancel and the result is actually the output of the "undelayed" plant model. If this is not the case, only the approximation is obtained.

The model output increment Δ_m is defined by the following formula:

$$\Delta_m = y_m^0(k+H) - y_m^0(k). \tag{13}$$

Prescribing the control goal

$$\Delta_p = \Delta_m \tag{14}$$

and taking into account Equations (11), (13), and (8), we obtain the FMBPC control law

$$u(k) = g_0^{-1}\Big(\big(y_r(k+H) - y_p^0(k) + y_m^0(k)\big) - \bar{\mathbf{C}}_m\bar{\mathbf{A}}_m^H\mathbf{x}_m^0(k) \\ - \bar{\mathbf{C}}_m\left(\bar{\mathbf{A}}_m^H - \mathbf{I}\right)\left(\bar{\mathbf{A}}_m - \mathbf{I}\right)^{-1}\bar{\mathbf{R}}_m\Big), \tag{15}$$

where g_0 stands for:

$$g_0 = \bar{\mathbf{C}}_m\left(\bar{\mathbf{A}}_m^H - \mathbf{I}\right)\left(\bar{\mathbf{A}}_m - \mathbf{I}\right)^{-1}\bar{\mathbf{B}}_m. \tag{16}$$

The control law of FMBPC in analytical form is finally obtained by introducing Equation (12) into Equation (15):

$$u(k) = g_0^{-1}\Big(\big(y_r(k+H) - y_p(k) + y_m(k)\big) - \bar{\mathbf{C}}_m\bar{\mathbf{A}}_m^H\mathbf{x}_m^0(k) \\ - \bar{\mathbf{C}}_m\left(\bar{\mathbf{A}}_m^H - \mathbf{I}\right)\left(\bar{\mathbf{A}}_m - \mathbf{I}\right)^{-1}\bar{\mathbf{R}}_m\Big). \tag{17}$$

In the following, it will be shown that the realizability of the control law, Equation (17) relies heavily on the relation between the coincidence horizon H and the relative degree of the plant ρ. In the case of discrete-time systems, the relative degree is directly related to the pure time-delay of the system transfer function. If the system is described in the state-space form, any form can be used in general, but the analysis is much simplified in the case of certain canonical descriptions. If the system is described in controllable canonical form in each fuzzy domain, then also the matrices $\bar{\mathbf{A}}_m$, $\bar{\mathbf{B}}_m$, and $\bar{\mathbf{C}}_m$ of the fuzzy model, Equation (36), take the controllable canonical form:

$$\bar{\mathbf{A}}_m = \begin{bmatrix} 0 & 1 & 0 & \dots & 0 \\ 0 & 0 & 1 & \dots & 0 \\ \vdots & \vdots & \vdots & \ddots & \vdots \\ 0 & 0 & 0 & \dots & 1 \\ -\bar{a}_n & -\bar{a}_{n-1} & -\bar{a}_{n-2} & \dots & -\bar{a}_1 \end{bmatrix}, \quad \bar{\mathbf{B}}_m = \begin{bmatrix} 0 \\ 0 \\ \vdots \\ 0 \\ 1 \end{bmatrix},$$

$$\bar{\mathbf{C}}_m = \begin{bmatrix} \bar{b}_n & \dots & \bar{b}_\rho & 0 & \dots & 0 \end{bmatrix}, \quad \bar{\mathbf{R}}_m = \begin{bmatrix} 0 \\ 0 \\ \vdots \\ 0 \\ \bar{r} \end{bmatrix}, \tag{18}$$

where $\bar{a}_j = \sum_{i=1}^{m} \beta_i a_{j_i}$, $j = 1, \dots, n$, $\bar{b}_j = \sum_{i=1}^{m} \beta_i b_{j_i}$, $j = \rho, \dots, n$, and $\bar{r} = \sum_{i=1}^{m} \beta_i (r_i/b_i)$, $j = 1, \dots, n$, and where the parameters a_{j_i}, b_{j_i} and r_i are state-space model parameters defined as in Equation (35). Note that the state-space system with matrices from Equation (19) has relative degree ρ what is reflected in the form of matrix $\bar{\mathbf{C}}_m$ – last $(\rho - 1)$ elements are equal to 0 while $\bar{b}_\rho \neq 0$.

Proposition 1.1. *If the coincidence horizon H is lower than the plant relative degree ρ $(H < \rho)$, then the control law, Equation* (17) *is not applicable.*

Proof. By taking into account the form of matrices in Equation (19), it can easily be shown that

$$\left(\bar{\mathbf{A}}_m^H - \mathbf{I}\right)\left(\bar{\mathbf{A}}_m - \mathbf{I}\right)^{-1}\bar{\mathbf{B}}_m = \begin{bmatrix} 0 \\ \vdots \\ 0 \\ 1 \\ \cdot \\ \vdots \\ \cdot \end{bmatrix}, \tag{19}$$

i.e., the first $(n - H)$ elements of the vector are zeros, then there is the element 1, followed by $(H - 1)$ arbitrary elements. It then follows from Equations (16) and (19) that $g_0 = 0$ if $\rho > H$, and consequently the control law cannot be implemented.

The closed-loop system analysis makes sense only in the case of non-singular control law. Consequently, the choice of H is confined to the interval $[\rho, \infty)$.

6.3.2. *Stability Analysis*

The stability analysis of the proposed predictive control can be performed using an approach of linear matrix inequalities (LMI) proposed in Wang *et al.* (1996) and Tanaka *et al.* (1996) or it can be done assuming the frozen-time theory (Leith and Leithead, 1998, 1999) which discusses the relation between the nonlinear dynamical system and the associated linear time-varying system. There also exist alternative approaches for stability analysis (Baranyi *et al.*, 2003; Blažič *et al.*, 2002; Perng, 2012; Precup *et al.*, 2007).

In our stability study, we have assumed that the frozen-time system given in Equation (36) is a perfect model of the plant, i.e., $y_p(k) = y_m(k)$ for each k. Next, it is assumed that there is no external input to the closed-loop system ($w = 0$) — an assumption often made when analysing stability of the closed-loop system. Even if there is external signal, it is important that it is bounded. This is assured by selecting stable reference model, i.e., $|a_r| < 1$. The results of the stability analysis are also qualitatively the same if the system operates in the presence of bounded disturbances and noise.

Note that the last term in the parentheses of the control law Equation (17) is equal to $g_0\bar{r}$. This is obtained using Equations (16) and (19). Taking this into account and considering the above assumptions the control law, Equation (17) simplifies to:

$$u(k) = g_0^{-1}\left(-\bar{\mathbf{C}}_m\bar{\mathbf{A}}_m^H\mathbf{x}_m^0(k)\right) - \bar{r}. \tag{20}$$

Inserting the simplified control law (20) into the model of the "undelayed" plant. Equation (7), we obtain:

$$\mathbf{x}_m(k+1) = \left(\bar{\mathbf{A}}_m - \bar{\mathbf{B}}_m g_0^{-1}\bar{\mathbf{C}}_m\mathbf{A}_m^H\right)\mathbf{x}_m^0(k). \tag{21}$$

The closed-loop state transition matrix is defined as:

$$\mathbf{A}_c = \bar{\mathbf{A}}_m - \bar{\mathbf{B}}_m g_0^{-1}\bar{\mathbf{C}}_m\bar{\mathbf{A}}_m^H. \tag{22}$$

If the system is in the controllable canonical form, the second term on the right-hand side of Equation (22) has non-zero elements only in the last row of the matrix, and consequently $\mathbf{A}_c$ is also in the Frobenius form. The interesting form of the matrix is obtained in the case $H = \rho$. If $H = \rho$, it can easily be shown that $g_0 = \bar{b}_\rho$ and that $\mathbf{A}_c$ takes the following form:

$$\mathbf{A}_c = \begin{bmatrix} 0 & 1 & 0 & 0 & \cdots & 0 \\ 0 & 0 & 1 & 0 & \cdots & 0 \\ 0 & 0 & 0 & 1 & \cdots & 0 \\ \vdots & \vdots & \vdots & \cdots & \ddots & \vdots \\ 0 & 0 & 0 & 0 & \cdots & 1 \\ 0 & \cdots & 0 & -\dfrac{\bar{b}_n}{\bar{b}_\rho} & \cdots & -\dfrac{\bar{b}_{\rho+1}}{\bar{b}_\rho} \end{bmatrix}. \tag{23}$$

The corresponding characteristic equation of the system is:

$$z^\rho \left(z^{n-\rho} + \frac{\bar{b}_{\rho+1}}{\bar{b}_\rho} z^{n-\rho-1} + \frac{\bar{b}_{\rho+2}}{\bar{b}_\rho} z^{n-\rho-2} + \cdots + \frac{\bar{b}_{n-1}}{\bar{b}_\rho} z + \frac{\bar{b}_n}{\bar{b}_\rho} \right) = 0. \tag{24}$$

The solutions of this equation are closed-loop system poles: ρ poles lie in the origin of the z-plane while the other $(n - \rho)$ poles lie in the roots of the polynomial $\bar{b}_\rho z^{n-\rho} + \bar{b}_{\rho+1} z^{n-\rho-1} + \cdots + \bar{b}_{n-1} z + \bar{b}_n$. These results can be summarized in the following proposition:

Proposition 1.2. *When the coincidence horizon is equal to the relative degree of the model ($H = \rho$), then $(n - \rho)$ closed-loop poles tend to open-loop plant zeros, while the rest (ρ) of the poles go to the origin of z-plane.*

The proposition states that the closed-loop system is stable for $H = \rho$ if the plant is minimum phase. When this is not the case, the closed-loop system would become unstable if H is chosen equal to ρ. In such case the coincidence horizon should be larger.

The next proposition deals with the choice of a very large coincidence horizon.

Proposition 1.3. *When the coincidence horizon tends to infinity ($H \to \infty$) and the open-loop plant is stable, the closed-loop system poles tend to open-loop plant poles.*

Proof. The proposition can be proven easily. In the case of stable plants, $\mathbf{A}_m$ is a Hurwitz matrix that always satisfies:

$$\lim_{H\to\infty} \mathbf{A}_m^H = 0. \tag{25}$$

Combining Equations (22) and (25), we arrive at the final result

$$\lim_{H\to\infty} \mathbf{A}_c = \mathbf{A}_m. \tag{26}$$

The three propositions give some design guidelines on choosing the coincidence horizon H. If $H < \rho$, the control law is singular and thus not applicable. If $H = \rho$, the closed-loop poles go to open-loop zeros, i.e., high-gain controller is being used. If H is very large, the closed-loop poles go to open-loop poles, i.e., low-gain controller is being used and the system is almost open-loop. If the plant is stable, the closed-loop system can be made stable by choosing coincidence horizon large enough.

6.3.3. *Practical Example — Continuous Stirred-Tank Reactor*

The simulated continuous stirred-tank reactor (CSTR) process consists of an irreversible, exothermic reaction, $A \to B$, in a constant volume reactor cooled by a single coolant stream, which can be modelled by the following equation (Morningred *et al.*, 1992):

$$\dot{C}_A^0 = \frac{q}{V}\left[C_{A0} - C_A^0\right] - k_0 C_A^0 \exp\left(\frac{-E}{RT}\right). \tag{27}$$

$$\begin{aligned}\dot{T} = {} & \frac{q}{V}(T_0 - T) - \frac{k_0 \Delta H}{\rho C_p} C_A^0 \exp\left(\frac{-E}{RT}\right) + \frac{\rho_c C_{pc}}{\rho C_p V} q_c \\ & \times \left[1 - \exp\left(-\frac{hA}{q_c \rho_c C_{pc}}\right)\right](T_{c0} - T).\end{aligned} \tag{28}$$

The actual concentration C_A^0 is measured with a time delay $t_d = 0.5$ min:

$$C_A(t) = C_A^0(t - t_d). \tag{29}$$

The objective is to control the concentration of A (C_A) by manipulating the coolant flow rate q_c. This model is a modified version of the first tank of a two-tank CSTR example from Henson and Seborg (1990). In the original model, the time delay was zero.

The symbol q_c represents the coolant flow rate (manipulated variable) and the other symbols represent constant parameters whose values are defined in Table 6.1. The process dynamics are nonlinear due to the Arrhenius rate expression which describes the dependence of the reaction rate constant on the temperature (T). This is why the CSTR exhibits some operational and control problems. The reactor presents multiplicity behavior with respect to the coolant flow rate q_c, i.e., if the coolant flow rate $q_c \in (11.1$ l/min, 119.7 l/min) there are three equilibrium concentrations C_A. Stable equilibrium points are obtained in the following cases:

- $q_c > 11.1$ l/min $\Rightarrow$ stable equilibrium point 0.92 mol/l $< C_A <$ 1 mol/l.
- $q_c < 111.8$ l/min $\Rightarrow$ stable equilibrium point $C_A < 0.14$ mol/l (the point where $q_c \approx 111.8$ l/min is a Hopf Bifurcation point).

If $q_c \in (11.1$ l/min, 119.7 l/min), there is also at least one unstable point for the measured product concentration C_A. From the above facts, one can see that the

Table 6.1: Nominal CSTR parameter values.

Measured product concentration	C_A	0.1 mol/l
Reactor temperature	T	438.54 K
Coolant flow rate	q_c	103.41 l min^{-1}
Process flow rate	q	100 l min^{-1}
Feed concentration	C_{A0}	1 mol/l
Feed temperature	T_0	350 K
Inlet coolant temperature	T_{c0}	350 K
CSTR volume	V	100 l
Heat transfer term	hA	7×10^5 cal min^{-1} K^{-1}
Reaction rate constant	$k0$	7.2×10^{10} min^{-1}
Activation energy term	E/R	1×10^4 K
Heat of reaction	ΔH	-2×10^5 cal/mol
Liquid densities	ρ, ρ_c	1×10^3 g/l
Specific heats	C_p, C_{pc}	1cal $\text{g}^{-1}\text{K}^{-1}$

CSTR exhibits quite complex dynamics. In our application, we are interested in the operation in the stable operating point given by $q_c = 103.41\ \text{l min}^{-1}$ and $C_A = 0.1$ mol/l.

6.3.3.1. *Fuzzy identification of the continuous stirred-tank reactor*

From the description of the plant, it can be seen that there are two variables available for measurement — measured product concentration C_A and reactor temperature T. For the purpose of control, it is certainly beneficial to make use of both although it is not necessary to feed back reactor temperature if one wants to control product concentration. In our case, the simple discrete compensator was added to the measured reactor temperature output:

$$\Delta q_{c_{ff}} = K_{ff}\,[T(k) - T(k-1)], \tag{30}$$

where K_{ff} was chosen to be 3, while the sampling time $T_s = 0.1$ min. The above compensator is a sort of the D-controller that does not affect the equilibrium points of the system (the static curve remains the same), but it does to some extent affect their stability. In our case the Hopf bifurcation point moved from $(q_c, C_A) = (111.8\ \text{l/min}, 0.14\ \text{mol/l})$ to $(q_c, C_A) = (116.2\ \text{l/min}, 0.179\ \text{mol/l})$. This means that the stability interval for the product concentration C_A expanded from $(0, 0.14\ \text{mol/l})$ to $(0, 0.179\ \text{mol/l})$. The proposed FMBPC will be tested on the compensated plant, so we need fuzzy model of the compensated plant.

The plant was identified in a form of discrete second-order model with the premise defined as $\mathbf{x}_p^T = [C_A(k)]$ and the consequence vector as $\mathbf{x}^T = [C_A(k), C_A(k-1), q_c(k - T_{D_m}), 1]$. The functions $\phi_j(\cdot)$ can be arbitrary smooth functions in general, although linear or affine functions are usually used. Due to

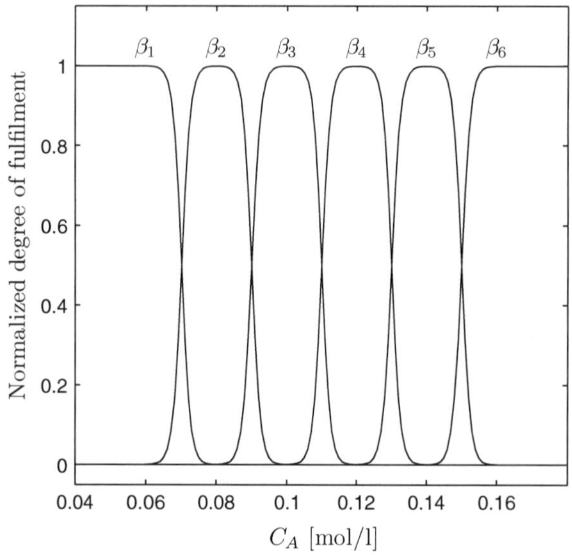

Figure 6.1: The membership functions.

strong nonlinearity the structure with six rules and equidistantly shaped gaussian membership functions was chosen. The normalized membership functions are shown in Figure 6.1.

The structure of the fuzzy model is the following:

$$\mathbf{R}_j\text{: } \mathbf{if}\ C_A(k)\ \mathbf{is}\ \mathbf{A}_j\ \mathbf{then}\ C_A(k+1)$$
$$= -a_{1j}C_A(k) - a_{2j}C_A(k-1) + b_{1j}q_c(k - T_{D_m}) + r_j \quad j = 1, \ldots, 6. \tag{31}$$

The parameters of the fuzzy form in Equation (31) have been estimated using least square algorithm where the data have been preprocessed using QR factorization (Moon and Stirling, 1999). The estimated parameters can be written as vectors $\mathbf{a}_1^T = [a_{11}, \ldots, a_{16}]$, $\mathbf{a}_2^T = [a_{21}, \ldots, a_{26}]$, $\mathbf{b}_1^T = [b_{11}, \ldots, b_{16}]$ and $\mathbf{r}_1^T = [r_{11}, \ldots, r_{16}]$. The estimated parameters in the case of CSTR are as follows:

$$\begin{aligned}
\mathbf{a}_1^T &= [-1.3462, -1.4506, -1.5681, -1.7114, -1.8111, -1.9157] \\
\mathbf{a}_2^T &= [0.4298, 0.5262, 0.6437, 0.7689, 0.8592, 0.9485] \\
\mathbf{b}_1^T &= [1.8124, 2.1795, 2.7762, 2.6703, 2.8716, 2.8500] \cdot 10^{-4} \\
\mathbf{r}_1^T &= [-1.1089, -1.5115, -2.1101, -2.1917, -2.5270, -2.7301] \cdot 10^{-2}
\end{aligned} \tag{32}$$

and $T_{D_m} = 5$.

After estimation of parameters, the TS fuzzy model Equation (31) was transformed into the state space form to simplify the procedure of obtaining the control law:

$$\mathbf{x}_m(k+1) = \sum_i \beta_i(\mathbf{x}_p(k))\left(\mathbf{A}_{m_i}\mathbf{x}_m(k) + \mathbf{B}_{m_i}u(k - T_{D_m}) + \mathbf{R}_{m_i}\right), \tag{33}$$

$$y_m(k) = \sum_i \beta_i(\mathbf{x}_p(k))\mathbf{C}_m\mathbf{x}_m(k), \tag{34}$$

$$\mathbf{A}_{m_i} = \begin{bmatrix} 0 & 1 \\ -a_{2_i} & -a_{1_i} \end{bmatrix} \quad \mathbf{B}_{m_i} = \begin{bmatrix} 0 \\ 1 \end{bmatrix} \quad \mathbf{C}_m = \begin{bmatrix} b_{1_i} & 0 \end{bmatrix} \quad \mathbf{R}_{m_i} = \begin{bmatrix} 0 \\ r_i/b_i \end{bmatrix}, \tag{35}$$

where the process measured output concentration C_A is denoted by y_m and the input flow q_c by u.

The frozen-time theory (Leith and Leithead, 1998, 1999) enables the relation between the nonlinear dynamical system and the associated linear time-varying system. The theory establishes the following fuzzy model

$$\begin{aligned} \mathbf{x}_m(k+1) &= \bar{\mathbf{A}}_m\mathbf{x}_m(k) + \bar{\mathbf{B}}_m u(k - T_{D_m}) + \bar{\mathbf{R}}_m, \\ y_m(k) &= \bar{\mathbf{C}}_m\mathbf{x}_m(k), \end{aligned} \tag{36}$$

where $\bar{\mathbf{A}}_m = \sum_i \beta_i(\mathbf{x}_p(k))\mathbf{A}_{m_i}$, $\bar{\mathbf{B}}_m = \sum_i \beta_i(\mathbf{x}_p(k))\mathbf{B}_{m_i}$, $\bar{\mathbf{C}}_m = \sum_i \beta_i(\mathbf{x}_p(k))\mathbf{C}_{m_i}$ and $\bar{\mathbf{R}}_m = \sum_i \beta_i(\mathbf{x}_p(k))\mathbf{R}_{m_i}$.

6.3.3.2. *Simulation results*

Reference tracking ability and disturbance rejection capability of the FMBPC control algorithm were tested experimentally on a simulated CSTR plant. The FMBPC was compared to the conventional PI controller.

In the first experiment, the control system was tested for tracking the reference signal that changed the operating point from nominal ($C_A = 0.1$ mol/l) to larger concentration values and back, and then to smaller concentration values and back. The proposed FMBPC used the following design parameters: $H = 9$ and $a_r = 0.96$. The parameters of the PI controller were obtained by minimising the following criterium:

$$C_{PI} = \sum_{k=0}^{400} (y_r(k) - y_{PI}(k))^2, \tag{37}$$

where $y_r(k)$ is the reference model output depicted in Figure 6.2, and $y_{PI}(k)$ is the controlled output in the case of PI control. This means that the parameters of the PI controller were minimized to obtain the best tracking of the reference

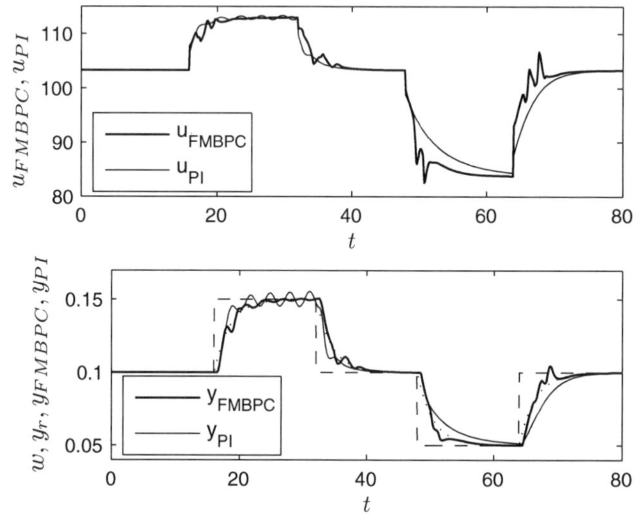

Figure 6.2: The performance of the FMBPC and the PI control in the case of reference trajectory tracking.

model output for the case treated in the first experiment. The optimal parameters were $K_P = 64.6454\ \text{l}^2\text{mol}^{-1}\text{min}^{-1}$ and $T_i = 0.6721$ min. Figure 6.2 also shows manipulated and controlled variables for the two approaches. In the lower part of the figure, the set-point is depicted with the dashed line, the reference model output with the dotted line, the FMBPC response with the thick solid line and the PI response with the thin solid line. The upper part of the figure represents the two control signals. The performance criteria obtained in the experiment are the following:

$$C_{\text{PI}} = \sum_{k=0}^{400} (y_r(k) - y_{PI}(k))^2 = 0.0165, \tag{38}$$

$$C_{\text{FMBPC}} = \sum_{k=0}^{400} (y_r(k) - y_{FMBPC}(k))^2 = 0.0061. \tag{39}$$

The disturbance rejection performance was tested with the same controllers that were set to the same design parameters as in the first experiment. In the simulation experiment, the step-like positive input disturbance of 3 l/min appeared and disappeared later. After some time, the step-like negative input disturbance of -3 l/min appeared and disappeared later. The results of the experiment are shown in Figure 6.3 where the signals are depicted by the same line types as in Figure 6.2. Similar performance criteria can be calculated as in the case of reference

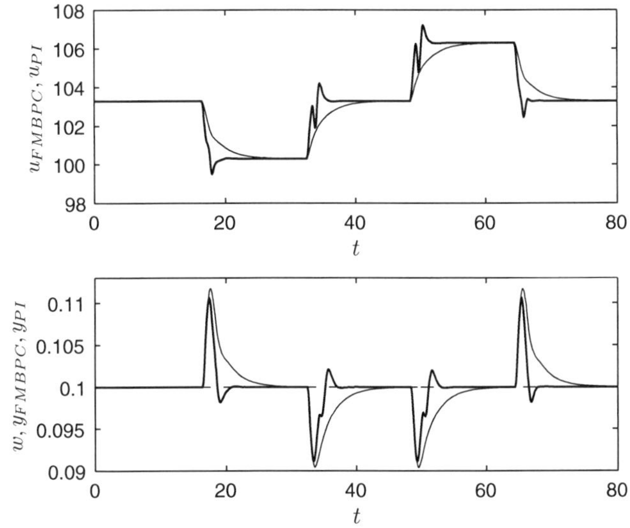

Figure 6.3: The control performance of the FMBPC and the PI control in the case of disturbance rejection.

tracking:

$$C_{\text{PI}} = \sum_{k=0}^{400} (y_r(k) - y_{PI}(k))^2 = 0.0076, \tag{40}$$

$$C_{\text{FMBPC}} = \sum_{k=0}^{400} (y_r(k) - y_{\text{FMBPC}}(k))^2 = 0.0036. \tag{41}$$

The obtained simulation results have shown that better performance criteria are obtained in the case of the FMBPC control in both control modes: The trajectory tracking mode and the disturbance rejection mode. This is obvious because the PI controller assumes linear process dynamics, while the FMBPC controller takes into account the plant nonlinearity through the fuzzy model of the plant. The proposed approach is very easy to implement and gives a high control performance.

6.4. Direct Fuzzy Model Reference Adaptive Control

We have already established that the fuzzy controllers are capable of controlling nonlinear plants. If the model of the plant is not only nonlinear but also unknown or poorly known, the solution becomes considerably more difficult. Nevertheless, several approaches exist to solve the problem. One possibility is to apply adaptive control. Adaptive control schemes for linear systems do not produce good results, although adaptive parameters try to track the "true" local linear parameters of the current operating point which is done with some lag after each operating-point change. To overcome this problem, adaptive control was extended in the 1980s and 1990s to time-varying and nonlinear plants (Krstić *et al.*, 1995).

It is also possible to introduce some sort of adaptation into the fuzzy controller. The first attempts at constructing a fuzzy adaptive controller can be traced back to Procyk and Mamdani (1979), where the so-called linguistic self-organizing controllers were introduced. Many approaches were later presented where a fuzzy model of the plant was constructed online, followed by control parameters adjustment (Layne and Passino, 1993). The main drawback of these schemes was that their stability was not treated rigorously. The universal approximation theorem (Wang and Mendel, 1992) provided a theoretical background for new fuzzy controllers (Pomares *et al.*, 2002; Precup and Preitl, 2006; Tang *et al.*, 1999; Wang and Mendel, 1992) whose stability was treated rigorously.

Robust adaptive control was proposed to overcome the problem of disturbances and unmodeled dynamics (Ioannou and Sun, 1996). Similar solutions have also been used in adaptive fuzzy and neural controllers, i.e., projection (Tong *et al.*, 2000), dead zone (Koo, 2001), leakage (Ge and Wang, 2002), adaptive fuzzy backstepping control (Tong and Li, 2012), etc. have been included in the adaptive law to prevent instability due to reconstruction error.

The control of a practically very important class of plants is treated in this section that, in our opinion, occurs quite often in process industries. The class of plants consists of nonlinear systems of arbitrary order but where the control law is based on the first-order nonlinear approximation. The dynamics not included in the first-order approximation are referred to as parasitic dynamics. The parasitic dynamics are treated explicitly in the development of the adaptive law to prevent the modeling error to grow unbounded. The class of plant also includes bounded disturbances.

The choice of simple nominal model results in very simple control and adaptive laws. The control law is similar to the one proposed by Blažič *et al.* (2003, 2012), but an extra term is added in this work where an adaptive law with leakage is presented (Blažič *et al.*, 2013). It will be shown that the proposed adaptive law is a natural way to cope with parasitic dynamics. The boundedness of estimated parameters, the tracking error and all the signals in the system will be proven if the leakage parameter σ' satisfies certain condition. This means that the proposed adaptive law ensures the global stability of the system. A very important property of the proposed approach is that it can be used in the consequent part of Takagi–Sugeno-based control. The approach enables easy implementation in the control systems with evolving antecedent part (Angelov *et al.*, 2001; Angelov and Filev, 2004; Angelov *et al.*, 2011; Cara *et al.*, 2010; Sadeghi–Tehran *et al.*, 2012). This combination results in a high-performance and robust control of nonlinear and slowly varying systems.

6.4.1. *The Class of Nonlinear Plants*

Our goal is to design control for a class of plants that include nonlinear time-invariant systems where the model behaves similarly to a first-order system at low frequencies (the frequency response is not defined for nonlinear systems so frequencies are meant here in a broader sense). If the plant were the first-order system (without parasitic dynamics), it could be described by a fuzzy model in the form of if-then rules:

$$\begin{aligned} &\textbf{if } z_1 \textbf{ is } A_{i_a} \textbf{ and } z_2 \textbf{ is } B_{i_b} \textbf{ then } \dot{y}_p = -a_i y_p + b_i u + c_i \\ &i_a = 1, \ldots, n_a \quad i_b = 1, \ldots, n_b \quad i = 1, \ldots, k, \end{aligned} \tag{42}$$

where u and y_p are the input and the output of the plant respectively, A_{i_a} and B_{i_b} are fuzzy membership functions, and a_i, b_i, and c_i are the plant parameters in the ith domain. Note the c_i term in the consequent. Such an additive term is obtained if a nonlinear system is linearized in an operating point. This additive term changes by changing the operating point. The term c_i is new comparing to the model used in Blažič *et al.* (2003, 2012). The antecedent variables that define the domain in which the system is currently situated are denoted by z_1 and z_2 (actually there can be only one such variable or there can also be more of them, but this does not affect the approach described here). There are n_a and n_b membership functions for the first and the second antecedent variables, respectively. The product $k = n_a \times n_b$ defines the number of fuzzy rules. The membership functions have to cover the whole operating area of the system. The output of the Takagi–Sugeno model is then given by the following equation

$$\dot{y}_p = \frac{\sum_{i=1}^{k} \left[\beta_i^0(\mathbf{x}_p)(-a_i y_p + b_i u + c_i)\right]}{\sum_{i=1}^{k} \beta_i^0(\mathbf{x}_p)}, \tag{43}$$

where $\mathbf{x}_p$ represents the vector of antecedent variables z_i (in the case of fuzzy model given by Equation (42), $\mathbf{x}_p = [z_1 \;\; z_2]^T$). The degree of fulfilment $\beta_i^0(\mathbf{x}_p)$ is obtained using the T-norm, which in this case is a simple algebraic product of membership functions

$$\beta_i^0(\mathbf{x}_p) = T(\mu_{A_{i_a}}(z_1), \mu_{B_{i_b}}(z_2)) = \mu_{A_{i_a}}(z_1) \cdot \mu_{B_{i_b}}(z_2), \tag{44}$$

where $\mu_{A_{i_a}}(z_1)$ and $\mu_{B_{i_b}}(z_2)$ stand for degrees of fulfilment of the corresponding fuzzy rule. The degrees of fulfilment for the whole set of fuzzy rules can be written in a compact form as

$$\boldsymbol{\beta}^0 = \left[\beta_1^0\ \beta_2^0 \ldots \beta_k^0\right]^T \in \mathbb{R}^k \tag{45}$$

or in a more convenient normalized form

$$\boldsymbol{\beta} = \frac{\boldsymbol{\beta}^0}{\sum_{i=1}^k \beta_i^0} \in \mathbb{R}^k. \tag{46}$$

Due to Equations (43) and (46), the first-order plant can be modeled in fuzzy form as

$$\dot{y}_p = -(\boldsymbol{\beta}^T\mathbf{a})y_p + (\boldsymbol{\beta}^T\mathbf{b})u + (\boldsymbol{\beta}^T\mathbf{c}), \tag{47}$$

where $\mathbf{a} = \left[a_1\ a_2 \cdots a_k\right]^T$, $\mathbf{b} = \left[b_1\ b_2 \cdots b_k\right]^T$, and $\mathbf{c} = \left[c_1\ c_2 \cdots c_k\right]^T$ are vectors of unknown plant parameters in respective domains ($\mathbf{a}, \mathbf{b}, \mathbf{c} \in \mathbb{R}^k$).

To assume that the controlled system is of the first order is a quite huge idealization. Parasitic dynamics and disturbances are therefore included in the model of the plant. The fuzzy model of the first order is generalized by adding stable factor plant perturbations and disturbances, which results in the following model (Blažič *et al.*, 2003):

$$\begin{aligned}\dot{y}_p(t) = &-(\boldsymbol{\beta}^T(t)\mathbf{a})y_p(t) + (\boldsymbol{\beta}^T(t)\mathbf{b})u(t) + (\boldsymbol{\beta}^T\mathbf{c}) \\ &- \Delta_y(p)y_p(t) + \Delta_u(p)u(t) + d(t),\end{aligned} \tag{48}$$

where p is a differential operator d/dt, $\Delta_y(p)$ and $\Delta_u(p)$ are stable strictly proper linear operators, while d is bounded signal due to disturbances (Blažič *et al.*, 2003).

Equation (48) represents the class of plants to be controlled by the approach proposed in the following sections. The control is designed based on the model given by Equation (47) while the robustness properties of the algorithm prevent the instability due to parasitic dynamics and disturbances.

6.4.2. *The Proposed Fuzzy Adaptive Control Algorithm*

A fuzzy model reference adaptive control is proposed to achieve tracking control for the class of plants described in the previous section. The control goal is that the plant output follows the output y_m of the reference model. The latter is defined by a first order linear system $G_m(p)$:

$$y_m(t) = G_m(p)w(t) = \frac{b_m}{p + a_m}w(t), \tag{49}$$

where $w(t)$ is the reference signal while b_m and a_m are the constants that define desired behavior of the closed system. The tracking error

$$\varepsilon(t) = y_p(t) - y_m(t), \tag{50}$$

therefore represents some measure of the control quality. To solve the control problem simple control and adaptive laws are proposed in the following sub-sections.

6.4.2.1. *Control law*

The control law is very similar to the one proposed by Blažič *et al.* (2003, 2012):

$$u(t) = \left(\boldsymbol{\beta}^T(t)\hat{\mathbf{f}}(t)\right) w(t) - \left(\boldsymbol{\beta}^T(t)\hat{\mathbf{q}}(t)\right) y_p(t) + \left(\boldsymbol{\beta}^T(t)\hat{\mathbf{r}}(t)\right), \tag{51}$$

where $\hat{\mathbf{f}}(t) \in \mathbb{R}^k$, $\hat{\mathbf{q}}(t) \in \mathbb{R}^k$, and $\hat{\mathbf{r}}(t) \in \mathbb{R}^k$ are the control gain vectors to be determined by the adaptive law. This control law is obtained by generalizing the model reference adaptive control algorithm for the first-order linear plant to the fuzzy case. The control law also includes the third term that is new with respect to the one in Blažič *et al.* (2012). It is used to compensate the $(\boldsymbol{\beta}^T\mathbf{c})$ term in Equation (48).

6.4.2.2. *Adaptive law*

The adaptive law proposed in this chapter is based on the adaptive law from Blažič *et al.* (2003). The e_1-modification was used in the leakage term in Blažič *et al.* (2012). An alternative approach was proposed in Blažič *et al.* (2012) where quadratic term is used the leakage. But a new adaptive law for $\hat{r}_i$ is also proposed here:

$$\begin{aligned}
\dot{\hat{f}}_i &= -\gamma_{fi} b_{\text{sign}} \varepsilon w \beta_i - \gamma_{fi}\sigma' w^2 \beta_i^2 (\hat{f}_i - \hat{f}_i^*) \quad i = 1, 2, \ldots, k, \\
\dot{\hat{q}}_i &= \gamma_{qi} b_{\text{sign}} \varepsilon y_p \beta_i - \gamma_{qi}\sigma' y_p^2 \beta_i^2 (\hat{q}_i - \hat{q}_i^*) \quad i = 1, 2, \ldots, k, \\
\dot{\hat{r}}_i &= -\gamma_{ri} b_{\text{sign}} \varepsilon \beta_i - \gamma_{ri}\sigma' \beta_i^2 (\hat{r}_i - \hat{r}_i^*) \quad i = 1, 2, \ldots, k,
\end{aligned} \tag{52}$$

where γ_{fi}, γ_{qi}, and γ_{ri} are positive scalars referred to as adaptive gains, $\sigma' > 0$ is the parameter of the leakage term, $\hat{f}_i^*$, $\hat{q}_i^*$, and $\hat{r}_i^*$ are the *a priori* estimates of the control gains $\hat{f}_i$, $\hat{q}_i$, and $\hat{r}_i$ respectively, and b_{sign} is defined as follows:

$$b_{\text{sign}} = \begin{cases} 1 & b_1 > 0, b_2 > 0, \ldots b_k > 0 \\ -1 & b_1 < 0, b_2 < 0, \ldots b_k < 0 \end{cases}. \tag{53}$$

If the signs of all elements in vector $\mathbf{b}$ are not the same, the plant is not controllable for some $\boldsymbol{\beta}$ ($\boldsymbol{\beta}^T\mathbf{b}$ is equal to 0 for this $\boldsymbol{\beta}$) and any control signal does not have an effect.

It is possible to rewrite the adaptive law, Equation (52) in the compact form if the control gain vectors $\hat{\mathbf{f}}$, $\hat{\mathbf{q}}$, and $\hat{\mathbf{r}}$ are defined as

$$\begin{aligned}\hat{\mathbf{f}}^T &= \left[\hat{f}_1\ \hat{f}_2 \ldots \hat{f}_k\right],\\ \hat{\mathbf{q}}^T &= \left[\hat{q}_1\ \hat{q}_2 \ldots \hat{q}_k\right],\\ \hat{\mathbf{r}}^T &= \left[\hat{r}_1\ \hat{r}_2 \ldots \hat{r}_k\right].\end{aligned} \tag{54}$$

Then the adaptive law, Equation (52), takes the following form:

$$\begin{aligned}\dot{\hat{\mathbf{f}}} &= -\mathbf{\Gamma}_f b_{\text{sign}} \varepsilon w \boldsymbol{\beta} - \mathbf{\Gamma}_f \sigma' w^2 \operatorname{diag}(\boldsymbol{\beta}) \operatorname{diag}(\boldsymbol{\beta})(\hat{\mathbf{f}} - \hat{\mathbf{f}}^*),\\ \dot{\hat{\mathbf{q}}} &= \mathbf{\Gamma}_q b_{\text{sign}} \varepsilon y_p \boldsymbol{\beta} - \mathbf{\Gamma}_q \sigma' y_p^2 \operatorname{diag}(\boldsymbol{\beta}) \operatorname{diag}(\boldsymbol{\beta})(\hat{\mathbf{q}} - \hat{\mathbf{q}}^*),\\ \dot{\hat{\mathbf{r}}} &= -\mathbf{\Gamma}_r b_{\text{sign}} \varepsilon \boldsymbol{\beta} - \mathbf{\Gamma}_r \sigma' \operatorname{diag}(\boldsymbol{\beta}) \operatorname{diag}(\boldsymbol{\beta})(\hat{\mathbf{r}} - \hat{\mathbf{r}}^*),\end{aligned} \tag{55}$$

where $\mathbf{\Gamma}_f \in \mathbb{R}^{k\times k}$, $\mathbf{\Gamma}_q \in \mathbb{R}^{k\times k}$, and $\mathbf{\Gamma}_r \in \mathbb{R}^{k\times k}$ are positive definite matrices, $\operatorname{diag}(\mathbf{x}) \in \mathbb{R}^{k\times k}$ is a diagonal matrix with the elements of vector $\mathbf{x}$ on the main diagonal, while $\hat{\mathbf{f}}^* \in \mathbb{R}^k$, $\hat{\mathbf{q}}^* \in \mathbb{R}^k$, and $\hat{\mathbf{r}}^* \in \mathbb{R}^k$ are the *a priori* estimates of the control gain vectors.

6.4.2.3. *The sketch of the stability proof*

The reference model Equation (49) can be rewritten in the following form:

$$\dot{y}_m = -a_m y_m + b_m w. \tag{56}$$

By subtracting Equation (56) from Equation (48), the following tracking-error model is obtained

$$\begin{aligned}\dot{\varepsilon} = -a_m \varepsilon &+ \left[(\boldsymbol{\beta}^T \mathbf{b})(\boldsymbol{\beta}^T \hat{\mathbf{f}}) - b_m\right] w - \left[(\boldsymbol{\beta}^T \mathbf{b})(\boldsymbol{\beta}^T \hat{\mathbf{q}}) + (\boldsymbol{\beta}^T \mathbf{a}) - a_m\right] y_p\\ &+ \left[(\boldsymbol{\beta}^T \mathbf{b})(\boldsymbol{\beta}^T \hat{\mathbf{r}}) + (\boldsymbol{\beta}^T \mathbf{c})\right] + \Delta_u(p) u - \Delta_y(p) y_p + d.\end{aligned} \tag{57}$$

Now we assume that there exist constant control parameters $\mathbf{f}^*$, $\mathbf{q}^*$, and $\mathbf{r}^*$ that stabilize the closed-loop system. This is a mild assumption and it is always fulfilled unless the unmodeled dynamics are unacceptably high. These parameters are only needed in the stability analysis and can be chosen to make the "diference" between the closed-loop system and the reference model small in some sense (the defintion of this "diference" is not important for the analysis). The parameters $\mathbf{f}^*$, $\mathbf{q}^*$, and $\mathbf{r}^*$ are sometimes called the "true" parameters because they result in the perfect tracking in the absence of unmodeled dynamics and disturbances. The parameter errors are defined as:

$$\tilde{\mathbf{f}} = \hat{\mathbf{f}} - \mathbf{f}^*,$$
$$\tilde{\mathbf{q}} = \hat{\mathbf{q}} - \mathbf{q}^*, \tag{58}$$
$$\tilde{\mathbf{r}} = \hat{\mathbf{r}} - \mathbf{r}^*.$$

The expressions in the square brackets in Equation (57) can be rewritten similarly as in Blažič *et al.* (2003):

$$\begin{aligned}
\left[(\boldsymbol{\beta}^T\mathbf{b})(\boldsymbol{\beta}^T\hat{\mathbf{f}}) - b_m\right] &= b_{\text{sign}}\boldsymbol{\beta}^T\tilde{\mathbf{f}} + \eta_f = b_{\text{sign}}\sum_{i=1}^{k}\beta_i\tilde{f}_i + \eta_f,\\
\left[(\boldsymbol{\beta}^T\mathbf{b})(\boldsymbol{\beta}^T\hat{\mathbf{q}}) + (\boldsymbol{\beta}^T\mathbf{a}) - a_m\right] &= b_{\text{sign}}\boldsymbol{\beta}^T\tilde{\mathbf{q}} + \eta_q = b_{\text{sign}}\sum_{i=1}^{k}\beta_i\tilde{q}_i + \eta_q,\\
\left[(\boldsymbol{\beta}^T\mathbf{b})(\boldsymbol{\beta}^T\hat{\mathbf{r}}) + (\boldsymbol{\beta}^T\mathbf{c})\right] &= b_{\text{sign}}\boldsymbol{\beta}^T\tilde{\mathbf{r}} + \eta_r = b_{\text{sign}}\sum_{i=1}^{k}\beta_i\tilde{r}_i + \eta_r,
\end{aligned} \tag{59}$$

where bounded residuals $\eta_f(t)$, $\eta_q(t)$, and $\eta_r(t)$ are introduced [the boundedness can be shown simply; see also (Blažič *et al.*, 2003)]. The following Lyapunov function is proposed for the proof of stability:

$$V = \frac{1}{2}\varepsilon^2 + \frac{1}{2}\sum_{i=1}^{k}\gamma_{fi}^{-1}\tilde{f}_i^2 + \frac{1}{2}\sum_{i=1}^{k}\gamma_{qi}^{-1}\tilde{q}_i^2 + \frac{1}{2}\sum_{i=1}^{k}\gamma_{ri}^{-1}\tilde{r}_i^2. \tag{60}$$

Calculating the derivative of the Lyapunov function along the solution of the system, Equation (57) and taking into account Equation (59) and adaptive laws, Equation (52), we obtain:

$$\begin{aligned}
\dot{V} &= \varepsilon\dot{\varepsilon} + \sum_{i=1}^{k}\gamma_{fi}^{-1}\tilde{f}_i\dot{\hat{f}}_i + \sum_{i=1}^{k}\gamma_{qi}^{-1}\tilde{q}_i\dot{\hat{q}}_i + \sum_{i=1}^{k}\gamma_{ri}^{-1}\tilde{r}_i\dot{\hat{r}}_i\\
&= -a_m\varepsilon^2 + \eta_f w\varepsilon - \eta_q y_p\varepsilon + \eta_r\varepsilon + \varepsilon\Delta_u(p)u - \varepsilon\Delta_y(p)y_p + \varepsilon d\\
&\quad - \sum_{i=1}^{k}\sigma' w^2\beta_i^2(\hat{f}_i - \hat{f}_i^*)\tilde{f}_i - \sum_{i=1}^{k}\sigma' y_p^2\beta_i^2(\hat{q}_i - \hat{q}_i^*)\tilde{q}_i - \sum_{i=1}^{k}\sigma'\beta_i^2(\hat{r}_i - \hat{r}_i^*)\tilde{r}_i.
\end{aligned} \tag{61}$$

In principle, the first term on the right-hand side of Equation (61) is used to compensate for the next six terms while the last three terms prevent parameter drift. The terms from the second one to the seventh one are formed as a product between the tracking error $\varepsilon(t)$ and a combined error $E(t)$ defined as:

$$E(t) = \eta_f(t)w(t) - \eta_q(t)y_p(t) + \eta_r(t) + \Delta_u(p)u(t) - \Delta_y(p)y_p(t) + d(t). \tag{62}$$

Equation (61) can be rewritten as:

$$\dot{V} = -a_m\left(\varepsilon^2 - \frac{E\varepsilon}{a_m}\right) - \sum_{i=1}^{k}\sigma' w^2\beta_i^2(\hat{f}_i - \hat{f}_i^*)\tilde{f}_i - \sum_{i=1}^{k}\sigma' y_p^2\beta_i^2(\hat{q}_i - \hat{q}_i^*)\tilde{q}_i - \sum_{i=1}^{k}\sigma'\beta_i^2(\hat{r}_i - \hat{r}_i^*)\tilde{r}_i. \tag{63}$$

The first term on the right-hand side of Equation (63) becomes negative if $|\varepsilon| > \frac{|E|}{a_m}$. If the combined error, were *a priori* bounded, the boundedness of the tracking error ε would be more or less proven. The problem lies in the fact that not only bounded signals $(w(t), \eta_f(t), \eta_q(t), \eta_r(t), d(t))$ are included in $E(t)$, but also the ones whose boundedness is yet to be proven $(u(t), y_p(t))$. If the system becomes unstable, the plant output $y_p(t)$ becomes unbounded and, consequently, the same applies to the control input $u(t)$. If $y_p(t)$ is bounded, it is easy to see from the control law that $u(t)$ is also bounded. Unboundedness of $y_p(t)$ is prevented by leakage terms in the adaptive law. In the last three terms in Equation (63) that are due to the leakage there are three similar expressions. They have the following form:

$$(\hat{f}_i(t) - \hat{f}_i^*)\tilde{f}_i(t) = (\hat{f}_i(t) - \hat{f}_i^*)(\hat{f}_i(t) - f_i^*). \tag{64}$$

It is simple to see that this expression is positive if either $\hat{f}_i > \max\{\hat{f}_i^*, f_i^*\}$ or $\hat{f}_i < \min\{\hat{f}_i^*, f_i^*\}$. The same reasoning applies to $\hat{q}_i$ and $\hat{r}_i$. This means that the last three terms in Equation (63) become negative if the estimated parameters are large (or small) enough. The novelty of the proposed adaptive law with respect to the one in Blažič *et al.* (2003), is in the qudratic terms with y_p and w in the leakage. These terms are used to help cancelling the contribution of εE in Equation (63):

$$\varepsilon E = \varepsilon\eta_f w - \varepsilon\eta_q y_p + \varepsilon\eta_r + \varepsilon\Delta_u(p)u - \varepsilon\Delta_y(p)y_p + \varepsilon d. \tag{65}$$

Since $\varepsilon(t)$ is the difference between $y_p(t)$ and $y_m(t)$ and the latter is bounded, $\varepsilon = O(y_p)$ when y_p tends to infinity. By analyzing the control law and taking into account stability of parasitic dynamics $\Delta_u(s)$ and $\Delta_y(s)$, the following can be concluded:

$$u = O(y_p),\ \Delta_u(p)u = O(y_p) \Rightarrow \varepsilon E = O(y_p^2). \tag{66}$$

The third term on the right-hand side of Equation (63) is $-(\hat{q}_i - \hat{q}_i^*)\tilde{q}_i O(y_p^2)$ which means that the "gain" $(\hat{q}_i - \hat{q}_i^*)\tilde{q}_i$ with respect to y_p^2 of the negative contributions to $\dot{V}$ can always become greater (as a result of adaptation) than the fixed gain of quadratic terms with y_p in Equation (65). The growth of the estimated parameters is also problematic because these parameters are control gains and high gains can induce instability in combination with parasitic dynamics. Consequently, σ' has to be chosen large enough to prevent this type of instability. Note that the stabilization in the presence of parasitic dynamics is achieved without using an explicit dynamic normalization that was used in Blažič *et al.* (2003).

The stability analysis of a similar adaptive law for linear systems was treated in Blažič *et al.* (2010) where it was proven that all the signals in the system are bounded and the tracking error converges to a residual set whose size depends on the modeling error if the leakage parameter σ' is chosen large enough with respect to the norm of parasitic dynamics. In the approach proposed in this chapter, the "modeling error" is $E(t)$ from Equation (62) and therefore the residual-set size depends on the size of the norm of the transfer functions $\|\Delta_u\|$ and $\|\Delta_y\|$, the size of the disturbance d, and the size of the bounded residuals $\eta_f(t)$, $\eta_q(t)$, and $\eta_r(t)$.

Only the adaptation of the consequent part of the fuzzy rules is treated in this chapter. The stability of the system is guaranteed for any (fixed) shape of the membership functions in the antecedent part. This means that this approach is very easy to combine with existing evolving approaches for the antecedent part. If the membership functions are slowly evolving, these changes introduce another term to $\dot{V}$ which can be shown not to be larger than $O(y_p^2)$. This means that the system stability is preserved by the robustness properties of the adaptive laws. If, however, fast changes of the membership functions occur, a rigorous stability analysis would have to be performed.

6.4.3. *Simulation Example — Three-Tank System*

A simulation example will be given that illustrates the proposed approach. A simulated plant was chosen since it is easier to make the same operating conditions than it would be when testing on a real plant. The simulated test plant consisted of three water tanks. The schematic representation of the plant is given in Figure 6.4. The control objective was to maintain the water level in the third tank by changing the inflow into the first tank.

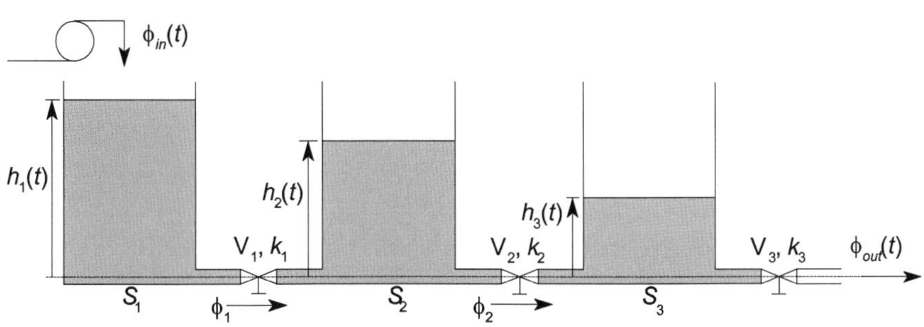

Figure 6.4: Schematic representation of the plant.

When modeling the plant, it was assumed that the flow through the valve was proportional to the square root of the pressure difference on the valve. The mass conservation equations for the three tanks are:

$$\begin{aligned} S_1\dot{h}_1 &= \phi_{in} - k_1\,\mathrm{sign}(h_1-h_2)\sqrt{|h_1-h_2|},\\ S_2\dot{h}_2 &= k_1\,\mathrm{sign}(h_1-h_2)\sqrt{|h_1-h_2|} - k_2\,\mathrm{sign}(h_2-h_3)\sqrt{|h_2-h_3|},\\ S_3\dot{h}_3 &= k_2\,\mathrm{sign}(h_2-h_3)\sqrt{|h_2-h_3|} - k_3\,\mathrm{sign}(h_3)\sqrt{|h_3|}, \end{aligned} \tag{67}$$

where ϕ_{in} is the volume inflow into the first tank, h_1, h_2, and h_3 are the water levels in three tanks, S_1, S_2, and S_3 are areas of the tanks cross-sections, and k_1, k_2, and k_3 are coefficients of the valves. The following values were chosen for the parameters of the system:

$$\begin{aligned} S_1 = S_2 = S_3 = 2\cdot 10^{-2}\mathrm{m}^2\\ k_1 = k_2 = k_3 = 2\cdot 10^{-4}\mathrm{m}^{5/2}\mathrm{s}^{-1}. \end{aligned} \tag{68}$$

The nominal value of inflow ϕ_{in} was set to $8\cdot 10^{-5}\mathrm{m}^3\mathrm{s}^{-1}$, resulting in steady-state values 0.48 m, 0.32 m, and 0.16 m for h_1, h_2, and h_3, respectively. In the following, u and y_p denote deviations of ϕ_{in} and h_3 respectively from the operating point.

By analyzing the plant, it can be seen that the plant is nonlinear. It has to be pointed out that the parasitic dynamics are also nonlinear, not just the dominant part as was assumed in deriving the control algorithm. This means that this example will also test the ability of the proposed control to cope with nonlinear parasitic dynamics. The coefficients of the linearized system in different operating points depend on u, h_1, h_2, and h_3 even though that only y_p will be used as an antecedent variable z_1 which is again violation of the basic assumptions but still produces fairly good results.

The proposed control algorithm was compared to a classical model reference adaptive control (MRAC) with e_1-modification. Adaptive gains γ_{fi}, γ_{qi}, and γ_{ri} in the case of the proposed approach were the same as γ_f, γ_q, and γ_r, respectively, in the case of MRAC. A reference signal was chosen as a periodic piece-wise constant function which covered quite a wide area around the operating point ($\pm 50\%$ of the nominal value). There were 11 triangular fuzzy membership functions (the fuzzification variable was y_p) used; these were distributed evenly across the interval $[-0.1, 0.1]$. As already said, the evolving of the antecedent part was not done in this work. The control input signal u was saturated at the interval $[-8\cdot 10^{-5}, 8\cdot 10^{-5}]$. No prior knowledge of the estimated parameters was available to us, so the initial parameter estimates were 0 for all examples.

The design objective is that the output of the plant follows the output of the reference model $0.01/(s+0.01)$. The reference signal was the same in all cases.

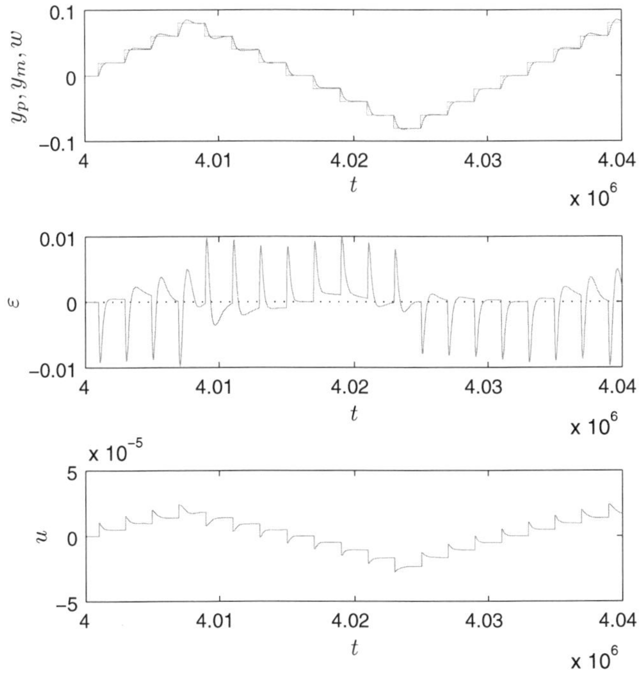

Figure 6.5: The MRAC controller — time plots of the reference signal and outputs of the plant and the reference model (upper figure), time plot of tracking error (middle figure), and time plot of the control signal (lower figure).

It consisted of a periodic signal. The results of the experiment with the classical MRAC controller with e_1-modification are shown in Figure 6.5.

We used the following design parameters: $\gamma_f = 10^{-4}, \gamma_q = 2 \cdot 10^{-4}, \gamma_r = 10^{-6}$, $\sigma' = 0.1$. Figures 6.6 and 6.7 show the results of the proposed approach, the former shows a period of system responses after the adaptation has settled, the latter depicts time plots of the estimated parameters. Since $\hat{\mathbf{f}}$, $\hat{\mathbf{q}}$, and $\hat{\mathbf{r}}$ are vectors, all elements of the vectors are depicted. Note that every change in the reference signal results in a sudden increase in tracking error ε (up to 0.01). This is due to the fact that zero tracking of the reference model with relative degree 1 is not possible if the plant has relative degree 3.

The experiments show that the performance of the proposed approach is better than the performance of the MRAC controller for linear plant which is expectable due to nonlinearity of the plant. Very good results are obtained in the case of the proposed approach even though that the parasitic dynamics are nonlinear and linearized parameters depend not only on the antecedent variable y_p but also on others. The spikes on ε in Figure 6.6 are consequences of the fact that the plant of 'relative degree' 3 is forced to follow the reference model of relative degree 1. These spikes are inevitable no matter which controller is used.

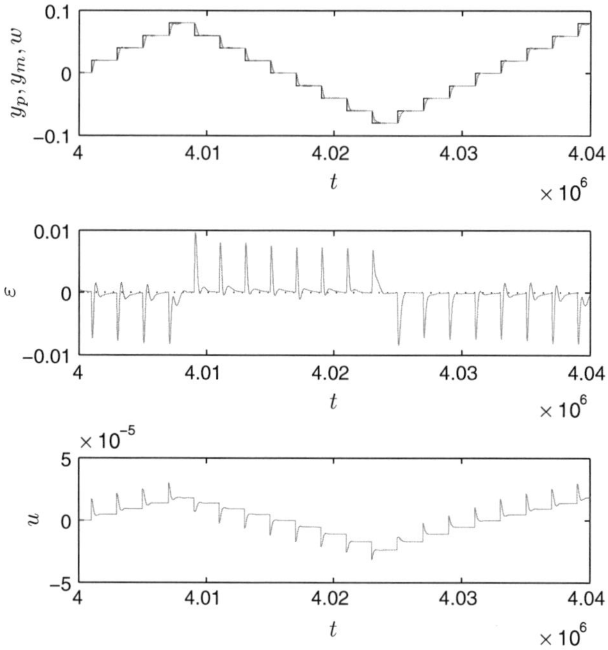

Figure 6.6: The proposed approach — time plots of the reference signal and outputs of the plant and the reference model (upper figure), time plot of tracking error (middle figure), and time plot of the control signal (lower figure).

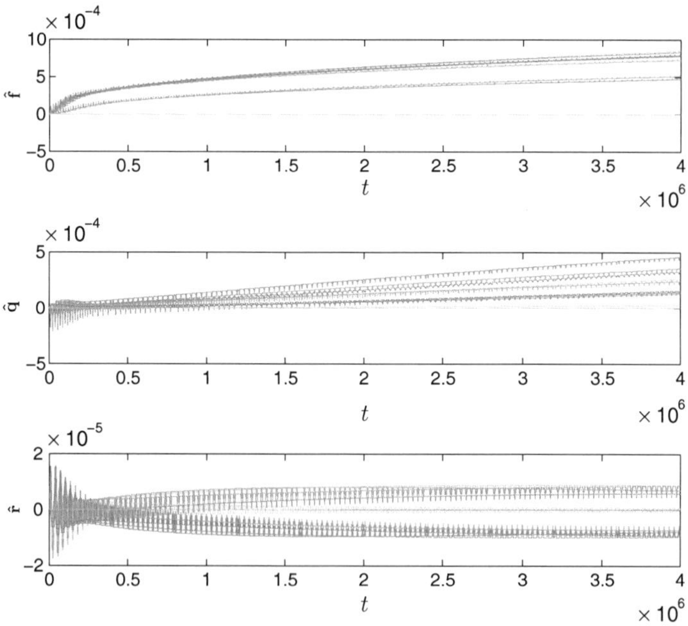

Figure 6.7: The proposed approach — time plots of the control gains.

The drawback of the proposed approach is relatively slow convergence since the parameters are only adapted when the corresponding membership is non-zero. This drawback can be overcome by using classical MRAC in the beginning when there are no parameter estimates or the estimates are bad. When the system approaches desired behavior, the adaptation can switch to the proposed one by initializing all elements of vectors $\hat{\mathbf{f}}$, $\hat{\mathbf{q}}$, and $\hat{\mathbf{r}}$ with estimated scalar parameters from the classical MRAC.

6.5. Conclusion

This chapter presents two approaches to the control of nonlinear systems. We chose these two solutions because they are easy to tune and easy to implement on the one hand, but they also guarantee the stability under some assumptions on the other. Both approaches also only deal with the rule consequents and are easy to extend to the variants with evolving antecedent part.

References

Abonyi, J., Nagy, L. and Szeifert, F. (2001). Fuzzy model-based predictive control by instantaneous linearization. *Fuzzy Sets Syst.*, 120(1), pp. 109–122.

Andone, D. and Hossu, A. (2004). Predictive control based on fuzzy model for steam generator. In *Proc. IEEE Int. Conf. Fuzzy Syst.*, Budapest, Hungary, 3, pp. 1245–1250.

Angelov, P., Buswell, R. A., Wright, J. and Loveday, D. (2001). Evolving rule-based control. In *Proc. of EUNITE Symposium*, pp. 36–41.

Angelov, P. and Filev, D. P. (2004). An approach to online identification of Takagi–Sugeno fuzzy models. *IEEE Syst. Man Cybern.*, pp. 484–498.

Angelov, P., Sadeghi–Tehran, P. and Ramezani, R. (2011). An approach to automatic real-time novelty detection, object identification, and tracking in video streams based on recursive density estimation and evolving Takagi–Sugeno fuzzy systems. *Int. J. Intell. Syst.*, 26(3), pp. 189–205.

Babuska, R. (1998). *Fuzzy Modeling for Control*. Kluwer Academic Publishers.

Baranyi, P., Tikk, D., Yam, Y. and Patton, R. J. (2003). From differential equations to PDC controller design via numerical transformation. *Comput. Ind.*, 51(3), pp. 281–297.

Bequette, B. W. (1991). Nonlinear control of chemical processes: A review. *Ind. Eng. Chem. Res.*, 30, pp. 1391–1413.

Blažič, S. and Škrjanc, I. (2007). Design and stability analysis of fuzzy model-based predictive control — a case study. *J. Intell. Robot. Syst.*, 49(3), pp. 279–292.

Blažič, S., Škrjanc, I. and Matko, D. (2002). Globally stable model reference adaptive control based on fuzzy description of the plant. *Int. J. Syst. Sci.*, 33(12), pp. 995–1012.

Blažič, S., Škrjanc, I. and Matko, D. (2003). Globally stable direct fuzzy model reference adaptive control. *Fuzzy Sets Syst.*, 139(1), pp. 3–33.

Blažič, S., Škrjanc, I. and Matko, D. (2010). Adaptive law with a new leakage term. *IET Control Theory Appl.*, 4(9), pp. 1533–1542.

Blažič, S., Škrjanc, I. and Matko, D. (2012). A new fuzzy adaptive law with leakage. In *2012 IEEE Conf. Evolving Adapt. Intell. Syst. (EAIS)*. Madrid: IEEE, pp. 47–50.

Blažič, S., Škrjanc, I. and Matko, D. (2013). A robust fuzzy adaptive law for evolving control systems. *Evolving Syst.*, 5(1), pp. 3–10. doi: 10.1007/s12530-013-9084-7.

Cara, A. B., Lendek, Z., Babuska, R., Pomares, H. and Rojas, I. (2010). Online self-organizing adaptive fuzzy controller: Application to a nonlinear servo system. In *2010 IEEE Int. Conf. Fuzzy Syst. (FUZZ)*, Barcelona, pp. 1–8. doi: 10.1109/FUZZY.2010.5584027.

Cervantes, L., Castillo, O. and Melin, P. (2011). Intelligent control of nonlinear dynamic plants using a hierarchical modular approach and type-2 fuzzy logic. In Batyrshin, I. and Sidorov, G. (eds.), *Adv. Soft Comput. Lect. Notes Comput. Sci.*, 7095, pp. 1–12.

Clarke, D. W., Mohtadi, C. and Tuffs, P. S. (1987). Generalized predictive control — part 1, part 2. *Autom.*, 24, pp. 137–160.

Cutler, C. R. and Ramaker, B. L. (1980). Dynamic matrix control — a computer control algorithm. In *Proc. ACC*. San Francisco, CA, paper WP5-B.

De Keyser, R. M. C., Van de Valde, P. G. A. and Dumortier, F. A. G. (1988). A comparative study of self-adaptive long-range predictive control methods. *Autom.*, 24(2), pp. 149–163.

Doyle, F. J., Ogunnaike, T. A. and Pearson, R. K. (1995). Nonlinear model-based control using second-order volterra models. *Autom.*, 31, pp. 697–714.

Figueroa, J. L. (2001). Piecewise linear models in model predictive control. *Latin Am. Appl. Res.*, 31(4), pp. 309–315.

Ge, S. and Wang, J. (2002). Robust adaptive neural control for a class of perturbed strict feedback nonlinear systems. *IEEE Trans. Neural Netw.*, 13(6), pp. 1409–1419.

Goldberg, R. R. (1976). *Methods of Real Analysis*. New York, USA: John Wiley and Sons.

Henson, M. A. (1998). Nonlinear model predictive control: current status and future directions. *Comput. Chem. Eng.*, 23, pp. 187–202.

Henson, M. A. and Seborg, D. E. (1990). Input–output linerization of general processes. *AIChE J.*, 36, p. 1753.

Ioannou, P. A. and Sun, J. (1996). *Robust Adaptive Control*. Upper Saddle River, New Jersey, USA: Prentice-Hall.

Johanyák, Z. C. and Papp, O. (2012). A hybrid algorithm for parameter tuning in fuzzy model identification. *Acta Polytech. Hung.*, 9(6), pp. 153–165.

Kim, J.-H. and Huh, U.-Y. (1998). Fuzzy model, based predictive control. In *Proc. IEEE Int. Conf. Fuzzy Syst.*, Anchorage, AK, pp. 405–409.

Koo, K.-M. (2001). Stable adaptive fuzzy controller with time varying dead-zone. *Fuzzy Sets Syst.*, 121, pp. 161–168.

Kosko, B. (1994). Fuzzy systems as universal approximators. *IEEE Trans. Comput.*, 43(11), pp. 1329–1333.

Krstić, M., Kanellakopoulos, I. and Kokotović, P. (1995). *Nonlinear and Adaptive Control Design*. New York, NY, USA: John Wiley and Sons.

Layne, J. R. and Passino, K. M. (1993). Fuzzy model reference learning control for cargo ship steering. *IEEE Control Syst. Mag.*, 13, pp. 23–34.

Leith, D. J. and Leithead, W. E. (1998). Gain-scheduled and nonlinear systems: dynamics analysis by velocity-based linearization families. *Int. J. Control*, 70(2), pp. 289–317.

Leith, D. J. and Leithead, W. E. (1999). Analyitical framework for blended model systems using local linear models. *Int. J. Control*, 72(7–8), pp. 605–619.

Li, N., Li, S. and Xi, Y. (2004). Multi-model predictive control based on the Takagi–Sugeno fuzzy models: a case study. *Inf. Sci. Inf. Comput. Sci.*, 165(3–4), pp. 247–263.

Lin, C.-H. (1997). Siso nonlinear system identification using a fuzzy-neural hybrid system. *Int. J. Neural Syst.*, 8(3), pp. 325–337.

Mamdani, E. (1974). Application of fuzzy algorithms for control of simple dynamic plant. *Proc. Inst. Electr. Eng.*, 121(12), pp. 1585–1588.

Moon, T. K. and Stirling, W. C. (1999). *Mathematical Methods and Algorithms for Signal Processing*. Upper Saddle River, New Jersey, USA: Prentice Hall.

Morningred, J. D., Paden, B. E. and Mellichamp, D. A. (1992). An adaptive nonlinear predictive controller. *Chem. Eng. Sci.*, 47, pp. 755–762.

Padin, M. S. and Figueroa, J. L. (2000). Use of cpwl approximations in the design of a numerical nonlinear regulator. *IEEE Trans. Autom. Control*, 45(6), pp. 1175–1180.

Passino, K. and Yurkovich, S. (1998). *Fuzzy Control*, Addison-Wesley.

Pedrycz, W. (1993). *Fuzzy Control and Fuzzy Systems*. Taunton, UK: Research Studies Press.

Perng, J.-W. (2012). Describing function analysis of uncertain fuzzy vehicle control systems. *Neural Comput. Appl.*, 21(3), pp. 555–563.

Pomares, H., Rojas, I., Gonzlez, J., Rojas, F., Damas, M. and Fernndez, F. J. (2002). A two-stage approach to self-learning direct fuzzy controllers. *Int. J. Approx. Reason.*, 29(3), pp. 267–289.

Precup, R.-E. and Hellendoorn, H. (2011). A survey on industrial applications of fuzzy control. *Comput. Ind.*, 62(3), pp. 213–226.

Precup, R.-E. and Preitl, S. (2006). PI and PID controllers tuning for integral-type servo systems to ensure robust stability and controller robustness. *Electr. Eng.*, 88(2), pp. 149–156.

Precup, R.-E., Tomescu, M. L. and Preitl, S. (2007). Lorenz system stabilization using fuzzy controllers. *Int. J. Comput., Commun. Control*, 2(3), pp. 279–287.

Procyk, T. J. and Mamdani, E. H. (1979). A linguistic self-organizing process controller. *Autom.*, 15, pp. 15–30.

Richalet, J. (1993). Industrial application of model based predictive control. *Autom.*, 29(5), pp. 1251–1274.

Richalet, J., Rault, A., Testud, J. L. and Papon, J. (1978). Model predictive heuristic control: Applications to industrial processes. *Autom.*, 14, pp. 413–428.

Roubos, J. A., Mollov, S., Babuska, R. and Verbruggen, H. B. (1999). Fuzzy model-based predictive control using takagi-sugeno models. *Int. J. Approx. Reason.*, 22(1–2), pp. 3–30.

Sadeghi–Tehran, P., Cara, A. B., Angelov, P., Pomares, H., Rojas, I. and Prieto, A. (2012). Self-evolving parameter-free rule-based controller. In *IEEE Proc. 2012 World Congr. Comput. Intell., WCCI-2012*, pp. 754–761.

Sun, H.-R., Han, P. and Jiao, S.-M. (2004). A predictive control strategy based on fuzzy system. In *Proc. 2004 IEEE Int. Conf. Inf. Reuse Integr.*, pp. 549–552. doi: 10.1109/1R1.20041431518.

Takagi, T. and Sugeno, M. (1985). Fuzzy identification of systems and its applications to modelling and control. *IEEE Trans. Syst., Man, Cybern.*, 15, pp. 116–132.

Tanaka, K. and Wang, H. O. (2002). *Fuzzy Control Systems Design and Analysis: A Linear Matrix Inequality Approach*. New York: John Wiley & Sons Inc.

Tanaka, K., Ikeda, T. and Wang, H. O. (1996). Robust stabilization of a class of uncertain nonlinear systems via fuzzy control: Quadratic stabilizability, h^{∞} control theory, and linear matrix inequalities. *IEEE Trans. Fuzzy Syst.*, 4(1), pp. 1–13.

Tang, Y., Zhang, N. and Li, Y. (1999). Stable fuzzy adaptive control for a class of nonlinear systems. *Fuzzy Sets Syst.*, 104, pp. 279–288.

Tong, S. and Li, Y. (2012). Adaptive fuzzy output feedback tracking backstepping control of strict-feedback nonlinear systems with unknown dead zones. *IEEE Trans. Fuzzy Systems*, 20(1), pp. 168–180.

Tong, S., Wang, T. and Tang, J. T. (2000). Fuzzy adaptive output tracking control of nonlinear systems. *Fuzzy Sets Syst.*, 111, pp. 169–182.

Vaščák, J. (2012). Adaptation of fuzzy cognitive maps by migration algorithms. *Kybernetes*, 41(3/4), pp. 429–443.

Škrjanc, I. and Matko, D. (2000). Predictive functional control based on fuzzy model for heat-exchanger pilot plant. *IEEE Trans. Fuzzy Systems*, 8(6), pp. 705–712.

Wang, H. O., Tanaka, K. and Griffin, M. F. (1996). An approach to fuzzy control of nonlinear systems: Stability and design issues. *IEEE Trans. Fuzzy Syst.*, 4(1), pp. 14–23.

Wang, L.-X. and Mendel, J. M. (1992). Fuzzy basis functions, universal approximation, and orthogonal least-squares learning. *IEEE Trans. Neural Netw.*, 3(5), pp. 807–814.

Ydstie, B. E. (1984). Extended horizon adaptive control. In *IFAC World Congr.* Budapest, Hungary, paper 14.4/E4.

Ying, H. G. (1997). Necessary conditions for some typical fuzzy systems as universal approximators. *Autom.*, 33, pp. 1333–1338.

Zadeh, L. A. (1973). Outline of a new approach to the analysis of complex systems and decision processes. *IEEE Trans. Syst., Man Cybern.*, SMC-3(1), pp. 28–44.

Chapter 7

Fuzzy Fault Detection and Diagnosis

Bruno Sielly Jales Costa

This chapter presents a thorough review of the literature in the field of fault detection and diagnosis (FDD), focusing, latter, on the strategies and applications based on fuzzy rule-based systems. The presented methods are classified into three main research lines: quantitative model-based, qualitative model-based and process history-based methods, and such division offers the reader an immediate glance about possible directions in the field of study. Introductory concepts and basic applications of each group of techniques are presented in a unified benchmark framework, enabling a fair comparison between the strategies. Many of the traditional and state-of-the-art approaches presented in the literature are referred in this chapter, allowing the reader to have a general overview of possible fault detection and diagnosis strategies.

7.1. Introduction

For four decades, fuzzy systems have been successfully used in a large scope of different industrial applications. Among the different areas of study, it is imperative to mention the work of Kruse *et al.* (1994) in the field of computer science, Pedrycz and Gomide (2007) in the field of industrial engineering, Lughofer (2011) in the field of data stream mining, Abonyi (2003) in the field of process control, Kerre and Nachtegael (2000) in the field of image processing and Nelles (2001) in the field of system identification.

One of the main advantages of a fuzzy system, when compared to other techniques for inaccurate data mining, such as neural networks, is that its knowledge basis, which is composed of inference rules, is very easy to examine and understand (Costa *et al.*, 2012). This format of rules also makes it easy to maintain and update the system structure. Using a fuzzy model to express the behavior of a real system in an understandable manner is a task of great importance, since the main "philosophy of fuzzy sets theory is to serve the bridge between the human understanding and the machine processing" (Casillas *et al.*, 2003). Regarding this matter, interpretability of fuzzy systems was the object of study of Casillas *et al.* (2003), Lughofer (2013), Gacto *et al.* (2011), Zhou and Gan (2008) and others.

Fault Detection and Diagnosis (FDD) is, without a doubt, one of the more beneficial areas for fuzzy theory, among the industrial applications scope (Mendonça *et al.*, 2006; Dash *et al.*, 2003). As concrete examples of applications of fuzzy sets and systems in the context of FDD, one can mention Serdio *et al.* (2014) and Angelov *et al.* (2006), where fuzzy systems are placed among top performers in residual-based data-driven FDD, and Lemos *et al.* (2013) and Laukonen *et al.* (1995), presenting fuzzy approaches to be used in the context of data-stream mining based FDD.

While FDD is still widely performed by human operators, the core of the task consists, roughly, of a sequence of reasoning steps based on the collected data, as we are going to see along this chapter. Fuzzy reasoning can be applied in all steps and in several different ways in the FDD task.

Applications of FDD techniques in industrial environments are increasing in order to improve the operational safety, as well as to reduce the costs related to unscheduled stoppages. The importance of the FDD research in control and automation engineering relies on the fact that prompt detection of an occurring fault, while the system is still operating in a controllable region, usually prevents or, at least, reduces productivity losses and health risks (Venkatasubramanian *et al.*, 2003c).

Many authors have, very recently, contributed to the FDD field of study, with extensive studies, compilations and thorough reviews. Korbicz *et al.* (2004) cover the fundamentals of model-based FDD, being directed toward industrial engineers, scientists and academics, pursuing the reliability and FDD issues of safety-critical industrial processes. Chiang *et al.* (2001) presents the theoretical background and practical techniques for data-driven process monitoring, which includes many approaches based on principal component analysis, linear discriminant analysis, partial least squares, canonical variate analysis, parameter estimation, observer-based methods, parity relations, causal analysis, expert systems and pattern recognition. Isermann (2009) introduces into the field of FDD systems the methods which have proven their performance in practical applications, including fault detection with signal-based and model-based methods, and fault diagnosis with classification and inference methods, in addition to fault-tolerant control strategies and many practical simulations and experimental results. Witczak (2014) presents a selection of FDD and fault-tolerant control strategies for nonlinear systems, from state estimation up to modern soft computing strategies, including original research results. Last but not the least, Simani *et al.* (2002) focuses on model identification oriented to the analytical approach of FDD, including sample case studies used to illustrate the application of each technique.

With the increasing complexity of the procedures and scope of the industrial activities, the Abnormal Event Management (AEM) is a challenging field of study nowadays. The human operator plays a crucial role in this matter since it has been shown that people responsible for AEM take incorrect decisions many times. Industrial statistics show that 70–90% of the accidents are caused by human errors (Venkatasubramanian *et al.*, 2003c; Wang and Guo, 2013). Moreover, there is much more behind the necessity of an automation of FDD processes; for instance, in several industrial environments, the efforts from the operators for a full coverage supervision of all variables and states of the system are very high, which results in severe costs for the company. Sometimes, a manual supervision is simply infeasible, for instance, in largely distributed systems (Chen *et al.*, 2006).

In this chapter, we present a short review on the FDD process, focusing, later, on the existing fuzzy techniques and applications.

7.2. Detection, Isolation and Identification

First, it is important to address some of the nomenclature and definitions in the field of research. The so-called *fault* is the departure from an operating state with an acceptable range of an observed variable or a calculated parameter associated with a process (Venkatasubramanian *et al.*, 2003c). A fault, hence, can be defined as a symptom (e.g., low flow of a liquid, high temperature on a pump) within the process. On the other hand, the event causing such abnormalities is called *failure*, which is also a synonym for *malfunction* or *root cause*.

In an industrial context, there are several different types of faults that could affect the normal operation of a plant. Among the different groups of malfunctions, one can list the following (Samantaray and Bouamama, 2008):

- Gross parameter changes, also known as parametric faults, refers to "disturbances to the process from independent variables, whose dynamics are not provided with that of the process" (Samantaray and Bouamama, 2008). As examples of parametric faults, one can list a change in the concentration of a reactant, a blockage in a pipeline resulting in a change of the flow coefficient and so on.
- Structural changes refers to equipment failures, which may change the model of the process. An appropriate corrective action to such abnormality would require the extraction of new modeling equations to describe the current faulty status of the process. Examples of structural changes are failure of a controller, a leaking pipe and a stuck valve.
- Faulty sensors and actuators, also known as additive faults (or depending on the model, multiplicative faults), refers to incorrect process inputs and outputs, and could lead the plant variables to beyond acceptable limits. Some examples of abnormalities in the input/output instruments are constant (positive or negative) bias, intermittent disturbances, saturation, out-of-range failure and so on.

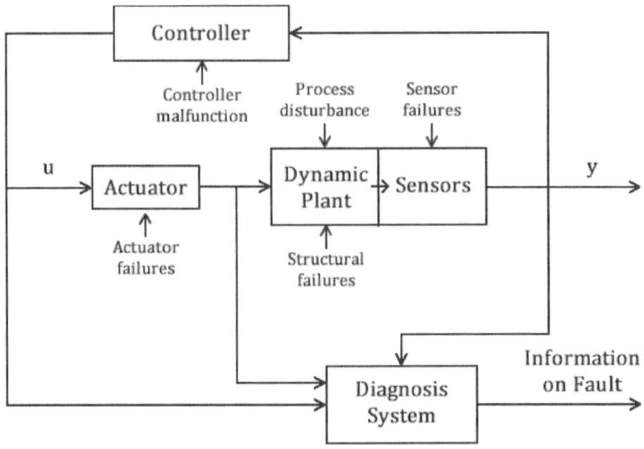

Figure 7.1: General FDD structure (Venkatasubramanian *et al.*, 2003c).

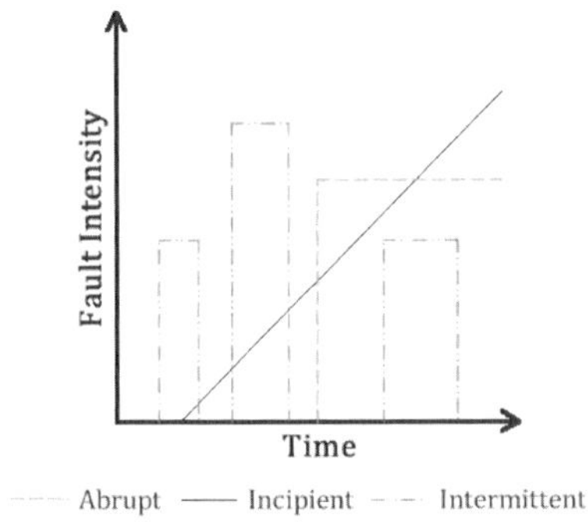

Figure 7.2: Types of faults regarding the time-variant aspect (Patan, 2008).

Figure 7.1 depicts a general process and diagnosis system framework.
Faults can also be classified in a time-variant aspect as

- Abrupt: A fault that abruptly/instantly changes the value of a variable (or a group of variables) from a constant value to another. It is often related to hardware damage.
- Incipient refers to slow parametric changes, where the fault gradually develops to a higher degree. It is usually more difficult to detect due to its slow time characteristics, however, it is less severe than an abrupt fault (Edwards *et al.*, 2010). A good example of an incipient fault is the slow degradation of a hardware component.
- Intermittent: A fault that appears and disappears, repeatedly, over time. A typical example is a partially damaged wiring or a loose connector.

It is important to highlight that a general abnormality is only considered a fault, if it is possible to recover from it, with appropriate control action, either automatic or with the operator intervention. In the past, passive approaches, making use of robust control techniques to ensure that the closed-loop system becomes insensitive to some mild failure situations, were used as a popular fault tolerance strategy (Zhou and Ren, 2001). Nowadays, the active FDD and recovery processes are given as the best solution, once they provide fault accommodation, enabling an update in the control action in order to adjust the controller, in the presence of a fault, to a new given scenario. Fault accommodation, also known as fault compensation, is addressed in Lin and Liu (2007), Efimov *et al.* (2011) and many others.

The entire process of AEM is often divided in a series of steps (usually detection, identification and isolation), which in fault-tolerant design is a fault diagnosis scheme. Although the number of steps may vary from author to author, the general idea remains the same.

The detector system (first stage) continuously monitors the process variables (or attributes) looking for symptoms (deviations on the variables values) and sends these symptoms to the diagnosis system, which is responsible for the classification and identification process.

Fault detection or anomaly detection is the first stage and it has extreme importance to FDD systems. In this stage, we are able to identify whether the system is working in a normal operating state or in a faulty mode. However, in this stage, vital information about the fault, such as physical location, length or intensity, are not provided to the operator (Silva, 2008).

The diagnosis stage presents its own challenges and obstacles, and can be handled independently from the first one. It demands different techniques and solutions, and can be divided in two sub-stages, called isolation and identification. The term isolation refers to determination of kind, location and time of detection of a fault, and follows the fault detection stage (Donders, 2002). Identification, on the other hand, refers to determination of size and time-variant behavior of a fault, and follows fault isolation.

The diagnosis stage, especially, is a logic decision-making process that generates qualitative data from quantitative data, and it can be seen as a classification problem. The task is to match each pattern of the symptom vector with one of the pre-assigned classes of faults, when existing, and the fault-free case (Frank and Köppen-Seliger, 1997). This process is also known in the literature as fault reasoning.

One last stage related to FDD applications is the task of recovering from an existing and detected fault. The action regarding the process reconfiguration needs to compensate the current malfunction in order to maintain the requirements for an acceptable operating state, when possible, or to determine the further sequence of events (controlled shutdown, for example). Although recovering/accommodation are related to the FDD scheme, we will focus only on the previous described stages.

In general, artificial intelligence-based techniques, such as neural networks, fuzzy systems and expert systems, can be applied in all stages of FDD. In the next sections, we will present some of the widely known approaches based on fuzzy systems.

7.2.1. *Quantitative Model-Based FDD Techniques*

In order to detect and prevent an anomalous state of a process, often, some type of redundancy is necessary. It is used to compare the current and actual state of the process to a state that is expected under those circumstances. Although the redundancy can be provided by extra hardware devices, which is what usually happens in high security processes, analytical redundancy can be used where the redundancy is supplied by a process model instead (Frisk, 2001).

With regard to process models, there are methods that require detailed mathematical models, and there are methods that only require the qualitative description of the model, as we present in the next sub-section.

When the process model is available, the detection of a fault using quantitative model-based techniques depends only on the analysis of the *residual* signal. The residual (e^r) is the difference between the current output (y) of the system and the estimated output ($\hat{y}$) based on the given model. In general, the residual is expected to be "null" or "nearly-null", when in a fault-free state, and considerably different from zero, in the presence of a fault. It should be noted that the design of an FDD system must consider the particularities of a real process (e.g., environmental noise, model uncertainties), which can slightly deviate the residual from zero and still not relate to a fault event.

Mathematical models can be available both to the normal state of operation of the process and to each previously known faulty state, indicating that model-based FDD systems are able not only to distinguish between fault-free and faulty states (detection), but also to identity different types and locations of faults (diagnosis). Figure 7.3 illustrates the general structure of a quantitative model-based FDD system.

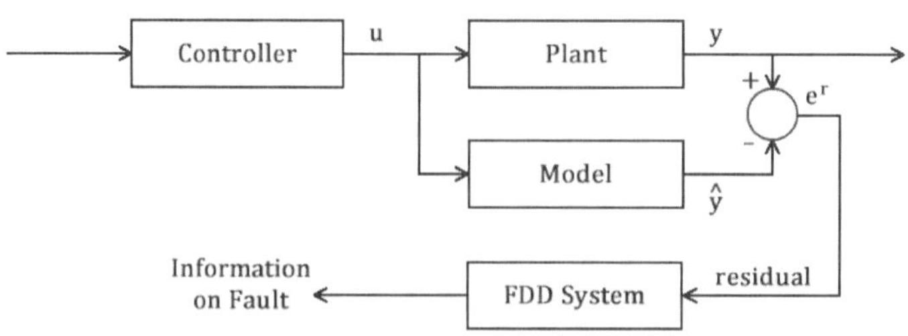

Figure 7.3: General structure of a quantitative model-based FDD system.

Many approaches to FDD using quantitative model-based methods were investigated in the literature. One can mention Venkatasubramanian *et al.* (2003c) and Isermann (2005) as two of the main references about the topic. In the first one, the authors present a systematic and comparative review of numerous quantitative model-based diagnostic methods from different perspectives, while in the latter one, the author includes a few detailed applications of such methods to a few different real industrial problems. Still regarding residual-based FDD approaches using analytical models, the reading of Chen and Patton (1999) and Simani *et al.* (2002) is highly recommended.

7.2.2. *Qualitative Model-Based FDD Techniques*

For this group of model-based techniques, the methods are based on the expertise of the operator, qualitative knowledge, and basic understanding about the physics, dynamics, and behavior of the process.

Qualitative models are particularly useful in the sense that even if accurate mathematical models are available for the process, it is often unpractical to obtain all information of the relevant physical parameters of the system, not to mention that external parameters, such as unpredictable disturbances, model uncertainties and so on, are not considered in quantitative models. Hence, FDD methods based on qualitative descriptors are particularly robust (Glass *et al.*, 1995).

Instead of crisp outputs and residual signals, qualitative models work with a qualitative database that feeds a discrepancy detector. The resulting signal, instead of a simple subtraction, is a qualitative discrepancy, based on the expected behavior, for the given state and the actual output of the system, where the qualitative database is a collection of expert knowledge in form of linguistic descriptions about fault-free and faulty states. Figure 7.4 details the general structure of a qualitative model-based FDD system.

Among the relevant work about the topic, it is imperative to mention Venkatasubramanian *et al.* (2003a). The authors present a complete review of the techniques based on qualitative model representations and search strategies in FDD,

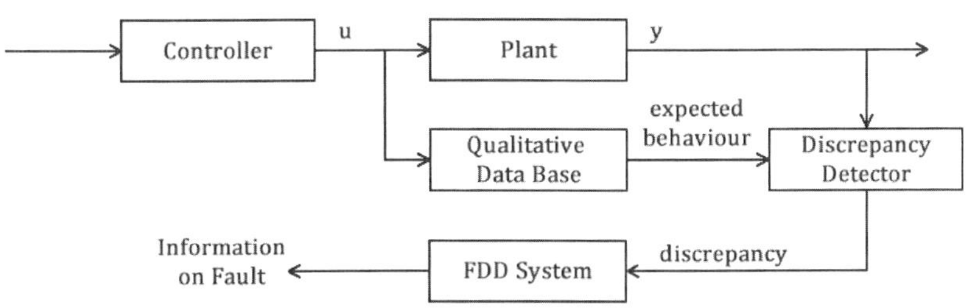

Figure 7.4: General structure of a qualitative model-based FDD system.

highlighting the relative advantages and disadvantages of these methods. Another work that is worth mentioning is Katipamula and Brambley (2005), the first of a two-part review, which summarizes some of the successful qualitative model-based techniques and, although applied exclusively to heating, ventilation and air-conditioning (HVAC) problems, the paper focuses on generic FDD and prognostics, providing a framework for categorizing, describing, and identifying methods, their primary strengths and weaknesses.

7.2.3. *Process History-Based FDD Techniques*

The third and last large group of methods for FDD refers to a particular type of techniques that is completely data-driven. Process history-based techniques do not require any knowledge, either quantitative or qualitative, about the process. Instead, they use massive historical information collected from the process. This data is, then, transformed and presented as *a priori* information to the FDD system through a process known as *feature extraction.*

Feature extraction (or feature selection) is responsible for reducing the dimensionality of the data, carefully extracting only the relevant information from the input dataset, which usually consists of the measured sensor outputs, namely observable variables (e.g., tank level, pump pressure), or calculated parameters, namely process attributes (e.g., error, pressure oscillation). Statistical methods, expert systems, and neural networks are often used in this type of approach. Figure 7.5 details the general structure of a process history-based FDD system.

As the literature references, one can mention Venkatasubramanian *et al.* (2003b) and Yang *et al.* (2003) as two very important works on the topic. In the first one, the authors present the third part of the literature review, focusing on the process history-based FDD methods. As the last part of the extensive study, the authors suggest that "no single method has all the desirable features one would like a diagnostic system to possess" and, in order to overcome the limitations of individual solution strategies, the use of hybrid FDD systems is often advised. The latter paper presents a survey on feature extraction, focusing on a variety of validated vibration feature extraction techniques, applied to rotating machinery.

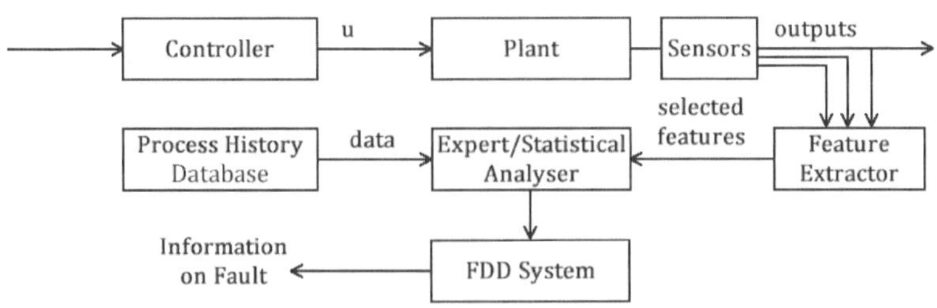

Figure 7.5: General structure of a process history-based FDD system.

7.3. Fuzzy Fault Detection and Identification

Fuzzy rule-based (FRB) systems are currently being investigated in the FDD and reliability research community as a powerful tool for modeling and decision-making (Serdio *et al.*, 2014; Angelov *et al.*, 2006; Lemos *et al.*, 2013; Laukonen *et al.*, 1995), together with neural networks and other more traditional techniques, such as nonlinear and robust observers, parity space methods and so on (Mendonça *et al.*, 2004a). Fuzzy sets theory makes possible the quantification of intrinsically qualitative statements, subjectivity and uncertainty.

The main concepts of fuzzy logic theory make it adequate for FDD. While the nonlinear fuzzy modeling can be very useful in the fault detection work, the transparent and human logic-related inference system is highly suitable for the fault diagnosis stage, which may not only include the expertise from the human operator, but also learn from experimental and/or simulation data. Another benefit of using fuzzy systems in FDD applications is the good performance in reproducing nonlinear mappings, and their abilities of generalization, since fuzzy systems are universal approximators, i.e., being able to model any degree of nonlinearity with an arbitrary desired degree of accuracy (Castro and Delgado, 1996). Hence, fuzzy logic-based systems for fault diagnosis can be advantageous, since they allow the incorporation of prior knowledge and their inference engines are easily understandable to the human operator (Mendonça *et al.*, 2004b).

The process of FDD, especially in its latter stage, can be viewed as a classification problem, which comes with certain particularities, when compared to other groups of applications. When dealing with a classification problem, it is useful to think about the system output as a fuzzy value, instead of a crisp value, skipping the defuzzification step. This way, the output of the FRB system can be presented as a label, which will represent the class of fault assigned to the current state of the process/plant.

Considering an input vector of crisp values $x \in R^n$, composed by the values of the selected process variables/attributes/features, a fuzzy inference rule basis $\Re$, with R rules, for a generic FDD system can be represented by

$$\begin{aligned}
\Re^1 &: \textbf{IF } \left(x_1 \textbf{ IS } A_{1,1} \textbf{ AND } x_2 \textbf{ IS } A_{1,2} \textbf{ AND...AND } x_n \textbf{ IS } A_{1,n}\right) \textbf{ THEN} \\
&\quad (y_1 \textbf{ IS } \text{“}\textit{Fault } 1\text{”}), \\
\Re^2 &: \textbf{IF } \left(x_1 \textbf{ IS } A_{2,1} \textbf{ AND } x_2 \textbf{ IS } A_{2,2} \textbf{ AND...AND } x_n \textbf{ IS } A_{2,n}\right) \textbf{ THEN} \\
&\quad (y_2 \textbf{ IS } \text{“}\textit{Fault } 2\text{”}), \\
&\vdots \\
\Re^R &: \textbf{IF } \left(x_1 \textbf{ IS } A_{R,1} \textbf{ AND } x_2 \textbf{ IS } A_{R,2} \textbf{ AND...AND } x_n \textbf{ IS } A_{R,n}\right) \textbf{ THEN} \\
&\quad (y_R \textbf{ IS } \text{“}\textit{Fault } R\text{”}),
\end{aligned}$$

where A is the set of fuzzy values for the input variables and y is the output of the system.

Note that the output y is inferred as the label representing each given class of fault, which can include the nature (e.g., structural, disturbances), the location (e.g., tank 1, pump, valve A), the type (e.g., leakage, off-set), the degree (e.g., mild, severe) of the fault, as well as can represent the normal state of operation of the plant. Such labels, of course, require linguistic encoding, based on the expert knowledge from the operator. A few unsupervised or semi-supervised approaches (for instance, the one to be presented in Section 7.3.5) are able to automatically create new rules from the knowledge extracted from data using non-specific labels. These labels, such as "Fault 1"and "Fault A" can, later, be correctly specified by the human operator to include the operation mode/fault class related to that rule.

The inference in a fuzzy rule-based FDD system can be produced using the well-known "winner-takes-it-all" rule (Angelov and Zhou, 2008):

$$L = L^{i*}, \quad i^* = \text{argmax}_{i=1}^{R}(\gamma^i), \tag{1}$$

where γ^i represents the degree of membership of the input vector $\vec{x}$ to the fuzzy set A^i, considering R inference rules.

As a general example of the application of FRB systems in FDD, we are going to use a benchmark problem, which will be presented and solved with different approaches in the next sub-sections.

7.3.1. *Benchmark Problem: First-Order Liquid Level Control in Experimental Tanks*

The selected problem is presented and well described in Costa *et al.* (2013) and used in many different applications (Costa *et al.*, 2010, 2012). The referred plant for this study is a two coupled water tanks module, developed by Quanser (2004).

The plant consists of a pump with a water basin. The pump thrusts water vertically to two quick connect, normally closed orifices "Out1" and "Out2". Two tanks mounted on the front plate are configured such that the flow from the first tank flows into the second tank and outflow from the second tank flows into the main water basin. The graphic representation of the plant is presented in Figure 7.6.

For didactic purposes, in this example, we refer to the simulated version of the referred plant, whose behavior is highly similar to the real version of the same didactic plant, however free of unpredictable environment noise and unrelated disturbances. Although the plant allows second-order control, since it is possible to control the level of the second tank, we will address only first-order aspect of the application, hence, measuring the level on the first tank.

The system consists, then, of two variables: (1) the voltage/control signal (u) applied to the motor/pump — input — which, for safety reasons, is limited to

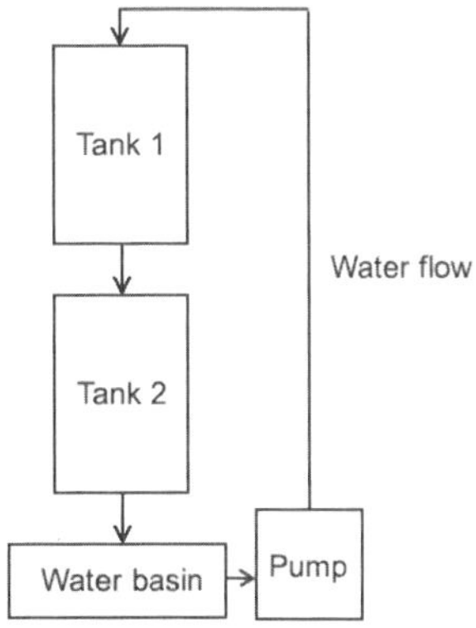

Figure 7.6: Graphic representation of the benchmark plant.

0–15V DC, and (2) the level (y) of the tank 1 — output — which can vary from 0 to 30 cm.

For the control application, which is not in the scope of this chapter, we use a very simple Proportional-Integral-Derivative (PID) controller, where the control signal (u) is calculated by

$$u(t) = K_p e(t) + K_i \int_0^t e(\tau) d\tau + K_d \frac{d}{dt} e(t), \tag{2}$$

where K_p is the proportional gain, K_i is the integral gain, K_d is the derivative gain, t is the current time instant and τ is the variable of integration. In this application, the sampling period for the discrete implementation is 1 s. The error, e, is calculated by

$$e = r - y, \tag{3}$$

where r is the reference/set point of the control application.

For all following examples, we will consider $r = 5$ cm, $K_p = 10$, $K_i = 0.1$ and $K_d = 0.1$. The resulting control chart, for a normal state of operation of the plant, is shown in Figure 7.7 and will serve as reference for the fault-free case.

In this example, we will consider a finite set of pre-specified faults, logically generated in the simulation environment. The total of six faults cover different natures, locations, types and degrees of faults that are easily found in common industrial applications, and is more than enough to present a basic review of the different types of fuzzy FDD systems. The set of defined faults is presented in Table 7.1.

The referred faults were independently and sequentially generated within the interval of data samples $k = [500, 800]$. Figure 7.8 presents the control behavior of the system in the presence of the faults (a) F_1 and (b) F_2 (actuator positive off-sets),

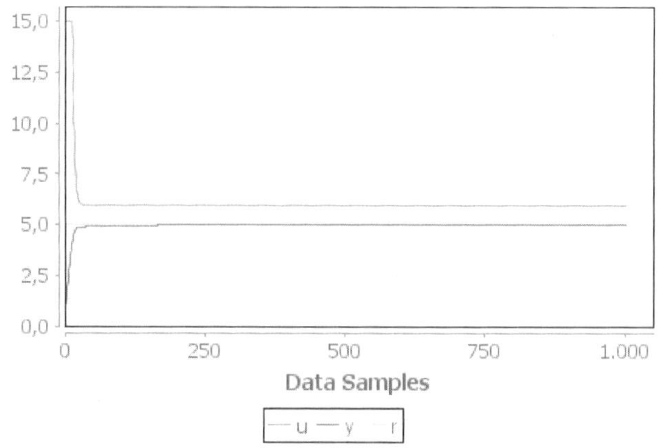

Figure 7.7: Normal state of operation of the plant.

Table 7.1: Pre-defined set of faults.

Fault	Nature	Location	Type	Degree
F_1	Actuator	Pump	Off-set	Mild
F_2	Actuator	Pump	Off-set	Severe
F_3	Structural	Tank 1	Leakage	Mild
F_4	Structural	Tank 1	Leakage	Severe
F_5	Actuator	Pump	Saturation	Mild
F_6	Actuator	Pump	Saturation	Severe

Figure 7.9 shows the control behavior of the system for the faults (a) F_3 and (b) F_4 (tank leakages) and Figure 7.10 illustrates the control behavior of the system for the faults (a) F_5 and (b) F_6 (actuator saturations).

In the following sub-sections, we will present two different basic fuzzy-based approaches for the proper detection and classification of the given set of faults and a short review of other applications in the literature.

7.3.2. *Quantitative Model-Based Fuzzy FDD*

In this first example, we develop a fuzzy classifier able to detect and identify different types and levels of faults based on (1) the previous knowledge of the mathematical model of the plant and (2) the expertise of the human operator. This approach was addressed in the literature by Zhao *et al.* (2009), Kulkarni *et al.* (2009), Mendonça *et al.* (2009) and many others.

The mathematical model of the two tanks module, which is necessary for quantitative model-based FDD approaches, is described in Meneghetti (2007). The flow provided by the pump, which is driven by a DC motor, is directly proportional to the voltage applied to the motor. For a first-order configuration, all the water flows

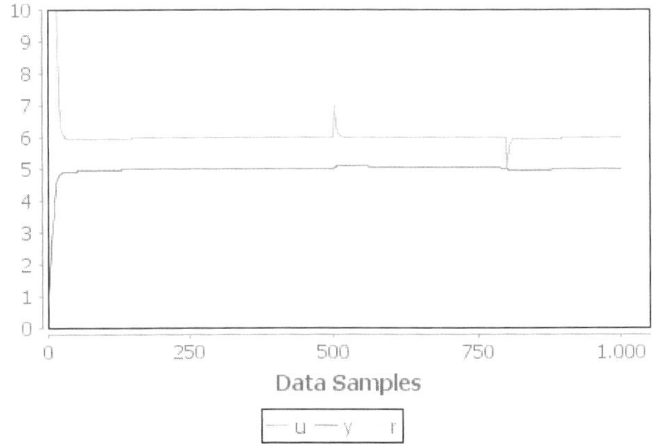

(a) Mild degree

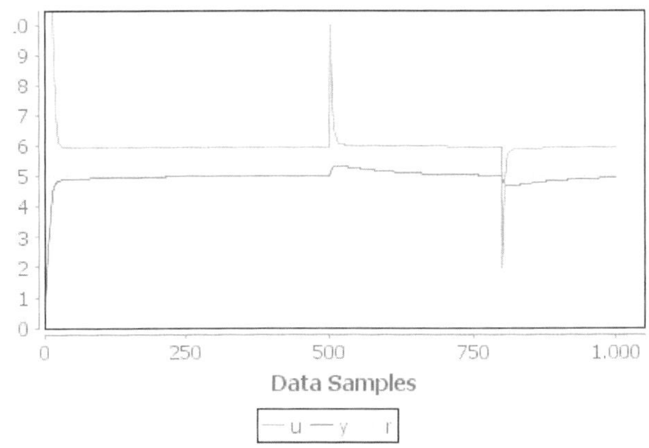

(b) Severe degree

Figure 7.8: Actuator positive off-set.

to tank 1. This variable is called input flow F_1^{in} and can be calculated by

$$F_1^{\text{in}} = K_m V_p [\text{cm}^3/\text{s}], \tag{4}$$

where V_p is the voltage applied to the motor and K_m is the pump constant, which, in this case, is $K_m = 250$.

The speed at which the liquid flows through the output orifice is given by Bernoulli equation for small orifices (Cengel *et al.*, 2012):

$$v^{\text{out}} = \sqrt{2gL_1} [\text{cm/s}], \tag{5}$$

where g is the gravity acceleration in $[\text{cm/s}^2]$ and L_1 is the water level in the tank 1. The *output flow* F_1^{out}, can be calculated by

$$F_1^{\text{out}} = a_1 v^{\text{out}} [\text{cm}^3/\text{s}], \tag{6}$$

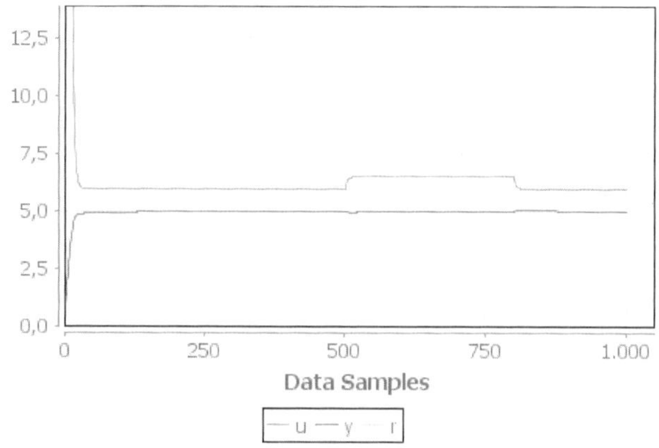

(a) Mild degree

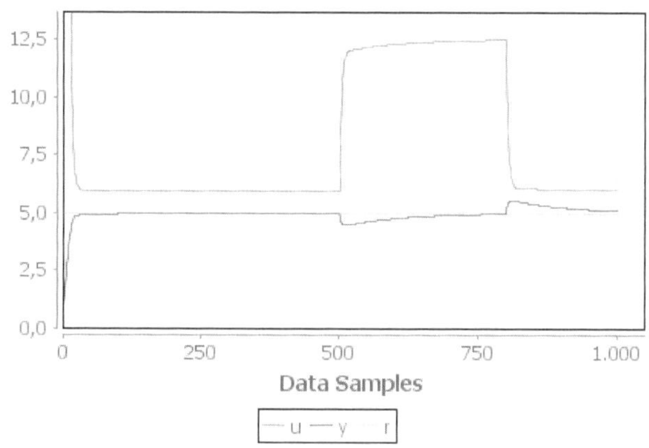

(b) Severe degree

Figure 7.9: Tank leakage.

where a_1 is the area of the tank 1 output orifice in [cm^2], which, in this case, is $a_1 = 0.47625\,\text{cm}^2$.

The level variation rate on tank 1 ($\dot{L}_1$) is given by the ratio between the volumetric variation rate ($\dot{V}$) and the area of the tank base (A_1) for $\dot{V} = F_1^{\text{in}} - F_1^{\text{out}}$.

Based on the given model of the plant, one can generate the residual of the output signal by analyzing the discrepancy between the outputs of the model and the actual process as

$$e_y^r = y - \hat{y}, \tag{7}$$

where e_y^r is the residual of the tank level (observable variable), $\hat{y}$ is the model output for the input control signal u, and y is the output measured by the sensor for the same input control signal.

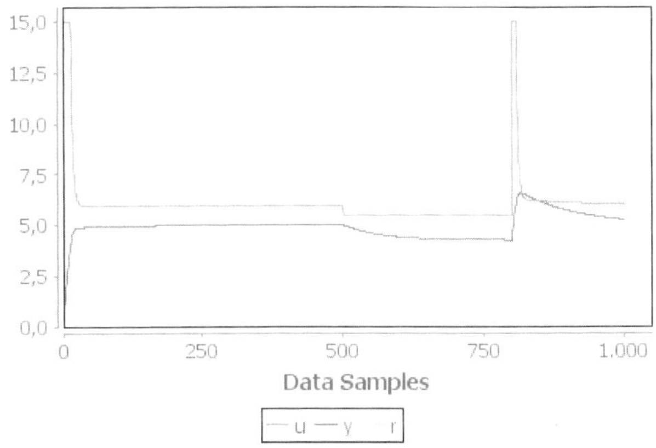

(a) Mild degree

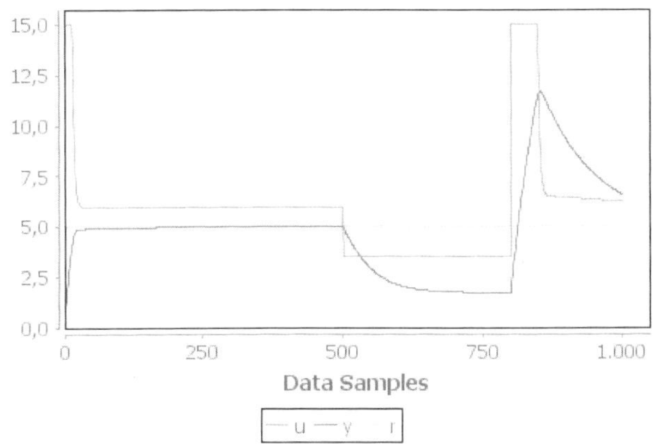

(b) Severe degree

Figure 7.10: Actuator saturation.

It is important to highlight that, in this case, within a normal state of operation of the plant (for $k < 500$ or $k > 800$), Equation (7) will generate a null residual, since we are working with a simulated and disturbance/noise-free application. In real online applications, due to the presence of noise and unpredicted disturbances, the residuals should be handled within a dynamic band or through other tolerance approaches. Figures 7.11–7.13 present the graphical representation of the residual evaluation signal e_y^r for the all previously described faults.

Note that all faults presented here can be classified as abrupt, since they are characterized by the nominal signal changing, abruptly by an unknown positive or negative value. For handling incipient faults, Carl *et al.* (2012) proposes that incipient faults can be approximated by a linear profile because they evolve slowly in time through the estimation of the time of injection and the slope of the signal.

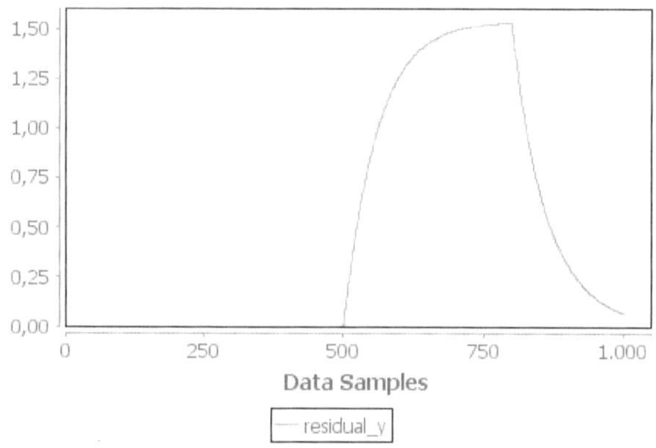

(a) Mild degree

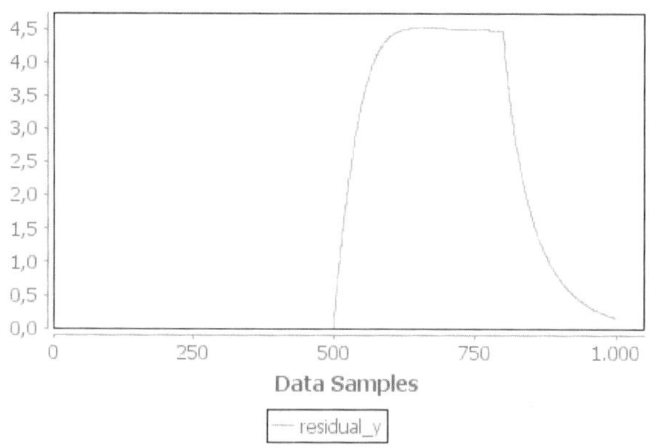

(b) Severe degree

Figure 7.11: Residual evaluation function of the fault "Actuator positive off-set".

Based on the behavior visualized in the charts, one can make a few assumptions about the fault classification from the generated residuals:

1. The faults F_1 and F_2, which are positive off-sets of the actuator, can be promptly detected and easily distinguished from the other ones, since the generated residual is positive, while, in the other cases, it is negative.
2. The faults F_3 and F_4, which are tank leakages, are difficult to distinguish from the faults F_5 and F_6, which are actuator saturations, since both residuals generated are negative. Although the ranges of the signals are considerably different, only the residual of the output e_y^r may not be enough for an effective classification. The use of additional signals, such as the control signal, might be recommended.

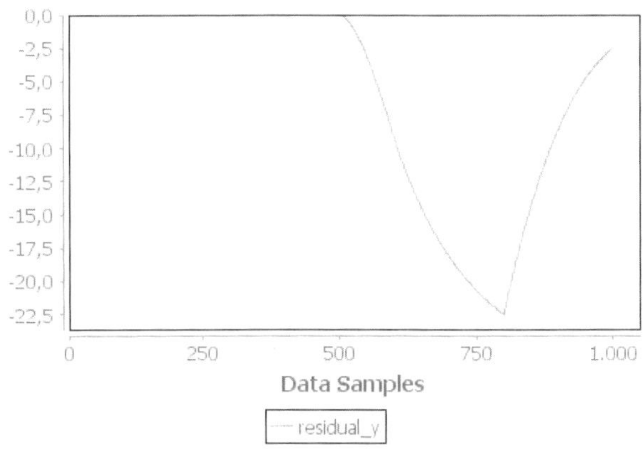

(a) Mild degree

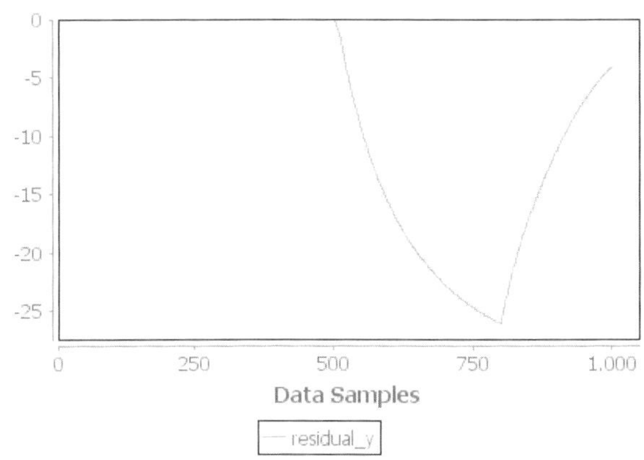

(b) Severe degree

Figure 7.12: Residual evaluation function of the fault "Tank leakage".

A Mamdani-type FRB system able to address this problem can be composed by one input variable (e_y^r), seven fuzzy sets as membership functions of the input variable ("negative_very_high", "negative_high", "negative_low", "negative_very_low", "zero", "positive_low" and "positive_high"), one output variable (*Fault*) and seven fuzzy sets as membership functions of the output variable ("F_1", "F_2", "F_3", "F_4", "F_5", "F_6" and "Normal"). One can model the input variable as shown in Figure 7.14 and the output variable as illustrated in Figure 7.15.

For didactic purposes, triangular and trapezoidal membership functions were used to model all fuzzy sets in these examples. Other types of functions are also encouraged (e.g., Gaussian, bell), especially when using automatic/adaptive approaches.

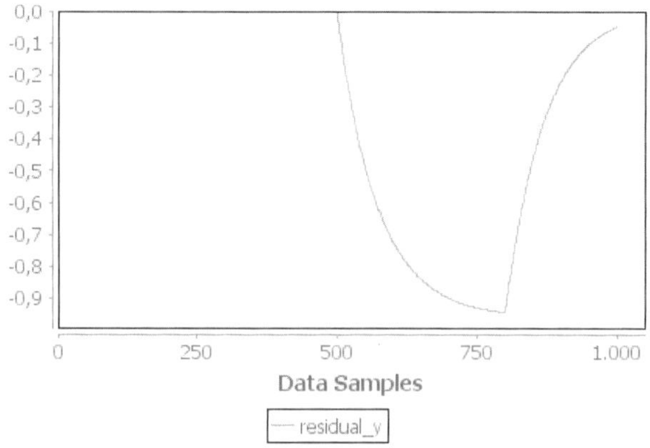

(a) Mild degree

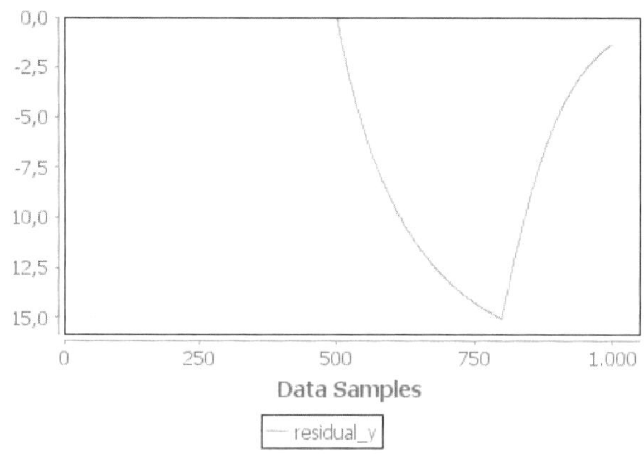

(b) Severe degree

Figure 7.13: Residual evaluation function of the fault "actuator saturation".

One can, then, propose the following fuzzy rule basis $\mathfrak{R}$ for the detection and classification of the defined faults:

$\mathfrak{R}^1$: **IF** (e_y^r **IS** positive$_{\text{low}}$ **THEN** (y_1 **IS** "$F_1 - ActuatorOffset - Mild$"),
$\mathfrak{R}^2$: **IF** (e_y^r **IS** positive$_{\text{high}}$ **THEN** (y_2 **IS** "$F_2 - ActuatorOffset - Severe$"),
$\mathfrak{R}^3$: **IF** (e_y^r **IS** negative$_{\text{high}}$ **THEN** (y_3 **IS** "$F_3 - TankLeakage - Mild$"),
$\mathfrak{R}^4$: **IF** (e_y^r **IS** negative_very_high **THEN** (y_4 **IS** "$F_4 - TankLeakage - Severe$"),
$\mathfrak{R}^5$: **IF** (e_y^r **IS** negative_very_low **THEN**
(y_5 **IS** "$F_5 - ActuatorSaturation - Mild$"),
$\mathfrak{R}^6$: **IF** (e_y^r **IS** negative$_{\text{low}}$ **THEN** (y_6 **IS** "$F_6 - ActuatorSaturation - Severe$"),
$\mathfrak{R}^7$: **IF** (e_y^r **IS** zero **THEN** $\big($$y_7$ **IS** "$Normaloperation''$$\big)$.

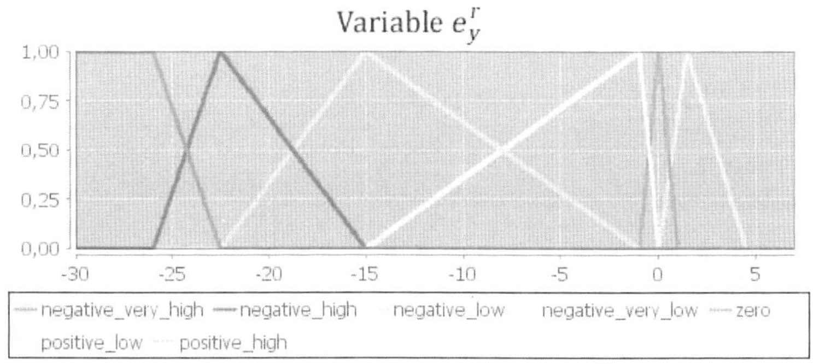

Figure 7.14: Membership functions of the input variable (e_y^r).

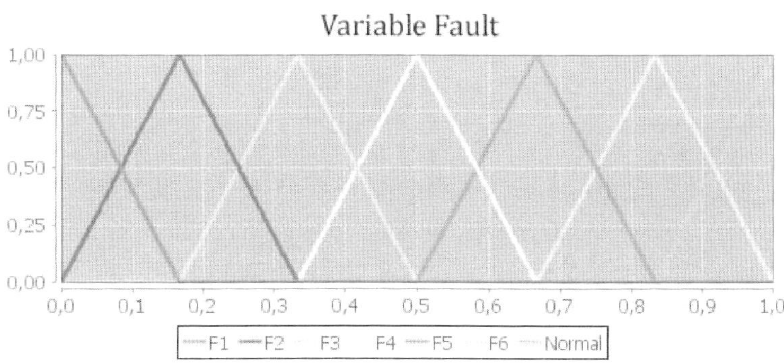

Figure 7.15: Membership functions of the output variable (*Fault*).

Now, for example, let us consider $e_y^r = 25$, at a given time instant, and the "winner-takes-it-all" rule for the output. The whole inference process, for all defined rules, is illustrated in Figure 7.16.

Note that in the left column, two rules (rules 3 and 4) are activated by the input value 25. The membership value of the output of rule 4 is greater than the one for rule 3. It is important to highlight that for the proposed type of fuzzy classifiers, the defuzzification process is ignored. This way, the output of the FRB system is the label "F_4", which is equivalent to the "Severe Leakage in Tank 1" fault.

7.3.3. *Qualitative Model-Based Fuzzy FDD*

As discussed in sub-section 7.2.1, although model-based FDD approaches are theoretically efficient, in practice, the dependence on the mathematical model is not appropriate for real applications. Even when this model is given, many times it does not consider variables that are usually present in industrial environments (e.g., process inertia, environment disturbances).

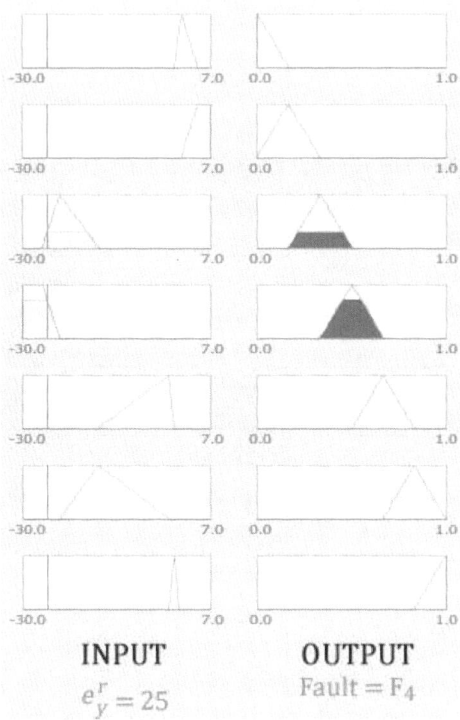

Figure 7.16: Detailed inference process for $e_y^r = 25$.

Starting from a similar point of view, one can consider using an FDD approach that is based on the previous knowledge of the process, however, the mathematical aspect is not necessary. A dynamics-based FDD system is very appropriate when the operator knows well the dynamics of the plant, its physics and behavior. This approach was addressed in the literature by Patton *et al.* (2000), Insfran *et al.* (1999) and many others.

Considering the previous FDD problem, one can make a few observations about the process in Figure 7.7, which illustrates the process in a normal state of operation:

1. In steady state ($k > 180$), the level (y) reaches the set-point (r) value, thus, the error (e) is zero ($e = r - y$).
2. Again, considering the steady state, the control signal (u) becomes constant/non-oscillatory, which means that the control signal variation (Δu) from time step $k - 1$ to time step k is zero ($\Delta u = u_k - u_{k-1}$).
3. Observations (1) and (2) are not true when the system is in a faulty state, as can be seen in Figures 7.17–7.19.

Considering two input variables *Err* (e) and *delta_u* (Δu), four fuzzy sets as membership functions of the variable Err ("negative", "zero", "positive_low"

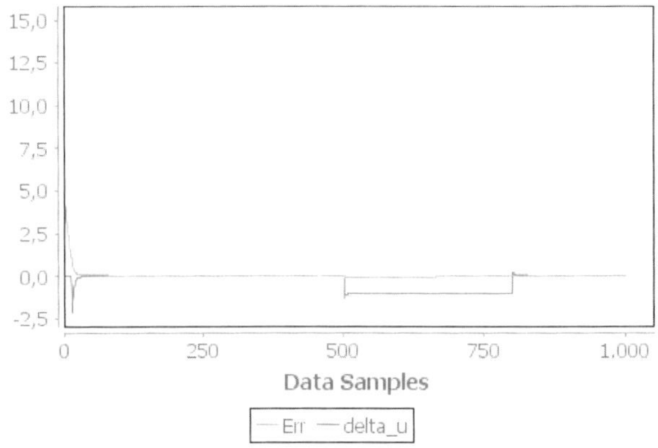

(a) Mild degree

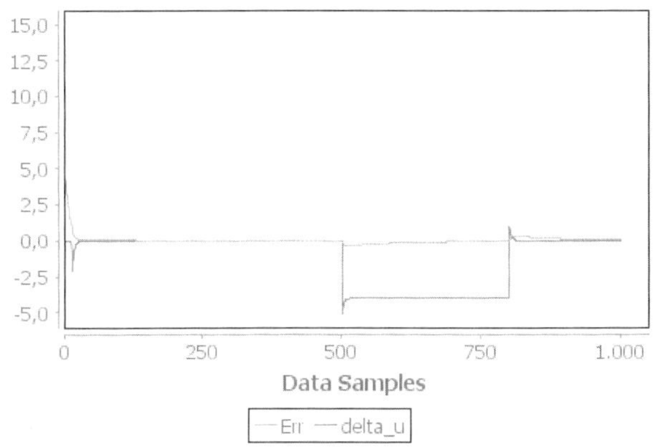

(b) Severe degree

Figure 7.17: Error and control signal variation on the fault "actuator positive off-set".

and "positive_high"), six fuzzy sets as membership functions of the variable *delta_u*("negative_high", "negative_low", "zero", "positive_low", "positive_medium" and "positive_high") and the same output variable (*Fault*) as the one presented in Figure 7.15, one can model the variables of the system as presented in Figures 7.20 and 7.21, which represent the input variables *Err* and *delta_u*, respectively.

Based on these membership functions, one can, then, propose the following Mamdani-type fuzzy rule basis $\mathfrak{R}$ for the detection and classification of the defined faults:

$$\mathfrak{R}^1 : \textbf{IF } (Err \textbf{ IS } \text{zero } \textbf{AND } delta\_u \textbf{ IS } \text{negative\_low } \textbf{THEN}$$
$$(y_1 \textbf{ IS } \text{“}F_1 - ActuatorOffset - Mild\text{”}),$$

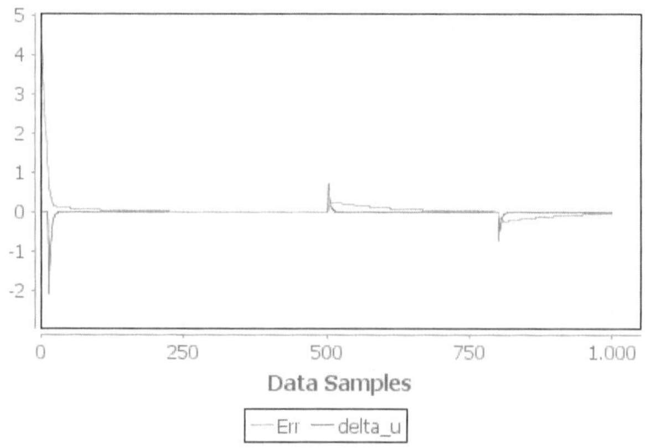

(a) Mild degree

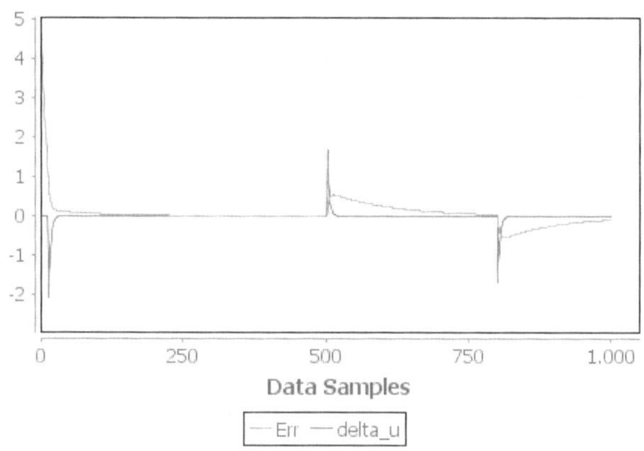

(a) Severe degree

Figure 7.18: Error and control signal variation on the fault "tank leakage".

$\mathfrak{R}^2$: **IF** (*Err* **IS** negative **AND** *delta_u* **IS** negative_high **THEN**
(y_2 **IS** "F_2 – *ActuatorOffset* – *Severe*"),

$\mathfrak{R}^3$: **IF** (*Err* **IS** positive_low **AND** *delta_u* **IS** *positive*_low **THEN**
(y_3 **IS** "F_3 – *TankLeakage* – *Mild*"),

$\mathfrak{R}^4$: **IF** (*Err* **IS** positive_low **AND** *delta_u* **IS** *positive_medium* **THEN**
(y_4 **IS** "F_4 – *TankLeakage* – *Severe*"),

$\mathfrak{R}^5$: **IF** (*Err* **IS** positive_low **AND** *delta_u* **IS** *positive_high* **THEN**
(y_4 **IS** "F_5 – *ActuatorSaturation* – *Mild*"),

$\mathfrak{R}^6$: **IF** (*Err* **IS** positive_high **AND** *delta_u* **IS** *positive_high* **THEN**
(y_4 **IS** "F_6 – *ActuatorSaturation* – *Severe*"),

$\mathfrak{R}^7$: **IF** (*Err* **IS** zero **AND** *delta_u* **IS** *zero* **THEN** (y_4 **IS** "*Normaloperation*").

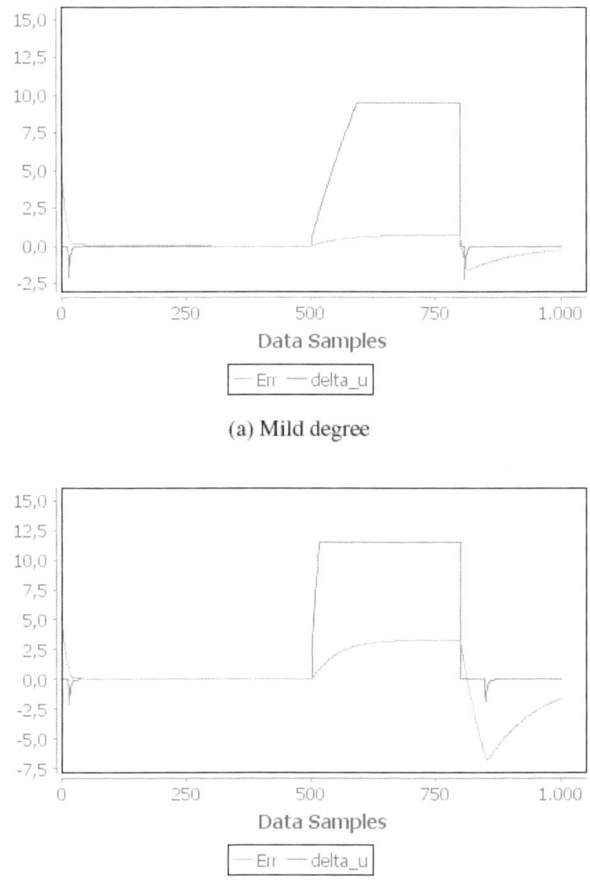

(a) Mild degree

(b) Severe degree

Figure 7.19: Error and control signal variation on the fault "actuator saturation".

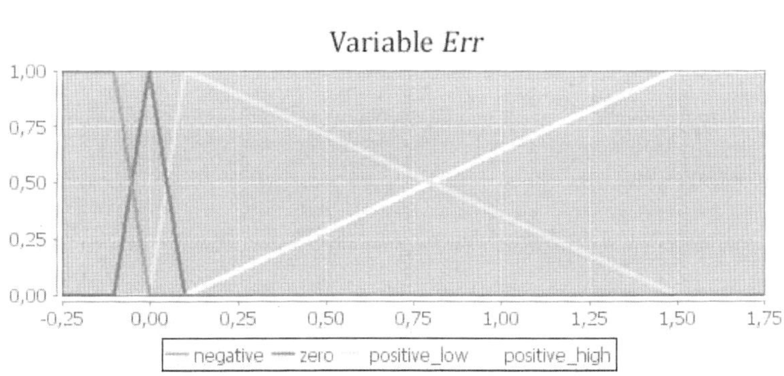

Figure 7.20: Membership functions of the input variable (*Err*).

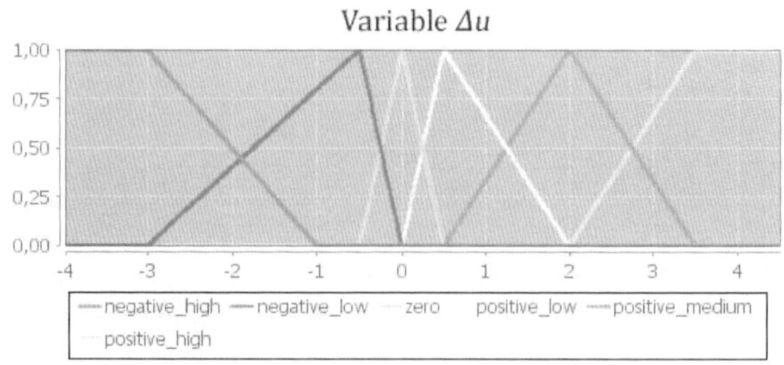

Figure 7.21: Membership functions of the input variable (*delta_u*).

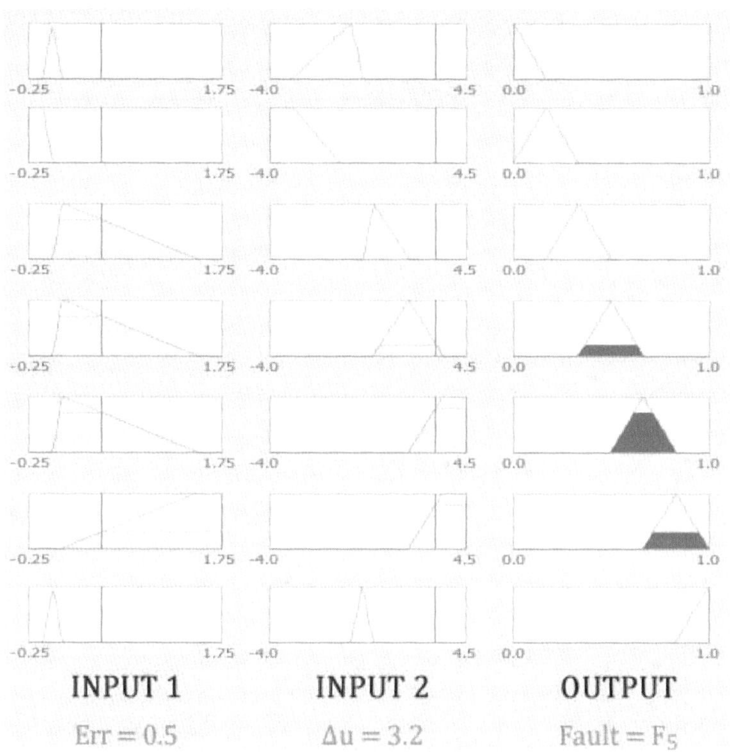

Figure 7.22: Detailed inference process for $Err = 0.5$ and $\Delta u = 3.2$.

As an illustrative example, let us consider $Err = 0.5$ and $delta\_u = 3.2$, at a given time instant, and the "winner-takes-it-all" rule for the output. The detailed inference process, for all defined rules, is illustrated in Figure 7.22.

Note that although the mathematical model of the process, in this particular case, is known, it was not needed in any part of the development of the system. Instead, we used some *a priori* information about the behavior of the system, relating the error and control signals to the normal or faulty states of operation.

7.3.4. *Process History-Based Fuzzy FDD*

If neither the mathematical and physics/dynamics/behavior models are available, the FDD system can still be based on the data itself. Process history-based FDD systems are commonly used in applications where either there is no prior knowledge available, quantitative or qualitative, or the operator chooses to rely only on the acquired historical process data.

Feature extraction — the main task of process history-based techniques — methods, which are used to transform large amounts of data in prior knowledge about the process, are many times based on the aspects of fuzzy theory. In this sub-section, we are not addressing the particular example presented in sub-section 7.3.1. Instead, we are addressing a few successful approaches of process history-based fuzzy FDD methods.

In Bae *et al.* (2005), a basic data mining application for FDD of induction motors is presented. The method is based on wavelet transform and classification models with current signals. Through a so-called "fuzzy measure of similarity", features of faults are extracted, detected and classified.

A multiple signal fault detection system for automotor vehicles is presented in Murphey *et al.* (2003). The paper describes a system that involves signal segmentation and feature extraction, and uses a fuzzy learning algorithm based on the signals acquired from good functional vehicles only. It employs fuzzy logic at two levels of detection and has been implemented and tested in real automation applications.

In Hu *et al.* (2005), a two-stage fault diagnosis method based on empirical mode decomposition (EMD), fuzzy feature extraction and support vector machines (SVM) is described. In the first stage, intrinsic mode components are obtained with EMD from original signals and converted into fuzzy feature vectors, and then the mechanical fault can be detected. In the following stage, these extracted fuzzy feature vectors are input into the multi-classification SVM to identify the different abnormal cases. The proposed method is applied to the classification of a turbo-generator set under three different operating conditions.

7.3.5. *Unsupervised/Semi-supervised Fuzzy Rule-Based FDD*

A new fully unsupervised autonomous FRB approach to FDD has been recently proposed (Costa *et al.*, 2014a, 2014b). The algorithm is divided into two sequential stages, detection and identification. In the first stage, the system is able to detect through a recursive density estimation method, whether there is a fault or not. If a fault is detected, the second stage is activated and, after a spatial distribution analysis, the fault is classified by a fuzzy inference system in a fully unsupervised manner. That means that the operator does not need to know all types, or even the number of possible faults. The fuzzy rule basis is updated at each data sample read, and the number of rules can grow if a new class of fault is detected. The classification is performed by an autonomous label generator, which can be assisted by the operator.

The detection algorithm is based on the recursive density estimation (RDE) (Angelov, 2012), which allows building, accumulating, and self-learning a dynamically evolving information model of "normality", based on the process data for particular specific plant, and considering the normal/accident-free cases only. Similarly, like other statistical methods [e.g., statistical process control (SPC)] (Cook *et al.*, 1997), RDE is an online statistical technique. However, it does not require that the process parameters follow Gaussian/normal distributions nor make other prior assumptions.

The fault identification algorithm is based on the self-learning and fully unsupervised evolving classifier algorithm called *AutoClass*, which is an AnYa-like FRB classifier and, unlike the traditional FRB systems (e.g., Mamdani, Takagi–Sugeno), AnYa does not require the definition of membership functions. The antecedent part of the inference rule uses the concepts of data clouds (Angelov and Yager, 2012) and relative data density, representing exactly the real distribution of the data.

A data cloud is a collection of data samples in the n-dimensional space, similar to the well-known data clusters, however, it is different since a data cloud forming is non-parametric and it does not have a specific shape or boundary (Angelov, 2012) and, instead, it follows the exact real data distribution. A given data sample can belong to all the data clouds with a different degree $\gamma \in [0; 1]$, thus the fuzzy aspect of the model is preserved.

The consequent of the inference rule in *AutoClass* is a zero-order Takagi–Sugeno crisp function, i.e., a class label $L_i = [1, K]$. The inference rules follow the construct of an AnYa-like FRB system (Angelov and Yager, 2012):

$$\Re^i : \mathbf{IF}(\vec{x} \sim \aleph^i)\mathbf{THEN}(L^i),$$

where $\Re^i$ is the i-th rule, $\vec{x} = [x_1, x_2, \ldots, x_n]^T$ is the input data vector, $\aleph^i \in \Re^n$ is the i-th data cloud and $\sim$ denotes the fuzzy membership expressed linguistically as "is associated with" or "is close to". The inference in *AutoClass* is produced using the "winner-takes-it-all" rule.

The degree of membership of the input vector x_k to the data cloud $\aleph^i$, defined as the relative local density, can be recursively calculated as (Angelov, 2012)

$$\gamma_k^i = \frac{1}{1 + \|x_k - \mu_k\|^2 + X_k - \|\mu_k\|^2} \tag{8}$$

where μ_k and X_k are updated by

$$\mu_k = \frac{k-1}{k}\mu_{k-1} + \frac{1}{k}x_k, \quad \mu_1 = x_1, \tag{9}$$

$$X_k = \frac{k-1}{k}X_{k-1} + \frac{1}{k}\|x_k\|^2, \quad X_1 = \|x_1\|^2. \tag{10}$$

Both stages of the proposed FDD approach can start "from scratch", from the very first data sample acquired, with no previous knowledge about the plant model or dynamics, training or complex user-defined parameters or thresholds. The generated fuzzy rules have no specific parameters or shapes for the membership functions and the approach is entirely data-driven.

The approach was implemented and tested in a real liquid level control application, using a Laboratory pilot plant for industrial process control, similar to the plant presented in sub-section 7.3.1, however, in industrial proportions. The fault-free behavior of the system, after a change of reference, is shown in Figure 7.23.

A larger set of faults was, then, generated, including actuator, leakage, stuck valves and disturbance-related faults. Figure 7.24 shows the detection stage of a sequence of fault events. While monitoring the oscillation of the error and control signals, the algorithm is able to detect the beginning (black bars) and end (grey bars) of the faults F_2, F_4, F_1 and F_9. In this stage, the system is responsible only for distinguishing the normal operation from a fault and considers only the steady state regime (which in Figure 7.23, for example, starts around 75s).

After a fault is detected, the identification/classification stage, based on the fuzzy algorithm *AutoClass* is activated. The data is spatially distributed in an n-dimensional feature space. In this particular example, two features were used — here called Feature 1 and Feature 2, thus $x = \{Feature\ 1, Feature\ 2\}$ —, where the first one is the period and the second one is the amplitude of the control signal.

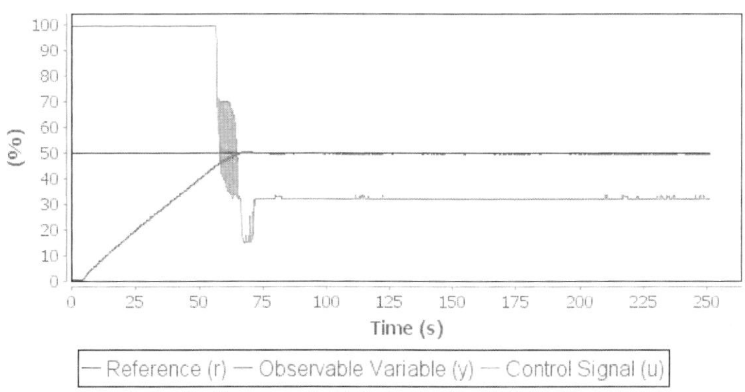

Figure 7.23: Fault-free state of operation of the plant.

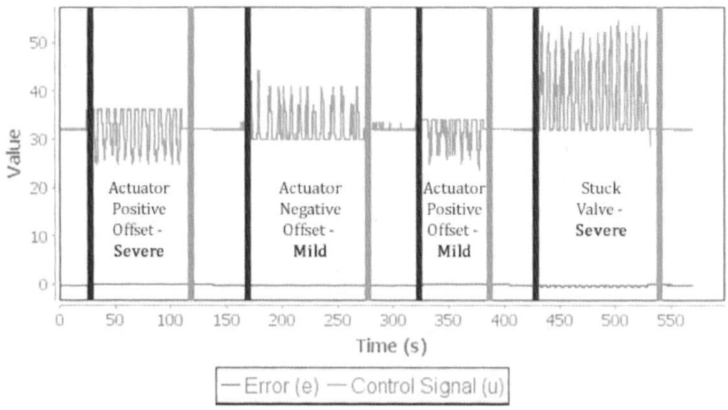

Figure 7.24: Detection of a sequence of faults using RDE.

Figure 7.25 shows the n-dimensional feature space after the reading of all data samples.

The fuzzy rule-based classifier, autonomously generated from the data stream, which consists of 5,600 data samples, is presented as follows:

$$\mathfrak{R}^1 : \textbf{IF}\left(\vec{x} \sim \aleph^1\right) \textbf{THEN} \left(\text{``}\mathit{Class}\ 1\text{''}\right),$$
$$\mathfrak{R}^2 : \textbf{IF}\left(\vec{x} \sim \aleph^2\right) \textbf{THEN} \left(\text{``}\mathit{Class}\ 2\text{''}\right),$$
$$\mathfrak{R}^3 : \textbf{IF}\left(\vec{x} \sim \aleph^3\right) \textbf{THEN} \left(\text{``}\mathit{Class}\ 3\text{''}\right),$$

with

$$\aleph^1 : c_1 = [0.416, 3.316] \text{ and } ZI_1 = [0.251, 0.756],$$
$$\aleph^2 : c_2 = [-0.513, 2.706] \text{ and } ZI_2 = [0.250, 0.601],$$
$$\aleph^3 : c_3 = [-0.416, 1.491] \text{ and } ZI_3 = [0.197, 0.451],$$

where c_i is the focal point (mean) and Z_i is the zone of influence of the cloud.

The fault classification procedure, which is only executed after the detection of a fault by the RDE-based detection algorithm (that is why no rule for the fault-free case was created), is quite unique in the sense that it autonomously and in a completely unsupervised manner (automatic labels) identifies the types of faults. Traditional models, such as neural networks, start to drift and a re-calibration is needed. This unsupervised and self-learning method does not suffer from such disadvantage because it is adapting and evolving.

It should be noted that the class labels are generated automatically in a sequence ("Class 1", "Class 2" and so on) as different faults are detected. Of course, these labels do not represent the actual type or location of the fault, but they are very useful to distinguish different faults. Since there is no training or pre-definition of faults or models, the correct labeling can be performed in a semi-supervised manner by

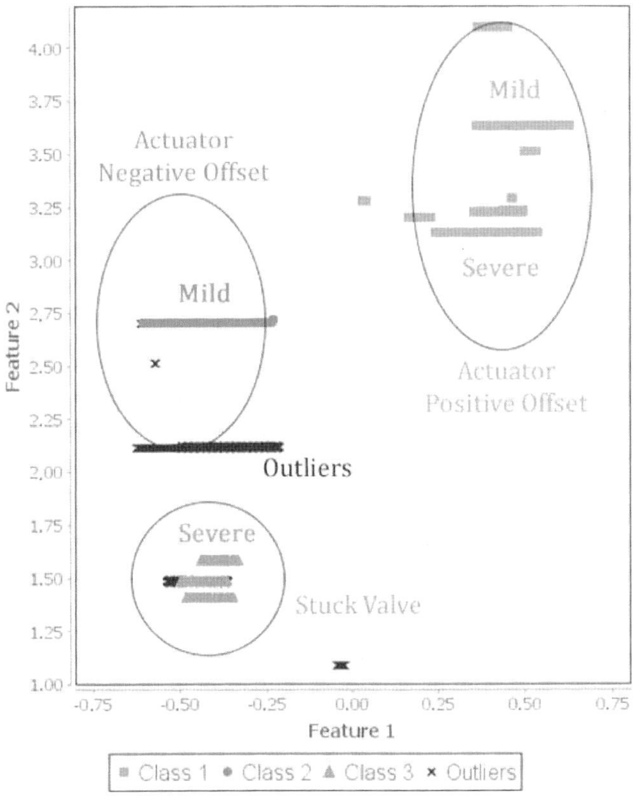

Figure 7.25: Classification and automatic labeling of the faults using *AutoClass*.

the human operators without requiring prompt/synchronized actions from the user. Moreover, in a semi-supervised approach, the operator should be able to merge, split and rename the generated clouds/rules/classes of faults, enabling the classification of faults/operation states that cannot be represented by compact/convex data clouds.

It is also important to highlight that even though the detection and classification process were presented separately, they are performed simultaneously, online, from the acquired data sample.

7.3.6. *Other Approaches to Fuzzy FDD*

Most of the methods for FDD addressed in the literature are problem-driven and, although classifiable into one of the three main groups of methods (quantitative, qualitative or process history-based), they still can be very different in many aspects. That said, we can still recommend the following literature.

Observation-based fault detection in robots is discussed in Sneider and Frank (1996). The supervision method proposed makes use of non-measurable process information. This method is reviewed and applied to the fault detection problem in an industrial robot, using dynamic robot models, enhanced by the inclusion of nonlinear friction terms. A fuzzy logic residual evaluation approach of model-based fault detection techniques is investigated for processes with unstructured disturbances, arising from model simplification.

In Simani (2013), the author proposes an approach based on analytical redundancy, focused on fuzzy identification oriented to the design of a set of fuzzy estimators for fault detection and identification. Different aspects of the fault detection problem are treated in the paper, such as model structure, parameter identification and residual generation and fault diagnosis techniques. The proposed approach is applied to a real diesel engine.

A model-based approach to FDD using fuzzy matching is proposed in Dexter and Benouarets (1997). The scheme uses a set of fuzzy reference models, obtained offline from simulation, which describes normal and, as an extension of the example given in Section 7.3.2, also describes faulty operation. A classifier based on fuzzy matching evaluates the degree of similarity every time the online fuzzy model is identified. The method also deals with any ambiguity, which may result from normal or faulty states of operation, or different types of faults, with similar symptoms at a given operating state.

A method for design of unknown fuzzy observers for Takagi–Sugeno (TS) models is addressed in Akhenak *et al.* (2009). The paper presents the development of a robust fuzzy observer in the presence of disturbances, which is used for detection and isolation of faults which can affect a TS model. The proposed methodology is applied to a simulated environment by estimating the yaw rate and the fault of an automatic steering vehicle.

In Gmytrasiewicz *et al.* (1990), Tanaka *et al.* (1983) and Peng *et al.* (2008), different approaches to fault diagnosis for systems based on fuzzy fault-tree analysis are discussed. These methods aim to diagnose component failures from the observation of fuzzy symptoms, using the information contained in a fault-tree. While in conventional fault-tree analysis, the failure probabilities of components of a system are treated as exact values in estimating the failure probability of the top event, a fuzzy fault-tree employs the possibility, instead of the probability, of failure, namely a fuzzy set defined in probability space.

Fault diagnosis based on trend patterns shown in the sensor measurements is presented in Dash *et al.* (2003). The process of trend analysis involves graphic representation of signal trends as temporal patterns, extraction of the trends, and their comparison, through a fuzzy estimation of similarity, to infer the state of the process. The technique is illustrated with its application for the fault diagnosis of an exothermic reactor.

In Lughofer and Guardiola (2008), and Skrjanc (2009), the authors present different approaches to the usage of fuzzy confidence intervals for model outputs in order to normalize residuals with the model uncertainty. While in the first paper, the authors evaluate the results based on high-dimensional measurement data from engine test benchmarks, in the latter one, the proposed method is used for a nonlinear waste-water treatment plant modeling.

In Oblak *et al.* (2007), the authors introduce an application of the interval fuzzy model in fault detection for nonlinear systems with uncertain interval-type parameters. An application of the proposed approach in a fault-detection system for a two-tank hydraulic plant is presented to demonstrate the benefits of the proposed method.

A fuzzy-genetic algorithm for automatic FDD in HVAC systems is presented in Lo *et al.* (2007). The proposed FDD system monitors the HVAC system states continuously by a fuzzy system with optimal fuzzy inference rules generated by a genetic algorithm. Faults are represented in different levels and are classified in an online manner, concomitantly with the rule basis tuning.

Last, but not least, the reader is referred to Rahman *et al.* (2010), Calado and Sá da Costa (2006), which present the literature reviews of neuro-fuzzy applications in FDD systems. These surveys present many applications of fault detection, isolation and classification, using neuro-fuzzy techniques, either single or combined, highlighting the advantages and disadvantages of each presented approach.

7.4. Open Benchmarks

The study and validation of new and existing FDD techniques is, usually, related to the use of well-known and already validated benchmarks. They are advantageous in the sense that they are enabling one to perform the experiments using real industrial data and serving as a fair basis of comparison to other techniques.

Among the most used benchmarks for FDD, we surely need to mention Development and Applications of Methods for Actuator Diagnosis in Industrial Control Systems (DAMADICS), first introduced in Bartys *et al.* (2006). DAMADICS is an openly available benchmark system based on the industrial operation of the sugar factory Cukrownia Lublin SA, Poland. The benchmark considers many details of the physical and electro-mechanical properties of a real industrial actuator valve operating under challenging process conditions.

With DAMADICS, it is possible to simulate 19 abnormal events, along with the normal operation, from three actuators. A faulty state is composed by the type of the fault followed by the failure mode, which can be abrupt or incipient. DAMADICS was successfully used as testing platform in many applications, such as Puig *et al.* (2006), Almeida and Park (2008), and Frisk *et al.* (2003).

Another important benchmark, worth mentioning, is presented in Blanke *et al.* (1995). The benchmark is based on an electro-mechanical position servo, part of

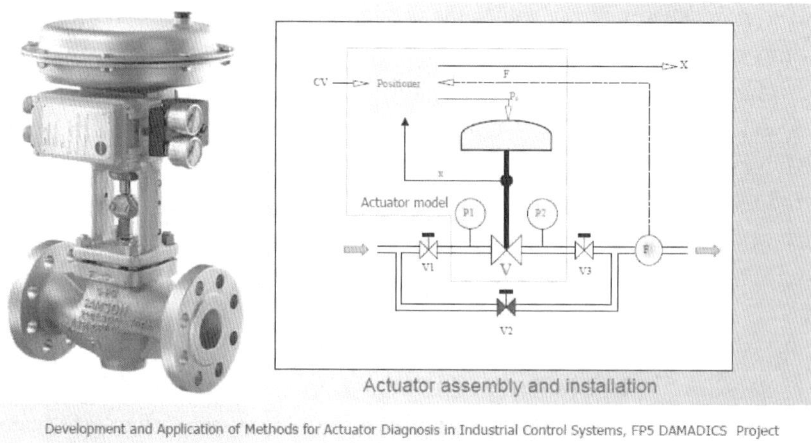

Figure 7.26: Actuator model of DAMADICS benchmark (Damadics, 1999).

a shaft rotational speed governor for large diesel engines, located in a test facility at Aalborg University, Denmark. Potential faults include malfunction of velocity, position measurements or motor power drive and, can be fast or incipient, depending on the parameters defined by the operator. The benchmark also enables the study of robustness, sensor noise and unknown inputs.

In Odgaard *et al.* (2009), the authors introduce a benchmark model for fault tolerant control of wind turbines, which presents a diversity of faulty scenarios, including sensor/actuator, pitch system, drive train, generator and converter system malfunctions. Last, but not least, Goupil and Puyou (2013) introduces a high-fidelity aircraft benchmark, based on a generic twin engine civil aircraft model developed by Airbus, including the nonlinear rigid-body aircraft model with a complete set of controls, actuator and sensor models, flight control laws, and pilot inputs.

7.5. Conclusions

A full overview of FDD methods was presented in this chapter with special attention to the fuzzy rule-based techniques. Basic and essential concepts of the field of study were presented, along with the review of numerous techniques introduced in the literature, from more traditional strategies, well-fitted in one of the three main categories of FDD techniques, to advanced state-of-the-art approaches, which combine elements and characteristics of multiple categories. A benchmark simulated study was introduced and used to illustrate and compare different types of methods, based either on quantitative/qualitative knowledge or on the data acquired from the process. A few other benchmark applications introduced in the literature were also referred, encouraging the reader to use them as tools for analysis/comparison. As previously suggested in other works, the use of hybrid FDD techniques, combining the best features of each group, is very often advised, since all groups of methods present their own advantages and disadvantages, and single methods frequently lack a number of desirable features necessary for an ideal FDD system.

References

Abonyi, J. (2003). *Fuzzy Model Identification for Control*. Boston, USA: Birkhäuser.

Akhenak, A., Chadli, M., Ragot, J. and Maquin, D. (2009). Design of observers for Takagi–Sugeno fuzzy models for fault detection and isolation. In *Proc. Seventh IFAC Symp. Fault Detect., Supervision Saf. Tech. Process., SAFEPROCESS*, 9.

Almeida, G. M. and Park, S. W. (2008). Fault detection and diagnosis in the DAMADICS benchmark actuator system — a hidden Markov model approach. In *Proc. 17th World Congr. Int. Fed. Autom. Control*, Seoul, Korea, July 6–11, pp. 12419–12424.

Angelov, P. (2012). *Autonomous Learning Systems: From Data to Knowledge in Real Time*. Hoboken, New Jersey: John Wiley and Sons.

Angelov, P., Giglio, V., Guardiola, C., Lughofer, E. and Lujan, J. M. (2006). An approach to model-based fault detection in industrial measurement systems with application to engine test benches. *Meas. Sci. Technol.*, 17(7), pp. 1809–1818.

Angelov, P. and Yager, R. (2012). A new type of simplified fuzzy rule-based systems. *Int. J. Gen. Syst.*, 41, pp. 163–185.

Angelov, P. and Zhou, X. (2008). Evolving fuzzy-rule-based classifiers from data streams. *IEEE Trans. Fuzzy Syst.*, 16, pp. 1462–1475.

Bae, H., Kim S., Kim, J. M. and Kim, K. B. (2005). Development of flexible and adaptable fault detection and diagnosis algorithm for induction motors based on self-organization of feature extraction. In *Proc. 28th Ann. German Conf. AI, KI 2005*, Koblenz, Germany, September 11–14, pp. 134–147.

Bartyś, M., Patton, R., Syfert, M., de lasHeras, S. and Quevedo, J. (2006). Introduction to the DAMADICS actuator FDI benchmark study. *Control Eng. Pract.*, 14(6), pp. 577–596.

Blanke, M., Bøgh, S. A., Jørgensen, R. B. and Patton, R. J. (1995). Fault detection for a diesel engine actuator: a benchmark for FDI. *Control Eng. Pract.*, 3(12), pp. 1731–1740.

Calado, J. and Sá da Costa, J. (2006). Fuzzy neural networks applied to fault diagnosis. In *Computational Intelligence in Fault Diagnosis*. London: Springer-Verlag, pp. 305–334.

Carl, J. D., Tantawy, A., Biswas, G. and Koutsoukos, X. (2012). Detection and estimation of multiple fault profiles using generalized likelihood ratio tests: a case study. *Proc. 16th IFAC Symp. Syst. Identif.*, pp. 386–391.

Casillas, J., Cordon, O., Herrera, F. and Magdalena, L. (2003). *Interpretability Issues in Fuzzy Modeling*. Berlin, Heidelberg: Springer-Verlag.

Castro, J. L. and Delgado, M. (1996). Fuzzy systems with defuzzification are universal approximators. *IEEE Trans. Syst., Man Cybern., Part B: Cybern.*, 26(1), pp. 149–152.

Cengel, Y. A., Turner, R. H. and Cimbala, J. M. (2012). *Fundamentals of Thermal-Fluid Sciences, Fourth Edition*. USA: McGraw Hill, pp. 471–503.

Chen, H., Jiang, G. and Yoshihira, K. (2006). Fault detection in distributed systems by representative subspace mapping. *Pattern Recognit., ICPR 2006, 18th Int. Conf.*, 4, pp. 912–915.

Chen, J. and Patton, R. J. (1999). *Robust Model-Based Fault Diagnosis for Dynamic Systems*. Boston, Massachusetts: Kluwer Academic Publishers.

Chiang, L. H. and Russell, E. L. and Braatz, R. D. (2001). *Fault Detection and Diagnosis in Industrial Systems*. London: Springer.

Chow, E. Y. and Willsky, A. S. (1984). Analytical redundancy and the design of robust failure detection systems. *IEEE Trans. Autom. Control*, 29(7), pp. 603–614.

Cook, G., Maxwell, J., Barnett, R. and Strauss, A. (1997). Statistical process control application to weld process. *IEEE Trans. Ind. Appl.*, 33, pp. 454–463.

Costa, B., Bezerra, C. G. and Guedes, L. A. (2010). Java fuzzy logic toolbox for industrial process control. In *Braz. Conf. Autom.* (*CBA*), Bonito-MS, Brazil: Brazilian Society for Automatics (SBA).

Costa, B., Skrjanc, I., Blazic, S. and Angelov, P. (2013). A practical implementation of self-evolving cloud-based control of a pilot plant. *IEEE Int. Conf., Cybern.* (*CYBCONF*), June 13–15, pp. 7, 12.

Costa, B. S. J., Angelov, P. P. and Guedes, L. A. (2014a). Fully unsupervised fault detection and identification based on recursive density estimation and self-evolving cloud-based classifier. *Neurocomputing* (Amsterdam), 1, p. 1.

Costa, B. S. J., Angelov, P. P. and Guedes, L. A. (2014b). Real-time fault detection using recursive density estimation. *J. Control, Autom. Elec. Syst.*, 25, pp. 428–437.

Costa, B. S. J., Bezerra, C. G. and de Oliveira, L. A. H. G. (2012). A multistage fuzzy controller: toolbox for industrial applications. *IEEE Int. Conf., Ind. Technol.* (*ICIT*), March 19–21, pp. 1142, 1147.

Damadics Project. (1999). In http://sac.upc.edu/proyectos-de-investigacion/proyectosue/damadics.

Dash, S., Rengaswamy, R. and Venkatasubramanian, V. (2003). Fuzzy-logic based trend classification for fault diagnosis of chemical processes. *Comput. Chem. Eng.*, 27(3), pp. 347–362.

Dexter, A. L. and Benouarets, M. (1997). Model-based fault diagnosis using fuzzy matching. *Trans. Syst., Man Cybern., Part A*, 27(5), pp. 673–682.

Ding, S. X. (2008). *Model-Based Fault Diagnosis Techniques: Design Schemes, Algorithms, and Tools*. Berlin, Heidelberg: Springer.

Donders, S. (2002). *Fault Detection and Identification for Wind Turbine Systems: A Closed-Loop Analysis*. Master's Thesis. University of Twente, The Netherlands: Faculty of Applied Physics, Systems and Control Engineering.

Edwards, C., Lombaerts, T. and Smaili, H. (2010). Fault tolerant flight control: a benchmark challenge. *Lect. Notes Control Inf. Sci.*, 399, Springer.

Efimov, D., Zolghadri, A. and Raïssi, T. (2011). Actuator fault detection and compensation under feedback control. *Autom.*, 47(8), pp. 1699–1705.

Frank, P. M. and Köppen-Seliger, B. (1997). Fuzzy logic and neural network applications to fault diagnosis. *Int. J. Approx. Reason.*, 16(1), pp. 67–88.

Frank, P. M. and Wünnenberg, J. (1989). Robust fault diagnosis using unknown input observer schemes. In Patton, R. J., Frank, P. M. and Clark, R. N. (eds.), *Fault Diagnosis in Dynamic Systems: Theory and Applications*. NY: Prentice Hall.

Frisk, E. (2001). *Residual Generation for Fault Diagnosis*. PhD Thesis. Linköping University, Sweden: Department of Electrical Engineering.

Frisk, E., Krys, M. and Cocquempot, V. (2003). Improving fault isolability properties by structural analysis of faulty behavior models: application to the DAMADICS benchmark problem. In *Proc. IFAC SAFEPROCESS'03*.

Gacto, M. J., Alcala, R. and Herrera, F. (2011). Interpretability of linguistic fuzzy rule-based systems: an overview of interpretability measures. *Inf. Sci.*, 20, pp. 4340–4360.

Glass, A. S., Gruber, P., Roos, M. and Todtli, J. (1995). Qualitative model-based fault detection in air-handling units. *IEEE Control Syst.*, 15(4), pp. 11, 22.

Gmytrasiewicz, P., Hassberger, J. A. and Lee, J. C. (1990). Fault tree-based diagnostics using fuzzy logic. *IEEE Trans. Pattern Anal. Mach. Intell.*, 12(11), pp. 1115–1119.

Goupil, P. and Puyou, G. (2013). A high-fidelity airbus benchmark for system fault detection and isolation and flight control law clearance. *Prog. Flight Dynam., Guid., Navigat., Control, Fault Detect., Avionics*, 6, pp. 249–262.

Hu, Q., He, Z. J., Zi Y., Zhang, Z. S. and Lei, Y. (2005). Intelligent fault diagnosis in power plant using empirical mode decomposition, fuzzy feature extraction and support vector machines. *Key Eng. Mater.*, 293–294, pp. 373–382.

Insfran, A. H. F., da Silva, A. P. A. and Lambert Torres, G. (1999). Fault diagnosis using fuzzy sets. *Eng. Intell. Syst. Elec. Eng. Commun.*, 7(4), pp. 177–182.

Isermann, R. (2009). *Fault Diagnosis Systems: An Introduction from Fault Detection to Fault Tolerance*. Berlin, Heidelberg: Springer.

Isermann, R. (2005). Model-based fault-detection and diagnosis — status and applications. *Annu. Rev. Control*, 29(1), pp. 71–85.

Katipamula, S., and Brambley, M. R. (2005). Methods for fault detection, diagnostics, and prognostics for building systems: a review, part I. *HVAC&R RESEARCH*, 11(1), pp. 3–25.

Kerre, E. E. and Nachtegael, M. (2000). *Fuzzy Techniques in Image Processing*. Heidelberg, New York: Physica-Verlag.

Korbicz, J., Koscielny, J. M., Kowalczuk, Z. and Cholewa, W. (2004). *Fault Diagnosis: Models, Artificial Intelligence and Applications*. Berlin, Heidelberg: Springer-Verlag.

Kruse, R., Gebhardt, J. and Palm, R. (1994). *Fuzzy Systems in Computer Science*. Wiesbaden: Vieweg-Verlag.

Kulkarni, M., Abou, S. C. and Stachowicz, M. (2009). Fault detection in hydraulic system using fuzzy logic. In *Proc. World Congr. Eng. Comput. Sci.* 2, *WCECS'2009*, San Francisco, USA, October 20–22.

Laukonen, E. G., Passino, K. M., Krishnaswami, V., Lub, G.-C. and Rizzoni, G. (1995). Fault detection and isolation for an experimental internal combustion engine via fuzzy identification. *IEEE Trans. Control Syst. Technol.*, 3(9), pp. 347–355.

Lemos, Caminhas, W and Gomide, F. (2013). Adaptive fault detection and diagnosis using an evolving fuzzy classifier. *Inf. Sci.*, 220, pp. 64–85.

Liang, Y., Liaw, D. C. and Lee, T. C. (2000). Reliable control of nonlinear systems. *IEEE Trans. Autom. Control*, 45(4), 706–710.

Lin, L. and Liu, C. T. (2007). Failure detection and adaptive compensation for fault tolerable flight control systems. *IEEE Trans. Ind. Inf.*, 3(4), pp. 322, 331.

Lo, C. H., Chan, P. T., Wong, Y. K., Rad, A. B. and Cheung, K. L. (2007). Fuzzy-genetic algorithm for automatic fault detection in HVAC systems. *Appl. Soft Comput.*, 7(2), pp. 554–560.

Lughofer, E. (2011). *Evolving Fuzzy Systems — Methodologies, Advanced Concepts and Applications*. Berlin, Heidelberg: Springer.

Lughofer, E. (2013). On-line assurance of interpretability criteria in evolving fuzzy systems: achievements, new concepts and open issues. *Inf. Sci.*, 251, pp. 22–46.

Lughofer, E. and Guardiola, C. (2008). Applying evolving fuzzy models with adaptive local error bars to on-line fault detection. *Proc. Genet. Evolving Fuzzy Syst.* Germany: Witten-Bommerholz, pp. 35–40.

Mendonça, L. F., Sousa, J. M. C. and Sá da Costa, J. M. G. (2004a). Fault detection and isolation using optimized fuzzy models. In *Proc. 11th World Congr., IFSA'2005*. Beijing, China, pp. 1125–1131.

Mendonça, L. F., Sousa, J. M. C. and Sá da Costa, J. M. G. (2004b). Fault detection and isolation of industrial processes using optimized fuzzy models. In Palade, V., Bocaniala, C. D. and Jain, L. C. (eds.), *Computational Intelligence in Fault Diagnosis*. Berlin Heidelberg: Springer, pp. 81–104.

Mendonça, L. F., Sousa, J. M. C. and Sá da Costa, J. M. G. (2009). An architecture for fault detection and isolation based on fuzzy methods. *Expert Syst. Appl. Int. J.*, 36(2), pp. 1092–1104.

Mendonça, L., Sousa, J. and da Costa, J. S. (2006). Fault detection and isolation of industrial processes using optimized fuzzy models. In Palade, V., Jain, L. and Bocaniala, C. D. (eds.), *Computational Intelligence in Fault Diagnosis*, *Advanced Information and Knowledge Processing*. London: Springer, pp. 81–104.

Meneghetti, F. (2007). Mathematical modeling of dynamic systems. *Lab. Keynotes* no. 2. Natal, Brazil: Federal University of Rio Grande do Norte (UFRN).

Murphey, Y. L., Crossman, J. and Chen, Z. (2003). Developments in applied artificial intelligence. In *Proc. 16th Int. Conf. Ind. Eng. Appl. Artif. Intell. Expert Syst., IEA/AIE 2003*. Loughborough, UK, June 23–26, pp. 83–92.

Nelles, O. (2001). *Nonlinear System Identification*. Berlin: Springer.

Oblak, S., Škrjanc, I. and Blažič, S. (2007). Fault detection for nonlinear systems with uncertain parameters based on the interval fuzzy model. *Eng. Appl. Artif. Intell.*, 20(4), pp. 503–510.

Odgaard, P. F., Stoustrup, J. and Kinnaert, M. (2009). Fault tolerant control of wind turbines — a benchmark model. In *Proc. Seventh IFAC Symp. Fault Detect., Supervision Saf. Tech. Process*. Barcelona, Spain, June 30–July 3, pp. 155–160.

Patan, K. (2008). Artificial neural networks for the modelling and fault diagnosis of technical processes. *Lect. Notes Control Inf. Sci.*, 377, Springer.

Patton, R. J., Frank, P. M. and Clark, R. N. (2000). *Issues of Fault Diagnosis for Dynamic Systems*. London: Springer-Verlag.

Pedrycz, W. and Gomide, F. (2007). *Fuzzy Systems Engineering: Toward Human-Centric Computing*. Hoboken, New Jersey: John Wiley & Sons.

Peng, Z., Xiaodong, M., Zongrun, Y. and Zhaoxiang, Y. (2008). An approach of fault diagnosis for system based on fuzzy fault tree. *Int. Conf. Multi Media Inf. Technol., MMIT'08*, December 30–31, pp. 697–700.

Puig, V., Stancu, A., Escobet, T., Nejjari, F., Quevedo, Q. and Patton, R. J. (2006). Passive robust fault detection using interval observers: application to the DAMADICS benchmark problem. *Control Eng. Pract.*, 14(6), pp. 621–633.

Quanser (2004). Coupled tanks user manual.

Rahman, S. A. S. A., Yusof, F. A. M. and Bakar, M. Z. A. (2010). The method review of neuro-fuzzy applications in fault detection and diagnosis system. *Int. J. Eng. Technol.*, 10(3), pp. 50–52.

Samantaray, A. K. and Bouamama, B. O. (2008). *Model-based Process Supervision: A Bond Graph Approach, First Edition*. New York: Springer.

Serdio, F., Lughofer, E., Pichler, K., Buchegger, T. and Efendic, H. (2014). Residual-based fault detection using soft computing techniques for condition monitoring at rolling mills. *Inf. Sci.*, 259, pp. 304–320.

Silva, D. R. C. (2008). *Sistema de Detecção e Isolamento de Falhas em Sistemas Dinâmicos Baseado em Identificação Paramétrica* (*Fault Detection and Isolation in Dynamic Systems Based on Parametric Identification*). PhD Thesis. Federal University of Rio Grande do Norte (UFRN), Brazil: Department of Computer Engineering and Automation.

Simani, S. (2013). Residual generator fuzzy identification for automotive diesel engine fault diagnosis. *Int. J. Appl. Math. Comput. Sci.*, 23(2), pp. 419–438.

Simani, S., Fantuzzi, C. and Patton, R. J. (2002). *Model-based Fault Diagnosis in Dynamic Systems Using Identification Techniques*. Berlin, Heidelberg: Springer-Verlag.

Skrjanc, I. (2009). Confidence interval of fuzzy models: an example using a waste-water treatment plant. *Chemometr. Intell. Lab. Syst.*, 96, pp. 182–187.

Sneider, H. and Frank, P. M. (1996). Observer-based supervision and fault detection in robots using nonlinear and fuzzy logic residual evaluation. *IEEE Trans. Control Syst. Technol.*, 4(3), pp. 274, 282.

Tanaka, H., Fan, L. T., Lai, F. S. and Toguchi, K. (1983). Fault-tree analysis by fuzzy probability. *IEEE Trans. Reliab.*, R-32(5), pp. 453, 457.

Venkatasubramanian, V., Rengaswamy, K. and Kavuri, S. N. (2003a). A review of process fault detection and diagnosis-part II: Qualitative models and search strategies. *Comput. Chem. Eng.*, 27, pp. 293–311.

Venkatasubramanian, V., Rengaswamy, K., Yin, K. and Kavuri, S. N. (2003b). A review of process fault detection and diagnosis-part III: Process history based methods. *Comput. Chem. Eng.*, 27, pp. 327–346.

Venkatasubramanian, V., Rengaswamy, K., Yin, K. and Kavuri, S. N. (2003c). A review of process fault detection and diagnosis-part I: Quantitative model-based methods. *Comput. Chem. Eng.*, 27, pp. 313–326.

Wang, P. and Guo, C. (2013). Based on the coal mine's essential safety management system of safety accident cause analysis. *Am. J. Environ. Energy Power Res.*, 1, pp. 62–68.

Witczak, M. (2014). *Fault Diagnosis and Fault-Tolerant Control Strategies for Nonlinear Systems: Analytical and Soft Computing Approaches*. Berlin, Heidelberg: Springer-Verlag.

Yang, H., Mathew, J. and Ma, L. (2003). Vibration feature extraction techniques for fault diagnosis of rotating machinery: a literature survey. In *Proc. Asia-Pac. Vib. Conf.*, Gold Coast, Australia, November 12–14.

Zhao, Y., Lam, J. and Gao. H. (2009). Fault detection for fuzzy systems with intermittent measurements. *IEEE Trans. Fuzzy Syst.*, 17(2), pp. 398–410.

Zhou, K. and Ren, Z. (2001). A new controller architecture for high performance, robust and fault-tolerant control. *IEEE Trans. Autom. Control*, 46(10), pp. 1613–1618.

Zhou, S. M. and Gan, J. Q. (2008). Low-level interpretability and high-level interpretability: a unified view of data-driven interpretable fuzzy systems modelling. *Fuzzy Sets Syst.*, 159(23), pp. 3091–3131.

Part II

Artificial Neural Networks and Learning Systems

Chapter 8

The ANN and Learning Systems in Brains and Machines

Leonid Perlovsky

8.1. The Chapter Preface

This chapter overviews mathematical approaches to learning systems and recent progress toward mathematical modeling and understanding of the mind mechanisms, higher cognitive and emotional functions, including cognitive functions of the emotions of the beautiful and the music. It is clear today that any algorithmic idea can be realized in a neural-network like architecture. Therefore, from a mathematical point of view, there is no reason to differentiate between Artificial Neural Networks (ANNs) and other algorithms. For this reason, words "algorithms," "neural networks," "machine learning," "artificial intelligence," "computational intelligence" are used in this chapter interchangeably. It is more important to acknowledge that the brain-mind is still a much more powerful learning device than popular ANNs and algorithms and try to understand why this is so. Correspondingly, this chapter searches for fundamental principles, which set the brain-mind apart from popular algorithms, for mathematical models of these principles, and for algorithms built on these models.

What does the mind do differently from ANN and algorithms? We are still far away from mathematical models deriving high cognitive abilities from properties of neurons, therefore mathematical modeling of the "mind" often is more appropriate than modeling the details of the brain, when the goal is to achieve "high" human-like cognitive abilities. The reader would derive a more informed opinion by reading this entire book. This chapter devotes attention to fundamental cognitive principles of the brain-mind, and their mathematical modeling in parallel with solving engineering problems. I also discuss experimental evidence derived from psychological, cognitive, and brain imaging experiments about mechanisms of the brain-mind to the extent it helps the aim: identifying fundamental principles of the mind.

The search for the fundamental principles of the brain-mind and their mathematical models begins with identifying mathematical difficulties behind hundreds of ANNs and algorithms. After we understand the fundamental reasons for the decades of failure of artificial intelligence, machine learning, ANN, and other approaches to modeling the human mind, and to developing mathematical techniques with the human mind power, then we turn to discussing the fundamental principles of the brain-mind (Perlovsky, 2010e).

The next section analyzes and identifies several mathematical difficulties common to wide groups of algorithms. Then we identify a single fundamental mathematical reason for computers failing behind the brain-mind. This reason is reliance of computational intelligence on classical logic.

This is an ambitious statement and the chapter analyzes mathematical as well as cognitive reasons for logic being the culprit of decades of mathematical and cognitive failures. Fundamental mathematical as well as psychological reasons are identified for "how and why" logic that used to be considered a cornerstone of science, turned out to be inadequate, when attempting to understand the mind.

Then, we formulate a mathematical approach that has overcome limitations of logic. It resulted in hundreds of times improvement in solving many classical engineering problems, and it solved problems that remained unsolvable for decades. It also explained what used to be psychological mysteries for long time. In several cognitive and brain-imaging experiments, it has been demonstrated to be an adequate mathematical model for brain-mind processes. Amazingly, this mathematical technique is simpler to code and use than many popular algorithms.

8.2. A Short Summary of Learning Systems and Difficulties They Face

Mathematical ideas invented in the 1950s and 1960s for learning are still used today in many algorithms, therefore let me briefly overview these ideas and identify sources of the mathematical difficulties (Perlovsky, 2001, 2002a).

Computational approaches to solving complex engineering problems by modeling the mind began almost as soon as computers appeared. These approaches in the 1950s followed the known brain neural structure. In 1949, Donald Hebb published what became known as the Hebb-rule: neuronal synaptic connections grow in strength, when they are used in the process of learning. Mathematicians and engineers involved in developing learning algorithms and devices in the early 1950s were sure soon computers would surpass by far the human minds in their abilities. Everybody knows today that Frank Rosenblatt developed a first ANN capable of learning, called Perceptron. Perceptron, however, could only learn to solve fairly simple problems. In 1969, Marvin Minsky and Seymour Papert mathematically proved limits to Perceptron learning.

Statistical pattern recognition algorithms were developed in parallel (Duda *et al.*, 2000). They characterized patterns by features. D features formed a D-dimensional classification space; features from learning samples formed distributions in this space, statistical methods were used to characterize the distributions and derive a classifier. One approach to a classifier design defined a plane, or a more complex surface in a classification space, which separated classes. Another approach became known as a nearest neighbor or a kernel method. In this case, neighborhoods in a classification space near known examples from each class are assigned to the class. The neighborhoods are usually defined using kernel functions (often bell-shaped curves, Gaussians). Use of Gaussian Mixtures to define neighborhoods is a powerful method; first attempts toward deriving such algorithms have been complex, and efficient convergence has been a problem (Titterington *et al.*, 1985). Eventually good algorithms have been derived (Perlovsky and McManus, 1991). Today Gaussian Mixtures are widely used (Mengersen *et al.*, 2011). Yet, these methods turned out to be limited by the dimensionality of classification space.

The problem with dimensionality was discovered by Richard Bellman (1962), who called it "the curse of dimensionality." The number of training samples has to grow exponentially (or combinatorially) with the number of dimensions. The reason is in the geometry of high-dimensional spaces: there are "no neighborhoods", most of the volume is concentrated on the periphery (Perlovsky, 2001). Whereas kernel functions are defined so that the probability of belonging to a class rapidly falls with the distance from a given example, in high-dimensional spaces volume growth may outweigh the kernel function fall; if kernels fall exponentially (like Gaussian), the entire "neighborhood" resides on a thin shell where the kernel fall is matched by the volume rise. Simple problems have been solved efficiently, but learning more complex problems seems impossible.

Marvin Minsky (1965) and many colleagues suggested that learning was too complex and premature. Artificial intelligence should use knowledge stored in computers. Systems storing knowledge in a form of "if, . . . , then, . . . ," rules are called expert systems and are still being used. But when learning is attempted, rules often depend on other rules and grow into combinatorially large trees of rules.

A general approach attempting to combine existing knowledge and learning was model-based learning popular in the 1970s and 1980s. This approach used parametric models to account for existing knowledge, while learning was accomplished by selecting the appropriate values for the model parameters. This approach is simple when all the data comes from only one mode, for example, estimation of a Gaussian distribution from data, or estimation of a regression equation.

When multiple processes have to be learned, algorithms have to split data among models and then estimate model parameters. I briefly describe one algorithm, multiple hypotheses testing (MHT), which is still used today (Singer *et al.*, 1974). To fit model parameters to the data, MHT uses multiple applications of a two-step process. First, an association step assigns data to models. Second, an estimation step estimates parameters of each model. Then a goodness of fit is computed (such as likelihood). This procedure is repeated for all assignments of data to models, and at the end model parameters corresponding to the best goodness of fit are selected. The number of associations is combinatorially large, therefore MHT encounters combinatorial complexity and could only be used for very simple problems.

In the 1970s, the idea of self-learning neural system became popular again. Since the 1960s, Stephen Grossberg continued research into the mechanisms of the brain-mind. He led a systematic exploitation of perceptual illusions for deciphering neural-mathematical mechanisms of perception — similar to I. Kant using typical errors in judgment for deciphering *a priori* mechanisms of the mind. But Grossberg's ideas seemed too complex for a popular following. Adaptive Resonance Theory (ART) became popular later (Carpenter and Grossberg, 1987); it incorporated ideas of interaction between bottom–up (BU), and top–down (TD), signals considered later.

Popular attention was attracted by the idea of Backpropagation, which overcame earlier difficulties of the Perceptron. It was first invented by Arthur Bryson and Yu-Chi Ho in 1969, but was ignored. It was reinvented by Paul Werbos in 1974, and later in 1986 by David Rumelhart, Geoffrey Hinton, and Ronald Williams. The Backpropagation algorithm is capable of learning connection weights in multilayer feedforward neural networks. Whereas an original single layer Perceptron could only learn a hyperplane in a classification space, two layer networks could learn multiple hyperplanes and therefore define multiple regions, three layer networks could learn classes defined by multiple regions.

Multilayer networks with many weights faced the problem of overfitting. Such networks can learn (fit) classes of any geometrical shape and achieve a good performance on training data. However, when using test data, which were not part of the training procedure, the performance could significantly drop. This is a general problem of learning algorithms with many free parameters learned from training data. A general approach to this problem is to train and test a neural network or a classifier on a large number of training and test data. As long as both training and testing performance continue improving with increasing number of free parameters, this indicates valid learning; but when increasing number of parameters results in poorer performance, this is a definite indication of overfitting. A valid training-testing procedure could be exceedingly expensive in research effort and computer time.

A step toward addressing the overfitting problem in an elegant and mathematically motivated way has been undertaken in the Statistical Learning Theory (SLT) (Vapnik, 1999). SLT seems one of the very few theoretical breakthroughs in learning theory. SLT promised to find a valid performance without overfitting in a classification space of any dimension from training data alone. The main idea of SLT is to find a few most important training data points (support vectors) needed to define a valid classifier in a classification sub-space of a small dimension. Support Vector Machines (SVMs) became very popular, likely due to a combination of elegant theory, relatively simple algorithms, and good performance.

However, SVM did not realize the theoretical promise of a valid optimal classifier in a space of any dimension. A complete theoretical argument why this promise has not been realized is beyond the scope of this chapter. A simplified summary is that for complex problems a fundamental parameter of the theory, the Vapnik–Chervonenkis dimension, turns out to be near its critical value. I would add that SLT does not rely on any cognitive intuition about brain-mind mechanisms. It does not seem that the SLT principles are used by the brain-mind. It could have been expected that if SLT would be indeed capable of a general optimal solution of any problem using a simple algorithm, its principles would have been discovered by biological algorithms during billions of years of evolution.

The problem of overfitting due to a large number of free parameters can be approached by adding a penalty function to the objective function to be minimized (or maximized) in the learning process (Setiono, 1997; Nocedal and Wright, 2006). A simple and efficient method is to add a weighted sum of squares of free parameters to a log likelihood or alternatively to the sum of squares of errors; this method is called Ridge regression. Practically, Ridge regression often achieves performance similar to SVM.

Recently, progress for a certain class of problems has been achieved using gradient boosting methods (Friedman *et al.*, 2000). The idea of this approach is to use an ensemble of weak classifiers, such as trees or stumps (short trees) and combine them until performance continues improving. These classifiers are weak in that their geometry is very simple. A large number of trees or stumps can achieve good performance. Why a large number of classifiers with many parameters do not necessarily over fit the data? It could be understood from SLT; one SLT conclusion is that overfitting occurs not just due to a large number of free parameters, but due to an overly flexible classifier parameterization, when a classifier can fit every little "wiggle" in the training data. It follows that a large number of weak classifiers can potentially achieve good performance. A cognitively motivated variation of this idea is Deep Learning, which uses a standard back-propagation algorithm with standard, feed-forward multilayer neural networks with many layers (here is the idea of "deep"). Variations of this idea under the names of gradient boosting, ensembles of trees, and deep learning algorithms are useful, when a very large amount of labeled training data is available (millions of training samples), while no good theoretical knowledge exists about how to model the data. This kind of problem might be encountered in data mining, speech, or handwritten character recognition (Hinton *et al.*, 2012; Meier and Schmidhuber, 2012).

8.3. Computational Complexity and Gödel

Many researchers have attempted to find a general learning algorithm to a wide area of problems. These attempts continue from the 1950s until today. Many smart people spent decades perfecting a particular algorithm for a specific problem, and when they achieve success they are often convinced that they found a general approach. The desire to believe in existence of a general learning algorithm is supported by the fact that the human mind indeed can solve a lot of problems. Therefore, cognitively motivated algorithms such as Deep Learning can seem convincing to many people. If developers of the algorithm succeed in convincing many followers, their approach may flourish for five or even 10 years, until gradually researchers discover that the promise of finding a general learning algorithm has not been fulfilled (Perlovsky, 1998).

Other researchers have been inspired by the fact that the mind is much more powerful than machine learning algorithms, and they have studied mechanisms of the mind. Several principles of mind operations have been discovered, nevertheless mathematical modeling of the mind faced same problems as artificial intelligence and machine learning: mathematical models of the mind have not achieved cognitive power comparable to mind. Apparently, mind learning mechanisms are different from existing mathematical and engineering ideas in some fundamental way.

It turned out that indeed there is a fundamental mathematical principle explaining in unified way previous failures of attempts to develop a general learning algorithm and model learning mechanisms of the mind. This fundamental principle has been laying bare and well known to virtually everybody in full view of the entire mathematical, scientific, and engineering community. Therefore, in addition to explaining this fundamental mathematical reason I will also have to explain why it has not been noticed long ago. It turned out that this explanation reveals a fundamental psychological reason preventing many great mathematicians, engineers, and cognitive scientists from noticing "the obvious" (Perlovsky, 2013c).

The relationships between logic, cognition, and language have been a source of longstanding controversy. The widely accepted story is that Aristotle founded logic as a fundamental mind mechanism, and only during the recent decades science overcame this influence. I would like to emphasize the opposite side of this story. Aristotle thought that logic and language are closely related. He emphasized that logical statements should not be formulated too strictly and language inherently contains the necessary degree of precision. According to Aristotle, logic serves to communicate already made decisions (Perlovsky, 2007c). The mechanism of the mind relating language, cognition, and the world Aristotle described as forms. Today we call similar mechanisms mental representations, or concepts, or simulators in the mind (Perlovsky 2007b; Barsalou, 1999). Aristotelian forms are similar to Plato's ideas with a marked distinction, forms are dynamic: their initial states, before learning, are different from their final states of concepts (Aristotle, 1995). Aristotle emphasized that initial states of forms, forms-as-potentialities, are not logical (i.e., vague), but their final states, forms-as-actualities, attained in the result of learning, are logical. This fundamental idea was lost during millennia of philosophical arguments. It is interesting to add Aristotelian idea of vague forms-potentialities has been resurrected in fuzzy logic by Zadeh (1965); and dynamic logic described here is an extension of fuzzy logic to a process "from vague to crisp" (Perlovsky, 2006a, 2006b, 2013d). As discussed below, the Aristotelian process of dynamic forms can be described mathematically by dynamic logic; it corresponds to processes of perception and cognition, and it might be the fundamental principle used by the brain-mind, missed by ANNs and algorithms (Perlovsky, 2012c).

Classical logic has been the foundation of science since its very beginning. All mathematical algorithms, including learning algorithms and ANNs use logic at some step, e.g., fuzzy logic uses logic when deciding on the degree of fuzziness; all learning algorithms and ANNs use logic during learning: training samples are presented as logical statements. Near the end of the 19th century, logicians founded formal mathematical logic, the formalization of classical logic. Contrary to Aristotelian warnings they strived to eliminate the uncertainty of language from mathematics. Hilbert (1928) developed an approach named formalism, which rejected intuition as a matter of scientific investigation and was aimed at formally defining scientific objects in terms of axioms or rules. In 1900, he formulated famous Entscheidungsproblem: to define a set of logical rules sufficient to prove all past and future mathematical theorems. This was a part of "Hilbert's program", which entailed formalization of the entire human thinking and language.

Formal logic ignored the dynamic nature of Aristotelian forms and rejected the uncertainty of language. Hilbert was sure that his logical theory described mechanisms of the mind. "The fundamental idea of my proof theory is none other than to describe the activity of our understanding, to make a protocol of the rules according to which our thinking actually proceeds" Hilbert (1928). However, Hilbert's vision of formalism explaining mysteries of the human mind came to an end in the 1930s, when Gödel (2001) proved internal inconsistency or incompleteness of formal logic. This development called Gödel theory is considered among most fundamental mathematical results of the previous century. Logic, that was believed to be a sure way to derive truths, a foundation of science, turned out to be basically flawed. This is a reason why theories of cognition and language based on formal logic are inherently flawed.

How exactly does Gödel's incompleteness of logic affect every day logical arguments, cognitive science, and mathematical algorithms?

Gödel, as most mathematical logicians, considered infinite systems, in which every entity is defined with absolute accuracy, every number is specified with infinite precision. Therefore, usual everyday conversations are not affected directly by Gödel's theory. However, when scientists, psychologists, cognitive scientists attempt to understand the mind, perfectly logical arguments can lead to incorrect conclusions. Consider first mathematical algorithms. When Gödel's argument is applied to a finite system, such as computer or brain, the result is not fundamental incompleteness, but computational complexity (Perlovsky, 2013c). An algorithm that upon logical analysis seems quite capable of learning how to solve a certain class of problems in reality has to perform "too many" computations. How many is too many? Most learning algorithms have to consider combinations of some basic elements. The number of combinations grows very fast. Combinations of 2 or 3 are "few". But consider 100, not too big a number; however the number of combinations of 100 elements is 100^{100}, this exceeds all interactions of all elementary particles in the Universe in its entire lifetime, any algorithm facing this many computations is incomputable.

It turns out that algorithmic difficulties considered previously are all related to this problem. For example, a classification algorithm needs to consider combinations of objects and classes. Neural network and fuzzy logic have been specifically developed for overcoming this problem related to logic, but as mentioned they still use logic at some step. For example, training is an essential step in every learning system, training includes logical statements, e.g.,"this is a chair". The combinatorial complexity follows as inadvertently as incompleteness in any logical system.

Combinatorial complexity is inadvertent and practically as "bad" as Gödel's incompleteness.

8.4. Mechanisms of the Mind. What the Mind does Differently?: Dynamic Logic

Although logic "does not work", the mind works and recognizes objects around us. This section considers fundamental mechanisms of the mind, and mathematics necessary to model them adequately. Gradually, it will become clear why Gödel's theory and the fundamental flaw of logic, while been known to all scientists since the 1930s, have been ignored when thinking about the mind and designing theories of artificial intelligence (Perlovsky, 2010a, 2013c).

Among fundamental mechanisms of the mind are mental representations. To simplify, we can think about them as mental imagery, or memories; these are mechanisms of concepts, which are fundamental for understanding the world: objects, scenes, events, as well as abstract ideas. Concepts model events in the world, for this reason they are also called mental models. We understand the world by matching concept-models to events in the world. In a "simple" case of visual perception of objects, concept-models of objects in memory are matched to images of objects on the retina.

Much older mechanisms are instincts (for historical reasons psychologists prefer to use the word "drives"). According to Grossberg–Levine theory of instincts and emotions (1987), instincts work like internal bodily sensors, e.g., our bodies have sensors measuring sugar level in blood. If it is below a certain level, we feel hunger. Emotions of hunger are transferred by neuron connections from instinctual areas in the brain to decision-making areas, and the mind devotes more attention to finding food.

This instinctual-emotional theory has been extended to learning. To find food, to survive we need to understand objects around us. We need to match concept-models of food to surrounding objects. This ability for understanding surroundings is so important for survival, that we have an inborn ability, an instinct that drives the mind to match concept-models to surrounding objects. This instinct is called the knowledge instinct (Perlovsky and McManus, 1991; Perlovsky, 2001, 2006a, 2007d). The neural areas of the brain participating in the knowledge instinct are discussed in (Levine and Perlovsky, 2008, 2010; Perlovsky and Levine, 2012). A mathematical model of the knowledge instinct (to simplify) is a similarity measure between a concept and the corresponding event. Satisfaction of any instinct is felt emotionally. There are specific emotions related to the knowledge instinct, these are aesthetic emotions (Perlovsky, 2001, 2014; Perlovsky *et al.*, 2011). Relations of aesthetic emotions to knowledge have been discovered by Kant (1790). Today it is known that these emotions are present in every act of perception and cognition. An experimental demonstration of existence of these emotions has been reported in (Perlovsky *et al.*, 2010). Their relations to emotions of the beautiful are discussed later.

Mental representations are organized in an approximate hierarchy from perceptual elements to objects, to scenes, to more and more abstract concepts (Grossberg, 1988). Cognition and learning of representations involves interactions between a higher and lower level of representations (more than two layers may interact). This interaction involves bottom–up signals, BU (from lower to higher levels) and top–down, TD (from higher to lower levels). In a simplified view of object perception, an object image is projected from eye retina to the visual cortex (BU), in parallel, representations of expected objects are projected from memory to the visual cortex (TD). In an interaction between BU and TD projections, they are matched. When a match occurs, the object is perceived.

We discussed in previous sections that artificial intelligence algorithms and neural networks for decades have not been able to model this mechanism, logic used in algorithms caused the problem of computational complexity. For example, ART neural network (Carpenter and Grossberg, 1987) matched BU and TD signals using a mathematical procedure of nearest neighbor. This procedure relies on logic at some algorithmic step (e.g., selecting neighbors) and faces combinatorial complexity. The MHT is another approach used for matching the BU and TD signals, as we discussed it faces the combinatorial complexity due to a logical step of assignment of data to models.

To solve the problem, a mathematical technique of dynamic logic (DL), has been created to avoid logic and follow the Aristotelian process of forms from potentialities to actualities. Instead of stationary statements of classical logic, DL is a process-logic, a process "from vague to crisp". This process starts with vague states, "potentialities"; the initial representations in DL are vague. DL thus predicts that mental representations and their initial projections to the visual cortex are vague. In interaction with crisp BU projections from retina, TD projections become crisp and match the BU projections, creating "actualities". How does this process avoid logic and overcome combinatorial complexity?

Compare DL to MHT, which uses logic for data-model assignment. Due to the vagueness of DL initial representations, all data are associated with all models-representations. Thus, a logical assignment step is avoided. DL does not need to consider combinatorially large number of assignments, and combinatorial complexity is avoided. What remains is to develop a mathematical procedure that gradually improves models and concurrently makes associations less vague. Before formulating this mathematical procedure in the next section, let us discuss experimental evidence that confirms the fundamental DL prediction: representations are vague.

Everyone can conduct a simple 1/2 minute experiment to glimpse into neural mechanisms of representations and BU–TD signal interactions. Look at an object in front of your eyes. Then close your eyes and imagine this object. The imagined object is not as clear and crisp as the same object with opened eyes. It is known that visual imaginations are produced by TD signals, projecting representations to the visual cortex. Vagueness of the imagined object testifies to the vagueness of its representation. Thus, the fundamental DL prediction is experimentally confirmed: representations are vague.

When you open your eyes, the object perception becomes crisp in all its details. This seems to occur momentarily, but this is an illusion of consciousness. Actually the process "from vague to crisp" takes quite long by neuronal measures, 0.6s, hundreds to thousands of neuronal interactions. But our consciousness works in such a way that we are sure, there is no "vague to crisp" process. We are not conscious of this process, and usually we are not conscious about vague initial states either.

This prediction of DL has been confirmed in brain imaging experiments (Bar *et al.*, 2006). These authors demonstrated that indeed initial representations are vague and usually unconscious. Also, the vague to crisp process is not accessible to consciousness. Indeed Aristotle's formulation of cognition as a process from vague potentialities to logical actualities was ahead of his time.

8.5. Mathematical Formulation of DL

DL maximizes a similarity L between the BU data $\boldsymbol{X}(n)$, $n = 1, \ldots, N$, and TD representations-models $\boldsymbol{M}(m)$, $m = 1, \ldots, \boldsymbol{M}$,

$$L = \prod_{n \in N} \sum_{m \in M} r(m) l(\boldsymbol{X}(n) | \boldsymbol{M}(m)). \tag{1}$$

Here $l(\boldsymbol{X}(n)|\boldsymbol{M}(m))$ are conditional similarities, later I denote them $l(n|m)$ for shortness; they can be defined so that under certain conditions they become the conditional likelihoods of data given the models, L becomes the total likelihood, and DL performs the maximum likelihood estimation. From the point of view of modeling the mind processes, DL matches BU and TD signals and implements the knowledge instinct. Coefficients $r(m)$, model rates, define a relative proportion of data described by model m; for $l(n|m)$ to be interpretable as conditional likelihoods $r(m)$ must satisfy a condition,

$$\sum_{m \in M} r(m) = 1. \tag{2}$$

A product over data index n does not assume that data are probabilistically independent (as some simplified approaches do, to overcome mathematical difficulties), relationships among data are introduced through models. Models $\boldsymbol{M}(m)$ describe parallel or alternative states of the system (the mind has many representations in its memories). Note, Equation (1) accounts for all possible alternatives of the data associations through all possible combinations of data and models-representations. Product over data index n of the sums of M models results in M^N items, this huge number is the mathematical reason for CC.

Learning consists in estimating model parameters, which values are unknown and should be estimated along with $r(m)$ in the process of learning. Among standard estimation approaches that we discussed is MHT (Singer *et al.*, 1974), which considers every item among M^N. Logically, this corresponds to considering separately every alternative association between data and models and choosing the best possible association (maximizing the likelihood). It is known to encounter CC.

DL avoids this logical procedure and overcomes CC as follows. Instead of considering logical associations between data and models, DL introduces continuous associations,

$$f(m|n) = r(m)l(n|m) \Big/ \sum_{m' \in M} r(m')l(n|m'). \tag{3}$$

For decades, associations between models and data have been considered an essentially discrete procedure. Representing discrete associations as continuous variables, Equation (3) is the conceptual breakthrough in DL. The DL process for the estimation of model parameters $\boldsymbol{S}_m$ begins with arbitrary values of these unknown parameters with one restriction; parameter values should be defined so that partial similarities have large variances. These high-variance uncertain states of models, in which models correspond to any pattern in the data, correspond to the Aristotelian potentialities. In the process of estimation, variances are reduced so that models correspond to actual patterns in data, Aristotelian actualities. This DL-Aristotelian process "from vague to crisp" is defined mathematically as follows (Perlovsky, 2001, 2006a, 2006b):

$$\frac{\mathrm{D}f(m|n)}{\mathrm{d}t} = f(m|n) \sum_{m' \in M} [{}_{\mathrm{mm'}} - f(m'|n)] \left[\frac{\partial \ln l(n|m')}{\partial \boldsymbol{M}_{m'}}\right] \left(\frac{\partial \boldsymbol{M}_{m'}}{\partial \boldsymbol{S}_{m'}}\right) \frac{\mathrm{d}\boldsymbol{S}_{m'}}{\mathrm{d}t},$$

$$\frac{\mathrm{d}\boldsymbol{S}_m}{\mathrm{d}t} = \sum_{n \in N} f(m|n) \left[\frac{\partial \ln l(n|m)}{\partial \boldsymbol{M}_m}\right] \frac{\partial \boldsymbol{M}_m}{\partial \boldsymbol{S}_{m,mm'}} = 1 \quad \text{if } m = m', 0 \text{ otherwise.} \tag{4}$$

Parameter t here is an internal time of the DL process; in digital computer implementation it is proportional to an iteration number.

A question might come up why DL, an essentially continuous process, seemingly very different from logic is called logic. This topic is discussed from a mathematical viewpoint in (Vityaev *et al.*, 2011, 2013; Kovalerchuk *et al.*, 2012). Here I would add that DL explains how logic emerges in the mind from neural operations: vague and illogical DL states evolve in the DL process to logical (or nearly logical) states. Classical logic is (approximately) an end-state of the DL processes.

Relations between DL, logic, and computation are worth an additional discussion (Perlovsky, 2013c). Dynamic logic is computable. Operations used by computers implementing dynamic logic algorithms are logical. But these logical operations are at a different level than human thinking. Compare the text of this chapter as stored in your computer and the related computer operations (assuming you have the book in e-version) to the human understanding of this chapter. The computer's operations are logical, but on a different level from your "logical" understanding of this text. A computer does not understand the meaning of this chapter the way a human reader does. The reader's logical understanding is on top of 99% of the brain's operations that are not "logical" at this level. Our logical understanding is an end state of many illogical and unconscious dynamic logic processes.

8.6. A Recognition-Perception DL Model

Here, I illustrate the DL processes "from vague to crisp" for object perception. These processes model interactions among TD and BU signals. In these interactions, vague top-level representations are matched to crisp bottom-level representations. As mentioned, Aristotle discussed perception as a process from forms-as-potentialities to forms-as-actualities 2400 years ago. Amazingly, Aristotle was closer to the truth than many ANNs and computational intelligence algorithms used today.

From an engineering point of view, this example solves a problem of finding objects in strong clutter (unrelated objects of no interest, noise). This is a classical engineering problem. For cases of clutter signals stronger than object signals this problem has not been solved for decades.

For this illustration, I use a simple example, still unsolvable by other methods. In this example, DL finds patterns-objects in noise-clutter. Finding patterns below noise can be an exceedingly complex problem. I briefly repeat here why for decades existing algorithms could not solve this type of problems. If an exact pattern shape is not known and depends on unknown parameters, these parameters should be found by fitting the pattern model to the data. However, when the locations and orientations of patterns are not known, it is not clear which subset of the data points should be selected for fitting. A standard approach for solving this kind of problem, which has already been mentioned, is multiple hypotheses testing, MHT (Singer *et al.*, 1974); this algorithm searches through all logical combinations of subsets and models and encounters combinatorial complexity.

In the current example, we are looking for 'smile' and 'frown' patterns in noise shown in Figure 8.1a without noise, and in Figure 8.1b with noise, as actually measured (object signals are about 2–3 times below noise and cannot be seen). This example models the visual perception "from vague to crisp". Even so, it is usually assumed that human visual system works better than any computer algorithm, this is not the case here. The DL algorithm used here models human visual perception, but human perception has been optimized by evolution for different types of patterns; the algorithm here is not as versatile as human visual system, it has been optimized for few types of patterns encountered here.

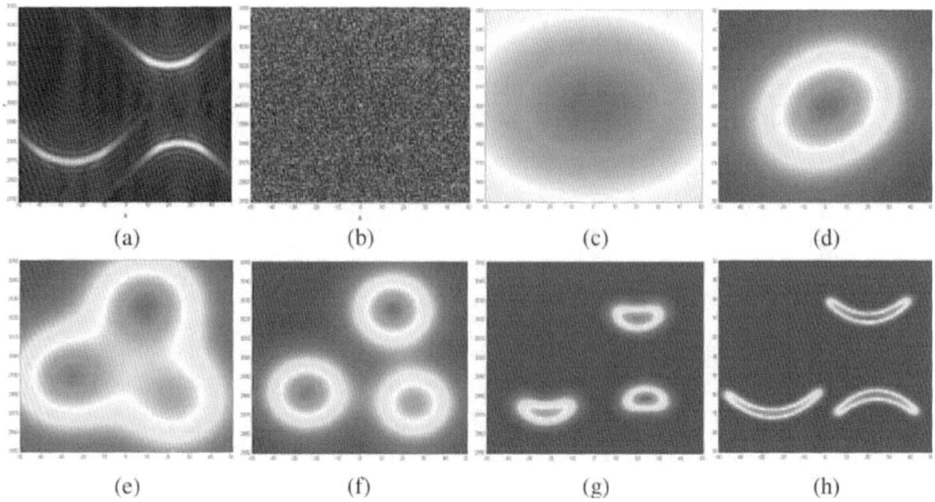

Figure 8.1: Finding 'smile' and 'frown' patterns in noise, an example of dynamic logic operation: (a) true 'smile' and 'frown' patterns are shown without noise; (b) actual image available for recognition (signals are below noise, signal-to-noise ratio is between $\frac{1}{2}$ and $\frac{1}{4}$, 100 times lower than usually considered necessary); (c) an initial fuzzy blob-model, the vagueness corresponds to uncertainty of knowledge; (d) through (h) show improved models at various steps of DL [Equations (3) and (4) are solved in 22 steps]. Between stages (d) and (e) the algorithm tried to fit the data with more than one model and decided, that it needs three blob-models to 'understand' the content of the data. There are several types of models: one uniform model describing noise (it is not shown) and a variable number of blob-models and parabolic models, which number, location, and curvature are estimated from the data. Until about stage (g) the algorithm 'thought' in terms of simple blob models, at (g) and beyond, the algorithm decided that it needs more complex parabolic models to describe the data. Iterations stopped at (h), when similarity (1) stopped increasing.

Several types of pattern models-representations are used in this example: parabolic models describing 'smiles' and 'frown' patterns (unknown size, position, curvature, signal strength, and number of models), circular-blob models describing approximate patterns (unknown size, position, signal strength, and number of models), and noise model (unknown strength). Mathematical description of these models and corresponding conditional similarities $l(n|m)$ are given in Perlovsky *et al.* (2011).

In this example, the image size is 100×100 points ($N = 10{,}000$ BU signals, corresponding to the number of receptors in an eye retina), and the true number of models is 4 (3+ noise), which is not known. Therefore, at least $M = 5$ models should be fit to the data, to decide that 4 fits best. This yields complexity of logical combinatorial search, $M^N = 10^{5000}$; this combinatorially large number is much larger than the size of the Universe and the problem was unsolvable for decades. Figure 8.1 illustrates DL operations: (a) true 'smile' and 'frown' patterns without noise, unknown to the algorithm; (b) actual image available for recognition;

(c) through (h) illustrate the DL process, they show improved models (actually $f(m|n)$ values) at various steps of solving DL Equations (3), and (4), a total of 22 steps until similarity continues improving (noise model is not shown; figures (c) through (h) show association variables, $f(m|n)$, for blob and parabolic models). By comparing (h) to (a), one can see that the final states of the models match patterns in the signal. Of course, DL does not guarantee finding any pattern in noise of any strength. For example, if the amount and strength of noise would increase 10-fold, most likely the patterns would not be found. DL reduced the required number of computations from combinatorial 10^{5000} to about 10^9. By solving the CC problem, DL was able to find patterns under the strong noise. In terms of signal-to-noise ratio, this example gives 10,000% improvement over the previous state-of-the-art.

The main point of this example is to illustrate the DL process "from vague-to-crisp," how it models the open-close eyes experiment described in Section 8.4, and how it models visual perception processes demonstrated experimentally in (Bar *et al.*, 2006). This example also emphasizes that DL is a fundamental and revolutionary improvement in mathematics and machine learning (Perlovsky 2009c, 2010c).

8.7. Toward General Models of Structures

The next "breakthrough" required for machine learning and for modeling cognitive processes is to construct algorithms with similar fast learning abilities that do not depend on specific parametric shapes, and that could address the structure of models. I describe such an algorithm in this section. For concreteness, I consider learning situations constructed from some objects among many other objects. I assume that the learning system can identify objects, however, which objects are important for constructing which situation and which objects are randomly present is unknown. Such a problem faces CC of a different kind from that considered above. Logical choice here would have to find structure of models: objects that form situations. Instead, DL concentrates on continuous parameterization of the model structure, which objects are associated with which situations (Ilin and Perlovsky, 2010).

In addition to situation learning, the algorithm given below solves the entire new wide class of problems that could not have been previously solved: structure of texts as they are built from words, structure of interaction between language and cognition, higher cognitive functions, symbols, grounded symbols, perceptual symbol system, creative processes, and the entire cognitive hierarchy (Barsalou, 1999; Perlovsky, 2007a, 2007b; Perlovsky and Ilin, 2012; Perlovsky and Levine, 2012; Perlovsky *et al.*, 2011). Among applications related to learning text structure, I demonstrate autonomous learning of malware codes in Internet messages (Perlovsky and Shevchenko, 2014). Each of these problems if approached logically would result in combinatorial complexity. Apparently, the DL ability to model continuous associations could be the very conceptual breakthrough that brings power of the mind to mathematical algorithms.

This further development of DL turns identifying a structure into a continuous problem. Instead of the logical consideration of a situation as consisting of its objects, so that every object either belongs to a situation or does not, DL considers every object as potentially belonging to a situation. Starting from the vague potentiality of a situation, to which every object could belong, the DL learning process evolves this into a model-actuality containing definite object, and not containing others.

Every observation, $n = 1, \ldots, N$, contains a number of objects, $j = 1, \ldots, J$. Let us denote objects as $x(n, j)$, here n enumerates observations, and j enumerates objects. As previously, $m = 1, \ldots, M$ enumerates situation-models. Model parameters, in addition to $r(m)$ are $p(m, j)$, potentialities of object j belonging to situation-models m. Data $x(n, j)$ have values 0 or 1; potentialities $p(m, j)$ start with vague value near 0.5 and in the DL process of learning they converge to 0 or 1. Mathematically this construct can be described as

$$l(n|m) = \prod_{j=1}^{J} p(m, j)^{x(n,j)} (1 - p(m, j))^{(1-x(n,j))}. \tag{5}$$

A model parameter $p(m, j)$, modeling a potentiality of object j being part of model m, starts the DL process with initial value near 0.5 (exact values 0.5 for all $p(m, j)$ would be a stationary point of the DL process, Equation (4)). Value $p(m, j)$ near 0.5 gives potentiality values (of $x(n, j)$ belonging to model m) with a maximum near 0.5, in other words, every object has a significant chance to belong to every model. If $p(m, j)$ converge to 0 or 1 values, these would describe which objects j belong to which models m.

Using conditional similarities, Equation (5) in the DL estimation process, Equation (4) can be simplified to an iterative set of Equations (3) and

$$p(m, j) = \sum_{n} f(m|n) x(n, j) \Big/ \sum_{n'} x(n', j); \tag{6}$$

both Equations (3) and (6) should be recomputed at each iteration.

Illustration of this DL algorithm is shown in Figure 8.2. Here, 16,000 simulated observations are shown on the left. They are arranged in their sequential order along the horizontal axis, n. For this simplified example, we simulated 1,000 total possible objects, they are shown along the vertical axis, j. Every observation has or does not have a particular object as shown by a white or black dot at the location (n, j). This figure looks like random noise corresponding to pseudo-random content of observations. On the right figure, observations are sorted so that observations

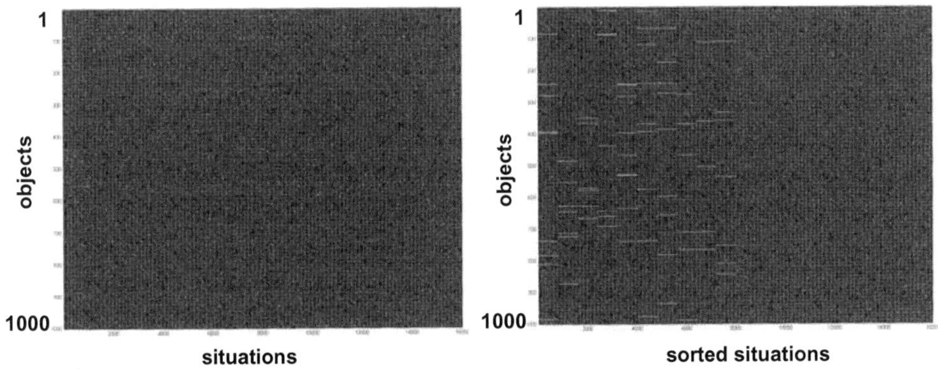

Figure 8.2: On the left are 16,000 observed situations arranged in their sequential order along the horizontal axis, n. The total number of possible objects is 1,000, they are shown along the vertical axis, j. Every observation has or does not have a particular object as shown by a white or black dot at the location (n, j). This figure looks like random noise corresponding to pseudo-random content of observations. On the right figure, observations are sorted so that observations having similar objects appear next to each other. These similar objects appear as white horizontal streaks. Most of observation contents are pseudo-random objects; about a half of observations have several similar objects. These observations with several specific objects observe specific situations, they reveal certain situation-models.

having similar objects appear next to each other. These similar objects appear as white horizontal streaks and reveal several groups of data, observations of specific situations. Most of observation contents are pseudo-random objects; about one-half of observations contain certain situations. These observations with specific repeated objects reveal specific situations, they identify certain situation-models.

Since the data for this example have been simulated, we know the true number of various situations, and the identity of each observation as containing a particular situation-model. All objects have been assigned correctly to their situations without a single error. Convergence is very fast and took two to four iterations (or steps) to solve Equation (4).

This algorithm has been also applied to autonomous finding of malware codes in Internet messages (Perlovsky and Shevchenko, 2014) by identifying groups of messages different from normal messages. In this application, messages are similar to observations in the previous application of situation learning; groups of messages correspond to situations, and n-grams correspond to objects. We applied this algorithm to a publicly available dataset of malware codes, KDD (Dua and Du, 2011; Gesher, 2013; Mugan, 2013). This dataset includes 41 features extracted from Internet packets and one class attribute enumerating 21 classes of four types of attacks. The DL algorithm identified all classes of malware and all malware messages without a single false alarm. This performance in terms of accuracy and speed is better than other published algorithms. An example of the algorithm performance

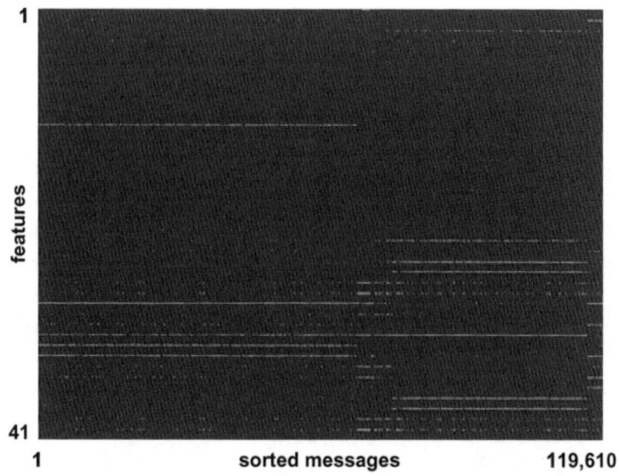

Figure 8.3: This figure shows sorted messages from six groups (one normal and five malware) of the KDD dataset (similar to Figure 8.2 right. I do not show unsorted messages, similar to Figure 8.2 left). Along the horizontal axis: 67,343 normal messages and a five malware codes 2,931 portsweep, 890 warezclient, 3,633 satan, 41,214 neptune, 3,599 ipsweep. Groups of malware are significantly different in size, and not all features important for a group are necessarily present in each vector belonging to the group, therefore the look of the figure is not as clear cut as Figure 8.2 right. Nevertheless all vectors are classified without errors, and without false alarms.

on this data is given in Figure 8.3. This application is a step toward autonomous finding of malware codes in Internet messages.

8.8. Modeling Higher Cognitive Functions, Including the Beautiful

Examples in previous sections addressed classical engineering problems that have not been solved for decades. In parallel they modeled the mind processes corresponding to classical psychological phenomena of perception and cognition. In this section, I begin considering "higher" cognitive functions, the entire hierarchy of the mind processes from objects to the very "top" of the mental hierarchy. These processes have not been so far understood in psychology, even so some of their aspects (e.g., language, the beautiful, music) have been analyzed in philosophy and psychology for thousands of years. From the engineering point of view, these problems are becoming important now as engineers attempt to construct human-like robots. As shown in the following sections, constructing robots capable of abstract thinking requires understanding of how cognition interacts with language. I also demonstrate that the beautiful and the music have specific fundamental cognitive functions, and understanding their mechanisms is paramount for constructing human-like robots (even at a level well below than the full power of the human mind).

The mathematical model of learning situations constructed from objects, considered in the previous section, is applicable to modeling the entire hierarchy of the mind. The mind is organized in an approximate hierarchy (Grossberg, 1988) from visual percepts, to objects, to situations, to more and more abstract concepts at higher levels, which contents I analyze later. The mathematical structure of the model given by Equations (3)–(5) is applicable to the entire hierarchy because it does not depend on specific designations of "objects", "situations", or "n-grams", used above. It is equally applicable to modeling interaction of BU and TD signals between any higher and lower levels in the hierarchy, and therefore modeling neural mechanisms of learning of abstract concepts from lower level concepts.

Let us turn to details of the knowledge instinct and related aesthetic emotions briefly discussed in Section 8.4. Interactions between BU and TD signals are driven by the inborn mechanism, instinct. At lower levels of the hierarchy involving object recognition, this instinct is imperative for finding food, detecting danger, and for survival (Perlovsky, 2007d). Therefore, the knowledge instinct at these levels acts autonomously. Tentative analysis of brain regions participating in the knowledge instinct have been analyzed in (Levine and Perlovsky, 2008, 2010; Perlovsky and Levine, 2012). The mathematical model of the knowledge instinct is given in the previous section, as DL maximization of similarity between mental representations (TD signals) at every level and those coming from a lower level BU signals. Motivation for improving knowledge and satisfaction or dissatisfaction with knowledge are felt as aesthetic emotions. Their connection to knowledge makes them "more spiritual" than basic emotions related to bodily instincts. Existence of these emotions has been experimentally confirmed (Perlovsky *et al.*, 2010). At higher levels of the mental hierarchy a person might experience "higher" aesthetic emotions. These are related to the beautiful as discussed below (Perlovsky, 2000).

Concept-representations at every level emerged in evolution with a specific purpose, to form higher-level more abstract concepts by unifying some subsets of lower-level ones. For example, a mental representation of "professor office" unifies lower level representations such as chairs, desk, computer, shelves, books, etc. At every higher level more general and abstract representations are formed. We know from DL and confirming experiments that higher-level representations are vaguer and less conscious than objects perceived with opened eyes. This vagueness and lesser consciousness is the "price" for generality and abstractness Perlovsky (2010d).

Continuing these arguments toward the top of the hierarchy we can come up with the hypothesis of the contents of representations at the top of the hierarchy. The "top" representation evolved with the purpose to unify the entire life experience and it is perceived as the meaning of life. Does it really exist? Let us repeat that top representations are vague and mostly unconscious, therefore the meaning of life does not exist the same way as a concrete object that can be perceived with opened eyes. Nevertheless, it really exists, similar to other abstract concepts-representation independently of subjective will. It is not up to one's will to accept or deny an objectively existing architecture of the brain-mind.

Every person can work toward improving one's understanding of the meaning of his or her life. Appreciation that one's life has a meaning is of utmost importance; thousands of years ago it could have been important for the individual survival. Today it is important for concentrating ones efforts on the most important goals, for attaining one's highest achievements. Improving these highest representations, even if it only results in the improved appreciation of existence of the meaning, leads to satisfaction of the knowledge instinct. The corresponding aesthetic emotions near the top of the hierarchy are felt as emotions of the beautiful (Perlovsky, 2000, 2002b, 2010b, 2010e, 2010f, 2014a).

This theory of beautiful is the scientific development of Kant's aesthetics (1790). Kant has been the first who related the beautiful to knowledge. But without the theory of the knowledge instinct, and the hierarchy of aesthetic emotions, he could not complete his aesthetic theory to his satisfaction. He could only formulate what the beauty "is not", in particular, he emphasized that the beautiful does not respond to any specific interests, it is purposeful, but its purpose is not related to any specific need. Today I reformulate this: emotions of the beautiful do not satisfy any of the bodily instincts, they satisfy the "higher and more spiritual" instinct for knowledge. Several times Kant has tried to come close to this scientific understanding, he has emphasized that the beautiful is purposive in some highest way, that it corresponds to some highest human interests, and that a better more precise formulation is needed, but he had to concede that "today we cannot" do this. This Kantian intuition was ahead of his time by far. His immediate follower Shiller (1895) misunderstood Kant and interpreted him as if the beautiful is disinterested, and therefore art exists for its own sake. This misunderstanding of the beautiful, its function in cognition, and the meaning of art persists till today. In tens of thousands of papers on art and aesthetics, the beautiful is characterized as disinterested, and "art for its own sake" (Perlovsky, 2010f).

I would add that often emotions of the beautiful are mixed up with sexual feelings. Of course, sex is among the most powerful instincts, it may involve all our abilities. However, emotions related to sex are driven by the instinct for procreation and therefore they fundamentally differ from the beautiful, which is driven by the instinct for knowledge.

Let us summarize the emotion of the beautiful as an aesthetic emotion related to the satisfaction of the knowledge instinct near the top of the mental hierarchy, related to the understanding of the meaning of life. It is a subjective emotion affected by the entire individual life experience, at the same time it objectively exists, being related to the fundamental structure of the human mind.

8.9. Language, Cognition, and Emotions Motivating their Interactions

Many properties of cognition and language have been difficult to understand because interactions between these two human abilities have not been understood. Do we think with language, or is language used only for communicating completed thoughts? Language and thinking are so closely related and intertwined that answering this question, requires a mathematical model corresponding to the known neural structures of the brain-mind. For many years, mathematical modeling of language and cognition has proceeded separately, without neurally-based mathematical analysis of how these abilities interact. So, we should not be surprised that existing robots are far away from human-like abilities for language and cognition. Constructing humanoid robots requires mathematical models of these abilities. A model of language-cognition interaction described in this section gives a mathematical foundation for understanding these abilities and for developing robots with human-like abilities. It also gives a foundation for understanding why higher human cognitive abilities, including ability for the beautiful sometimes may seem mysterious (Perlovsky, 2004, 2005, 2009a).

A cognitive hierarchy of the mind has been illustrated in Figure 8.4. However, analysis in this section demonstrates that such a hierarchy cannot exist without language. The human mind requires a dual hierarchy of language-cognition illustrated in Figure 8.5 (Perlovsky, 2005, 2007a, 2009a, 2009b, 2011, 2013b;

Figure 8.4: The hierarchy of cognition from sensory-motor signals at the "lower" levels to objects, situations, and more abstract concepts. Every level contains a large number of mental representations. Vertical arrows indicate interactions of BU and TD signals.

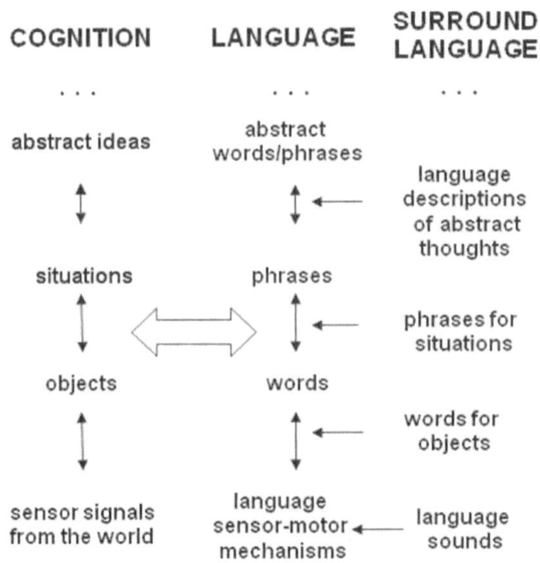

Figure 8.5: The dual hierarchy. Language and cognition are organized into approximate dual hierarchy. Learning language is grounded in the surrounding language throughout the hierarchy (indicated by thin horizontal arrows). Learning the cognitive hierarchy is grounded in experience only at the very "bottom." The rest of the cognitive hierarchy is mostly grounded in language. Vertical arrows indicate interactions of BU and TD signals. A wide horizontal arrow indicates interactions between language and cognition; for abstract concepts these are mostly directed from language to cognition.

Perlovsky and Ilin, 2010, 2013; Tikhanoff *et al.*, 2006). The dual hierarchy model explains many facts about thinking, language, and cognition, which has remained unexplainable and would be considered mysteries, if not so commonplace. Before we describe how the dual hierarchy is modeled by equations discussed in Section 8.6, let us list here some of the dual model explanations and predictions (so that the mathematical discussion later will be associated with specific human abilities).

(1) The dual model explains functions of language and cognition in thinking: cognitive representations model surrounding world, relations between objects, events, and abstract concepts. Language stores culturally accumulated knowledge about the world, yet language is not directly connected to objects, events, and situations in the world. Language guides acquisition of cognitive representations from random percepts and experiences, according to what is considered worth learning and understanding in culture. Events that are not described in language are likely not even noticed or perceived in cognition.

(2) Whereas language is acquired early in life, acquiring cognition takes a lifetime. The reason is that language representations exist in surrounding language "ready-made," acquisition of language requires only interaction with language

speakers, but does not require much life experience. Cognition on the opposite requires life experience.

(3) This is the reason why abstract words excite only language regions of brain, whereas concrete words excite also cognitive regions (Binder *et al.*, 2005). The dual model predicts that abstract concepts are often understood as word descriptions, but not in terms of objects, events, and relations among them.

(4) In this way, the dual model explains why children can acquire the entire hierarchy of language including abstract words without experience necessary for understanding them.

(5) DL is the basic mechanism for learning language and cognitive representations. The dual model suggests that language representations become crisp after language is learned (5–7 years of age), this corresponds to language representations being crisp and near logical. However, cognitive representations remain vague for two reasons. First, as we have discussed, this vagueness is necessary for the ability to perceive objects and events in their variations. Second, this vagueness is a consequence of limited experience; ability to identify cognitive events and abstract concepts in correspondence with language improves with experience; the vagueness is also the meaning of "continuing learning", this takes longer for more abstract and less used concepts. How do these two different aspects of vagueness co-exist? Possibly, various concrete representations are acquired with experience; vague representations are still retained for perception of novelty. At lower levels, this occurs automatically, at higher levels individual efforts are necessary to maintain both concrete and vague representations (we know that some minds get "closed" with experience).

(6) The dual model gives mathematical description of the recursion mechanism (Perlovsky and Ilin, 2012). Whereas Hauser *et al.* (2002) postulate that recursion is a fundamental mechanism in cognition and language, the dual model suggests that recursion is not fundamental, hierarchy is a mechanism of recursion.

(7) Another mystery of human-cognition, not addressed by cognitive or language theories, is basic human irrationality. This has been widely discussed and experimentally demonstrated following discoveries of Tversky and Kahneman (1974), leading to the 2002 Nobel Prize. According to the dual hierarchy model, the "irrationality" originates from the dichotomy between cognition and language. Language is crisp and conscious while cognition might be vague and ignored when making decisions. Yet, collective wisdom accumulated in language may not be properly adapted to one's personal circumstances, and therefore be irrational in a concrete situation. In the 12th century, Maimonides wrote that Adam was expelled from paradise because he refused original thinking using his own cognitive models, but ate from the tree of knowledge and acquired collective wisdom of language (Levine and Perlovsky, 2008).

The same Equations (4) or (3) and (5) that we have used to model the cognitive hierarchy are used for the mathematical modeling of the dual language-cognition model. Modeling the dual hierarchy differs from modeling cognition in that every observation, situation-collection of lower level signals, now includes both language and cognitive representations from lower levels. In the DL processes [Equations (4) and (5)], language hierarchy is acquired first (during early years of life); it is learned according to abstract words, phrases, and higher-level language representations existing in the surrounding language. Most cognitive representations remain vague for a while. As more experience is accumulated, cognitive representations are acquired corresponding to already existing language representations. This joint acquisition of both language and cognition corresponds to the wide horizontal arrow in Figure 8.5. In this way, cognitive representations are acquired from experience guided by language.

As some cognitive representations become crisper and more conscious, this establishes more reliable connections between representation and events in the world. This provides learning feedback, grounding for learning of both cognition and language. Thus, both cognition and language are grounded not only in language, but also in the surrounding world. Language representations correspond to some extent to the world. At lower levels of the hierarchy, levels of objects and situations, these processes are supported by the fact that objects can be directly observed; situations can be observed to some extent after acquisition of the corresponding cognitive ability. At more abstract levels, these connections between language and the world are more sporadic, some connections of abstract language and cognitive representations could be more or less conscious, correspondingly more or less concrete could be understanding of abstract events and relations in the world.

Higher up in the hierarchy, less of cognitive representations ever become fully conscious, if they maintain an adequate level of generality and abstractness. Two opposing mechanisms are at work here (as already mentioned). First, vagueness of representations is a necessary condition for being able to perceive novel contents (we have seen it in the "open–close" eyes experiment). Second, vague contents evolve toward concrete contents with experience. Therefore, more concrete representations evolve with experience, while vague representations remain. This depends on experience and extent to which cultural wisdom contained in language is acquired by an individual. People differ in extents and aspects of culture they become conscious of at the higher levels. Majority of cognitive contents of the higher abstract concepts remain unconscious. This is why we can discuss in detail the meaning of life and the beautiful using language, but significant part of higher cognitive contents forever remain inaccessible to consciousness.

Interactions among language, cognition, and the world require motivation. The inborn motivation is provided by the knowledge instinct. Language acquisition is driven by its aspect related to the language instinct (Pinker, 1994). Certain mechanisms of mind may participate in both language and knowledge instinct, and division between language and knowledge instinct is not completely clear-cut. This area remains "grey" in our contemporary knowledge. More experimental data are needed to differentiate the two. I would emphasize that the language instinct drives language acquisition, its mechanisms "stop" at the border with cognition, and the language instinct does not concern improvement of cognitive representations and connecting language representations with the world.

Mechanisms of the knowledge instinct connecting language and cognition are experienced as emotions. These are special aesthetic emotions related to language. As we have discussed, these interactions are mostly directed from language to cognition, and correspondingly these emotions–motivations necessary for understanding language cognitively (beyond "just" words) are "more" on the language side. For cognitive mechanisms to be "interested" in language, to be motivated to acquire directions from language, there has to be an emotional mechanism in language accomplishing this motivation. These emotions of course must be of ancient origin, they must have been supporting the very origin of language and originating pre-linguistically. These emotions are emotional prosody of language.

In the pre-linguistic past, animal vocalizations did not differentiate emotion-evaluation contents from conceptual-semantic contents. Animals' vocal tract muscles are controlled from the ancient emotional center (Deacon, 1989; Lieberman, 2000). Sounds of animal cries engage the entire psyche, rather than concepts and emotions separately. Emergence of language required emancipation of voicing from uncontrollable emotions (Perlovsky, 2004, 2009a, 2009b). Evolution of languages proceeded toward reducing emotional content of language voice. Yet, complete disappearance of emotions from language would make language irrelevant for life, meaningless. Connections of language with cognition and life require that language utterances remain emotional. This emotionality motivates connecting language with cognition. Some of these prosodial emotions correspond to basic emotions and bodily needs; yet there is a wealth of subtle variations of prosodial emotions related to the knowledge instinct and unrelated to bodily needs. I would add that the majority of everyday conversations may not relate to exchange of semantic information as in scientific presentations; majority of information in everyday conversations involve emotional information, e.g., information about mutual compatibility among people. This wealth of emotions we hear in poetry and in songs.

Emotionality of language prosody differs among languages; this impacts entire cultures. It is interesting to note that during the recent 500 years, during the transition from Middle English to Modern English, significant part of emotional connections between words and their meanings has been lost. I repeat, these emotions came from millennial past and subconsciously control the meanings of utterances and thoughts; disappearance (to significant extent) of these emotions makes English a powerful tool of science and engineering, including social engineering. There are differences between these areas of fast changes in contemporary life. Results of scientific and engineering changes, such as new drugs, new materials, and new transportation methods usually are transparent for society. Positive changes are adopted, when in doubt (such as genetic engineering) society can take evaluative measures and precautions. Social engineering is different, changes in values and attitudes usually are considered to be results of contemporary people to be smarter in their thinking than our predecessors. Identifying which part of these changes is due to autonomous changes in language, which are not under anybody's conscious control, should be an important part of social sciences.

The dual hierarchy model explains how language influences cognition. A more detailed development of this model can lead to explaining and predicting cultural differences related to language, so called Sapir–Whorf Hypothesis (SWH) (Whorf, 1956; Boroditsky, 2001). Prosodial emotions are influenced by grammar, leading to Emotional SWH (Perlovsky, 2009b; Czerwon, *et al.*, 2013). It follows that languages influence emotionalities of cultures, in particular, the strength of emotional connections between words and their meanings. This strength of individual "belief" in the meaning of words can significantly influence cultures and their evolution paths.

Understanding prosodial emotions and their functions in cognition, developing appropriate mathematical models is important not only for psychology and social science but also for artificial intelligence and ANNs, for developing human–computer interface and future robots with human level intelligence.

8.10. Music Functions in Cognition

2400 years ago Aristotle (1995) asked "why music, being just sounds, reminds states of the soul?" Why an ability to perceive sounds emotionally and to create such sounds could emerge in evolution? Darwin (1871) called music "the greatest mystery". Does computational intelligence community need to know the answer? Can we contribute to understanding of this mystery? The explanation of the mystery of music has been obtained from the dual model considered in the previous section. Music turns out to perform cognitive functions of utmost importance, it enables accumulation of knowledge, it unifies human psyche split by language, and it makes the entire evolution of human culture possible. Enjoying music is not just good for spending time free from job; enjoying music is fundamental for cognition. Humanoid robots need to enjoy music, otherwise cognition is not possible. To understand cognitive functions of music, music origin and evolution, we first examine an important cognitive mechanism counteracting the knowledge instinct, the mechanism of cognitive dissonances.

Cognitive dissonances (CD) are discomforts caused by holding conflicting cognitions. Whereas it might seem to scientists and engineers that conflicts in knowledge are welcome as they inspire new thinking, in fact CD are particularly evident when a new scientific theory is developed; new ideas are usually rejected. It is not just because of opposition of envious colleagues, it is also because of genetically inherited mechanism of CD. CD is among "the most influential and extensively studied theories in social psychology" (e.g., Alfnes *et al.*, 2010). CDs are powerful anti-knowledge mechanisms. It is well known that CD discomforts are usually resolved by devaluing and discarding a conflicting piece of knowledge (Festinger, 1957; Cooper, 2007; Harmon-Jones *et al.*, 2009); we discuss it in detail later. It is also known that awareness of CD is not necessary for actions to reduce the conflict (discarding conflicting knowledge); these actions are often fast and act without reaching conscious mechanisms (Jarcho *et al.*, 2011).

I would emphasize that every mundane element of knowledge to be useful must differ from innate knowledge supplied by evolution or from existing knowledge acquired through experience. Otherwise the new knowledge would not be needed. For new knowledge to be useful it must to some extent contradict existing knowledge. Can new knowledge be complementary rather than contradictory? Since new knowledge emerges by modifying previous knowledge (Simonton, 2000; Novak, 2010), there must always be conflict between the two. Because of this conflict between new and previous knowledge CD theory suggests that new knowledge should be discarded. This process of resolving CD by discarding contradictions is usually fast, and according to CD theory new knowledge is discarded before its usefulness is established. But accumulating knowledge is the essence of cultural evolution, so how human cultures could evolve? A powerful cognitive-emotional mechanism evolved to overcome CD, discomforts of contradictory knowledge, so that human evolution became possible.

A language phrase containing a new piece of knowledge, in order to be listened to without an immediate rejection, should come with a sweetener, a positive emotion sounding in the voice itself. In the previous section, we discussed that this is the purpose of language prosody. However, emotions of language have been reduced in human evolution, whereas knowledge has been accumulated and stronger emotions have been needed to sustain the evolution. The human mind has been rewired for this purpose. Whereas animal vocalization is controlled from the ancient emotional center, the human mind evolved secondary emotional centers in the cortex, partially under voluntary control, governing language vocalization. In the process of language evolution human vocalization split into highly semantic and low emotional language, and another type of vocalization, highly emotional and less semantic, connected to the primordial emotional center governing the entire psyche; this highly emotional vocalization unifying psyche gradually evolved into music. The powerful emotional mechanism of music overcame cognitive dissonances, it enables us and our predecessors to maintain contradictory cognitions and unify psyche split by language (Perlovsky, 2006a, 2010a, 2012a, 2012b, 2013a).

Pre-language animals' mind is unified. A monkey seeing an approaching tiger understands the situation conceptually (danger), is afraid emotionally (fear), behaves appropriately (jumps on a tree) and cries in monkey language for itself and for the rest of the pack ("tiger", in monkey language). However, all of these are experienced as a unified state of the mind, a monkey cannot experience emotions and concepts separately. A monkey does not contemplate the meaning of his life. Humans, in contrast, possess a remarkable degree of differentiation of their mental states. Emotions in humans have separated from concepts and from behavior. This differentiation destroyed the primordial unity of the psyche. With the evolution of language the human psyche lost its unity — the inborn connectedness of knowledge, emotions, and behavior. The meaning of our life, the highest purpose requiring the utmost effort is not obvious and not defined for us instinctively; the very existence of the meaning is doubtful. However, the unity of psyche is paramount for concentrating the will, and for achieving the highest goal. While part of the human voice evolved into language, acquired concrete semantics, lost much of its emotionality, and split our mental life into many disunited goals, another part of the voice evolved into a less concretely semantic but powerfully emotional ability — music — helping to unify the mental life (Perlovsky, 2006a, 2012a, 2012b, 2013a).

8.11. Theoretical Predictions and Experimental Tests

Mathematical models of the mind have been used for designing cognitive algorithms; these algorithms based on DL solved several classes of engineering problems considered unsolvable, reaching and sometimes exceeding power of the mind. A few examples have been discussed in this chapter, many others can be found in the referenced publications (e.g., Perlovsky *et al.*, 2011). These engineering successes suggest that DL possibly captures some essential mechanisms of the mind making it more powerful than past algorithms. In addition to solving engineering problems, mathematical models of the mind have explained mechanisms that could not have been understood and made predictions that could be tested experimentally. Some of these predictions have been tested and confirmed, none has been disproved. Experimental validations of DL predictions are summarized below.

The first and most fundamental prediction of dynamic logic is vagueness of mental representations and the DL process "from vague to crisp". This prediction has been confirmed in brain imaging experiments for perception of objects

(Bar *et al.*, 2006), and for recognition of contexts and situations (Kveraga *et al.*, 2007). DL is a mechanism of the knowledge instinct. The knowledge instinct theory predicts the existence of special emotions related to knowledge, aesthetic emotions. Their existence has been demonstrated in (Perlovsky *et al.*, 2010). This also confirms of existence of the knowledge instinct.

The dual hierarchy theory of language-cognition interaction predicts that language and cognition are different mechanisms. Existence of separate neural mechanisms for language and cognition has been confirmed in (Price, 2012). The dual hierarchy theory predicts that perception and understanding of concrete objects involves cognitive and language mechanisms, whereas cognition of abstract concepts is mostly due to language mechanisms. This has been confirmed in (Binder *et al.*, 2005).

The dual hierarchy emphasizes fundamental cognitive function of language emotionality, language prosody influences strength of emotional connections between sounds and meanings; these connections are the foundations of both language and cognition. The strengths of these emotional connections could differ among languages, affecting cultures and their evolution, leading to Emotional SWH. Various aspects of this hypothesis have been confirmed experimentally. Guttfreund (1990) demonstrated that Spanish is more emotional than English; Harris *et al.* (2003) demonstrated that emotional connections between sounds and meanings in Turkish are stronger than in English; these have been predicted based on grammatical structures of the corresponding languages (Perlovsky, 2009b). Czerwon *et al.* (2013) demonstrated that this emotional strength depends on grammar as predicted in Perlovsky (2009b).

A theory of musical emotions following from the dual model predicts that music helps unifying mental life, overcoming CD and keeping contradictory knowledge. This prediction has been confirmed in (Masataka and Perlovsky, 2012a, 2012b), which describes a modified classical CD experiment (Aronson and Carlsmith, 1963); in the original experiment children devalued a toy if they were told not to play with it. The desire 'to have' contradicts the inability 'to attain'; this CD is resolved by discarding the value of a toy. Masataka and Perlovsky modified this experiment by adding music played in the background. With music, the toy has not been devalued, contradictory knowledge could be retained. Another experiment explained the so-called Mozart effect: student's academic test performance improved after listening to Mozart (Rauscher *et al.*, 1993). These results started a controversy resolved in (Perlovsky *et al.*, 2013). This publication demonstrated that the Mozart effect is the predicted overcoming of CD: as expected from CD theory students allocate *less* time to more difficult and stressful tests; with music in the background students *can* tolerate stress, allocate *more* time to stressful tests, and improve grades. These results have been further confirmed in (Cabanac *et al.*, 2013):

students selecting music classes outperformed other students in all subjects. Another experiment demonstrated that music helps overcoming cognitive interference. A classical approach to creating cognitive interference is Stroop effect (Stroop, 1935). Masataka and Perlovsky (2013) demonstrated that music played in the background reduced the interference.

8.12. Future Research

Future engineering research should develop the large-scale implementation of the dual hierarchy model and demonstrate joint learning of language and cognition in robotics and human–computer integrated systems. Scientifically oriented research should use agent systems with each agent possessing a mind with language and cognitive abilities (the dual hierarchy). Such systems could be used for studying evolution of languages including grammar along with evolution of cultures. This will open directions toward studying evolution of cognitive dissonances and aesthetic emotions. Future research should address brain mechanisms of the knowledge instinct. A particularly understudied area is functions of emotions in cognition. Several directions for research in this area are outlined below.

Emotions of language prosody have only been studied in cases of intentionally strongly-emotional speech. These emotions are recognized without language in all societies, and unify us with non-human animals. Non-intentional prosodial emotions that are inherent functions of languages and connect language sounds to meanings should be studied. The dual model predicts fundamental importance of these emotions in language-cognition interaction.

Emotional SWH made a number of predictions about prosodial emotions and their connections to language grammar. In particular, this theory predicts that emotional links between sounds and meanings (words and objects-events they designate) are different in different languages, and the strengths of these links depend on language grammar in a predictable way (Perlovsky, 2009b): languages with more inflections have stronger emotional links between sounds and meanings. These predictions have been confirmed for English, Spanish, and Turkish (Guttfreund, 1990; Harris *et al.*, 2003; Czerwon, *et al.*, 2013). More experiments are needed to study connections between language structure, its emotionality, and cultural effects.

Among the greatest unsolved problems in experimental studies of the mind is how to measure the wealth of aesthetic emotions. Bonniot-Cabanac *et al.* (2012) initiated experimental studying of CD emotions. These authors demonstrated existence of emotions related to CD, their fundamental difference from basic emotions, and outlined steps toward demonstrating a very large number of these emotions. Possibly, a most direct attempt to "fingerprint" aesthetic emotions is to measure neural networks corresponding to them (Wilkins *et al.*, 2012). Three specific difficulties are faced when attempting to instrumentalize (measure) a variety of aesthetic emotions.

The first is a limitation by words. In the majority of psychological experiments measuring emotions, they are described using words. But English words designate a limited number of different emotions, about 150 words designate between 6 and 20 different emotions (depending on the author; e.g., Petrov *et al.*, 2012). Musical emotions that evolved with a special purpose not to be limited by low emotionality of language cannot be measured in all their wealth by emotional words. Second difficulty is "non-rigidity" of aesthetic emotions. They are recent in evolutionary time. Whereas basic emotions evolved hundreds of millions of years ago, aesthetic emotions evolved no more than two million years ago, and possibly more recently. This might be related to the third difficulty, subjectivity. Aesthetic emotions depend not only on stimuli, but also on subjective states of experiment participants. All experimental techniques today rely on averaging over multiple measurements and participants. Such averaging likely eliminates the wealth of aesthetic emotions, such as musical emotions, and only most "rigid" emotions remain.

This chapter suggests that mental representations near the top of the hierarchy of the mind are related to the meaning of life. Emotions related to improvement of the contents of these representations are related to the emotions of the beautiful. Can this conjecture be experimentally confirmed? Experimental steps in this direction have been made in (Biederman and Vessel, 2006; Zeki *et al.*, 2014).

References

Alfnes, F., Yue, C. and Jensen, H. H. (2010). Cognitive dissonance as a means of reducing hypothetical bias. *Eur. Rev. Agric. Econ.*, 37(2), pp. 147–163.

Aronson, E. and Carlsmith, J. M. (1963). Effect of the severity of threat on the devaluation of forbidden behavior. *J. Abnor. Soc. Psych.*, 66, 584–588.

Aristotle. (1995). *The Complete Works: The Revised Oxford Translation*, Barnes, J. (ed.). Princeton, NJ, USA: Princeton University Press.

Bar, M., Kassam, K. S., Ghuman, A. S., Boshyan, J., Schmid, A. M., Dale, A. M., Hämäläinen, M. S., Marinkovic, K., Schacter, D. L., Rosen, B. R. and Halgren, E. (2006). Top-down facilitation of visual recognition. *Proc. Natl. Acad. Sci. USA*, 103, pp. 449–54.

Barsalou, L. W. (1999). Perceptual symbol systems. *Behav. Brain Sci.*, 22, pp. 577–660.

Bellman, R. E. (1961). *Adaptive Control Processes.* Princeton, NJ: Princeton University Press.

Biederman, I. and Vessel, E. (2006). Perceptual pleasure and the brain. *Am. Sci.*, 94(3), p. 247. doi: 10.1511/2006.3.247.

Binder, J. R., Westbury, C. F., McKiernan, K. A., Possing, E. T. and Medler, D. A. (2005). Distinct brain systems for processing concrete and abstract concepts. *J. Cogn. Neurosci.*, 17(6), pp. 1–13.

Bonniot-Cabanac, M.-C., Cabanac, M., Fontanari, F. and Perlovsky, L. I. (2012). Instrumentalizing cognitive dissonance emotions. *Psychol.*, 3(12), pp. 1018–1026. http://www.scirp.org/journal/psych.

Boroditsky, L. (2001). Does language shape thought? Mandarin and English speakers' conceptions of time. *Cogn. Psychol.*, 43(1), pp. 1–22.

Bryson, A. E. and Ho, Y.-C. (1969). *Applied Optimal Control: Optimization, Estimation, and Control.* Lexington, MA: Xerox College Publishing, p. 481.

Cabanac, A., Perlovsky, L. I., Bonniot-Cabanac, M.-C. and Cabanac, M. (2013). Music and academic performance. *Behav. Brain Res.*, 256, pp. 257–260.

Carpenter, G. A. and Grossberg, S. (1987). A massively parallel architecture for a self-organizing neural pattern recognition machine. *Comput. Vis., Graph., Image Process.*, 37, pp. 54–115.

Cooper, J. (2007). *Cognitive Dissonance: 50 Years of a Classic Theory.* Los Angeles, CA: Sage.

Czerwon, B., Hohlfeld, A., Wiese, H. and Werheid, K. (2013). Syntactic structural parallelisms in?uence processing of positive stimuli: Evidence from cross-modal ERP priming. *Int. J. Psychophysiol.*, 87, pp. 28–34.

Darwin, C. R. (1871). *The Descent of Man, and Selection in Relation to Sex.* London: John Murray Publishing House.

Deacon, T. W. (1989). The neural circuitry underlying primate calls and human language. *Human Evol.*, 4(5), pp. 367–401.

Dua, S. and Du, X. (2011). *Data Mining and Machine Learning in Cybersecurity.* Boca Raton, FL: Taylor & Francis.

Duda, R. O., Hart, P. E. and Stork, D. G. (2000). *Pattern Classification, Second Edition.* New York: Wiley-Interscience.

Festinger, L. (1957). *A Theory of Cognitive Dissonance.* Stanford CA: Stanford University Press.

Friedman, J., Hastie, T. and Tibshirani, R. (2000). Additive logistic regression: a statistical view of boosting (With discussion and a rejoinder by the authors). *Ann. Statist.*, 28(2), pp. 337–655.

Gödel, K. (2001). *Collected Works, Volume I, "Publications 1929–1936"*, Feferman, S., Dawson, Jr., J. W., and Kleene, S. C. (eds.). New York, USA: Oxford University Press.

Grossberg, S. (1988). *Neural Networks and Natural Intelligence.* Cambridge: MIT Press.

Grossberg, S. and Levine, D. S. (1987). Neural dynamics of attentionally modulated Pavlovian conditioning: blocking, inter-stimulus interval, and secondary reinforcement. *Psychobiol.*, 15(3), pp. 195–240.

Guttfreund D. G. (1990). Effects of language usage on the emotional experience of Spanish–English and English–Spanish bilinguals. *J. Consult. Clin. Psychol.*, 58, pp. 604–607.

Harmon-Jones, E., Amodio, D. M. and Harmon-Jones, C. (2009). Action-based model of dissonance: a review, integration, and expansion of conceptions of cognitive conflict. In M. P. Zanna (ed.), *Adv. Exp. Soc. Psychol.*, Burlington: Academic Press, 41, 119–166.

Harris, C. L., Ayçiçegi, A. and Gleason, J. B. (2003). Taboo words and reprimands elicit greater autonomic reactivity in a first language than in a second language. *Appl. Psycholinguist.*, 24, pp. 561–579.

Hauser, M. D., Chomsky, N. and Fitch, W. T. (2002). The faculty of language: what is it, who has it, and how did it evolve? *Science*, 298, pp. 1569–1570. doi: 10.1126/science.298.5598.156.

Hilbert, D. (1928). The foundations of mathematics. In van Heijenoort, J. (ed.), *From Frege to Gödel.* Cambridge, MA, USA: Harvard University Press, p. 475.

Hinton, G., Deng, L., Yu, D., Dahl, G. E. and Mohamed, A. (2012). Deep neural networks for acoustic modeling in speech recognition: the shared views of four research groups. *IEEE Signal Process. Mag.*, 29(6).

Ilin, R. and Perlovsky, L. I. (2010). Cognitively inspired neural network for recognition of situations. *Int. J. Nat. Comput. Res.*, 1(1), pp. 36–55.

Jarcho, J. M., Berkman, E. T. and Lieberman, M. D. (2011). The neural basis of rationalization: cognitive dissonance reduction during decision-making. *SCAN*, 6, pp. 460–467.

Kant, I. (1790). *The Critique of Judgment*, Bernard, J. H. (Trans.). Amherst, NY: Prometheus Books.

Kveraga, K., Boshyan, J. and Bar, M. (2007). Magnocellular projections as the trigger of top–down facilitation in recognition. *J. Neurosci.*, 27, pp. 13232–13240.

Levine, D. S. and Perlovsky, L. I. (2008). Neuroscientific insights on biblical myths: simplifying heuristics versus careful thinking: scientific analysis of millennial spiritual issues. *Zygon, J. Sci. Religion*, 43(4), pp. 797–821.

Levine, D. S. and Perlovsky, L. I. (2010). Emotion in the pursuit of understanding. *Int. J. Synth. Emotions*, 1(2), pp. 1–11.

Lieberman, P. (2000). *Human Language and Our Reptilian Brain*. Cambridge: Harvard University Press.

Masataka, N. and Perlovsky, L. I. (2012a). Music can reduce cognitive dissonance. Nature Precedings: hdl:10101/npre.2012.7080.1. http://precedings.nature.com/documents/7080/version/1.

Masataka, N. and Perlovsky, L. I. (2012b). The efficacy of musical emotions provoked by Mozart's music for the reconciliation of cognitive dissonance. *Scientific Reports* 2, Article number 694. doi:10.1038/srep00694. http://www.nature.com/srep/2013/130619/srep02028/full/srep02028.html.

Masataka, N. and Perlovsky, L. I. (2013). Cognitive interference can be mitigated by consonant music and facilitated by dissonant music. *Scientific Reports* 3, Article number 2028. doi:10.1038/srep02028. http://www.nature.com/srep/2013/130619/srep02028/full/srep02028.html.

Minsky, M. (1968). *Semantic Information Processing*. Cambridge, MA: MIT Press.

Meier, U. and Schmidhuber, J. (2012). Multi-column deep neural networks for image classification. *IEEE Conf. Comput. Vis. Pattern Recognit.* (*CVPR*), 16–21 June, Providence, R1, pp. 3642–3649.

Mengersen, K., Robert, C. and Titterington, M. (2011). *Mixtures: Estimation and Applications*. New York: Wiley.

Nocedal, J. and Wright, S. J. (2006). *Numerical Optimization, Second Edition*. Berlin, Heidelberg: Springer.

Novak. J. D. (2010). Learning, creating, and using knowledge: concept maps as facilitative tools in schools and corporations. *J. e-Learn. Knowl. Soc.*, 6(3), pp. 21–30.

Perlovsky, L. I. (1998). Conundrum of combinatorial complexity. *IEEE Trans. PAMI*, 20(6), pp. 666–670.

Perlovsky, L. I. (2000). Beauty and mathematical intellect. *Zvezda*, 9, pp. 190–201 (Russian).

Perlovsky, L. I. (2001). *Neural Networks and Intellect: Using Model-Based Concepts*. New York: Oxford University Press.

Perlovsky, L. I. (2002a). Physical theory of information processing in the mind: concepts and emotions. *SEED On Line J.*, 2(2), pp. 36–54.

Perlovsky, L. I. (2002b). Aesthetics and mathematical theories of intellect. *Iskusstvoznanie*, 2(2), pp. 558–594.

Perlovsky, L. I. (2004). Integrating language and cognition. *IEEE Connect.,* 2(2), pp. 8–12.

Perlovsky, L. I. (2005). Evolving agents: communication and cognition. In Gorodetsky, V., Liu, J. and Skormin, V. A. (eds.), *Autonomous Intelligent Systems: Agents and Data Mining*. Berlin, Heidelberg, Germany: Springer-Verlag, pp. 37–49.

Perlovsky, L. I. (2006a). Toward physics of the mind: concepts, emotions, consciousness, and symbols. *Phys. Life Rev.*, 3(1), pp. 22–55.

Perlovsky, L. I. (2006b). Fuzzy dynamic logic. *New Math. Nat. Comput.*, 2(1), pp. 43–55.

Perlovsky, L. I. (2007a). Symbols: integrated cognition and language. In Gudwin, R. and Queiroz, J. (eds.), *Semiotics and Intelligent Systems Development*. Hershey, PA: Idea Group, pp. 121–151.

Perlovsky, L. I. (2007b). Modeling field theory of higher cognitive functions. In Loula, A., Gudwin, R. and Queiroz, J. (eds.), *Artificial Cognition Systems*. Hershey, PA: Idea Group, pp. 64–105.

Perlovsky, L. I. (2007c). The mind vs. logic: Aristotle and Zadeh. *Soc. Math. Uncertain. Crit. Rev.*, 1(1), pp. 30–33.

Perlovsky, L. I. (2007d). Neural dynamic logic of consciousness: the knowledge instinct. In Perlovsky, L. I. and Kozma, R. (eds.), *Neurodynamics of Higher-Level Cognition and Consciousness*. Heidelberg, Germany: Springer Verlag, pp. 73–108.

Perlovsky, L. I. (2009a). Language and cognition. *Neural Netw.*, 22(3), pp. 247–257. doi:10.1016/j.neunet.2009.03.007.

Perlovsky, L. I. (2009b). Language and emotions: emotional Sapir–Whorf hypothesis. *Neural Netw.*, 22(5–6), pp. 518–526. doi:10.1016/j.neunet.2009.06.034.

Perlovsky, L. I. (2009c). 'Vague-to-crisp' neural mechanism of perception. *IEEE Trans. Neural Netw.*, 20(8), pp. 1363–1367.

Perlovsky, L. I. (2010a). Musical emotions: functions, origin, evolution. *Phys. Life Rev.*, 7(1), pp. 2–27. doi:10.1016/j.plrev.2009.11.001.

Perlovsky, L. I. (2010b). Intersections of mathematical, cognitive, and aesthetic theories of mind, *Psychol. Aesthetics, Creat., Arts*, 4(1), pp. 11–17. doi:10.1037/a0018147.

Perlovsky, L. I. (2010c). Neural mechanisms of the mind, Aristotle, Zadeh, & fMRI. *IEEE Trans. Neural Netw.*, 21(5), pp. 718–33.

Perlovsky, L. I. (2010d). The mind is not a kludge. *Skeptic*, 15(3), pp. 51–55.

Perlovsky L. I. (2010e). Physics of the mind: concepts, emotions, language, cognition, consciousness, beauty, music, and symbolic culture. *WebmedCentral Psychol.*, 1(12), p. WMC001374. http://arxiv.org/abs/1012.3803.

Perlovsky, L. I. (2010f). Beauty and art. cognitive function, evolution, and mathematical models of the mind. *WebmedCentral Psychol.*, 1(12), p. WMC001322. http://arxiv.org/abs/1012.3801.

Perlovsky L. I. (2011). Language and cognition interaction neural mechanisms. *Comput. Intell. Neurosci.*, Article ID 454587. Open Journal. doi:10.1155/2011/454587. http://www.hindawi.com/journals/cin/contents/.

Perlovsky, L. I. (2012a). Emotions of "higher" cognition. *Behav. Brain Sci.*, 35(3), pp. 157–158.

Perlovsky, L. I. (2012b). Cognitive function, origin, and evolution of musical emotions. *Musicae Scientiae*, 16(2), pp. 185–199. doi: 10.1177/1029864912448327.

Perlovsky, L. I. (2012c). Fundamental principles of neural organization of cognition. *Nat. Precedings*: hdl:10101/npre.2012.7098.1. http://precedings.nature.com/documents/7098/version/1.

Perlovsky, L. I. (2013a). A challenge to human evolution — cognitive dissonance. *Front. Psychol.*, 4, p. 179. doi: 10.3389/fpsyg.2013.00179.

Perlovsky, L. I. (2013b). Language and cognition — joint acquisition, dual hierarchy, and emotional prosody. *Front. Behav. Neurosci.*, 7, p. 123. doi:10.3389/fnbeh.2013.00123. http://www.frontiersin.org/Behavioral_Neuroscience/10.3389/fnbeh.2013.00123/full.

Perlovsky, L. I. (2013c). Learning in brain and machine — complexity, Gödel, Aristotle. *Front. Neurorobot.* doi: 10.3389/fnbot.2013.00023. http://www.frontiersin.org/Neurorobotics/10.3389/fnbot.2013.00023/full.

Perlovsky, L. I. (2014a). Aesthetic emotions, what are their cognitive functions? *Front. Psychol*, 5, p. 98. http://www.frontiersin.org/Journal/10.3389/fpsyg.2014.00098/full; doi:10.3389/fpsyg.2014.0009.

Perlovsky, L. I. and Ilin, R. (2010). Neurally and mathematically motivated architecture for language and thought. Brain and language architectures: where we are now? *Open Neuroimaging J.*, Spec. issue, 4, pp. 70–80. http://www.bentham.org/open/tonij/openaccess2.htm.

Perlovsky, L. I. and Ilin, R. (2012). Mathematical model of grounded symbols: perceptual symbol system. *J. Behav. Brain Sci.*, 2, pp. 195–220. doi:10.4236/jbbs.2012.22024. http://www.scirp.org/journal/jbbs/.

Perlovsky, L. I. and Ilin, R. (2013). CWW, language, and thinking. *New Math. Nat. Comput.*, 9(2), pp. 183–205. doi:10.1142/S1793005713400036. http://dx.doi.org/10.1142/S1793005713400036.

Perlovsky, L. I. and Levine, D. (2012). The Drive for creativity and the escape from creativity: neurocognitive mechanisms. *Cognit. Comput.* doi:10.1007/s12559-012-9154-3. http://www.springerlink.com/content/517un26h46803055/. http://arxiv.org/abs/1103.2373.

Perlovsky, L. I. and McManus, M. M. (1991). Maximum likelihood neural networks for sensor fusion and adaptive classification. *Neural Netw.*, 4(1), pp. 89–102.

Perlovsky, L. I. and Shevchenko, O. (2014). Dynamic Logic Machine Learning for Cybersecurity. In Pino, R. E., Kott, A. and Shevenell, M. J. (eds.), *Cybersecurity Systems for Human Cognition Augmentation*. Zug, Switzerland: Springer.

Perlovsky, L. I., Bonniot-Cabanac, M.-C. and Cabanac, M. (2010). Curiosity and pleasure. *WebmedCentral Psychol.*, 1(12), p. WMC001275. http://www.webmedcentral.com/article_view/1275. http://arxiv.org/ftp/arxiv/papers/1010/1010.3009.pdf.

Perlovsky, L. I., Deming, R. W. and Ilin, R. (2011). *Emotional Cognitive Neural Algorithms with Engineering Applications. Dynamic Logic: From Vague to Crisp.* Heidelberg, Germany: Springer.

Perlovsky, L. I., Cabanac, A., Bonniot-Cabanac, M.-C. and Cabanac, M. (2013). Mozart effect, cognitive dissonance, and the pleasure of music. arxiv 1209.4017; *Behavioural Brain Research*, 244, 9–14.

Petrov, S., Fontanari, F. and Perlovsky, L. I. (2012). Subjective emotions vs. verbalizable emotions in web texts. *Int. J. Psychol. Behav. Sci.*, 2(5), pp. 173–184. http://arxiv.org/abs/1203.2293.

Pinker, S. (1994). *The Language Instinct: How the Mind Creates Language*. New York: William Morrow.

Price, C. J. (2012). A review and synthesis of the first 20 years of PET and fMRI studies of heard speech, spoken language and reading. *Neuroimage*, 62, pp. 816–847.

Rauscher, F. H., Shaw, L. and Ky, K. N. (1993). Music and spatial task performance. *Nature*, 365, p. 611.

Rumelhart, D. E., Hinton, G. E. and Williams, R. J. (1986). Learning representations by back-propagating errors. *Nature*, 323(6088), pp. 533–536.

Schiller, F. (1895). In Hinderer, W. and Dahlstrom, D. (eds.), *Essays, German Library, Volume 17*. GB, London: Continuum Pub Group.

Schmidhuber, J. (2015). Deep learning in neural networks: An overview. *Neural Networks*. 61, pp. 85–117, doi: 10.1016/j.neu-net.2014.09.003.

Setiono, R. (1997). A penalty-function approach for pruning feedforward neural networks. *Neural Comput.*, 9(1), pp. 185–204.

Simonton, D. K. (2000). Creativity. Cognitive, personal, developmental, and social aspects. *Am. Psychol.*, 55(1), pp. 151–158.

Singer, R. A., Sea, R. G. and Housewright, R. B. (1974). Derivation and evaluation of improved tracking filters for use in dense multitarget environments. *IEEE Trans. Inf. Theory*, IT-20, pp. 423–432.

Stroop, J. R. (1935). Studies of interference in serial verbal reactions. *J. Exp. Psych.*, 18, pp. 643–682.

Tikhanoff, V., Fontanari, J. F., Cangelosi, A. and Perlovsky, L. I. (2006). Language and cognition integration through modeling field theory: category formation for symbol grounding. In *Book Series in Computer Science, Volume 4131*. Heidelberg: Springer.

Titterington, D. M., Smith, A. F. M. and Makov, U. E. (1985). *Statistical Analysis of Finite Mixture Distributions*. New York: John Wiley & Sons.

Tversky, A. and Kahneman, D. (1974). Judgment under uncertainty: heuristics and biases. *Science*, 185, pp. 1124–1131.

Vapnik, V. (1999). *The Nature of Statistical Learning Theory, Second Edition*. New York: Springer-Verlag.

Vityaev, E. E., Perlovsky, L. I., Kovalerchuk, B. Y. and Speransky, S. O. (2011). Probabilistic dynamic logic of the mind and cognition. *Neuroinformatics*. 5(1), pp. 1–20.

Vityaev, E. E., Perlovsky, L. I., Kovalerchuk, B. Y. and Speransky, S. O. (2013). Pro invited article. *Biologically Inspired Cognitive Architectures*, 6, pp. 159–168.

Werbos, P. J. (1974). *Beyond Regression: New Tools for Prediction and Analysis in the Behavioral Sciences*. PhD thesis. Boston, USA: Harvard University.

Whorf, B. (1956). *Language, Thought, and Reality: Selected Writings of Benjamin Lee Whorf*. Carroll, J. B. (ed.). Cambridge: MIT Press.

Wilkins, R. W., Hodges, D. A., Laurienti, P. J., Steen, M. R. and Burdette, J. D. (2012). Network science: a new method for investigating the complexity of musical experiences in the brain. *Leonardo*, 45(3), pp. 282–283.

Zadeh, L. A. (1965). Fuzzy sets. *Inf. Control*, 8, pp. 338–352.

Zeki, S., Romaya, J. P., Benincasa, D. M. T. and Atiyah, M. F. (2014). The experience of mathematical beauty and its neural correlates. *Human Neurosci.*, 8, Article 68. www.frontiersin.org.

Chapter 9

Introduction to Cognitive Systems

Péter Érdi and Mihály Bányai

The chapter reviews some historical and recent trends in understanding natural and developing artifical cognitive systems. One of the fundamental concepts of cognitive science, i.e., mental representation, is discussed. The two main directions, symbolic and connectionist (and their combinaton: hybrid) architectures are analyzed. Two main cognitive functions, memory and language, are specifically reviewed. While the pioneers of cognitive science neglected neural level studies, modern cognitive neuroscience contributes to the understanding of neural codes, neural representations. In addition, cognitive robotics builds autonomous systems to realize intelligent sensory-motor integration.

9.1. Representation and Computation

9.1.1. *Representations*

Cognitive science (CS), the interdisciplinary study of the mind, deals on the one hand with the understanding of the human mind and intelligence and on the other hand with the construction of an artificial mind and artificial cognitive systems. Its birth was strongly motivated by the information processing paradigm, thus CS aims to explain thinking as a computational procedure acting on representational structures. Historically, Kenneth Craik (Craik, 1943) argued that the mind does not operate directly on external reality, but on **internal models**, i.e., on representations. CS predominantly assumes that the mind has **mental representations** and computational manipulations on these representations are used to understand and simulate thinking. "... He emphasizes the three processes of translation, inference, and retranslation: "the translation of external events into some kind of neural patterns by stimulation of the sense organs, the interaction and stimulation of other neural patterns as in 'association', and the excitation by these effectors or motor patterns." Here, Craik's paradigm of stimulus-association-response allows the response to be affected by association with the person's current model but does not sufficiently invoke the active control of its stimuli by the organism ..." (Arbib *et al.*, 1997, p. 38). Different versions of representations, such as logic, production rules (Newell and Simon, 1972), semantic networks of concepts (Collins and Quillian, 1969; Quillian, 1968), frames (Minsky, 1974), schemata (Bobrow and Norman, 1975), scripts (Schank and Abelson, 1977), and mental models,[1] analogies, images (Shepard, 1980) have been suggested and analyzed in terms of their representation and computational power, neural plausibility, etc. (Thagard, 2005). It is interesting to see that while behaviorism famously ignored the study of mental events, cognitive science, although it was born by attacking behaviorism in the celebrated paper of Chomsky on Skinner (Chomsky, 1959), was also intentionally ignorant: neural mechanisms were not really in the focus of the emerging interdisciplinary field. Concerning the mechanisms of neural-level and mental level representations, Churchland and Sejnowski (Churchland and Sejnowski, 1990) argued that representations and computations in the brain seem to be very different from the ones offered by the traditional symbol-based cognitive science.

9.1.2. *Symbolic Representation*

9.1.2.1. *The physical symbol system hypothesis*

The physical symbol system hypothesis served as the general theoretical framework for processing information by serial mechanism, and local symbols. It stated that physical symbol system has the necessary and sufficient means for general intelligent action (Newell and Simon, 1976) and serves as the general theoretical framework for processing information by serial mechanism, and local symbols. It is necessary, since anything capable of intelligent action is a physical symbol system. It is sufficient, since any relevant physical symbol system is capable of intelligent action. The hypothesis is based on four ideas

- Symbols are physical patterns.
- Symbols can be combined to form more complex structures of symbols.
- Systems contain processes for manipulating complex symbol structures.
- The processes for representing complex symbol structures can themselves by symbolically represented within the system.

Thinking and intelligence was considered as problem solving. For well-defined problems, the problem space (i.e., branching tree of achievable situations) was searched by algorithms. Since problem spaces proved to be too large to be searched

[1]The phrase mental models has a specific, more technical meaning in Johnson-Lairds work than in Craiks account (Johnson-Laird, 1983).

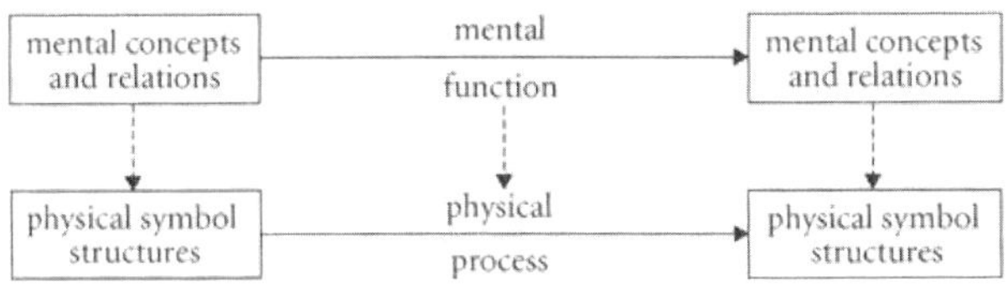

Figure 9.1: The assumed relationship between mental concepts and symbol structures.

by brute-force algorithms, selective search algorithms were used by defining **heuristic** search rules.

9.1.3. *Connectionism*

While the emergence of connectionism is generally considered as the reaction for the not sufficiently rapid development of the symbolistic approach, it had already appeared during the golden age of cybernetics related to the McCulloch–Pitts (MCP) models.

9.1.3.1. *MCP model*

In 1943, McCulloch, one of the two founding fathers of cybernetics (the other was Norbert Wiener), and the prodigy Walter Pitts published a paper with the title "A Logical Calculus of the Ideas Immanent in Nervous System", which was probably the first experiment to describe the operation of the brain in terms of interacting neurons (McCulloch and Pitts, 1943), for historical analysis see (Abraham, 2002; Arbib, 2000; Piccinini, 2004).

The MCP model was basically established to capture the logical structure of the nervous system. Therefore, cellular physiological facts known even that time were intentionally neglected.

The MCP networks are composed by multi-input ($x_i, i = 1, \ldots, n$) single output (y) threshold elements. The state of one element (neuron) of a network is determined by the following rule: $y = 1$, if the weighted sum of the inputs is larger than a threshold, and $y = 0$, in any other case:

$$y = \begin{cases} 1, \text{ if } \sum_i w_i x_i > \Theta \\ 0, \text{ otherwise.} \end{cases} \tag{1}$$

Such a rule describes the operation of all neurons of the network. The state of the network is characterized at a fixed time point by a series of zeros and ones, i.e., by a binary vector, where the dimension of the vector is equal with the number of neurons of the network. The updating rule contains an arbitrary factor: during one-time step either the state of *one* single neuron or of the *all* neurons can be modified. The former materializes asynchronous or serial processing, the latter materializes synchronous or parallel processing.

Obviously, the model contains neurobiological simplifications. The state is binary, the time is discrete, the threshold and the wiring are fixed. Chemical and electrical interactions are neglected, glia cells are also not taken into consideration. McCulloch and Pitts showed that a large enough number of synchronously updated neurons connected by appropriate weights could perform many possible computations.

Since all Boolean functions can be calculated by loop-free (or feed-forward) neuronal networks, and all finite automata can be simulated by neuronal networks (loops are permitted, i.e., recurrent networks), von Neumann adapted the MCP model to the logical design of the computers. The problem of the brain–computer analogy/disanalogy was a central issue of early cybernetics, in a sense revived by the neurocomputing boom from the mid-eighties. More precisely, the metaphor has two sides ("computational brain" versus "neural computer"). There are several different roots of the early optimism related to the power of the brain–computer analogy. We will review two of them. First, both elementary computing units and neurons were characterized as digital input–output devices, suggesting an analogy at even the elementary hardware level. Second, the equivalence (more or less) had been demonstrated between the mathematical model of the "control box" of a computer as represented by the state-transition rules for a Turing machine, and of the nervous system as represented by the. Binary vectors of "0"s and "1"s represented the state of the computer and of the brain, and their temporal behavior was described by the updating rule of these vectors. In his posthumously published book *The Computer and the Brain*, John von Neumann (von Neumann, 1958) emphasized the particular character of "neural mathematics": "... The logics and mathematics in the central nervous system, when viewed as languages, must structurally be essentially different from those languages to which our common experience refers ...".

The MCP model (i) introduced a formalism whose refinement and generalization led to the notion of finite automata (an important concept in computability theory); (ii) is a technique that inspired the notion of logic design of computers; (iii) was used to build neural network models to connect neural structures and functions by dynamic models; (iv) offered the first modern computational theory of brain and mind.

One possible generalization of the MCP model is that the threshold activation function is substituted by a g activation function.

9.1.3.2. *Hebbian learning rules*

Hebb marked a new era by introducing his learning rule and resulted in the sprouting of many new branches of theories and models on the mechanisms and algorithms of learning and related areas.

Two characteristics of the original postulate (Hebb, 1949) played key role in the development of post-Hebbian learning rules. First, in spite of being biologically motivated, it was a verbally described, *phenomenological* rule, without having view on detailed physiological mechanisms. Second, the idea seemed to be extremely convincing, therefore it became a widespread theoretical framework and a generally applied formal tool in the field of neural networks. Based on these two properties, the development of Hebb's idea followed two main directions. First, the postulate inspired an intensive and long lasting search for finding the *molecular* and *cellular* basis of the learning phenomena — which have been assumed to be Hebbian — thus this movement has been absorbed by neurobiology. Second, because of its computational usefulness, many variations evolved from the *biologically inspired* learning rules, and were applied to huge number of very different problems of artificial neural networks, without claiming any relation to biological foundation.

The simplest Hebbian learning rule can be formalized as:

$$\frac{d}{dt} w_{ij}(t) = k\, a_i(t)\, a_j(t), \quad k > 0. \tag{2}$$

This rule expresses the conjunction among pre- and post-synaptic elements (using neurobiological terminology) or associative conditioning (in psychological terms), by a simple product of the actual states of pre- and post-synaptic elements, $a_i(t)$ and $a_i(t)$. A characteristic and unfortunate property of the simplest Hebbian rule is that the synaptic strengths are ever increasing.

Long-term potentiation (LTP) was first discovered in the hippocampus and is very prominent there. LTP is an increase in synaptic strength that can be rapidly induced by brief periods of synaptic stimulation and which has been reported to last for hours *in vitro*, and for days and weeks *in vivo*.

The LTP (and later the LTD) after their discovery, have been regarded as the physiological basis of Hebbian learning. Subsequently, the properties of the LTP and LTD became more clear, and the question arises, whether the LTP and LTD could really be considered as the microscopical basis of the phenomenological Hebb type learning. Formally, the question is that how to specify the general functional F to serve as a learning rule with the known properties of LTP and LTD. Recognizing the existence of this gap between biological mechanisms and the long-used Hebbian learning rule, there have been many attempts to derive the corresponding phenomenological rule based on more or less detailed neurochemical mechanisms.

Spike Timing Dependent Plasticity (STDP), a temporally asymmetric form of Hebbian learning induced by temporal correlations between the spikes of pre- and post-synaptic neurons, has been discovered (Bi and Poo, 1998) and extensively studied (Sjoestrom and Gerstner, 2010). For reviews of post-Hebbian learning algorithms and models of synaptic plasticity, see e.g., (Érdi and Somogyvári, 2002; Shouval, 2007).

9.1.3.3. *Learning in artificial neural networks*

The MCP model supplemented with Hebb's concept about the continuously changing connectivities led to the pattern recognizing algorithm, famously called as the Perceptron (Rosenblatt, 1962). Actually, by using the modern terminology, the Hebbian rules belong to the class of unsupervised learning rule, while the Perceptron implements supervised learning

The Perceptron is a classifier defined as

$$f(x) = w^T x + b. \tag{3}$$

The classification rule is $sign(f(x))$. The learning rule is to perform the following updates if the classifier makes an error:

$$w^{t+1} = w^t + yx, \tag{4}$$

$$b^{t+1} = b^t + y. \tag{5}$$

A version of the single layer perceptron uses the **delta** learning rule. It is a gradient descent method, and adapts the weights to minimize the deviation between the target value and the actual value, The delta rule for the modification of the synaptic weights w_{ji} is given as

$$\delta w_{ji} = \alpha(t_j - y_j)g'(h_j)x_i. \tag{6}$$

Here, α is the learning rate, t_j and y_j are the target and actual output values of neuron j, h_j is the weighted some of the individual input x_is.

Famously, the Perceptron can solve linearly separable problems (Minsky and Papert, 1969) only, and such kinds of networks are not able to learn, e.g., the XOR function.

Multilayer perceptrons supplemented with another learning algorithm (Werbos, 1974), i.e., with the backpropagation (BP) algorithm overcame the limitations of the single-layer Perceptron. BP is a generalization of the delta rule to multilayered feedforward networks. Is based on by using the chain rule to iteratively compute gradients for each layer, and it proved to be a useful algorithm.

BP algorithm has two parts. First, there is a forward activity propagation followed by the backpropagation of the output to calculate the delta quantities for each neuron. Second, the gradient is calculated and the update of the weight is determined.

Connectionist (what else?) networks consisting of simple nodes and links are very useful for understanding psychological processes that involve parallel constraint satisfaction. (Neo!) connectionism has been revitalized and became a popular alternative of the symbolistic approach from the mid-eighties, when the two volumes of Parallel Distributed Processing: Explorations in the Microstructure of Cognition were published (Rumelhart and McClelland, 1986). An early successful application was an (artificial) neural network to predict the past tense of English verbs.

9.1.3.4. *Newer developments*

After the initial success, multilayer perceptrons with BP started to show their limitations with more complex classifications tasks. Multiple branches of machine learning techniques originated from generalization attempts of neural architectures.

One such advancement was the introduction of support vector machines (SVM) (Cortes and Vapnik, 1995) by Vapnik and Cortes. The mathematical structure is formally equivalent to a perceptron with one hidden layer of which the size may be potentially infinite. The goal of the optimization algorithm used to tune the network's parameters is to find a classification boundary that maximizes distance from data points in separated classes. Decision boundaries may be nonlinear if data is transformed into the feature space using a kernel function of appropriate choice. SVMs produce reproducible, optimal (in a certain sense) classifications based on a sound theory. They may be successfully applied in problems where data is not overly high-dimensional with relatively simple underlying structure, but might be very noisy.

Another direction of development of neural networks is deep learning. The basic idea is to stack multiple processing layers of neurons on top of each other forming a hierarchical model structure. Some of the most successful applications use the stochastic neuron instead of the deterministic one, where the probability of assuming one of the binary states is determined by a sigmoid function of the input.

$$\Pr(s_i = 1) = \frac{1}{1 + e^{-\sum_{j=1}^{N} W_{ij} x_i + b_i}}. \tag{7}$$

Stochastic networks may represent probability distributions over latent variables by the samples generated as the network is updated according to Equation (7). Such neurons may be connected in an undirected (that is, symmetric) manner, forming Boltzmann machines (Salakhutdinov and Hinton, 2009), which can be trained in an unsupervised fashion on unlabeled datasets by the contrastive divergence algorithm (Hinton, 2002). Directed versions of similar networks may also trained unsupervisedly by the wake-sleep algorithm (Hinton *et al.*, 1995).

To solve supervised classification problems, the first deep architectures were convolutional networks that solved the translation invariance of learned features by binding together of weights in processing layers. Boltzmann machines may be transformed into classification engines by refining the unsupervisedly pre-trained weights by back propagation of labeled data. Deep networks may be successfully applied to very high-dimensional data with complicated structure if the high signal-to-noise ratio is sufficiently high.

9.1.4. *Engineering Perspectives*

In terms of philosophical approaches, debates became less sharp, since the physical symbol system hypothesis which stated that [a] physical symbol system has the necessary and sufficient means for general intelligent action. In the technical application symbol, manipulation was the only game in town for many years.

9.1.4.1. *General problem solver*

General Problem Solver (GPS) was a computer program created in 1959 by Herbert A. Simon, J.C. Shaw, and Allen Newell and was intended to work as a universal problem solver machine. Formal symbolic problems were supposed to be solved by GPS. Intelligent behavior, as automatic theorem proving, and chess playing were paradigmatic examples of the ambitious goals. GPS, however, solved simple problems such as the Towers of Hanoi, that could be sufficiently formalized, it could not solve any real-world problems due to the combinatorial explosion. Decomposition of the task into subtasks and goals into subgoals somewhat helped to increase the efficiency of the algorithms.

9.1.4.2. *Expert systems*

Expert systems (also called as **knowledge-based** systems) were one of the most widely used applications of classical artificial intelligence. Their success was due to restricted use for specific fields of applications. The general goal has been to convert human knowledge to formal electronic consulting service. Generally it has two parts, the knowledge base and the inference machine. The central core of the inference machines is the rule-base, i.e., set of rules of inference that are used in reasoning. Generally, these systems use IF-THEN rules to represent knowledge. Typically, systems had from a few hundred to a few thousand rules.

The whole process resembles to medical diagnosis, and actually the first applications were towards medicine. For an introduction to expert systems, see e.g., (Jackson, 1998).

9.1.4.3. *Knowledge representation and reasoning*

Knowledge representation (KR) is a field of artificial intelligence aiming to represent certain aspects of the world to solve complex problems by using formal methods, such as automatic reasoning.

As it was suggested (Davis *et al.*, 1993).

"...

- A KR is most fundamentally a surrogate, a substitute for the thing itself, used to enable an entity to determine consequences by thinking rather than acting, i.e., by reasoning about the world rather than taking action in it.
- It is a set of ontological commitments, i.e., an answer to the question: In what terms should I think about the world?
- It is a fragmentary theory of intelligent reasoning, expressed in terms of three components: (i) the representation's fundamental conception of intelligent reasoning; (ii) the set of inferences the representation sanctions; and (iii) the set of inferences it recommends.
- It is a medium for pragmatically efficient computation, i.e., the computational environment in which thinking is accomplished. One contribution to this pragmatic efficiency is supplied by the guidance a representation provides for organizing information so as to facilitate making the recommended inferences.
- It is a medium of human expression, i.e., a language in which we say things about the world.

..."

In recent years, KR and reasoning has also derived challenges from new and emerging fields including the semantic web, computational biology, and the development of software agents and of ontology-based data management.

9.1.5. *Philosophical Perspectives*

9.1.5.1. *Methodological solipsism*

Jerry Fodor suggested methodological solipsism (Fodor, 1980) as a research strategy in cognitive science. He adopts an extreme **internalist** approach: the content of beliefs is determined by what is in the agent's head, and nothing to do with what is in the world. Mental representations are internally structured much like sentences in a natural language, in that they have both syntactic structure and a compositional semantics.

There are two lines of opinions, while classical cogntivism is based on the representational hypothesis supplemented by the internal world assumption, other approaches have other categories in their focus. Two of them are briefly mentioned here: **intentionality** and **embodied cognition**.

9.1.5.2. *Intentionality*

Searle (Searle, 1983, 1992) rejected the assumption undisputed from Craik to Simon that the representational mind/brain operates on formal internal models detached from the world and argued instead that its main feature is intentionality, a term which has been variously viewed as synonymous with connectedness, aboutness, meaningfulness, semantics or straightforwardly consciousness. Searle argued that the representational and computational structures that have typically been theorized in cognitive science lack any acceptable ontology. He argued that they are not being observable or understandable, so these structures just cannot exist.

9.1.5.3. *Situated or embodied cognition*

A seemingly different attempt to overcome the difficulties of methodological solipsism is to work with agents so simple as to not need a knowledge base at all, and basically don't need representations. The central hypothesis of embodied cognitive science is that cognition emerges from the interaction of brain, the whole body, and of its environment. What does it mean to understand a phenomenon? A pragmatic answer is to synthesize the behavior from elements. Many scientists believe if they are able to build a mathematical model based on the knowledge of the mechanism to reproduce a phenomenon and predict some other phenomena by using the same model framework, they understand what is happening in their system. Alternatively, instead of building a mathematical model one may wish to construct a robot. Rodney Brooks at MIT is an emblematic figure with the goal of building humanoid robots (Brooks, 2002). Embodied cognitive science now seems to be an interface between neuroscience and robotics: the features of embodied cognitive systems should be built both into neural models, and robots, and the goal is to integrate sensory, cognitive and motor processes. (Or even more, traditionally, emotions were neglected, as factors which reduce the cognitive performance. It is far from being true.)

9.2. Architectures: Symbolic, Connectionist, Hybrid

9.2.1. *Cognitive Architectures: What? Why? How?*

9.2.1.1. *Unified theory of cognition*

Alan Newell (Newell, 1990) spoke about the unified theory of cognition (UTC). Accordingly, there is single set of mechanisms that account for all of cognition (using the term broadly to include perception and motor control). UTC should be a theory to explain (i) the adaptive response of an intelligent system to environmental changes; (ii) the mechanisms of goal seeking and goal-driven behavior[2]; (iii) how to use symbols and (iv) how to learn from experience. Newell's general approach inspired

[2]One of the two founding papers of cybernetics addressed this problem (Rosenblueth and Bigelow, 1943).

his students and others to establish large software systems, cognitive architectures, to implement cognitions.

"Cognitive architecture is the overall, essential structure and process of a domain-generic computational cognitive model, used for a broad, multiple-level, multiple-domain analysis of cognition and behavior . . ." (Sun, 2004). They help to achieve two different big goals: (i) to have a computational framework to model and simulate real cognitive phenomena: (ii) to offer methods to solve real-world problems.

Two key design properties that underlie the development of any cognitive architecture are memory and learning (Duch *et al.*, 2007). For a simplified taxonomy of cognitive architectures, see Section 9.2.1.1.

Symbolic architectures focus on information processing using high-level symbols or declarative knowledge, as in the classical AI approach. Emergent (connectionist) architectures use low-level activation signals flowing through a network consisting of relatively simple processing units, a bottom-up process relaying on the emergent self-organizing and associative properties. Hybrid architectures result from combining the symbolic and emergent (connectionist) paradigms.

The essential features of cognitive architectures have been summarized (Sun, 2004). It should show (i) ecological realism, (ii) bio-evolutionary realism, (iii) cognitive realism and (iv) eclecticism of in methodologies and techniques. More specifically, it cannot be neglected that (i) cognitive systems are situated in sensory-motor system, (ii) the understanding in human cognitive systems can be seen from an evolutionary perspective, (iii) artificial cognitive systems should capture some

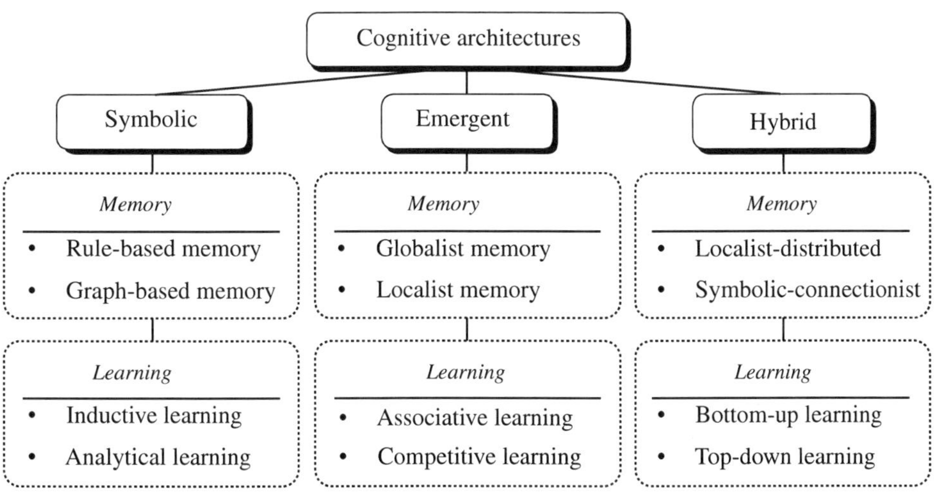

Figure 9.2: Simplified taxonomy of cognitive architectures. From Duch *et al.* (2007).

significant features of human cognition, (iv) at least for the time being multiple perspectives and approaches should be integrated.

9.2.2. *The State, Operator and Result (SOAR) Cognitive Architecture*

SOAR is a classic example of expert rule-based cognitive architecture designed to model general intelligence (Laird, 2012; Milnes *et al.*, 1992).

SOAR is a general cognitive architecture that integrates knowledge-intensive reasoning, reactive execution, hierarchical reasoning, planning, and learning from experience, with the goal of creating a general computational system that has the same cognitive abilities as humans. In contrast, most AI systems are designed to solve only one type of problem, such as playing chess, searching the Internet, or scheduling aircraft departures. SOAR is both a software system for agent development and a theory of what computational structures are necessary to support human-level agents.

Based on theoretical framework of knowledge-based systems seen as an approximation to physical symbol systems, SOAR stores its knowledge in the form of production rules, arranged in terms of operators that act in the problem space, that is the set of states that represent the task at hand. The primary learning mechanism in SOAR is termed chunking, a type of analytical technique for formulating rules and macro-operations from problem solving traces. In recent years, many extensions of the SOAR architecture have been proposed: reinforcement learning to adjust the preference values for operators, episodic learning to retain history of system evolution, semantic learning to describe more abstract, declarative knowledge, visual imagery, emotions, moods and feelings used to speed up reinforcement learning and direct reasoning. SOAR architecture has demonstrated a variety of high-level cognitive functions, processing large and complex rule sets in planning, problem solving and natural language comprehension.

9.2.3. *Adaptive Control of Thought-Rational (ACT-R)*

We follow here the analysis of (Duch *et al.*, 2007). ACT-R is a cognitive architecture: a theory about how human cognition works. It is both a hybrid cognitive architecture and theoretical framework for understanding and emulating human cognition (Anderson, 2007; Anderson and Bower, 1973). Its intention is to construct a software system that can perform the full range of human cognitive functions. The algorithm is realistic at the cognitive level, and weakly realistic in terms of neural mechanisms. The central components of ACT-R comprise a set of modules of perceptual-motor schemas, memory system, a buffer and a pattern matcher. The perceptual-motor modules basically serve as an interface between the system and the external world. There are two types of memory modules in ACT-R: declarative memory (DM) and procedural memory (PM). Both are realized by symbolic-connectionist structures, where the symbolic level consists of productions (for PM) or chunks (for DM), and the sub-symbolic level of a massively parallel connectionist structure. Each symbolic construct (i.e., production or chunk) has a set of sub-symbolic parameters that reflect its past usage and control its operations, thus enabling an analytic characterization of connectionist computations using numeric parameters (associative activation) that measure the general usefulness of a chunk or production in the past and current context. The pattern matcher is used to find an appropriate production.

ACT-R implements a top-down learning approach to adapt to the structure of the environment. In particular, symbolic constructs (i.e., chunks or productions) are first created to describe the results of a complex operation, so that the solution may be available without recomputing the next time a similar task occurs. When a goal, declarative memory activation or perceptual information appears it becomes a chunk in the memory buffer, and the production system guided by subsymbolic processes finds a single rule that responds to the current pattern. Sub-symbolic parameters are then tuned using Bayesian formulae to make the existing symbolic constructs that are useful more prominent. In this way, chunks that are often used become more active and can thus be retrieved faster and more reliably. Similarly, productions that more likely led to a solution at a lower cost will have higher expected utility, and thus be more likely chosen during conflict resolution (i.e., selecting one production among many that qualify to fire).

9.3. Cognitive Functions

9.3.1. *General Remarks*

Cognitive functions are related to mental processes, such as attention, learning, memory, language comprehension and production, reasoning, problem solving, planning, decision-making, etc. The mental processes can be realized by conscious or unconscious mechanisms. As an illustration, two topics, **memory** and **language** are briefly reviewed here.

9.3.2. *Multiple Memory Systems*

As also detailed in Section 9.4.4.2, knowledge stored in the human brain can be classified into sparable memory systems. An important division can be made in terms of duration of recallability. Short-term memories serve as a temporary storage, that helps the execution of everyday tasks, and pre-store certain information that can later be soldified into long-term memories.

Long-terms memory can be divided into three subsystems according to function. The first is procedural memory, encoding how to swim or draw a flower. The second is episodic memory, that can store past events, similar to the scenes of a movie. And the third, semantic memory, is everything that we know about the world in a more or less context-invariant manner.

Different memory systems clearly interact, as sensory information needs to be interpreted according to semantic knowledge in order to be efficiently stored in short-term or episodic memory, which is in turn built into the semantic web of knowledge. However, there is evidence that different systems may operate separately from each other, as illustrated by the case of H.M., a patient with severe epilepsy who had to have hippocampal lobotomy. He retained his semantic knowledge about the world and his procedural skills, together with the ability to acquire new procedural knowledge, but he completely lost the ability to form new episodic memory patterns (he had anterograde amnesia).

A model for the operation of multiple memory systems on a cognitive level was proposed by Tulving (1985).

9.3.3. *Language Acquisition, Evolution and Processing*

9.3.3.1. *What is language?*

Language is a system of symbols used to communicate ideas among two or more individuals. Normatively, it must be learnable by children, spoken and understood by adults, and capable of expressing ideas that people normally communicate in a social and cultural context.

9.3.3.2. *Cognitive approach to linguistics*

As Paul Thagard reviews, the cognitive approach to linguistics raises a set of fundamental questions:

- How does the mind turn sounds into words (phonology)?
- How does the mind turn words into sentences (syntax)?
- How does the mind understand words and sentences (semantics)?
- How does the mind understand discourse (semantics, pragmatics)?
- How does the mind generate discourse?
- How does the mind translate between languages?
- How does the mind acquire the capacities just described?
- To what extent is knowledge of language innate?

Hypotheses about how the mind uses language should be tested:

- Symbolic
  - — Linguistic knowledge consists largely of rules that govern phonological and syntactic processing.

  - — The computational procedures involved in understanding and generating language are largely rule-based.
  - — Language learning is learning of rules.
  - — Many of these rules are innate.
  - — The leading proponent of this general view has been Noam Chomsky.
  - — Rule-based models of language comprehension and generation have been developed e.g., in the SOAR system and within other frameworks.
- Connectionist
  - — Linguistic knowledge consists largely of statistical constraints that are less general than rules and are encoded in neural networks.
  - — The computational procedures involved in understanding and generating language are largely parallel constraint satisfaction.

9.3.3.3. *Language acquisition*

As it is well-known, behaviorists psychology considered language as a learned habit, and famously one of the starting points of the cognitive science was Chomsky's attack on Skinner's concepts (Chomsky, 1959). Chomsky's theory of generative grammar, approaches to children's acquisition of syntax (Chomsky, 1965) led to the suggestion of having a **universal grammar**. In a somewhat different context, it is identified with **language faculty** based on the *modularity of the mind* (Fodor, 1983) or the **language instinct** (Pinker, 2007). Language acquisition seems to be now a cognitive process that emerges from the interaction of biological and environmental components.

9.3.3.4. *Language evolution*

Is language mediated by a sophisticated and highly specialized "language organ" that is unique to humans and emerged completely out of the blue as suggested by Chomsky? Or was there a more primitive gestural communication system already in place that provided a scaffolding for the emergence of vocal language?

Steven Pinker and Paul Bloom (1990) argued for an adaptationist approach to language origins. Rizzolatti's (2008) discovery of the mirror neurons offered a new perspective of language evolution. A mirror neuron is a neuron that fires both when an animal acts and when the animal observes the same action performed by another. The mirror neuron hypothesis leads to a neural theory of language evolution reflected in Figure 9.3.

9.3.4. *Language processing*

Early AI has strong interest in (natural) language processing (NPL). One of the pioneers of AI, Terry Winograd created a software (SHRDLU) to understand a

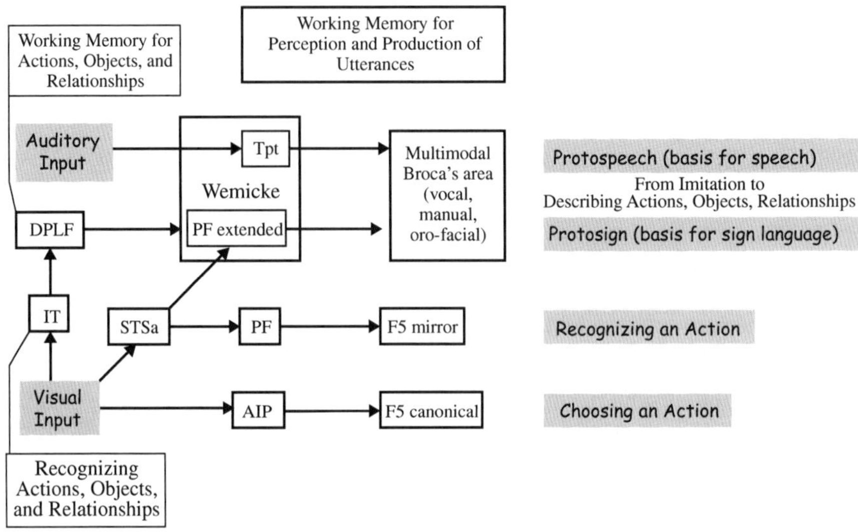

Figure 9.3: Model of the influence of protosign upon the mirror system and its impact on the evolution of language (Arbib, 2005).

language about a "toy world" (Winograd, 1972). SHRDLU was instructed to move various objects around in the "blocks world" containing various basic objects: blocks, cones, balls, etc. The system also had some memory to store the names of the object. Its success generated some optimism, but the application of the adopted strategy for real world problems remained restricted.

The new NPL systems are mostly based on machine learning techniques, often by using statistical inference. Initially the big goal was to make "machine translation". Nowadays, there are many tasks of NPL, some of them listed here: speech recognition (including speech segmentation), information extraction/retrieval are related more to syntactic analysis, while sentiment analysis and automatic summarization needs semantic/pragmatic analysis (see e.g., Jurafsky and Marti, 2008).

9.4. Neural Aspects

9.4.1. *Biological Overview*

9.4.1.1. *Hierarchical organization*

Cognitive functions are realized by the nervous system of animals and humans. The central computing element of these systems is the cortex, which connects to the outside world and the body through sensors and actuators. The cortex can be regarded as a hierarchy of networks operating at different scales. The basic building block of the cortex is the neuron (Ramón y Cajal, 1909), a spatially extended cell that connects to other such cells by synapses. These are special regions of the cell membrane, where electrical changes can trigger the release of certain molecules in the intercellular space. These molecules, the neurotransmitters, may bind to the receptor proteins of the other cell of the synapse, changing its membrane potential (the difference between the electric potential of intracellular and extracellular space, maintained by chemical concentration gradients). Additionally, the membrane potential dynamics of the neurons may produce action potentials (also called spikes or firing), sudden changes that propagate along the elongated axon of the cell to the synapses, triggering transmitter release.

9.4.1.2. *Chemical systems of cellular operation*

Protein interaction networks support the life cycle of every living cell, but neurons are equipped with additional machinery enabling them to transmit electrical impulses to each other, possibly over large distances as described above. The transmitters in each synapse may be excitatory or inhibitory, depending on the direction of their effect on the postsynaptic membrane potential. A single cell may only form either excitatory or inhibitory synapses. The principal excitatory cells in the cortex are called pyramidal cells. Synaptic signalling and connected cellular machineries are operated by the interaction of hundreds of proteins and other molecules and ions (Ma'ayan *et al.*, 2005).

9.4.1.3. *The network of cells*

According to our current knowledge, the human brain consists of 10^{11} neurons, each receiving and giving about 10^4 synapses. Most of these cells are formed by the time the child is born, but neurogenesis occurs during adulthood as well, to a lesser extent (Zhao *et al.*, 2008). Synapses can be formed, eliminated and changed in transmission efficacy by sensory experiences.

The cortical network of neurons is not uniformly connected, but organized according to architectural principles. On the surface of the cortical tissue we find the grey matter, which consists of cell bodies, and below the white matter, which is mostly axons and axonal bundles connecting distant neurons. Grey matter is organized into horizontal layers, which differ in the relative number of the cells of different types in them. Most of the cortex has six layers, some areas have five or less.

The horizontal organization of cortical tissue is much less well understood than the vertical in terms of layers. A candidate for such a structure is the concept of cortical column as proposed by Mountcastle (1997). Micro-columns consist of about 80 pyramidal neurons developed from the same stem cell, and macro-columns consist about 8,000 pyramidal cells. Columnar organization is expressed to a variable degree in different areas of the cortex.

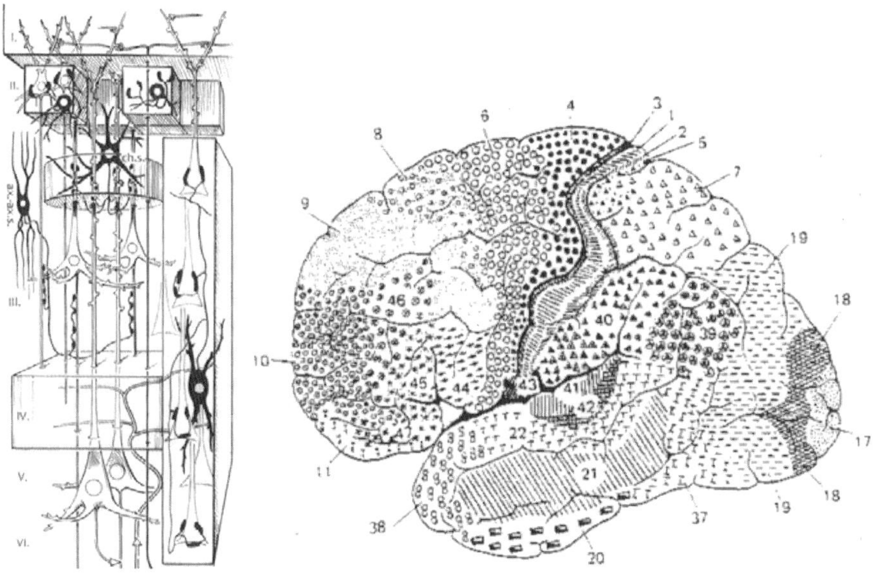

Figure 9.4: Anatomy of neural networks. Left: cellular connectivity in the cortex by Szentágothai. Right: cortical areas by Brodmann.

A central question about cortical networks is whether a repeated local connectivity pattern between cells exists over all or most of the cortex. Such a hypothetized module is called the *canonical microcircuit*. Connectivity between layers exhibits a certain level of constancy as noted by Szentágothai (1983), thus it may serve as a candidate for the canonical microcircuit (depicted in Figure 9.4). Mapping of such connectivity patterns is possible by axonal tracing (Lanciego and Wouterlood, 2011).

9.4.1.4. *Areas by anatomy and function*

Due to the huge number of neurons in the brain, it is useful to define macroscopic units in their network. As the cortex is indeed clustered in terms of connectivity and consists of highly specialized regions in terms of involvement in different behavioral tasks, this partition can be constructed according to anatomical and functional measures. The classical specification of 52 cortical areas was given by Brodmann (depicted in Figure 9.4), and was refined by generations of anatomists and physiologists since then (Strotzer, 2009).

We can often associate certain functions to areas by measuring their population activity during the execution of different tasks. Sensory areas deal with the primary processing of the external input of the nervous system. Further processing and combination of information happens in the associative areas. The hippocampus is a widely studied area that is involved in the formation and recall of memory patterns.

Higher level cognitive functions such as decision-making, attention, control over other areas and planning are associated with the prefrontal areas. The output of the nervous system is produced in the motor areas. Highly specialized areas exist for some specific tasks like face recognition or processing and production of speech.

Cortical areas are connected by axons and axonal bundles in both local and nonlocal manners. Mapping of this network is possible by Diffusion Tensor Imaging (Iturria-Medina *et al.*, 2008) together with axonal tracing.

9.4.2. *The Neural Code*

9.4.2.1. *Membrane potential, spikes and cortical state*

A central question of neuroscience is which physiological phenomena of the neurons are responsible for transmitting information and exactly how. Current consensus is that the membrane potential and the spikes are the most important. There are other signaling pathways in the nervous system that may have modulatory effects on information transfer between cells (Vizi *et al.*, 2004).

If we measure the electric field generated by a large population of neurons (the local field potential, LFP), we can observe periodicity with different frequencies. Based on such spectra and other characteristics of the LFP, one can define cortical states in various ways (Harris and Thiele, 2011). REM and non-REM sleep and wakefulness may be defined as macroscopical states of the cortex, one may observe regular transitions to more synchronous and asynchronous global spiking behavior of neurons, there may be local up- and downstates in sensory areas on the $\sim$100 ms scale, and the phase of different spectral components of the LFP may define a point in a state space of a dynamical system too. The importance and function of all of these definitions of cortical states is actively debated and far from being settled.

A detailed mathematical model of membrane potential dynamics of a neuron was given by Hodgkin and Huxley (Hodgkin and Huxley, 1952). Different hypotheses about the neural code can be expressed as models abstracting away certain aspects of this physiologically realistic description.

9.4.2.2. *Temporal and phase codes*

Temporal code hypotheses assume that the exact timing of the spikes of a neuron are relevant regarding information transfer, discarding the shape of the spike. The mathematical model that formalizes the temporal coding hypothesis is the leaky-integrate-and-fire neuron (LIF), looking back to a long history in science (Abbott, 2005). The dynamics of this model is given by the following equation:

$$\tau \frac{dV}{dt} = -V(t) + RI(t), \tag{8}$$

where V is the membrane potential of the cell, I is any input current from synapses and R is synaptic resistance. We have to define a firing threshold θ, an equilibrium potential V_0, a refractory period τ_r and a refractory potential V_r to make the model complete. In a simulation, we would compute the trajectory of the system according to Equation (8), and if V reaches θ, we record a spike, and set V to V_r for time τ_r, and then to V_0. By defining a synaptic model that describes $I(t)$ depending on presynaptic spike times, we can build networks of LIF neurons to simulate population behavior.

Phase coding hypotheses assume that spike timing is relevant in relation to the phase of some periodic component of the averaged population activity. These oscillations are hypothetized to implement different cognitive functions. Waking state of the cortex is characterized by beta (15–30 Hz) and gamma (30–80 Hz) oscillations (Bressler, 1990). Whether they are the way neural systems implement information processing (Buzsáki, 2004) or an epiphenomenon of computational algorithms and stimulus properties (Bastos *et al.*, 2012) is still to be settled.

9.4.2.3. *Rate codes*

Rate coding hypotheses assume that the exact timing of the spikes is not important, only the frequency with which they occur. The model formalizing such hypotheses is the rate neuron, defined at a discrete time step as follows:

$$r = sig\left(\sum_{i=1}^{D} w_i u_i - \theta\right) \tag{9}$$

with r being the firing rate of a neuron with D input synapses, w_i the efficacy of synapse i, u_i the firing rate of the presynaptic neuron of the same synapse, θ the firing threshold parameter, and $sig()$ a sigmoid nonlinear function. These model neurons can be used to construct networks without additional elements. Such a network corresponds to the artificial neural network (ANN) paradigm used in machine learning.

Double codes combine the rate and temporal coding aspects, for an example see Lengyel *et al.* (2003).

9.4.2.4. *Neural computation*

Computation denotes the mathematical transformation that neurons implement on their inputs to create their outputs. In the tradition of cybernetics, neurons and the brain were regarded as logical devices, carrying out the computation of logical functions. This idea gave rise to the ANN approach to artificial intelligence problems, and a simplified version of the rate model, the McCullogh–Pitts neuron (McCulloch and Pitts, 1943). In this model, instead of the sigmoid nonlinearity, we use a step function, thus the output of the neuron becomes binary, making the networks of such units equivalent to a logical function.

The rate and logical neurons implement the mathematical operation of linear separation of inputs (networks of them combine several decision boundaries solving nonlinear classification too). This operation can be regarded as one of the computational primitives found by physiologists and proposed by computationalists, which also includes linear filtering, exponentiation, divisive normalization (Carandini and Heeger, 2012) and coordinate basis transformation enabling classification (DiCarlo, 2012).

Similar to the quest for the canonical microcircuit, a central question in neuroscience is whether there is a basic computational unit in terms of microcircuitry. Attempts have been made to find an universal computational role for the structural microcircuit (Bastos *et al.*, 2012) and the cortical column (George and Hawkins, 2009).

9.4.3. *Neural Representations*

Representations associate with neural code the specific quantities it should carry information about, let that be some descriptor of the environment, expectation of the outcome an action, knowledge about a concept or a property of another neural population's activity. These quantities can be described with numerical variables, that serve as building blocks of representations.

If we add formal rules describing relationships between variables, we get a structure equivalent to a formal language, that the natural systems use to store, process and transmit information. This is the internal model that the brain builds from sensory experiences, and what we call neural representation. There may be multiple mathematical frameworks in which one can formulate such models, and a principal goal of neuroscience is to discover which one or more of these is actually related to neural activity. Such a discovery heavily relies on the ability to predict not only behavioral, but physiological quantities, which is no easy task to do at the current state of our knowledge, as even the measurement of these values can be rather challenging.

9.4.3.1. *Perception as inference*

The idea that sensory perception can be regarded as inference about unobserved quantities describing the environment based on observed sensory activations has deep roots in the history of science (see Helmholtz (Von Helmholtz, 1866) and Alhacen (Smith, 2001)). Such inference requires the building of models of the environment and the world that store previous experiences is a parsimonious manner, allowing the animal or human to calculate estimates of directly unobserved quantities.

9.4.3.2. *Dynamic models*

Dynamical systems may represent knowledge in the structure of their phase space (Strogatz, 2006) and autonomous dynamics. Through learning (which is to adjust the parameters of the system, as described in Section 9.4.4.3), several attractors of different nature can be formed in this state space, which may correspond to values of latent quantities describing the environment.

In dynamical systems, the trajectory itself can be regarded as the process of inference. Its starting point (or boundary condition, depending of the modeling framework) is the input to the system, and the attractor where the trajectory ends, be it a point or loop, is the inferred quantity.

Artificial neural networks are a special class of dynamical systems with a close structural correspondence to biological neural systems. Feed-forward networks are universal function approximators, and as such, can be regarded as black box models of knowledge, where a set of adjustable basis functions (hidden units of the network) are used to store a mapping from inputs to outputs without interpreting the activations of the bases.

Chaotic behavior expressed by some dynamical systems can serve as a candidate for modeling spontaneous associations. Chaotic itinerancy is one such theory, where trajectories jump from one attractor-like region to another (Tsuda, 1991).

9.4.3.3. *Probabilistic models*

There is ample evidence that the brain calculates with the uncertainty of the represented quantities. The source of this uncertainty may be sensory noise or unobserved properties of the environment. Probability theory offers a consistent way to model these phenomena. From the different interpretations of probabilities, cognitive models use the one that regards the framework as an extension of logic (Jaynes, 2003), and probabilities as measures of available information about quantities. Probabilistic cognitive modeling has been interlocked with the normative modeling approach, advocated by Barlow (Barlow, 1990) and Wiener (Rosenblueth *et al.*, 1943).

Probabilistic models define a joint probability distribution over variables defining the environment of the observer, including quantities directly observable by its sensors, and latent variables, such as the identity of objects in a scene. These models describe the process of generating the observables from the latents, so one can create synthetic stimuli with statistics similar to measured stimuli. The inversion of such a model allows the observer to infer the distribution of latent values given some observations, and to learn the regularities of the environment as parameters.

Physical causality is not represented in probabilistic generative models *per se*, but one may argue that human reasoning is inherently causal instead of probabilistic, and augment the framework of probabilities with concepts directly describing to causal relationships, as described by Pearl (2000).

Probabilistic models may be defined to incorporate the temporal evolution of variables or distributions, thus describing dynamic phenomena. Dynamic models with latent variables can describe cognitive processes, such as the inference of invariant features in sensory data by slow feature analysis (Wiskott and Sejnowski, 2002).

9.4.3.4. *How do neurons correspond to variables?*

One of the central questions of neuroscience is how do neurons represent variables of internal models. Many different proposals exist, and the question is far from being settled. If we assume that a specific neuron is responsible for a given variable of the internal model, we have to choose a physiological quantity that will represent the value of that variable at any given point of time. One option is to use the membrane potential of the cell, but one can define a time bin and a spike count, or an instantaneous firing rate without binning. Whether a single variable is represented by only one neuron or more is also unknown. A certain amount of redundancy exists in neural circuitry as representations are robust to minor injuries, but this can be realized by all different variables with heavy dependence too.

The visual system is one of the better understood regions of the cortex in terms of representation. Neurons in the primary visual cortex have receptive fields (that is, the set of inputs that they respond to) resembling wavelet functions, sensitive to edges with a preferred orientation and spatial frequency (Hubel and Wiesel, 1968). Neurons with similar receptive fields are closer to each other, forming a columnar structure, thus connecting modular anatomical architecture to function. In higher-order visual areas one can find neurons responsive to specific concepts, such as people (Quiroga, 2005). Intermediary levels of representation are less well understood, there are competing proposals about the quantities that are represented by neurons of these areas (Ziemba *et al.*, 2013).

If we assume that the probabilistic brain hypothesis is correct, we need the neurons to represent probability distributions of model variables instead of single values. This can also be realized in multiple ways. One is probabilistic population coding (PPC), which aims to represent distributions in a parametric manner (Ma *et al.*, 2006). Another concept is the sampling hypothesis, where the above-mentioned neuronal properties encode a sample from the probability distribution of the corresponding variable (Fiser *et al.*, 2010). The sampling hypothesis also creates a connection to a class of practical machine learning algorithms (Neal, 1992).

9.4.4. *Learning Internal Models*

9.4.4.1. *Plasticity in the brain*

Storage of information in the brain is realized by the changing strength of coupling between neurons either through the variation of synaptic strengths or the number of synapses. Multiple biological mechanisms exist that implement changes in synaptic connectivity depending on neural activity.

Short-term plasticity (STP) lasts on the timescale of hundreds of milliseconds or seconds. The biological mechanism behind the facilitatory type of STP is the increased probability of transmitter release in connection with spike-dependent presynaptic calcium dynamics. Conversely, depressive effect is exerted by the depletion of transmitters due to frequent spiking. Whether a synapse shows facilitatory or depressive behavior depends on the specific cell type to which it belongs.

Long-term plasticity has effects potentially for decades. It is implemented by a complicated interaction between synaptic proteins and gene regulatory systems.

9.4.4.2. *Memory systems of the brain*

Similar to plasticity mechanisms, memory systems can be categorized into short and long term storages. Long term memory has multiple distinct subsystems with different goals, separability of which is proven by lesion studies. Motor memory stores sequences of movements that may be executed in certain situations (such as riding a bicycle).

Episodic memory stores autobiographical scenes or short sequences of events that we observed once. Conversely, semantic memory stores the context-independent knowledge about the world including concepts, connections, mechanisms or rules. It is the internal model that describes our best ideas about how the world works. There is a performance advantage of having an episodic memory instead of just the semantic model of the environment as reliable estimates of model parameters are costly in terms of data (Lengyel and Dayan, 2007).

Episodic memories contain snapshots of collections of context-dependent information. To construct a generally valid model of the environment, one has to extract invariant concepts from these snapshots, and organize them into a structure that balances good predictions and compact representation. Such extraction may be described as the construction of concept-trees from scenes (Battaglia and Pennartz, 2011). The *consolidation* of episodic memories into semantic knowledge is hypothetized to be one of the functions of sleeping. The interplay between episodic hypothesized and semantic memories is bidirectional, as we need semantic knowledge to construct parsimonious descriptions of episodes and scenes.

The most widely studied type of short term memory is the working memory. This is a temporary storage operating on a time scale of order of a second or hundred milliseconds. The brain uses this functionality to coordinate everyday tasks. Experiments show that the persistent activity (that is, increased population firing) of certain prefrontal areas correlate with working memory functionality. Separate working memory systems exist for different sensory systems to process signals of that modality. Capacity of the human working memory is around seven objects (anything that is stored in the semantic memory), leading to hypotheses that this functionality may be implemented by cortical oscillations described in Section 9.4.2.2, the capacity resulting from the ratio of their frequencies.

9.4.4.3. *Learning problems and rules*

Learning as a mathematical problem involves adjusting the parameters of a model so that it minimizes some error function. Learning problems may be categorized into three families based on the nature of the available information and the goal.

In unsupervized or representational settings, we have a set of observations. The goal of the learner is to create a model that captures the regularities in the data. The learned model may be used for inference of latent variables or predicting future observations. A simple learning rule for adjusting weight parameters in neural models for unsupervized problems was proposed by Hebb (1949). This spike-timing dependent plasticity rule states that if a neuron's firing elicits firing in another with great reliability, the coupling between the two should be strengthened (in discrete time models this means simultaneous activation). This rule can modified in many different ways to incorporate additional assumptions about the system to be modeled (Dayan and Abbott, 2001).

In supervized settings, we have a set of input–output pairs and the goal is to learn the mapping between the two sets of variables. The learned model may be used to predict outputs for new inputs. Here we can construct an explicit error function to minimize from the desired and the produced output for each input. A learning rule using gradient descent to find a local minimum in such a function is called the delta rule, or error backpropagation for feedforward neural networks (Rumelhart *et al.*, 1985), or Rosenblatt's algorithm for a single McCulloch–Pitts neuron.

In reinforcement learning (RL) settings, the learner is acting in an environment described by a state space. At each step, we observe the state of the environment and a possibly sparse reward signal, based on which we have to choose an action. The goal is to maximize reward in a long run, for which we need to learn values of visited states and generalize them to unvisited ones. Pavlovian conditioning and the Rescorla–Wagner rule can be regarded as simple examples of an RL paradigm. A general RL problem my be solved with the temporal difference learning rule (Sutton and Barto, 1998) that adjusts estimated state values based on the prediction error of the reward signal. A state space may be represented by neural networks, an idea that served as the basis of successful proof-of-concept applications (Mnih *et al.*, 2013). In the brain, neural systems using dopamine as neurotransmitter, population activity is thought to encode reward prediction (Waelti *et al.*, 2001).

9.4.4.4. *Storage of information in neural systems*

Mapping between different variables can be stored in a feedforward network of rate neurons trained in a supervized manner. These mappings can be generalized to inputs never seen, with varying efficiency. Another classical way to store patterns in a neurons is to use a Hopfield network (Hopfield, 1982), which is a recursive system of McCulloch–Pitts neurons with symmetric weights. Elements of the learning set can be stored in the weight matrix of the network using a Hebbian learning rule. This creates point attractors in the phase space of the system at the patterns to store (and unfortunately at some other patterns), so when applying a new activation to the network, it will converge to the closest stored vector.

A probabilistic extension of the Hopfield network is the Boltzmann machine (Ackley *et al.*, 1985), which is able to store probability distributions of binary (and with some extensions, other) variables. The MCP neurons are replaced with probabilistic ones, making the neuron draw a sample from a Bernoulli distribution at each time step. A network may have unobserved variables too, for which the learning rule sets the weights so that on the observed units the activation statistics matches that of the training set up to pairwise correlations.

9.4.5. *Measuring Cognitive Systems*

To assess the validity of different modeling approaches to cognitive systems, one needs to collect data from the brain. In general, this is a very challenging task due to the enormous number of computing units and potentially relevant physiological quantities, and to the invasive nature of most direct measurement techniques in existence today.

9.4.5.1. *Electrophysiology*

As we believe that electric properties of the neurons are central to their information processing, direct measurement of membrane potentials is a primary goal. Single cells can be measured with high accuracy with the patch-clamp technique, which is limited in the number of possible parallel recordings. If one would like to measure population activity, extracellular electrodes or electrode arrays can record the LFP. However, such recordings pose rather challenging mathematical problems when one tries to obtain more direct information of cellular activity either by current source density reconstruction (Somogyvári *et al.*, 2012), or spike train reconstruction by waveform clustering (Buzsáki, 2004).

Such invasive techniques can only be used in animal experiments, and in humans only in the case when a patient needs electrophysiological localization of damaged tissue to be removed by surgery. A non-invasive electrophysiological technique is the electroencephalogram (EEG), which records the neural electric field outside of the skull, providing a temporally detailed picture of macroscopic changes in population activity of neurons. However, EEG is limited in the sense of localization of the source of specific patterns. The magnetoencephalogram (MEG) is somewhat better in this regard in return for a vastly higher price compared to the low-cost EEG.

9.4.5.2. *Other imaging methods*

Indirect measurements of cellular activity record a physical quantity that can be regarded a proxy to the electric activity of the cells. Methods based on magnetic resonance (MR) are very popular due to their noninvasive nature and high spatial resolution over the whole brain. When applied for functional imaging (fMRI), localization of activated brain areas is possible, however the temporal resolution is in the order of a second, thus one cannot see temporally detailed responses. Seeing the activity of single cells is generally not possible with fMRI today, however, there are some advancements in this direction (Radecki *et al.*, 2014).

Imaging techniques are not only useful to localize task-specific activity, but it is also possible to infer functional connectivity from such data. Interaction networks of brain areas are also task-specific or related to a resting state. Connectivity analysis usually relies on a model of area and stimulus interactions (Friston *et al.*, 2003), and applicable to compare different groups of subjects. One direction of application is the characterization of neurological diseases, such as schizophrenia, which is thought to be a disconnection syndrome (Bányai *et al.*, 2011).

Some other functional imaging methods also promise better quality data about cellular activity. These include intrinsic optical imaging, voltage sensitive dyes and calcium imaging.

9.4.5.3. *Psychophysics*

Cognitive models can make many predictions about performance in different tasks. These can be checked without making invasive or otherwise expensive measurements of neural activity and provide indirect evidence about the plausibility of different models. Psychophysics was founded in the 19th century by Fechner

(Fechner, 1907), and since then it is a very important tool for cognitive science. Sensory classification tasks measured in psychophysical experiments also shed light on the nature of representations in the cortex. For example, in the visual areas, the structure low-level representations in the visual cortex can be examined by texture stimuli (as introduced by Julesz (1962)). Higher-level representations of objects is phenomenologically described by Gestalt psychology (Koffka, 2013). These results can be combined with physiology to assess the relevance of particular models on the neural level.

9.5. Cognitive Robotics

9.5.1. *Challenges of Automation*

9.5.1.1. *Typical settings and problems*

Nowadays, robotics is starting to leave behind the assembly line and the futuristic demos on tech shows and university press events. Everyday interaction with autonomous machines is a prospect of the near future, either in the form of a software running on a general-purpose computer or a custom-built hardware that moves around. Examples of autonomous machines in testing or production phase include self-driving cars, drone swarms and speech recognition and synthetization systems available in mobile computing devices.

As the problems such agents need to solve resemble the situations living organisms find themselves every day, we will find that a strong parallelism exists between the tools used for modeling neural cognitive systems and the ones used to produce adaptive behavior in machines. These methods, together with other effective algorithms, are undergoing rapid improvement in the fields of machine learning and artificial intelligence. When creating physically embodied agents, these methods need to be augmented by advancements from mechanical, electrical and software engineering, control theory and signal processing, and in terms of adaptive algorithms, a larger emphasis is placed on strategy learning and decision-making. Thus, cognitive robotics is formed as a cooperation between diverse fields of multiple scientific disciplines.

Applications of such robots go beyond civil use, as military or astronautical purposes create a major drive to these developments all around the globe.

9.5.1.2. *Building models of the environment and the agent*

The core problem of adaptive behavior is to represent the world and the robot itself in an efficient manner to support perception, decision and action. Formation of such representations is closely related to the phenomenon of internal models in the human brain, as detailed in Section 9.4.3. However, when building a robot, different constraints are in effect regarding the cost of certain computations or storage. Thus, for every problem in cognitive neuroscience there is a parallel problem in machine learning, where instead of asking what is the way nature solves a given task, we seek the optimal solution with respect to the constraint of the computational architecture at hand.

The knowledge the agent needs to represent include the encoding of existing objects, their properties, relationships between them, concepts as correlation of objects in time or space and the agent itself, that is, the possible actions it can take and their effects on the environment. Unlike to the study of biological systems, the language of representation and code of communication are not restricted in artificial agents by anything but the capabilities of their hardware.

In realistic settings, we typically cannot define a good representation by hand. Thus, automatic formation of representation is often defined as an unsupervised learning problem, where the optimal representation is sought in such a way that it supports optimal decision (classification, action selection) the best. Unsupervised learning algorithms exist for many modeling frameworks (Ghahramani, 2004), and with the advent of large-scale datasets (typically at companies providing websites where users can store media content) they can be tested in problems with near-realistic complexity.

9.5.1.3. *Learning architectures*

One of the central concepts of cybernetics was the theory of feedback loops that can implement adaptive control for autonomous agents. The simplest problems may be solved without adaptation, as illustrated by the Braitenberg vehicles (Braitenberg, 1986) modeling primitive animal behavior. More complex problems require the use of adaptive dynamical systems that are modifying their parameters based on optimality criteria as a feedback mechanism.

In complex environments, generalization to unseen situations is of primary importance, as the agent has typically no chance of exploring all possible states or inputs, thus it has to extrapolate to unseen ones based on some metric of the state or input space. Artificial neural networks (see Section 9.4.3.2) are universal function approximators with good generalization properties, and they form the basis of many problem models in autonomous agents.

If the robot needs to represent the uncertainty of modelled quantities, probabilistic models can be employed (Bishop, 2006). Advantages of this approach are that probability is a framework unifying many different modeling and algorithmic approaches on a principled ground, and it may be regarded as a natural extension to binary logic representing belief in propositions (Jaynes, 2003). Moreover, the framework of graphical models provides an intuitive language of model creation and improvement.

Probabilistic neural networks combine the two approaches. They are the state-of-the-art solution to many benchmark and real-world problems, as they can be trained with effective algorithms in unsupervised and supervised settings as well.

9.5.2. *Sensory Processing*

9.5.2.1. *Learning invariances*

The basic task of processing a sensory input is to classify it according to different criteria, e.g., the presence of a specific object or object type in it. To perform such classifications, one has to differentiate regularities of the phenomenon to discover from regularities arising due to finite data (for example, when deciding whether we see a lion, we have take into account the fact that lions may appear in various positions in front of various backgrounds, but if we have seen only male lions, one without a mane might be misclassified).

Learning invariances is a potentially very challenging task, in which humans exhibit a performance which is hardly matched by any algorithm so far, especially in terms of robustness to change of context.

9.5.2.2. *Image processing*

Many robotic applications need to deal with some form of visual input in the form of images or video streams. Typically, one needs to segment the images to detect the presence of certain objects. Invariances that need to be handled during visual object recognition include rotation, translation, resizing (possibly due to perspective), change of background and possibly color, relative position of parts or stretching.

For the purpose of testing and development of algorithms, several benchmark databases exist, such as the MNIST database of handwritten images and the ImageNet database with lots of labels attached to the images by humans.

The most successful solutions for image classification are deep neural networks that capitalize on the hierarchical nature of image composition by fitting a layered architecture to observations. Unsupervised pre-training of layers can enhance the performance greatly, as it constructs a representation that is related to the inherent statistics of the input set (which may contain much more data than the set we have labels provided for), which can be refined by adding the information of the available labels in a supervised manner.

9.5.2.3. *Speech processing*

Effective interaction with humans is mostly possible through speech. It is different from visual input in the sense that it is typically lower dimensional, but temporally extended sequential data with high autocorrelations.

To model such a dataset, one needs to employ dynamical models that explicitly represent temporal dependence. The class of Hidden Markov Models (HMMs) offers the simplest solution to this problem. More complex, nonlinear relationships may be captured by recurrent neural networks, in which feedback loops are placed on processing layers representing time. Learning algorithms defined for feedforward networks may be extended for such loopy architectures relatively easily.

Speech processing solutions are possibly the branch of robotics that pervaded everyday life the most in the form of mobile phone software that not only processes, but also produces speech. This may be accomplished by constructing a world model that defines not only the grammar but topical relationships between words.

9.5.2.4. *Understanding content*

The hardest problems of signal processing can be described as semantic analysis, as we typically look for the meaning of the input by making sense of a visual scene or an uttered sentence. This cannot be accomplished solely on the basis of pattern mining, but one needs to construct a world model that effectively encodes relationships between concepts. Semantics can indeed be defined as a higher level in the hierarchy of syntaxes.

In visual processing, slow feature analysis (Wiskott and Sejnowski, 2002) aims to detect temporally stable objects, creating object hierarchies builtding up visual scenes. In natural language processing, document topic models, such as Latent Dirichlet Allocation (LDA) (Blei *et al.*, 2003) try to model word correlations by identifying document categories.

We can also attempt to discover the model structure that describes the data best instead of hand-picking it. Model selection or structure learning (Kemp and Tenenbaum, 2008) is the unsupervised discovery of the model form that can fit to the observations best.

9.5.3. *Decision-Making*

9.5.3.1. *Utility and cost functions*

When deciding about which action to take, it is not enough to determine what is the effect of the options according to the internal model, we also have to define how desirable those outcomes are. This can be described by a cost or utility function that encodes the undesirability or equivalently, the desirability of situations or actions.

As Kahneman and Tversky (Tversky and Kahneman, 1981) noted, cost functions of humans deviate from expected reward, reflecting priorities auxiliary to the task at hand (they also show that equivalent reformulation of problems lead to different decisions, which behavior is best kept at minimum in artificial agents).

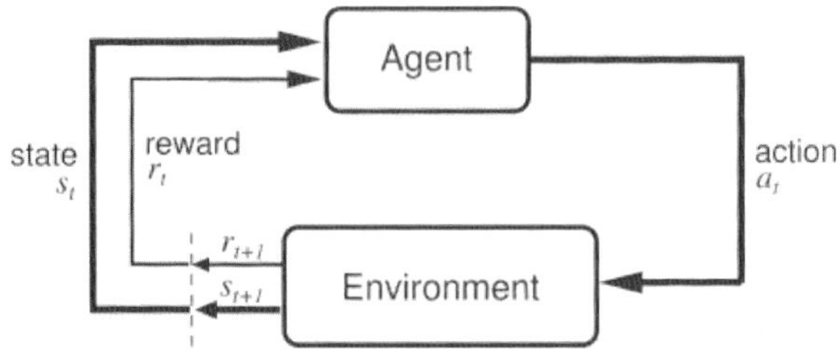

Figure 9.5: Agent-environment interplay in a MDP.

Simple decision-making protocols may be defined on the basis of predefined cost functions, but more complex problems require the adaptation of the estimation of such costs or values based on experience.

9.5.3.2. *Strategy learning*

For learning strategies, it is useful to model the environment and the agent as a set of states and associated rewards, a set of actions, and a transition probability function defined on triplets of two states and an action. Such a model is called a Markov Decision Process (MDP), and reinforcement learning methods operate on it to find the best strategy to collect reward.

Finding the optimal action to take at each state of the environment is a reinforcement learning (RL) problem as described in Section 9.4.4.3. Well-performing RL solvers update their belief about values of states using some variant of the temporal difference (TD) learning rule:

$$V(s_t) \leftarrow V(s_t) + \alpha\left[r_{t+1} + \gamma V(s_{t+1}) - V(s_t)\right], \tag{10}$$

where s_t is the state the environment is in at time t, V is the belief about the value of the state, r is the reward signal, γ and α are parameters of the update rule. The TD rule makes use of the error in the prediction of subsequent reward by the estimated value of a state. Action selection may either be based on a separately learned state transition probability function, or the estimation of a state-action value function instead of a state-value.

Reinforcement learning using a neural representation was used to create proof-of-concept applications playing games against human players (Tesauro, 1995) and in virtual environments (Mnih *et al.*, 2013).

9.5.3.3. *Active learning*

In MDP environments, actions of the agent influence the learning process greatly, as data collection is dependent of the actual chain of states it visits. Thus, it is important to choose an action selection strategy that maximizes reward in the long run by finding the best strategy, and when it is reasonable to assume that the agent won't find any better, employ it. This is the classic exploration versus exploitation dilemma (Sutton and Barto, 1998), which is usually resolved in a way that initially the agent act random to explore the environment as much as possible, and as reward accumulates, thus state value estimations get more reliable, it chooses the best action with a proportionally greater probability. This way we can ensure that in theory (that is, with an arbitrary amount of learning epochs) the globally optimal strategy can be found.

9.5.3.4. *Learning to move mechanical bodies*

Moving machines can take many forms. One category is vehicle-like, such as cars, drones (Virágh *et al.*, 2014) or submarines, which have simpler movement patterns and easier to control, in return they are limited in terms of terrain difficulty. Alternatively, robots may mimic living organisms not only in terms of behavior, but also physical form. These solutions include bipedals, four-legged robots mimicking dogs (Touretzky and Tira-Thompson, 2005) or mules, and structures with more legs. A great advantage of such constructions is that they can manage more difficult terrains such as rocks or steps.

Complex movement of animal-like structures can be copied from actual animals. By motion capture techniques, one can record the movement of an animal or a human to time series of coordinates, and look for periodic patterns or other primitives in them that can be transcribed to the robot's program.

Optimal movement can be and often is obtained by reinforcement learning. Then the state is defined by some parametrization of the joints or motors of the robot, and the reward function is constructed in such a way that it encourages the reaching of a goal or keeping moving, and punishes loss of stability. This way complex movement patterns can be acquired without having (or being able at all) to describe them in terms of joint coordinates.

9.5.3.5. *Cooperative agents*

Agents aiming for optimal behavior in realistic settings need to take into account other goal-directed entities acting in the environment. Moreover, if the agents share the same goal, they can perform better (or solve otherwise intractable tasks) in a cooperative manner. A simple form of this behavior can be observed in insect colonies that inspired a class of optimization algorithms, Ant Colony Optimization (ACO). More generally, swarm intelligence is a field of research where complex behavior is assembled as a cooperation between simple individual agents (Bonabeau *et al.*, 1999).

A higher level of cooperation can be realized not only on the behavioral, but on the hardware level, where simple agents perform the self-assemby of a more complicated structure (Gro *et al.*, 2006).

Strategy learning in a cooperative setting may be approached by reinforcement learning techniques, however, such a situation can only be modelled by a partially observable MDP (POMDP) due to the fact that effects of actions of other agents may confound the state transitions of the environment. Optimal behavior in a POMDP is a heavily researched problem (Buşoniu *et al.*, 2010).

Cooperative RL is a very ambitious goal in general, but advancements can be realized and tested in well-controlled game situations, such as the RoboCup annual football championship organized in different categories exclusively for teams of robotic agents.

9.6. Conclusion

In this chapter, we reviewed the philosophical and mathematical treatment of cognitive systems modeling, including directions that aim to understand biological systems, and to build artificial solutions to problems encountered by living organisms. We gave an overview of the basic approaches of cognitive modeling, symbolic, connectionist and hybrid, and the computational tools and architectures that can be used to model phenomena in either of those settings. Possibilities of connecting the computational picture to biological neurons were shown, and applications where cognitive principles were successfully adopted in artificial systems were overviewed.

The chapter is meant to be an introduction to the very diverse field of cognitive science, with the references serving as pointers to the branches of study mentioned. We hoped to convey a picture of the frontier in the great endeavor to understand the human brain as it stood in 2014. As the reader surely concluded based on the fragmentary nature of success stories, we are only at the beginning of the work. We are starting to grasp concepts in sufficient detail to predict behavior and sometimes even physiology, but assembling a composite picture will require much more effort. The central question of such an integrated model will be the nature of neural codes and representations, as advancing in those topics may allow cognitive science to be a proper natural science with predictive models and repeatable experiments. Nowadays, multiple large-scale programs are being initiated in neuroscience aiming for an integrative approach, and their results are expected to unfold in the next decade.

The most complex problems in cognitive science, such as social systems or the hard problem of consciousness, may also be addressed in a more satisfying manner when we have a more complete understanding of the formal treatment of thinking and problem solving systems.

References

Abbott, L. F. (2005). Lapicque's introduction of the integrate-and-fire model neuron (1907). *Brain Res. Bull.*, pp. 1–2.

Abraham, T. (2002). (Physio)logical circuits: The intellectual origins of the Mcculloch–Pitts neural networks. *J. Hist. Behav. Sci.*, 38, pp. 3–25.

Ackley, D. H., Hinton, G. E. and Sejnowski, T. J. (1985). A learning algorithm for boltzmann machines. *Cognit. Sci.*, 9(1), pp. 147–169.

Anderson, J. R. (2007). *How Can the Human Mind Occur in the Physical Universe?* New York: Oxford University Press.

Anderson, J. R. and Bower, G. H. (1973). *Human Associative Memory*. Washington: Winston and Sons.

Arbib, M. (2000). Warren Mcculloch's search for the logic of the nervous system. *Perspect. Biol. Med.*, 43, pp. 193–216.

Arbib, M., Érdi, P. and Szentágothai, J. (1997). *Neural Organization: Structure, Function, and Dynamics*. Cambridge, MA: MIT Press.

Arbib, M. A. (2005). From monkey-like action recognition to human language: An evolutionary framework for neurolinguistics. *Behav. Brain Sci.*, 28, pp. 105–168.

Barlow, H. B. (1990). Conditions for versatile learning, Helmholtz's unconscious inference, and the task of perception. *Vis. Res.*, 30(11), pp. 1561–1571.

Bastos, A. M., Usrey, W. M., Adams, R. A., Mangun, G. R., Fries, P. and Friston, K. J. (2012). Canonical microcircuits for predictive coding. *Neuron*, 76(4), pp. 695–711.

Battaglia, F. P. and Pennartz, C. M. A. (2011). The construction of semantic memory: Grammar-based representations learned from relational episodic information. *Fronti. Comput. Neurosci.*, 5, p. 36.

Bi, G. and Poo, M. (1998). Synaptic modifications in cultured hippocampal neurons: Dependence on spike timing, synaptic strength, and postsynaptic cell type. *J. Neurosci.*, 18, pp. 10464–10472.

Bishop, C. M. (2006). *Pattern Recognition and Machine Learning*, Vol. 1. New York: Springer.

Blei, D. M., Ng, A. Y. and Jordan, M. I. (2003). Latent dirichlet allocation. *J. Mach. Learn. Res.*, 3, pp. 993–1022.

Bobrow, D. and Norman, D. (1975). Some principles of memory schemata. In Bobrow, D. and Collins, A. (eds.) *Representation and Understanding*. New York: Academic Press.

Bonabeau, E., Dorigo, M. and Theraulaz, G. (1999). From natural to artificial swarm intelligence.

Braitenberg, V. (1986). *Vehicles: Experiments in Synthetic Psychology*. Cambridge: MIT Press.

Bressler, S. L. (1990). The gamma wave: A cortical information carrier? *Trends Neurosci.*, 13(5), pp. 161–162.

Brooks, R. (2002). *Flesh and Machines: How Robots Will Change Us*. New York: Pantheon Books.

Buzsáki, G. (2004). Large-scale recording of neuronal ensembles. *Nat. Neurosci.*, 7(5), pp. 446–451.

Buzsáki, G. (2004). Neuronal oscillations in cortical networks. *Science*, 304(5679), pp. 1926–1929.

Buşoniu, L., Babuška, R. and De Schutter, B. (2010). Multi-agent reinforcement learning: An overview. In *Innovations in Multi-Agent Systems and Applications — 1*. Berlin, Heidelberg: Springer, pp. 183–221.

Bányai, M., Diwadkar, V. A. and Érdi, P. (2011). Model-based dynamical analysis of functional disconnection in schizophrenia. *NeuroImage*, 58(3), pp. 870–877.

Carandini, M. and Heeger, D. J. (2012). Normalization as a canonical neural computation. *Nat. Rev. Neurosci.*, 13(1), pp. 51–62.

Chomsky, N. (1959). A review of B. F. Skinner's verbal behavior. *Lang.*, 35, pp. 26–58.

Chomsky, N. (1965). *Aspects of the Theory of Syntax*. Cambdridge: MIT Press.

Churchland, P. and Sejnowski, T. (1990). Neural representation and neural computation. *Philos. Perspect.*, 4, pp. 343–382.

Collins, A. and Quillian, M. (1969). Retrieval time for semantic memories. *J. Verbal Learn. Verbal Behav.*, 8, pp. 240–48.

Cortes, C. and Vapnik, V. (1995). Support-vector networks. *Mach. Lear.*, 20(3), pp. 273–297.

Craik, K. (1943). *The Nature of Explanation*. Cambridge: Cambridge University Press.

Davis, R., Shrobe, H., and Szolovits, P. (1993). What is a knowledge representation? *AI Mag.*, 14(1), pp. 17–33.

Dayan, P. and Abbott, L. F. (2001). *Theoretical Neuroscience*, Vol. 31. Cambridge, MA: MIT press.

DiCarlo, J. J., Zoccolan, D. and Rust, N. C. (2012). Perspective. *Neuron*, 73(3), pp. 415–434.

Duch, W., Oentaryo, R. and Pasqueier, M. (2007). Cognitive architectures: Where do we go from here? In Wang, P., Goertzel, B. and Franklin, S. (eds.), *Front. Artif. Intell. Appl.*, 171, pp. 122–136.

Érdi P. and Somogyvári, Z. (2002). Post-hebbian learning algorithms. In Arbib, M. (ed.), *The Handbook of Brain Theory and Neural Networks, Second Edition*. Cambridge, MA: MIT Press, pp. 533–539.

Fechner, G. T. (1907). *Elemente der Psychophysik*, Vol. 2. Breitkopf & Härtel.

Fiser, J., Berkes, P., Orbán, G. and Lengyel, M. (2010). Statistically optimal perception and learning: From behavior to neural representations. *Trends Cognit. Sci.*, 14(3), pp. 119–130.

Fodor, J. (1980). Methodological solipsism considered as a research strategy in cognitive psychology. *Behav. Brain Sci.*, 3, pp. 63–109.

Fodor, J. (1983). *The Modularity of Mind: An Essay on Faculty Psychology*. Cambridge: MIT Press.

Friston, K. J., Harrison, L. and Penny, W. (2003). Dynamic causal modelling. *NeuroImage*, 19(4), pp. 1273–1302.

George, D. and Hawkins, J. (2009). Towards a mathematical theory of cortical micro-circuits. *PLoS Comput. Biol.*, 5(10), p. e1000532.

Ghahramani, Z. (2004). Unsupervised Learning. In *Advanced Lectures on Machine Learning*. Berlin, Heidelberg: Springer, pp. 72–112.

Gro, R., Bonani, M., Mondada, F. and Dorigo, M. (2006). Autonomous self-assembly in swarm-bots. *IEEE Trans. Robot.*, 22(6), pp. 1115–1130.

Harris, K. D. and Thiele, A. (2011). Cortical state and attention. *Nat. Rev. Neurosci.*, 12(9), pp. 509–523.

Hebb, D. O. (1949). *The Organisation of Behavior, a Neuropsychological Theory*. New York: Wiley.

Hebb, D. O. (1949). *The Organization of Behavior: A Neuropsychological Approach*. New York: John Wiley & Sons.

Hinton, G. E. (2002). Training products of experts by minimizing contrastive divergence. *Neural Comput.*, 14(8), pp. 1771–1800.

Hinton, G. E., Dayan, P., Frey, B. J. and Neal, R. M. (1995). The "wake–sleep" algorithm for unsupervised neural networks. *Science*, 268(5214), pp. 1158–1161.

Hodgkin, A. L. and Huxley, A. F. (1952). A quantitative description of membrane current and its application to conduction and excitation in nerve. *J. Physiol.*, 117(4), pp. 500–544.

Hopfield, J. J. (1982). Neural networks and physical systems with emergent collective computational abilities. In *Proc. Nat. Acad. Sci.*, 79(8), pp. 2554–2558.

Hubel, D. H. and Wiesel, T. N. (1968). Receptive fields and functional architecture of monkey striate cortex. *J. Physiol.*, 195(1), pp. 215–243.

Iturria-Medina, Y., Sotero, R. C., Canales-Rodríguez, E. J., Alemán-Gómez, Y. and Melie-García, L. (2008). Studying the human brain anatomical network via diffusion-weighted MRI and graph theory. *NeuroImage*, 40(3), pp. 1064–1076.

Jackson, P. (1998). *Introduction To Expert Systems, Third Edition*. USA: Addison Wesley.

Jaynes, E. T. (2003). *Probability Theory: The Logic of Science*. Cambridge: Cambridge University Press.

Johnson-Laird, P. (1983). *Mental Mgedit rodels: Towards a Cognitive Science of Language, Inference, and Consciousness*. Cambridge: Cambridge University Press.

Julesz, B. (1962). Visual pattern discrimination. *IRE Trans. Inf. Theory*, 8(2), pp. 84–92.

Jurafsky, D. and Marti, J. (2008). *Speech and Language Processing: An Introduction to Natural Language Processing, Speech Recognition, and Computational Linguistics, Second Edition*. Englewood Cliffs, NJ: Prentice-Hall.

Kemp, C. and Tenenbaum, J. B. (2008). The discovery of structural form. *Proc. Nation. Acad. Sci.*

Koffka, K. (2013). *Principles of Gestalt Psychology*. Routledge.

Laird, J. (2012). *The Soar Cognitive Architecture*. Cambridge: MIT Press.

Lanciego, J. L. and Wouterlood, F. G. (2011). A half century of experimental neuroanatomical tracing. *J. Chem. Neuroanat.*, 42(3), pp. 157–183.

Lengyel, M. and Dayan, P. (2007). Hippocampal contributions to control: The third way. *Adv. Neural Inf. Process. Syst.*

Lengyel, M., Szatmáry, Z. and Érdi, P. (2003). Dynamically detuned oscillations account for the coupled rate and temporal code of place cell firing. *Hippocampus*, 13(6), pp. 700–714.

Ma'ayan, A., Jenkins, S. L., Neves, S., Hasseldine, A., Grace, E., Dubin-Thaler, B., Eungdamrong, N. J., Weng, G., Ram, P. T., Rice, J. J., Kershenbaum, A., Stolovitzky, G. A., Blitzer, R. D. and Iyengar, R. (2005). Formation of regulatory patterns during signal propagation in a Mammalian cellular network. *Science*, 309(5737), pp. 1078–1083.

Ma, W. J., Beck, J. M., Latham, P. E. and Pouget, A. (2006). Bayesian inference with probabilistic population codes. *Nat. Neurosci.*, 9(11), pp. 1432–1438.

McCulloch, W. and Pitts, W. (1943). A logical calculus of the ideas immanent in nervous system. *Bull. Math. Biophys.*, 5(4), pp. 115–133.

Milnes, B., Pelton, G., Doorenbos, R., Laird, M., Rosenbloom, P. and Newell, A. (1992). A specification of the soar cognitive architecture in z. Technical Report. Pittsburgh, PA, USA: Carnegie Mellon Univ.

Minsky, M. (1974). A framework for representing knowledge. *Technical Report*. Cambridge: MIT AI Laboratory Memo 306.

Minsky, M. and Papert, S. (1969). *Perceptrons: An Introduction to Computational Geometry*. Cambridge, MA: MIT Press.

Mnih, V., Kavukcuoglu, K., Silver, D., Graves, A., Antonoglou, I., Wierstra, D. and Riedmiller, M. (2013). Playing atari with deep reinforcement learning.

Mountcastle, V. B. (1997). The columnar organization of the neocortex. *Brain*, 120(Pt 4), pp. 701–722.

Neal, R. M. (1992). Connectionist learning of belief networks. *Artif. Intell.*, 56(1), pp. 71–113.

Newell, A. (1990). *Unified Theories of Cognition*. Cambridge, MA: Harvard University Press.

Newell, A. and Simon, H. (1972). *Human Problem Solving*. Englewood Cliffs, NJ: Prentice-Hall.

Newell, A. and Simon, H. (1976). Computer science as empirical enquiry: Symbols and search. *Commun. Assoc. Comput. Mach.*, 19, pp. 113–126.

Pearl, J. (2000). *Causality: Models, Reasoning and Inference*, Vol. 29, Cambridge: Cambridge University Press.

Piccinini, G. (2004). The first computational theory of mind and brain: A close look at Mcculloch and Pitts's 'logical calculus of ideas immanent in nervous activity'. *Synthese.*, 141, pp. 175–215.

Pinker, S. (2007). *The Language Instinct: How the Mind Creates Language*. New York: Harper Perennial Modern Classics.

Pinker, S. and Bloom, P. (1990). Natural language and natural selection. *Behav. Brain Sci.*, 13, pp. 707–784.

Quillian, M. (1968). Semantic memory. In Minsky, M. (ed.), *Semantic Information Processing*. Cambridge, MA: MIT Press.

Quiroga, R. Q., Reddy, L., Kreiman, G., Koch, C. and Fried, I. (2005). Invariant visual representation by single neurons in the human brain. *Nature*, 435(7045), pp. 1102–1107.

Radecki, G., Nargeot, R., Jelescu, I. O., Le Bihan, D. and Ciobanu, L. (2014). Functional magnetic resonance microscopy at single-cell resolution. *Aplysia Californica. Proc. Nation. Acad. Sci.*, 111(23), pp. 8667–8672.

Ramón y Cajal, S. (1909). *Histologie du systéme nerveux de l'homme et des vertebras*. Maloine.

Rizzolatti, G., Sinigaglia, C. and Anderson, F. (2008). *Mirrors in the Brain: How Our Minds Share Actions and Emotions*. New York, US: Oxford University Press.

Rosenblatt, F. (1962). *Principles of Neurodynamics*. Washington, DC: Spartan Books.

Rosenblueth, A. and Bigelow, J. (1943). Behaviour, purpose and teleology. *Philos. Sci.*, 10, pp. 18–24.

Rosenblueth, A., Wiener, N. and Bigelow, J. (1943). Behavior, purpose and teleology. *Philos. Sci.*, 10(1943), S. 18–24.

Rumelhart, D. and McClelland, J. (1986). *Parallel Distributed Processing: Explorations in the Microstructure of Cognition*. Cambridge, MA: MIT Press.

Rumelhart, D. E., Hinton, G. E. and Williams, R. J. (1985). Learning internal representations by error propagation.

Salakhutdinov, R. R. and Hinton, G. E. (2009). Deep boltzmann machines. *Proc. Int. Conf. Artif. Intell. Stat.*, pp. 448–455.

Schank, R. and Abelson, R. (1977). *Scripts, Plans, Goals and Understanding*. Hillsdale, NJ: Erlbaum.

Searle, J. (1983). *Intentionality: An Essay in the Philosophy of Mind.* Cambridge: Cambridge University Press.

Searle, J. (1992). *The Rediscovery of the Mind.* Cambridge, MA: MIT Press.

Shepard, R. (1980). *Internal Representations: Studies in Perception, Imagery, and Cognition.* Bradford: Montgomery, VT.

Shouval, H. (2007). Models of synaptic plasticity. http://www.scholarpedia.org/article/.

Sjoestrom, J. and Gerstner, W. (2010). Spike-timing dependent plasticity. http://www.scholarpedia.org/article/.

Smith, A. M. (2001). *Alhacen's Theory of Visual Perception: A Critical Edition, with English Translation and Commentary, of the First Three Books of Alhacen's De Aspectibus, the Medieval Latin Version of Ibn Al-Haytham's Kitab al-Manazir*, Vol. 1. USA: American Philosophical Society.

Somogyvári, Z., Cserpán, D., Ulbert, I. and Érdi, P. (2012). Localization of single-cell current sources based on extracellular potential patterns: The spike CSD method. *Eur. J. Neurosci.*, 36(10), pp. 3299–3313.

Strogatz, S. H. (2006). *Nonlinear Dynamics and Chaos (With Applications to Physics, Biology, Chemistry*. Perseus Publishing.

Strotzer, M. (2009). One century of brain mapping using brodmann areas. *Clin. Neuroradiol.*

Sun, R. (2004). Desiderata for cognitive architectures. *Philos. Psychol.*, 17, pp. 341–373.

Sutton, R. S. and Barto, A. G. (1998). *Introduction to Reinforcement Learning*. Cambridge: MIT Press.

Szentágothai, J. (1983). The modular architectonic principle of neural centers. In *Reviews of Physiology, Biochemistry and Pharmacology*, Vol. 98. Berlin, Heidelberg: Springer, pp. 11–61.

Tesauro, G. (1995). Temporal difference learning and TD-Gammon. *Commun. ACM.*

Thagard, P. (2005). *Mind: Introduction to Cognitive Science, Second Edition*. Cambridge, MA: MIT Press.

Touretzky, D. S. and Tira-Thompson, E. J. (2005). Tekkotsu: A framework for AIBO cognitive robotics, *Proceedings of the National Conference on Artificial Intelligence*, Vol. 20(4), Menlo Park CA; Cambridge, MA; London: AAAI Press; MIT Press, p. 1741.

Tsuda, I. (1991). Chaotic itinerancy as a dynamical basis of hermeneutics in brain and mind. *World Futures: J. Gen. Evol.*, 32(2–3), pp. 167–184.

Tulving, E. (1985). How many memory systems are there? *Am. Psychol.*, 40(4), p. 385.

Tversky, A. and Kahneman, D. (1981). The framing of decisions and the psychology of choice. *Science*, 211(4481), pp. 453–458.

Virágh, C., Vásárhelyi, G., Tarcai, N., Szörényi, T., Somorjai, G., Nepusz, T. and Vicsek, T. (2014). Flocking algorithm for autonomous flying robots. *Bioinspir. Biomim.*, 9(2), p. 025012.

Vizi, E. S., Kiss, J. P. and Lendvai, B. (2004). Nonsynaptic communication in the central nervous system. *Neuroche. Int.*, 45(4), pp. 443–451.

von Neumann, J. (1958). *The Computer and the Brain*. New Haven: Yale Univ. Press.

Von Helmholtz, H. (1866). *Handbuch der physiologischen Optik: mit 213 in den Text eingedruckten Holzschnitten und 11 Tafeln*. Vol. 9, Voss.

Waelti, P., Dickinson, A. and Schultz, W. (2001). Dopamine responses comply with basic assumptions of formal learning theory. *Nature*, 412(6842), pp. 43–48.

Werbos, P. (1974). *Beyond Regression: New Tools for Prediction and Analysis in the Behavioral Sciences*. PhD thesis. Cambridge: Harvard University.

Winograd, T. (1972). *Understanding Natural Language*. Waltham, MA: Academic Press.

Wiskott, L. and Sejnowski, T. J. (2002). Slow feature analysis: Unsupervised learning of invariances. *Neural Comput.*, 14(4), pp. 715–770.

Zhao, C., Deng, W. and Gage, F. H. (2008). Mechanisms and functional implications of adult neurogenesis. *Cell*, 132(4), pp. 645–660.

Ziemba, C. M., Heeger, D. J., Simoncelli, E. P., Movshon, J. A. and Freeman, J. (2013). A functional and perceptual signature of the second visual area in primates. *Nat. Neurosci.*, 16(7), pp. 1–12.

Chapter 10

A New View on Economics with Recurrent Neural Networks

Hans-Georg Zimmermann, Ralph Grothmann and Christoph Tietz

The identification of dynamical systems for forecasting and diagnosis plays an important role in technology as well as in economics. The special challenge in economics is that less *a priori* knowledge is available and the focus lies on the modeling of observed dynamical systems. We will explain our considerations in an economical framework, nevertheless, most of them can be applied to technical examples too.

System identification and forecasting in economics can be split. On the one hand, there are volume (e.g., demand- or load-) forecasting support marketing tasks, on the other hand there are price forecasts, which are essentially financial market forecasts. Market models are often not far away from being world models, presenting an extreme challenge.

Neural networks can not only meet this challenge but also provide unique insights into the nature and hidden structure of the identification problem.

10.1. Understanding Economics

This chapter shows the different challenges in marcoeconomics, business economics and finance which can be met with the help of neural networks (NN). The mathematics of NN allow insights into the market analysis which would not be possible without this approach.

10.1.1. *Markets as Recurrent Dynamical Systems*

Markets are high-dimensional, nonlinear systems. The dimensionality stems from the worldwide interactions between multiple agents, individual decisions of the agents can be seen as step functions which cause a nonlinear dynamic. An argument which is often used to defend linear models is that a Tailor expansion can be used to build a model and it is legitimate to start with the first term of the expansion to analyze a preliminary linear model. Especially in a fast changing world such an argument is questionable because a Tailor expansion can only be accurate around the expansion point. This will never be good enough in a world with fast changing dynamics.

Instead of modeling a complete market at once, let us focus first on the behavior of a single decision-maker, a trader. She has thousands of numbers available to her, arriving continuously from the data providers. Somewhere in these numbers the worldwide activity of the relevant markets is described. No one can grasp such an amount of information, therefore information filtering is an essential part of the decision-making process. This information filtering differs between traders, sometimes even conceptually like in the different systems of chartists or fundamentalists. With this focus of attention, a trader analyzes price changes in the market. The outcome of this analysis is an opinion about the emergence of a future market pattern. If the trader is confident of her analysis, she will sign a business contract.

These three steps — filtering, aggregation of information and decision-making can be efficiently described with the mathematical model of a single neuron (see the lower right of Figure 10.1). The filtering is realized by some zero weights on the incoming connections, the aggregation is modelled as a weighted sum and the decision step can be seen as evaluation of a nonlinear transfer function.

One trader alone does not make a market. Only the interaction between traders in a complex sequence of decisions and actions constitutes the dynamics of a market. The decisions observed over time can be discretized in form of a recurrent dynamical system with state equations as given in the upper right of Figure 10.1. A state s_t with observations u_t leads to the new state s_{t+1}. The state transformation equation defines the microeconomic picture of the interaction between all the microscopic

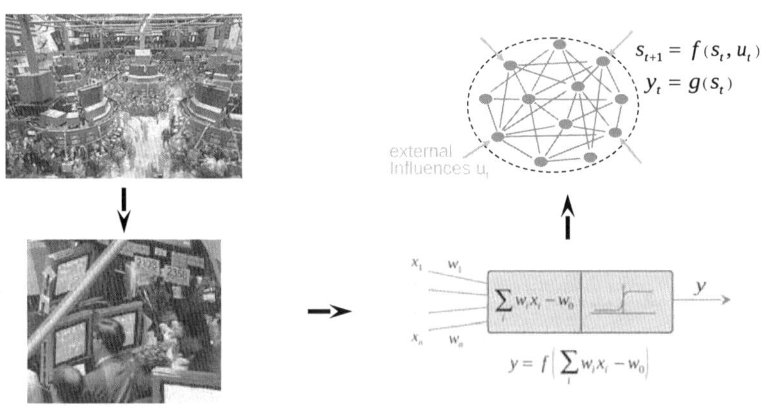

A neuron is a decision model combining information filtering & aggregation & switching.
A neural network can be seen as interaction of decisions and hence, as a market model.

Figure 10.1: Neural networks — from decision models to markets.

decisions of individual traders. Unfortunately, we are not able to observe the complete microscopic dynamics. We can only observe the macroscopic result of all these decisions as the behavior of the market. The output equation of the dynamical system bridges the gap between micro- and macro-economics with g as the bridging function and y_t as the observable subject of the market.

Is this simple mathematical model powerful enough to reproduce the different types of behavior in real markets? If indvidual decisions are uncorrelated, the overall market behavior might be very simple. On the other hand, if all the individual decisions correlate, then the behavior of real markets can become extremely chaotic. We will show that neural models are powerful enough to capture different types of markets. Model types do not have to be altered for different market conditions, neural models offer a reasonable microeconomic model and not only functional assumptions. Finally, we find at the core of neural models the adaptability of state transition and output functions to observed data.

10.1.2. *Improving Business Economics with Recurrent Neural Networks*

Business economics requires precise forecasts in order to enhance the quality of planning throughout the value chain. The complex planning and decision-making scenarios generally require the forecast to take account of a wide range of influencing factors with largely nonlinear cause and effect relationships.

An important application is demand forecasting for production control. One main challenge is the partial knowledge about the world, as competitors do not offer information about their decision-making. To overcome this lack of information, forecasting models can use the time-recursive structure of the observations to reconstruct information about the surrounding world which is not directly observable.

A second difficulty is that a demand forecast has to be applicable to new products which initially cannot provide training data over extended time intervals. Nevertheless, a reasonable demand forecast is necessary for production planning.

A third challenge arises where forecasts for a very large amount of variables have to be calculated. This is a typical situation in load forecasting (electricity, water or gas). If a load forecast has to be calculated for each quarter of an hour over one day, there are 96 variables to predict in form of a load curve. As will be shown in Section 10.3, Recursive Neural Networks (RNNs) which match the time recursive structure of the forecasting problem allow the simultaneous forecast of all 96 variables based on only one model.

10.1.3. *Understanding Finance with Recurrent Neural Networks*

The ability to forecast is a central requirement for rational decision-making, since the merit of any decision is always measured by its consequence in the future. This applies in particular to the financial sector, for example, in exchange rate trading or capital investment. The best known forecasting techniques in this context is chart analysis, which only evaluates data from the analyzed time series itself in the past. In contrast, fundamental analysis attempts to describe the actual dynamics of the market processes. The success of chart analyses is hampered by the low volume of input information, while that of a fundamental analysis is limited by the complexity of the market and the fact that it disregards the psychological factors influencing decision-making.

Section 10.4.1 introduces the network architecture of Historically Consistent Neural Networks (HCNNs), which is especially well suited for financial market models. It breaks up the common distinction between input and output values of a network and closes the modeled dynamical system by regarding all input and output values external to the network commonly as uniform observables. Its capabilities are demonstrated with results from modeling copper markets at the European Energy Exchange (EEX) and the London Metal Exchange (LME). This network architecture is refined in Section 10.4.2 to make better use of the available training information and speed up the training.

Markets can show different regimes, which can be characterized as based on (causal) historical developments, on (retro-causal) motivation and expectations or a mixture of both. We show in Sections 10.4.4 and 10.4.5, how the prior knowledge about these regimes can be coded in neural network architectures which extend the basic HCNN to Causal-Retro-Causal Historical Consistent Neural Networks (CRCNNs) which are finally able to model the copper markets we introduced earlier.

As mentioned in Section 10.1.1, Neural Networks can offer market models but for valuable decision support, a quantitative analysis of the underlying uncertainty has to be added. A typical analysis in finance is the tradeoff between expectation and risk of a position. Causal and retro-causal models offer a new view on uncertainty in forecasting, because for these models uncertainty is not seen as an essential part of the world. It is caused by the non-unique reconstruction of non-observable (hidden) variables in a model. Section 10.5 shows how this concept of uncertainty based on hidden variables allows a quantitative analysis of uncertainty and risk which surpasses commonplace distribution assumptions. We apply this analysis to the forecast of the Dow Jones Industrial Index (DJX) which illustrates the immediate consequences for auction pricing.

10.2. Recurrent Neural Networks

10.2.1. *Small Recurrent Neural Networks*

Starting with the view of a market as a deterministic dynamical system with a microeconomic state transition and an output equation bridging the gap to the macroeconomic observables, we can formally assume a vector time series y_τ which is created by a dynamical system with discrete time τ using a state transition and output equation (Haykin, 1994), given as:

$$\begin{aligned} \text{state transition} \quad s_\tau &= f(s_{\tau-1}, u_\tau), \\ \text{output equation} \quad y_\tau &= g(s_\tau). \end{aligned} \tag{1}$$

The time-recurrent state transition equation $s_\tau = f(s_{\tau-1}, u_\tau)$ describes the current state s_τ by means of a function of the previous state s_τ and of the external influences u_τ. The system formulated in the state transition equation can therefore be interpreted as a partially autonomous and partially externally driven dynamic. We call this an *open dynamical system.*

The output equation, also called observer equation $y_\tau = g(s_\tau)$, uses the non-observable system state s_τ in every time step τ to calculate the output of the dynamical system y_τ. The data-driven system identification is based on the selected parameterized functions $f()$ and $g()$. We choose the parameters in $f()$ and $g()$ such that the quadratic error function [see Equation (2)] is minimized.

$$\frac{1}{T}\sum_{\tau=1}^{T}\left(y_\tau - y_\tau^d\right)^2 \rightarrow \min_{f,g}. \tag{2}$$

The two functions $f()$ and $g()$ are thus estimated such that the average distance between the observed data y_τ^d and the system outputs y_τ across a number of observations $\tau = 1, \ldots, T$ is minimal.

So far, we have given a general description of the state transition and the output equation for open dynamical systems. Without loss of generality, we can specify the functions $f()$ and $g()$ by means of a Recurrent Neural Network (RNN) (Schäfer and Zimmermann, 2006; Zimmermann *et al.*, 2002), as:

$$\begin{aligned} \text{state transition} \quad s_\tau &= \tanh(As_{\tau-1} + Bu_\tau), \\ \text{output equation} \quad y_\tau &= Cs_\tau. \end{aligned} \tag{3}$$

Equation (3) specifies an RNN with weight matrices A, B, and C. It is designed as a nonlinear state-space model, which is able to approximate any continuos functions $f()$ and $g()$ on a compact domain (Hornik *et al.*, 1989), over a finite time horizon. We choose the hyperbolic tangent tanh as the transfer function for the state transitions $s_{\tau-1} \rightarrow s_\tau$. The output equation is specified as a linear function. The RNN output is generated by a superposition of two components: (i) the autonomous dynamics (coded in matrix A), which accumulates information in the state vectors over time (memory), and (ii) the influence of external factors (coded in matrix B).

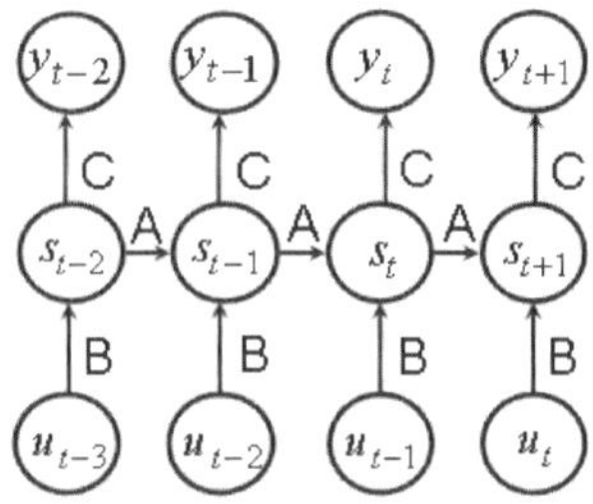

Figure 10.2: Basic RNN unfolded in time with shared weights A, B, and C.

Without loss of generality, we can assume a linear output equation in Equation (3). Any nonlinearity in the output equation could be merged with the state transition equation. For details see Schäfer and Zimmermann (2006).

The temporal system identification implies that we have to determine appropriate matrices A, B, and C, which minimize the error function Equation (2). We apply the technique of finite unfolding in time (Rumelhart *et al.*, 1986) to solve this task. The underlying idea of finite unfolding is that any RNN can be rewritten as an equivalent iterated Feedforward Neural Network, as long as the matrices A, B, and C are identical over all time steps (shared weights). Figure 10.2 depicts the resulting RNN in a simplified representation, where the transfer functions are located inside the nodes of a graph with the connections encapsulating the weight matrices.

One advantage of shared matrices is the moderate number of free parameters (weights), which reduces the risk of overfitting (Zimmermann and Neuneier, 2000). The actual training is conducted using error backpropagation through time (EBTT) together with a stochastic learning rule (Rumelhart *et al.*, 1986; Werbos, 1974). For algorithmic solutions, the reader is referred to the overview article by B. Pearlmatter (Pearlmatter, 2001).

10.2.2. *Overshooting*

The basic idea of the previous section defines a frame for all our modeling tasks. We can now add further architectural elements to the neural networks to code prior information in the network topology. This helps to control the training process and constrains the basic gradient descent of the backpropagation training algorithm to favor solutions which match the additional side conditions. Constraints can either be introduced from observations of past training attempts or from knowledge about the structure of the modeled dynamical system.

Predicting load curves (e.g., for electricity), a stable forecast often has to be generated over multiple time steps into the future. A problem often observed during training of RNNs for this application is that RNNs tend to focus on only the most recent external influences in order to explain the system dynamics. This has the

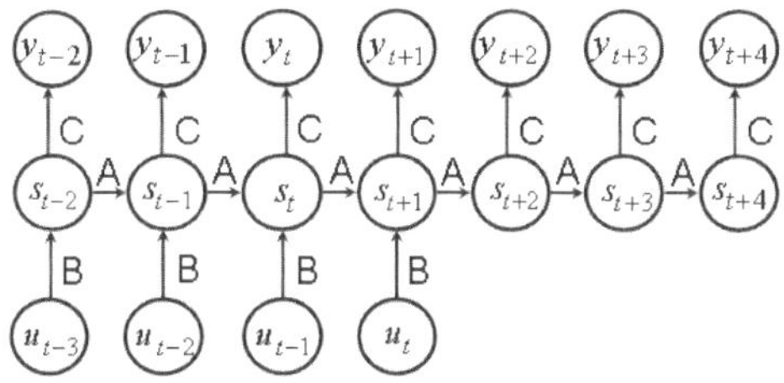

Figure 10.3: RNN incorporating overshooting.

consequence that forecasts can be only generated for a small number of steps before the model becomes unstable. To balance the information flow and extend the stable forecast range, we use a technique called overshooting. Overshooting extends the autonomous part of the system dynamics (coded in matrix A) into the future (here $\tau+2$, $\tau+3$, $\tau+4$) (Zimmermann and Neuneier, 2000) (see Figure 10.3). With the iterated application of the shared weight matrix A we can compute consistent multi-step forecasts. A corresponding RNN architecture is depicted in Figure 10.3.

For the RNN, we typically use an input preprocessing $u_\tau = x_\tau - x_{\tau-1}$ as the transformation for the raw data x. This avoids trends in the input or target variables of the RNN. The missing external inputs $u_{\tau>0}$ in the forecast part of the network can be interpreted as an assumption of a constant environment ($u_{\tau>0} \approx 0$). The effectiveness of overshooting depends on the strength of the autonomous dynamics. The stronger the autonomous flow is, the better the forecast accuracy for the overshooting time steps will be. A network with more time steps in the overshooting part will put higher emphasis on learning the autonomous part of the dynamic. It will accumulate a larger number of error gradients for the adaption of the state transition matrix A from the forecast part of the network during training. In this way the number of forecast steps implicitly determines the emphasis, which the training algorithm puts on the autonomous component of the system dynamic.

Summarizing, we can state that overshooting generates additional valuable forecast information about the identified dynamical systems and acts as a regularization method for the training.

10.3. Error Correction

Another problem, often encountered in demand forecast applications, is the incomplete observability of the market and a high noise level of the observed data. Under these conditions, system identification often fails and produces models that only have learned the input data by heart (overfitting) and do not show the desirable generalization capabilities.

To recapitulate the basic form of a dynamical system, we can use Equation (4) to identify the temporal relationships between states of a deterministic dynamical system by setting up a memory in form of the states in a state transition equation, as long as we have a complete description of all external forces influencing the system.

$$\begin{aligned} s_\tau &= f(s_{\tau-1}, u_\tau), \\ y_\tau &= g(s_\tau). \end{aligned} \tag{4}$$

If we are unable to identify the underlying system dynamics due to insufficient input information or unobserved influences, we can interpret the observed model error at a preceding time step as an indicator that our model will be misleading at a later point in time. Using this error as an additional input for the state transition, we extend Equation (4) to obtain Equation (5)

$$\begin{aligned} s_\tau &= f\left(s_{\tau-1}, u_\tau, y_{\tau-1} - y_{\tau-1}^d\right), \\ y_\tau &= g(s_\tau). \end{aligned} \tag{5}$$

Once a perfect description of the underlying dynamics has been learned, the extension of Equation (5) is no longer required, because the observed model error at $t-1$ approaches *zero*. Hence, modeling the dynamical system, one could directly refer to Equation (4). In all other situations, the model uses its own error flow as an indicator for unexpected shocks. This is similar to the MA part of a linear ARIMA model [*ARIMA* stands for *A*utoregressive *I*ntegrated *M*oving *A*verage model, which utilizes both linear autoregressive components and stochastically moving average-components derived from the observed model error to fit a time series, see (Wei, 1990)]. Since we are working with state space models, we do not need delayed error corrections.

Another resemblance bears to Kalman Filters, where the model error is used to improve the system identification. In contrast to the online adaptation in the Kalman approach, we try to identify a fixed nonlinear system which is able to handle external shocks. By using such a system, we cannot avoid an error when the external shock appears. Instead, our task is to adapt fast to the new situation. Such a strategy significantly decreases the rote learning of false causalities and will improve the generalization ability of our model.

10.3.1. *Error Correction Neural Networks*

A first neural network implementation of the error correction equations in Equation (5) can be written as:

$$\begin{aligned} s_\tau &= \tanh\left(As_{\tau-1} + Bu_\tau + D\left(Cs_{\tau-1} - y_{\tau-1}^d\right)\right), \\ y_\tau &= Cs_\tau. \end{aligned} \tag{6}$$

The term Cs_{t-1} recomputes the previous output y_{t-1} and compares it with the observed data y^d_{t-1}. The transformation matrix D is necessary to adjust different dimensionalities in the state transition equation. It is important to note that the identification of the above model framework is ambiguous, creating numerical instabilities. The main reason is the autoregressive structure between s_{t-1} and s_t which can either be coded in matrix A or in DC. We can disambiguate Equation (6) into the form in Equation (7) utilizing $\grave{A} = A + DC$.

$$\begin{aligned} s_\tau &= \tanh\left(\grave{A}s_{\tau-1} + Bu_\tau + Dy^d_{\tau-1}\right), \\ y_\tau &= Cs_\tau. \end{aligned} \tag{7}$$

The framework of Equation (7) is algebraically equivalent to Equation (6) and avoids numerical instabilities. Unfortunately, by using Equation (7), the explicit error information provided by external shocks is lost, since it is no longer measured as a deviation from zero. Neural networks that use tanh as the transfer function are, on the other hand, well known to be numerically most stable, when the model variables fluctuate around zero, which fits best to the finite state space $(-1; 1)^n$ spanned by the tanh nonlinearity.

Fortunately, we can rewrite Equations (6) and (7) again as shown in Equation (8) in an error correction form, measuring the difference between the expected value Cs_{t-1} and the observation y^d_{t-1}. The disambiguation is here a consequence of the additional nonlinearity.

$$\begin{aligned} s_\tau &= \tanh\left(As_{\tau-1} + Bu_\tau + D\tanh\left(Cs_{\tau-1} - y^d_{\tau-1}\right)\right), \\ y_\tau &= Cs_\tau. \end{aligned} \tag{8}$$

The system identification, Equation (9), is now a parameter optimization task adjusting the weights of the *four* matrices A, B, C, D.

$$\frac{1}{T} \cdot \sum_{\tau=1}^{T} \left(y_\tau - y^d_\tau\right)^2 \to \min_{A,B,C,D}. \tag{9}$$

10.3.2. *Unfolding in Time for Error Correction Neural Networks*

Next, we translate the formal description of Equation (8) into a network architecture named Error Correction Neural Network (ECNN).

The ECNN architecture (Figure 10.4) is best understood, if one analyzes the dependency between the elements in one unfolding segment of the network with $s_{t-1}, u_t, z_{t-1} = Cs_{t-1} - y^d_{t-1}$ and s_t.

We can identify two types of inputs to the model: The external inputs u_t directly influence the state transition $s_{t-1} \to s_t$. The second input type are the targets y^d_{t-1}, where only the difference between the internally expected output y_{t-1} and

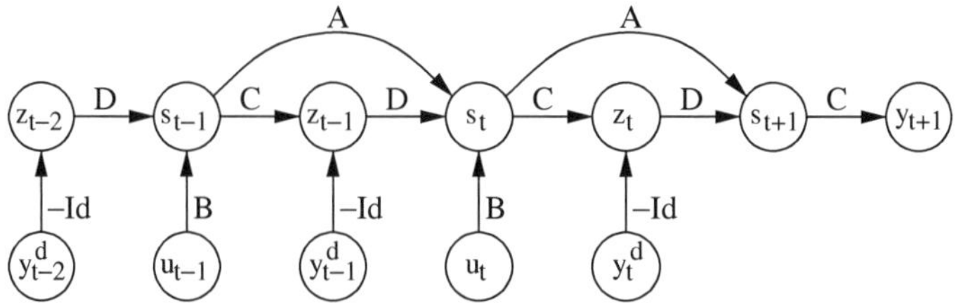

Figure 10.4: Error correction neural network.

the observation y^d_{t-1} has an impact on the state calculation for s_t. Note that $-Id$ is the negative of an identity matrix which is kept constant during the network training.

This design allows an elegant handling of missing values in the series of target vectors: If there is no compensation of the internal expected value $y_{t-1} = Cs_{t-1}$, the system automatically generates a replacement. A special case occurs at the time $t+1$. At this point in time, we have no compensation of the internal expected value and thus the system computes a forecast.

The outputs of the ECNN, which generate error information during the learning phase, are the $z_{t-\tau}$. Note that the target values for the outputs $z_{t-\tau}$ are *zero*, because we want to optimize the compensation mechanism between the expected values $y_{t-\tau}$ and their observations $y^d_{t-\tau}$.

The ECNN avoids another problem of the basic RNN networks (see Figure 10.2 in Section 10.2.1): In the *finite* unfolding of a RNN, no information about a valid initial state vector s_0 is available at the beginning of the training. Usually, an initial state of zero is used to initialize the state sequence. Only later in the training, a consistent initial state value can be learned. From the initial state, the network can only gradually adapt to a valid initial state vector. This burdens the system identification process, because the network not only has to identify the dynamical system but also needs to adapt, to correct the assumed initial state vector. The ECNN on the other hand uses the error correction mechanism to compensate for the initial state misrepresentation already in the first state transition. This can stabilize and speed up the training process significantly.

10.3.3. *Combining Overshooting & ECNN*

A combination of the basic ECNN presented in Section 10.3.1 and the overshooting technique of Section 10.2.2 is shown in Figure 10.5.

In addition to the advantages of overshooting described in Section 10.2.2, it has a further effect on the learning of the ECNN. A forecast provided by the ECNN is in general based on the modeling of the recursive structure of a dynamical system (coded in the matrix A) and the error correction mechanism, which acts

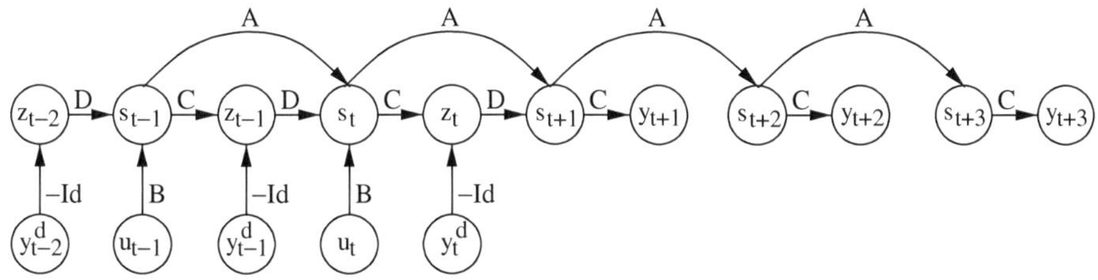

Figure 10.5: Combining overshooting and error correction neural networks.

as external input (coded in C and D). Overshooting puts emphasis on the training of the autoregressive substructure in the forecast part of the network, stabilizing it for long term forecasts. Of course, we have to supply the additional target values $y_{t+1}, y_{t+2}, y_{t+3}, \ldots,$ for the overshooting part of the network. Nevertheless does the number of parameters (weights) of the network not increase, compared to the standard ECNN in Figure 10.4. Overshooting only adds network structure which moderates the training process to favor solutions with desirable qualities (here the stability of long term forecasts).

10.3.4. *Variant–Invariant Separation*

One characteristic of load forecast applications is the high number of input variables. In this section we will show, how a technique called variant–invariant separation can be used to reduce the complexity of the modeling task. The basic idea is that of a coordinate transformation. We will introduce the technique using the example of a pendulum like the one shown in Figure 10.6.

One naïve way to describe the pendulum dynamic could state the coordinates of all the points along the pendulum axis (an infinite number of values) and their temporal shifts. Of course, nobody would describe a pendulum in this way. Instead, the description can be simplified, if we separate it into one variant (the angle φ, which changes over time) and the invariants (all points of the pendulum always lie on its axis).

We learn from this exercise that an appropriate coordinate transformation can lead to tremendous simplifications in the modeling of dynamics if we separate variants and invariants. Our goal is to describe a dynamical system with a minimum number of variants.

A typical example for this technique is the forecasting of yield curves in economy, where we can compress ten or more maturities of interest rates to a small number of variants (for the German economy, the standard yield curves can be reduced to only three variants). From the forecasts of only these variants we can predict the complete yield curve. Another example is tactical portfolio management.

Instead of forecasting every individual stock, we can compress the task by e.g., only predicting market sectors.

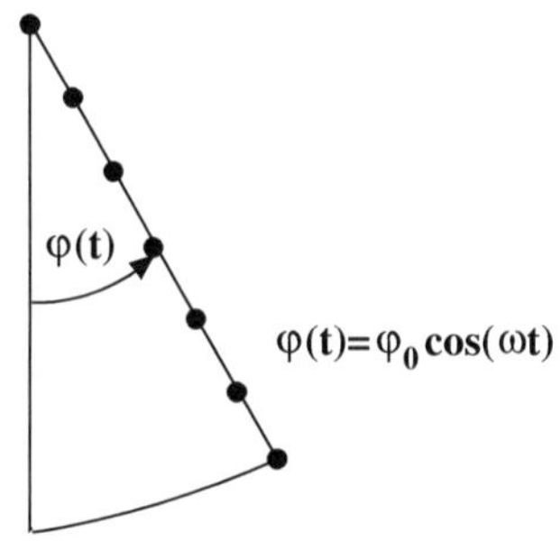

Figure 10.6: The dynamic of a pendulum can be separated in only one variant, the angle φ, and an infinite number of invariants.

10.3.5. *Variant–Invariant Separation with Neural Networks*

The translation of the variant–invariant separation to a neural network architecture is shown in Figure 10.7.

In this network, the internal state variables s_t, s_{t+1} play the role of the variants, which develop over time with the help of the forecast transition function $f()$. The variants are separated from the invariants by the compressor function $g()$. The decompressor function $h()$ combines the forecast of the variants with the invariants to reconstruct the complete dynamic.

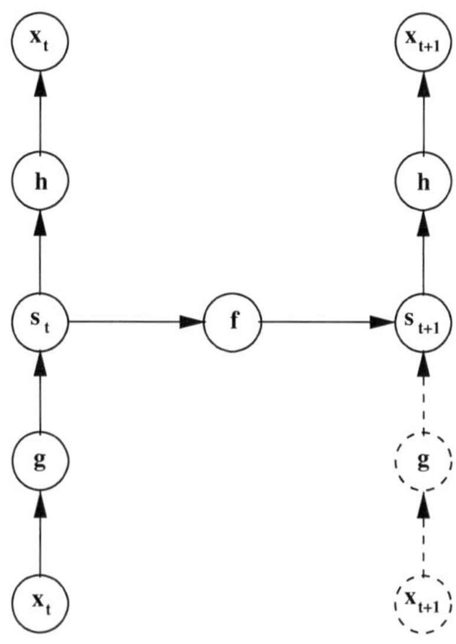

Figure 10.7: Variant–invariant separation by neural networks.

Although the general description of the variant–invariant separation can easily be stated without referring to neural networks at all, the realization is a typical neural network approach in the way that it uses concatenations of functional systems. Training the subsystems of compression/decompression and forecast is then adequately implemented using the EBTT algorithm.

10.3.6. *Combining Variant–Invariant Separation with ECNN*

In this section, we merge the concept of dimension reduction with the ECNN architecture. One might expect that merging both architectures leads to a very large interconnected structure. In Figure 10.8, we show a different approach. The compressor-decompressor network (also called *bottleneck network*) on the left-hand side is only seemingly disconnected from the ECNN network on the right-hand side. The weight matrices E and F are shared between both networks, combining the compression/decompression functionality of the bottleneck network with the forecast functionality of the ECNN. Training both networks together combines the search for an optimal coordinate transformation with the system identification.

In addition to the ECNN presented in Section 10.3.3, we introduced two new matrices E and F which parameterize compression and decompression respectively. The ECNN calculates the state transitions of the dynamical system on a state vector which has been compressed to the minimal dimension of vector x_t instead of the high dimensional vector y_t. It is important to note that the ECNN requires $-y_t^d$ as inputs in order to generate $-x_t^d$ in the z_t layer. In this way, the internal forecasts $x_t = Cs_{t-1}$ can be compensated by the transformed target data $-x_t^d = F(-y_t^d)$.

Applying this architeture to a number of real world modeling tasks, we found that the training of the combined neural network (Figure 10.8) is very robust, i.e., the coordinate transformation and the forecast can be trained simultaneously. For models with very high dimensionality it is also feasible, to first train the bottleneck network, then freeze the compressor and decompressor weights, train the ECNN and finally train both components together for a final optimization. Furthermore, node pruning algorithms are applicable to the x_t layer to support the dimension reduction.

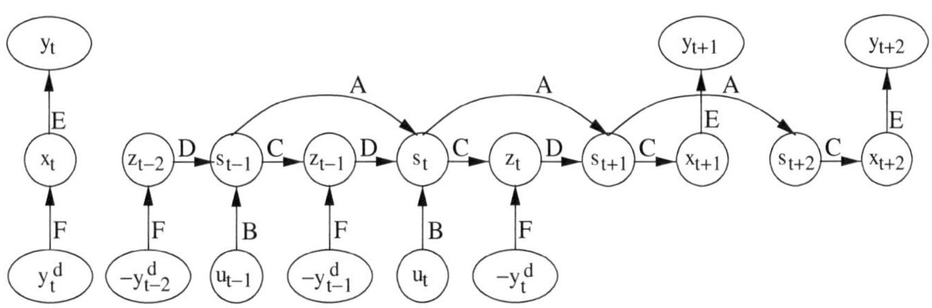

Figure 10.8: Combining variant–invariant separation and forecasting.

10.4. High Dimensional Dynamical Systems

10.4.1. *Historically Consistent Neural Networks (HCNN)*

Many real-world technical and economic applications can be seen in the context of large systems in which various (nonlinear) dynamics interact over time. Unfortunately, only a small subset of variables can be observed. From the subset of observed variables and their dynamics we have to reconstruct the hidden variables of the large system in order to understand the overall system dynamics. Here the term *observables* includes the input and output variables of conventional modeling approaches (i.e., $y_\tau := (y_\tau, u_\tau)$).

With the concept of observables, we can identify a consistency problem in the overshooting extensions of the RNN (Figure 10.3) and ECNN (Figure 10.5) architectures. On the output side, these networks provide forecasts for the observables y_τ, whereas they assume on the input side that the same observables y_τ can be kept constant and their influence on the (autonomous) dynamic can be neglected. This contradiction can be remedied, if we give up the distinction between input and output variables for a network but only regard observables. They describe the external state of the dynamical system for which we can compare measured observables with our forecast for the same observables. In this way, we can close the dynamical system.

The consequence of this concept is an architecture which we call HCNN. This model class follows our design principles for the modeling of large dynamical systems and overcomes the conceptual weakness described above. Equation (10) formulates the HCNN.

$$\begin{aligned} &\text{state transition} && s_\tau = A\tanh(s_{\tau-1}), \\ &\text{output equation} && y_\tau = [Id, 0]s_\tau. \end{aligned} \tag{10}$$

The joint dynamic for all observables is characterized in the HCNN by the sequence of states s_τ. For convenience, the observables ($i = 1, \ldots, N$) are arranged on the first elements of the state vector s_τ, followed by the non-observable (hidden) variables. The matrix $[Id, 0]$ is constant and extracts the observables from the state vector. The initial state s_0 is described as a bias vector. The bias s_0 and the matrix A are the only free parameters of the HCNN.

Like standard RNNs (Figure 10.2), HCNNs are also universal approximators. The proof for the RNN can be found in Schäfer and Zimmermann (2006). Figure 10.9 outlines the proof for HCNNs. It can be divided into six steps:

1. The output equation is shifted one-time step into the future and the resulting $s_{\tau+1}$ is substituted by the state transition equation.
2. By combining outputs and state variables into an extended state we derive an extended state transition equation. The output of the system is derived from the first components of the extended internal state.

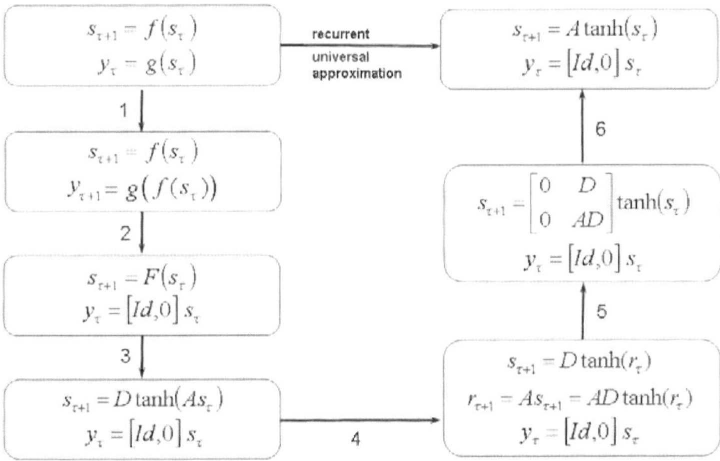

Figure 10.9: Proof of the universal approximation capabilities for HCNNs.

3. For the extended state transition equation, we apply the feedforward universal approximation theorem. At least for a finite time horizon this guarantees a small approximation error. Note that in RNNs at least one large component of the state vector together with the tanh transfer function can mimic a bias vector. Thus, we have omitted the explicit notation of a bias vector in the equations.
4. In this step, we remove one of the two matrices within the state transition equation. We apply a state transformation $r_\tau = As_\tau$. This results in two state transition equations.
5. The two-state transition equations can be reorganized into one-state transition, which combines the linear parts of the equations in one matrix.
6. Rewriting this matrix results in the claimed formulation for closed systems.

In contrast to the RNN and ECNN formulations in Equations (3) and (8), we shift in Equation (10) the application of matrix A in front of the tanh transfer function. This has the advantage that the system states — and thus also the system outputs — are not limited to the finite state space $(-1; 1)^n$, which is usually created by the tanh nonlinearity. The output equation has a simple and application independent form. Note that only the leading elements of the state vector are observable.

Figure 10.10 depicts the HCNN architecture. In this network architecture, the HCNN states s_τ are realized as hidden layers with identity transfer functions. The intermediate states r_τ use the usual tanh squashing. The forecasts are supplied by the output layers y_τ. There are no target values available for the future time steps. The forecast values $y_{\tau>t}$ can be read out at the corresponding future time steps of the network.

Since the HCNN model has no inputs, we have to unfold the neural network along the complete data history. This is different from small recurrent neural

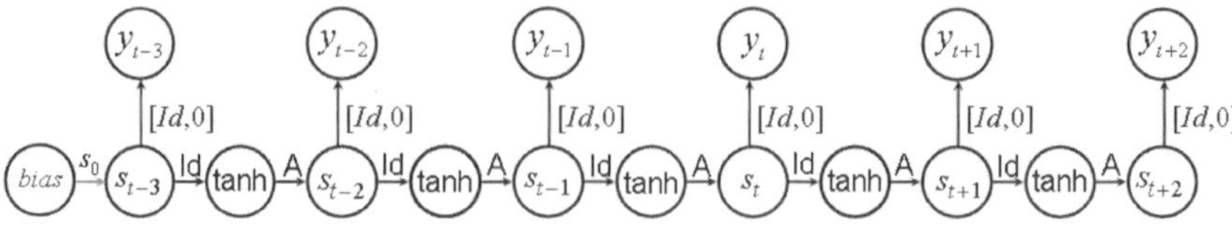

Figure 10.10: HCNN.

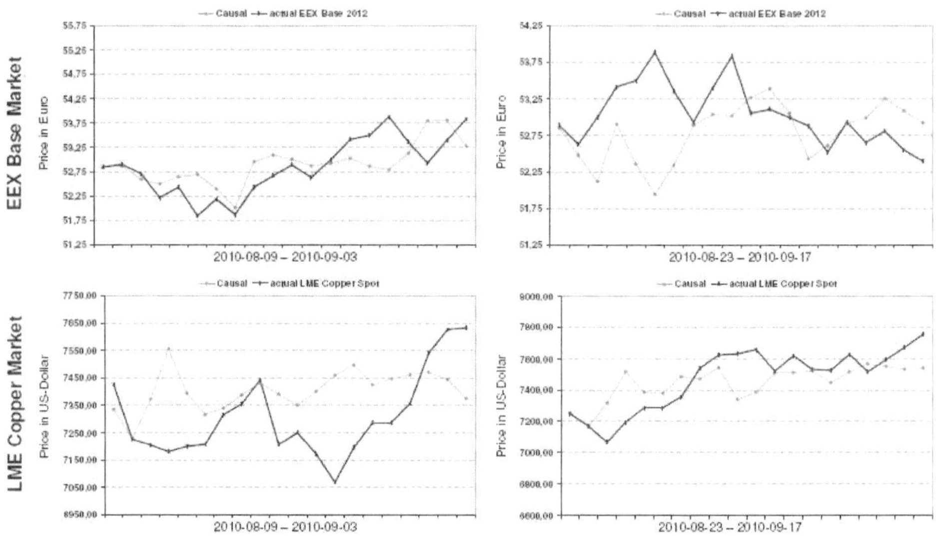

Figure 10.11: Forecasting EEX and LME future contracts over 20 days with HCNNs.

networks (see e.g., Figure 10.3), where we construct training data patterns in form of sliding windows. The HCNN learns the large dynamic from a single history of observations (i.e., a single training data pattern). For our commodity price forecasts, we unfold the HCNN over 440 trading days in the past to predict the next 20 days.

We applied the HCNN to forecast the market price development over the next 20 trading days of electricity and copper future contracts traded on the European Energy Exchange (EEX) and the London Metal Exchange (LME) respectively. Figure 10.11 compares the HCNN forecasts with the actual future prices for two forecast horizons. The HCNN model produces good forecasts for the first forecast horizon of the EEX market and the second horizon of the LME market. It fails in the other cases. We will analyze these failures in depth in Section 10.4.4.

10.4.2. *Architectural Teacher Forcing (ATF) for HCNNs*

In practice, we observe that HCNNs are difficult to train since the models do not use any input signals and are unfolded across the complete dataset. ATF makes the best possible use of the data from the observables and accelerates the training of the HCNN (Pearlmatter, 2001; Williams and Zipser, 1989; Zimmermann *et al.*, 2012).

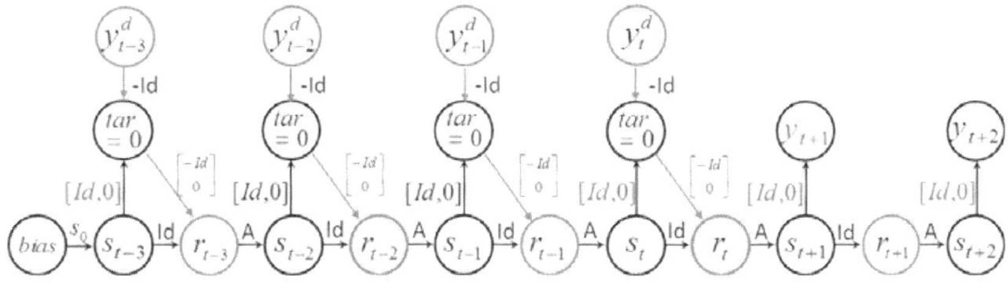

Figure 10.12: HCNN with ATF.

It was originally introduced as an extension to the algorithmic training procedures of RNNs. Here we integrate the idea into the network architecture, so we can continue to use the unmodified EBTT training algorithm (Haykin, 1994). The HCNN with integrated teacher forcing is shown in Figure 10.12.

In this network, the calculated values for all observables up to time $\tau = t$ are replaced with the actual observations in the next unfolding step. For this, we adapt the network architecture: As a first change, the output layers of the HCNN are given fixed zero target values. The negative observed values $-y_\tau^d$ for the observables are then added to the output, forcing the HCNN to produce the expected values y_τ to compensate.

As we constructed the HCNN in its plain form, the intermediate state vectors r_τ receive a copy of the state vectors s_τ which contain in their first elements the network output for the observables. If we now feed back the difference between the network outputs and the expected values to the intermediate state vectors, we can correct the calculated values to the observed values as shown in Figure 10.12, providing the next unfolding step with the correct values

$$y_\tau^d = y_\tau - \left(y_\tau - y_\tau^d\right). \tag{11}$$

For later reference let us call Equation (11), the teacher forcing identity. All connection matrices of the teacher forcing mechanism are kept constant. Only the transition matrix A is adapted to transform the corrected intermediate state to the state of the next unfolding step.

By definition, we cannot provide observables for the future time steps. Here, the system is iterated exclusively on the expected values. This turns an open dynamical system into a closed one. The HCNN architecture in Figure 10.12 is equivalent to the architecture in Figure10.10, if it has converged to zero error in the training. In this case we have found a solution for the original problem.

10.4.3. *Sparsity, Dimensionality versus Connectivity and Memory*

HCNNs may have to model many observables in parallel over time depending on the modeled system. The result is high dimensional dynamical systems (e.g., in our commodity price models we use $\dim(s) = 300$) which are unfolded over many time steps. Backpropagation training with a fully connected state transition matrix A of such dimensions is numerically instable: In the forward pass the nonlinear squashing function of the network reliably prevents the uncontrolled growth of propagated values. Nevertheless in the backward pass, the derivative of the sqashing function may fail to prevent the uncontrolled growth of the propagated error values leading to instable training. One way to avoid this problem is to use a sparse matrix A.

We have to answer the question, which dimensionality and which sparsity to choose. In Zimmermann *et al.* (2006), we showed that dimensionality and sparsity are related to another pair of meta-parameters: connectivity (con) and memory length (mem). Connectivity is defined as the number of nonzero elements in each row of matrix A. The memory length is the number of unfolding steps building the memory window from which we have to collect information in order to reach a Markovian state, i.e., the state vector could accumulate all required information from the past. We propose the following parameterization for the state dimension $\dim(s)$ and sparsity (Zimmermann *et al.*, 2006):

$$\text{Dimension of } A\text{: } \dim(s) = \text{con} \cdot \text{mem}, \tag{12}$$

$$\text{Sparsity of } A\text{: sparsity} = \text{rnd}\left(\frac{\text{con}}{\text{mem} \cdot \text{con}}\right) = \text{rnd}\left(\frac{1}{\text{mem}}\right). \tag{13}$$

Equation (13) represents the insight that a sparse system conserves information over more time steps before the information diffuses in the network. As an artificial example, compare a shift register with a fully connected matrix. The shift register requires only one connection from one time step to the next and acts as memory whereas a fully connected matrix masks the information passed from one time step to the next with the superposition of information.

Let us assume that we have initialized the state transition matrix as a sparse matrix A with uniform random sparsity. Following Equation (13), the denser parts of A can model faster sub-dynamics within the overall dynamic, while the highly sparse parts of A can focus on slow subsystems which require more memory. The sparse random initialization allows the combined modeling of systems on different time scales.

Unfortunately, Equation (12) favors very large dimensions. Our earlier work [see (Zimmermann *et al.*, 2006)] started with the setting of the system memory length mem, because for RNNs the memory length is equal to the number of the past unfolding steps. On the other hand, connectivity has to be chosen higher than the number of the observables. Working with HCNNs, the memory length becomes less important because we unfold the neural network along the complete data horizon. Here, the connectivity plays the major role. Empirical tests provided the rule of thumb that the EBTT algorithm remains stable with a connectivity less than or equal to 50 (con $\leq$ 50). To balance the computational performance, we usually limit the state dimensionality to $\dim(s) = 300$. This implies a sparsity of $50/300 \approx 17\%$. We leave the fine tuning of the parameters to the EBTT learning algorithm.

Matrix A is initialized with a randomly chosen sparsity grid. It is not optimized by e.g., pruning algorithms. We counter possible initialization biases towards inferior learned models with ensemble forecasts which average individual solutions learned with different random initializations.

We conducted ensemble experiments with different sparsity grids versus ensembles based on a constant sparsity grid. We found that the average of the ensemble as well as the ensemble spread are unaffected by the initialization of the sparsity grid (for more details on ensemble forecasting, see Section 10.5). It should be noted that these considerations hold only for large systems.

10.4.4. *Retro-Causal Historical Consistent Neural Networks*

A market dynamic can often be explained by a causal analysis of the dynamical system, i.e., we explain the system behavior at present time exclusively with a superposition of the historical development. Unfortunately, a causal model might lack in performance when the dynamic of interest results from rational decision-making and planning, where the anticipation of the future together with a superordinated goal (e.g., profit or utility maximization) plays an important role. Rational planning implies an information flow from an expected future state of the system backwards in order to make an optimal decision at present time given a specific target resp. reward function. Therefore, we have to formulate a model in which the information flows from the future backwards to the past. Inspired by the standard (causal) HCNN (see Figure 10.10), we define a RCNN by

$$\text{state transition } s_\tau = \tanh(A' s_{\tau+1}), \tag{14}$$

$$\text{output equation } y_\tau = [Id, 0] s_\tau, \tag{15}$$

where the internal state s_τ depends on the future state $s_{\tau+1}$ and the observables y_τ are derived from the internal state s_τ. In a causal HCNN the dynamic evolves in time from an initial state s_0 as a cause and effect model coded in the state transition equation. In a retro-causal HCNN, the dynamic is described by a final future state s_T together with a retro-causal state transition equation for effect and cause modeling. The retro-causal state transition is coded in matrix A'. Opposite to causal HCNNs, retro-causal HCNNs use error information up to the end of the future unfolding and forecasting is based on the estimation of the final state s_T.

Given the equations of the retro-causal HCNN [Equation (10)], we sketch the architecture of the RCNN in Figure 10.13. Likewise to the causal HCNN, the RCNN is trained using the EBTT algorithm and the architectural realization of teacher forcing (Haykin, 1994; Pearlmatter, 2001; Williams and Zipser, 1989).

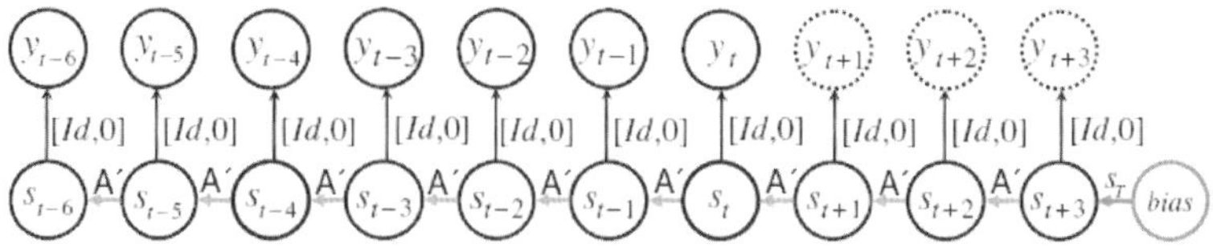

Figure 10.13: Architecture of the RCNN.

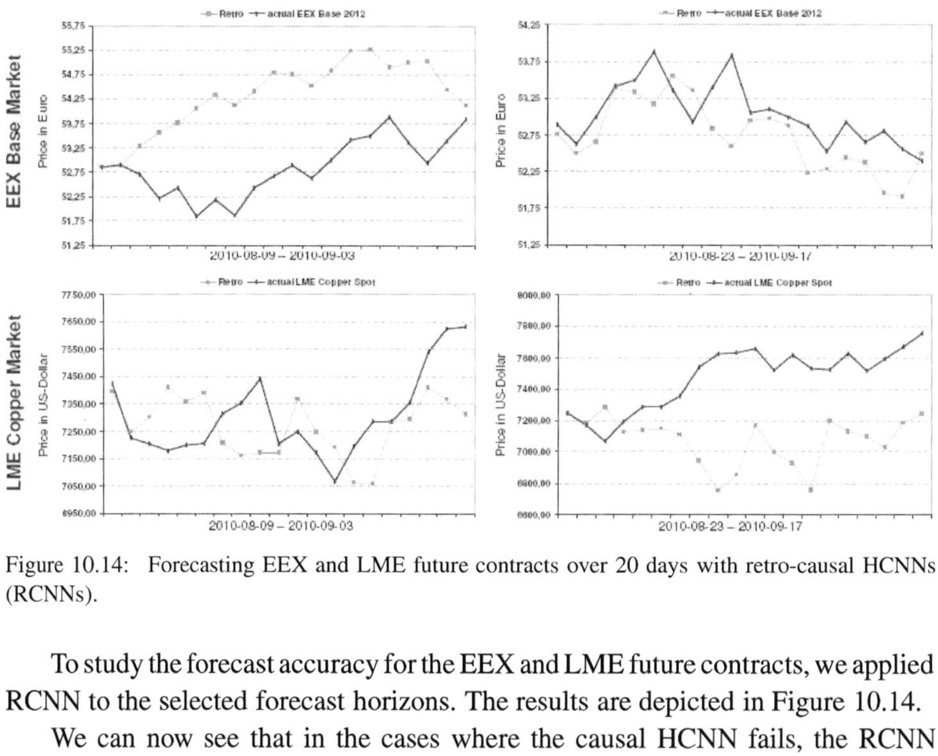

Figure 10.14: Forecasting EEX and LME future contracts over 20 days with retro-causal HCNNs (RCNNs).

To study the forecast accuracy for the EEX and LME future contracts, we applied RCNN to the selected forecast horizons. The results are depicted in Figure 10.14.

We can now see that in the cases where the causal HCNN fails, the RCNN is able to provide an accurate forecast of the market dynamic (see Figures 10.11 and 10.14). However, we do not know *ex ante* whether the market is under a causal or retro-causal regime. Next we want to combine both modeling approaches in an integrated model to handle both market regimes properly.

10.4.5. *Causal-Retro-Causal Historical Consistent Neural Networks (CRCNN)*

CRCNN combine a causal and a retro-causal information flow in an integrated neural model given by

$$\text{state transition } s_\tau = \tanh\left(\left[As_{\tau-1}, A's'_{\tau+1}\right]\right), \tag{16}$$

$$\text{output equation } y_\tau = [Id, 0]s_\tau + [Id, 0]s'_\tau. \tag{17}$$

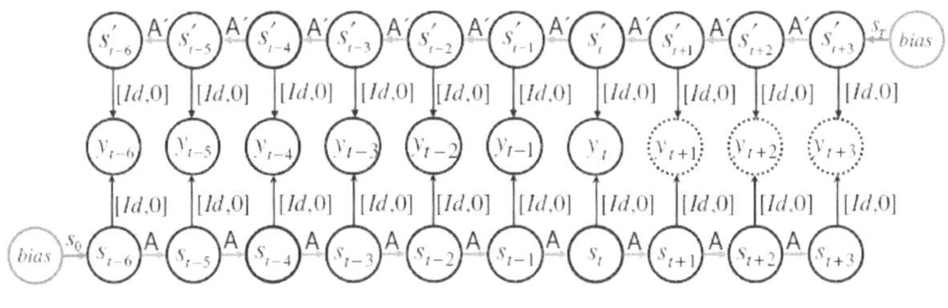

Figure 10.15: Architecture of the CRCNN.

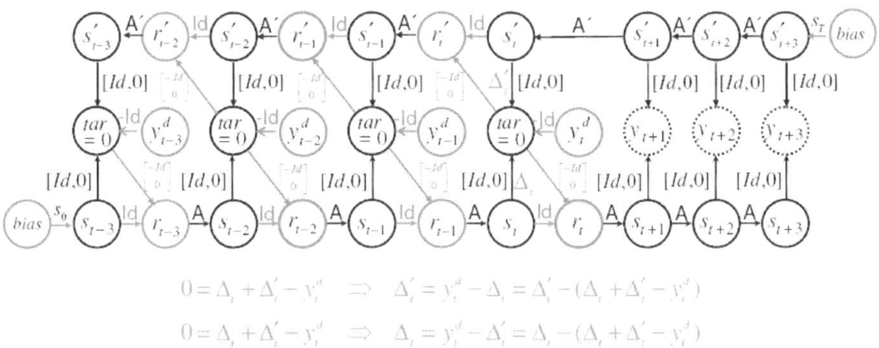

Figure 10.16: Extended CRCNN incorporating a Teacher Forcing (TF) mechanism.

The state transition equation s_τ of the CRCNN, Equation (16) is the sum of causal and retro-causal influences. The dynamic of all observables is explained by a sequence of causal states s_τ using the transition matrix A to explain the causal information flow and of retro-causal states s'_τ using the transition matrice A' for the retro-causal information flow. The output equation [Equation (16)], computes the observables y_τ by adding the causal and retro-causal information. Based on Equations (16) and (17), we can formulate the unfolded network architecture for the CRCNN shown in Figure 10.15.

Like for the basic HCNN, the CRCNN is unfolded over the entire time interval of available data, i.e., we learn the unique complete history of the system. As we did for the basic HCNN in Section 10.4.2, we also add architectural teacher forcing as shown in Figure 10.16.

The fundamental idea of the CRCNN architecture is that for the causal and the retro-causal part of the network, the error of one part is compensated by the opposite part. This has consequences for the teacher forcing mechanism, as the state correction for one part of the network should only correct the portion of the difference between calculated and observed values which is not explained by the opposite part of the network. If we denote the output contributions of the two network parts with $[Id, 0]s_\tau = \delta_\tau$ and $[Id, 0]s'_\tau = \delta'_\tau$, we can rewrite the teacher forcing identity from

Equation (11) for the CRCNN is

$$\delta_\tau^d = \delta_\tau - \left(\delta_\tau + \delta'_\tau - y_\tau^d\right), \tag{18}$$

$$\delta_\tau'^d = \delta'_\tau - \left(\delta_\tau + \delta'_\tau - y_\tau^d\right). \tag{19}$$

It is important to note that over the training of the network, the ratio of δ_τ to δ'_τ will adapt to the market regime, so in contrast to the simple case of the HCNN, the teacher forcing of the CRCNN cannot produce the definite correction values but it still provides best estimates of the correction based on the current contribution of the network parts.

The CRCNN (as well as the HCNN and the RCNN) models the dynamics of all observables and hidden variables in parallel. Thus, high-dimensional state transition matrices A and A' are required. For numerical stability, we again recommend to initialize these matrices with a (random) sparse connectivity. The degree of sparsity is chosen with respect to the metaparameters connectivity and memory length [see Equation (13) in Section 10.4.3].

Our CRCNN architecture relies on the assumption that the network can learn the balance between the causal and the retro-causal parts of the network from the presented data. This has the consequence that for all possible extensions of our CRCNN architecture, extreme care has to be applied, not to introduce asymmetries in the network architecture. Any asymmetry in the network would favor one of the network parts and introduce a serious modeling bias. Even in a perfect symmetric architecture, the modeling of the market regime may fail if the wrong part of the network arrives faster at a local minimum than the part which later could model the market regime better. Training is not guaranteed to provide the best possible model. Our solution for this problem is to train multiple models with random initializations and view the complete trained model ensemble as the modeling result. We will elaborate on this idea in the following section.

Figure 10.17 depicts the impact of our modeling efforts to predict the EEX and LME future contracts for the selected time periods.

The combination of the causal and retro-causal information flow within an integrated CRCNN is able to provide an accurate prediction for all future contracts under consideration. The trained CRCNN is able to detect beforehand if the market is governed by a causal or retro-causal regime as well as a mixture thereof, since the causal and retro-causal information flows are dynamically combined during the training of the CRCNN.

10.5. Uncertainty and Risk

The experience gained during the latest financial crisis has triggered a far-reaching discussion on the limitations of quantitative forecasting models and made investors

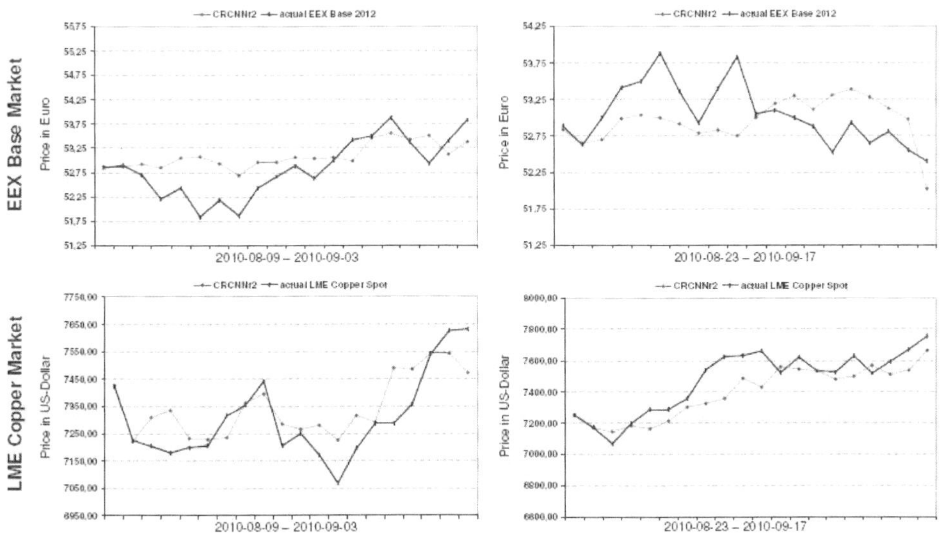

Figure 10.17: Forecasting EEX and LME future contracts over 20 days with CRCNN.

very conscious of risk (Föllmer, 2009). In order to understand risk distributions, traditional risk management uses diffusion models. Risk is understood as a random walk, in which the diffusion process is calibrated by the observed past error of the underlying model (McNeil *et al.*, 2005). In contrast, this section focuses on ensemble forecasts in order to provide important insights into complex risk relationships. These insights stem from the reconstruction of internal (unobserved) model variables which complement the observable description of the modeled system.

If the system identification is calculated repeatedly for HCNNs or CRCNNs with varying start conditions, an ensemble of solutions will be produced, which all have been trained to a forecast error of zero on the training data, but produce different predictions for the future. Since every HCNN or CRCNN model can produce a perfect description of the observed data, the complete ensemble is the true solution. A way to simplify the forecast is to take the arithmetical average of the individual ensemble members as the expected value, provided that the ensemble histogram is unimodal in every time step.

In addition to the expected forecast value, we consider the bandwidth of the ensemble, i.e., its distribution. The form of the ensemble is governed by differences in the reconstruction of the hidden system variables from the observables: for every finite number of observations there is an infinite number of explanation models which describe the data perfectly, but differ in their forecasts, since the observations make it possible to reconstruct the hidden variables in different forms during the training. In other words, our risk concept is based on the partial observability of

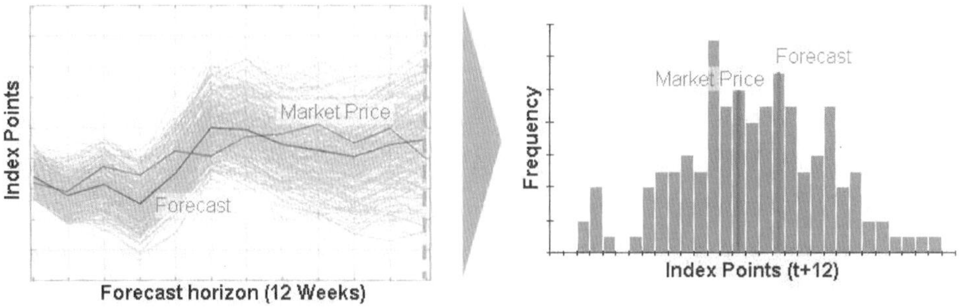

Figure 10.18: HCNN ensemble forecast for the DJX (12 weeks forecast horizon), left, and associated index point distribution for the ensemble in time step $t + 12$, right.

the world, leading to different reconstructions of the hidden variables and thus, different future scenarios. Since all scenarios are perfectly consistent with the history, we do not know which of the scenarios describes the future trend best and risk emerges.

This approach directly addresses the model risk. For HCNN and CRCNN models, we claim that the model risk is equal to the forecast risk. The reasons can be summarized as follows: First, HCNNs are universal approximators which are therefore able to describe every market scenario. Second, the form of the ensemble distribution is caused by an underlying dynamic, which interprets the market dynamics as the result of interacting decisions (Zimmermann, 1994). Third, in experiments we have shown that the ensemble distribution is independent of the model configuration details, if we build large models and large ensembles.

Let us exemplify our risk concept: The diagram (Figure 10.18, left) shows our approach applied to the Dow Jones Industrial Index (DJX). For the ensemble, a HCNN was used to generate 250 individual forecasts for the DJX.

For every forecast date, all individual forecasts of the ensemble members together define the empirical density function, i.e., a probability distribution over many possible market prices at a single point in time [see Figure 10.18, right]. It is noticeable that the actual development of the DJX is found always within the ensemble channel [see gray lines, Figure 10.18, left]. The expected value for the forecast distribution is also an adequate point forecast for the DJX [see Figure 10.18, right]. For further discussion of ensembles and their visual analysis with heat maps, see also Köpp *et al.* (2014).

10.6. Conclusion

At the beginning of this chapter we claimed that the mathematics of neural networks allows unique insights into market analysis. With the modeling techniques presented in the previous sections we are now in the position to review this claim.

First of all we have shown that we can model economy as dynamical systems. The universal approximation property makes our neural networks a strong tool which is not limited by hidden *a priori* structures in the models as, e.g., linear models would be.

Our strongest model building tool is a collection of neural network architectures which lets us add *a priori* information about dynamical systems to our networks without demanding specialized training algorithms for each new problem. Let us review which architectural designs make neural networks well suited for the challenges of the three economic systems we covered:

Business Economics: One application here is demand forecasting. This problem is characterized by a small number of variables modeled as a state space model which has to cope with incomplete knowledge about external variables — the competitors will not reveal their decision process. Our network architecture for this problem is the ECNN (Figure 10.5). Its error correction mechanism handles unknown influences and shocks in the data.

Our second application is load forecasting. Here, a large number of observations is typically available and we use variant–invariant separation in bottleneck networks to reduce the dimensionality of the problem. ECNN networks can then be applied to the low dimensional variant state space (Figure 10.8). The inverse of the dimension reduction transforms the low dimensional forecasts back to the high dimensional external description.

Macro-Economics: To forecast commodity prices, we have to model worldwide dynamical systems. The decisions of a large number of actors superpose, which we model with state transitions in recurrent neural networks. The resulting price is an observable macro-economic variable.

We cannot hope to reduce the dimensionality of this problem and neither is it suitable to introduce external influences in the past which we would have to assume as constant beyond the present. Our HCNN architecture with teacher forcing (Figure 10.12) solves this problem initially for causal market regimes. The governing idea is, to close the modeled dynamical system and regard all input and output variables just as observables which we have to explain in our model.

Unfortunately, many real markets are not only driven by a purely causal information flow. Expectation and motivation driven markets demand an inversed, retro-causal flow. Additionally, markets can change their regime dynamically which calls for combined causal-retro-causal models which we realized in the form of the CRCNN (Figure 10.16). Teacher forcing can be adapted to these models which completes our architectural toolbox.

To choose the right architecture for an economic modeling problem means to understand the basic mechanisms which characterize the modeled market. Each of our architectural variants emphasizes individual market dynamics we have observed and which helped us to gain a deeper understanding of our modeling tasks. Where we found elements missing from our toolbox we designed new architectures and analyzed their behavior.

Finance: The challenge in finance is to balance risc and expected return. For this, a deeper understanding of risk has to be acquired. The standard view on risk begins with the assumption that risk and uncertainty are external elements which behave like a random walk and have to be added to the model and its forecast.

In our approach, uncertainty is a consequence of the non-unique reconstruction of hidden (non-observable) variables in our large dynamical models. With a finite history of data we can train an ensemble of different models which all fit the data and are therefore valid models which differ in the reconstruction of the hidden variables and of course in their forecasts. We claim that uncertainty is not the uncertainty of building the one correct model but the distribution of the forecasts from our model ensembles. We argue that the universal approximation property of our models allows us to catch any complexity of the world on a finite time horizon. We can also show empirically that for large models the distribution of model forecasts is invariant beyond a minimum ensemble size and over many model architectures.

In our projects, we have studied several thousand ensemble distributions so far. Understanding more about their microstructure is an ongoing topic of our research.

References

Casdagli, M., Eubank, S., Farmer, J. D. and Gibson, J. (1991). State space reconstruction in the presence of noise. *Physica D*, 51, pp. 52–98.

Elton, E. J., Gruber, M. J., Brown, St. J. and Goetzmann, W. N. (2007). *Modern Portfolio Theory and Investment Analysis*, Seventh Edition. New York: John Wiley & Sons.

Elman, J. L. (1990). Finding structure in time. *Cognit. Sci.*, 14, pp. 179–211.

Föllmer, H. (2009). Alles richtig und trotzdem falsch?, Anmerkungen zur finanzkrise und finanzmathematik. MDMV 17/2009, pp. 148–154.

Gibson, J. F., Farmer, D. J., Casdagli, M. and Eubank, S. (1992). An analytic approach to practical state space reconstruction. *Physica D*, 57.

Haykin, S. (1994). *Neural Networks. A Comprehensive Foundation*. New York: Macmillan College Publishing.

Haykin, S. (2008). *Neural Networks and Learning Machines, Third Edition*. Upper Saddle River, NJ: Prentice Hall.

Hornik, K., Stinchcombe, M. and White, H. (1989). Multilayer feedforward networks are universal approximators. *Neural Netw.*, 2, pp. 359–366.

Köpp, C., von Mettenheim, H.-J. and Breitner, M. H. (2014). Decision analytics mit heatmap-visualisierung von mehrschrittigen ensembledaten. *Wirtschaftsinformatik*, 56(3), pp. 147–157.

Medsker, L. R. and Jain, L. C. (1999). *Recurrent Neural Networks: Design and Application*. CRC Press Int. Series Comput. Intell., No. I.

McNeil, A., Frey, R. and Embrechts, P. (2005). *Quantitative Risk Management: Concepts, Techniques and Tools*. Princeton, New Jersey: Princeton University Press.

Neuneier, R. and Zimmermann, H. G. (1998). How to train neural networks. In *Neural Networks: Tricks of the Trade*. Berlin: Springer-Verlag, pp. 373–423.

Ott, E., Sauer, T. and Yorke, J. A. (eds.) (1994). *Coping with Chaos*. New York: Wiley.

Packard, N., Crutchfield, N. H., Farmer, J. D. and Shaw. R. S. (1980). Geometry from a time series. *Phys. Rev. Lett.*, 45, pp. 712–716.

Pearlmatter, B. (1995). Gradient calculations for dynamic recurrent neural networks: A survey. In *IEEE Trans. Neural Netw.*, 6(5), pp. 1212–1228.

Pearlmatter, B. (2001). Gradient calculations for dynamic recurrent neural networks. In *A Field Guide to Dynamical Recurrent Networks*. New York, USA: IEEE Press, pp. 179–206.

Rumelhart, D. E., Hinton, G. E. and Williams, R. J. (1986). Learning internal representations by error propagation. In Rumelhart, D. E. and McClelland, J. L. (eds.), *Parallel Distributed Processing: Explorations in the Microstructure of Cognition, Volume I: Foundations*. Cambridge, MA: MIT Press/Bradford Books.

Sauer, T., Yorke, J. A. and Casdagli, M. (1991). Embedology. *J. Stat. Phys.*, 65(3/4), pp. 579–616.

Schäfer, A. M. and Zimmermann, H.-G. (2006). Recurrent neural networks are universal approximators. *ICANN*, 1, pp. 632–640.

Takens, F. (1981). Detecting strange attractors in turbulence. In Rand, D. A. and Young, L. S. (eds.), *Dynamical Systems and Turbulence*, 898, *Lect. Notes Math.* Springer, pp. 366–381.

Wei, W. W. S. (1990). *Time Series Analysis: Univariate and Multivariate Methods*. New York: Addison-Wesley Publishing Company.

Werbos, P. J. (1974). *Beyond Regression: New Tools for Prediction and Analysis in the Behavioral Sciences*. PhD Thesis. Cambridge, MA: Harvard University.

Werbos, P. J. (1994). *The Roots of Backpropagation. From Ordered Derivatives to Neural Networks and Political Forecasting*. NY: Wiley.

Williams, R. J. and Zipser, D. (1989). A learning algorithm for continually running fully recurrent neural networks. *Neural Comput.*, 1(2), pp. 270–280.

Zimmermann, H. G., Grothmann, R. and Neuneier, R. (2002). Modeling of dynamical systems by error correction neural networks. In Soofi, A. and Cao, L. (eds.), *Modeling and Forecasting Financial Data, Techniques of Nonlinear Dynamics*. Dordrecht, Netherlands: Kluwer.

Zimmermann, H. G., Grothmann, R., Schäfer, A. M. and Tietz, Ch. (2006). Modeling large dynamical systems with dynamical consistent neural networks. In Haykin, S., Principe, J. C., Sejnowski, T. J. and McWhirter, J. (eds.), *New Directions in Statistical Signal Processing: From systems to brain*. Cambridge, MA: MIT Press.

Zimmermann, H. G., Grothmann R., Tietz Ch. and v. Jouanne-Diedrich, H. (2011). Market modeling, forecasting and risk analysis with historical consistent neural networks. In Hu, B. (ed.), *Oper. Res. Proc. 2010, Select. Papers Annu. Int. Conf. German OR Soc. (GOR)*. Munich, Sept 2010. Berlin and Heidelberg: Springer.

Zimmermann, H. G., Grothmann, R. and Tietz, C. (2012). Forecasting market prices with causal-retro-causal neural networks. In Klatte, D., Lüthi, H.-J. and Schmedders, K. (eds.), *Oper. Res. Proc. 2011, Select. Papers Int. Conf. Oper. Res. 2011 (OR 2011)*. Zurich, Switzerland: Springer.

Zimmermann, H. G. (1994). Neuronale Netze als Entscheidungskalkül. In Rehkugler, H. and Zimmermann, H. G. (eds.), *Neuronale Netze in der Ökonomie, Grundlagen und wissenschaftliche Anwendungen*. Munich: Vahlen.

Zimmermann, H. G. and Neuneier, R. (2000). Neural network architectures for the modeling of dynamical systems. In Kolen, J. F. and Kremer, S. (eds.), *A Field Guide to Dynamical Recurrent Networks*. New York, USA: IEEE Press.

Chapter 11

Evolving Connectionist Systems for Adaptive Learning and Pattern Recognition: From Neuro-Fuzzy-, to Spiking- and Neurogenetic

Nikola Kasabov

This chapter follows the development of a class of neural networks called evolving connectionist systems (ECOSs). ECOSs combine the adaptive/evolving learning ability of neural networks and the approximate reasoning and linguistically meaningful explanation features of symbolic representation, such as fuzzy rules. This review paper includes hybrid expert systems, evolving neuro-fuzzy systems, spiking neural networks, neurogenetic systems, and quantum inspired systems, all discussed from the point of few of their adaptability and model interpretability. The chapter covers both methods and their numerous applications for data modeling, predictive systems, data mining, pattern recognition, across application areas of: engineering, medicine and health, neuroinformatics, bioinformatics, adaptive robotics, etc.

11.1. Early Neuro-Fuzzy Hybrid Systems

The human brain uniquely combines low level neuronal learning in the neurons and the connections between them and higher level abstraction leading to knowledge discovery. This is the ultimate inspiration for the development of the evolving connectionist systems described in this paper.

In the past 50 years or so, several seminal works in the areas of neural networks (Amari, 1967, 1990) and fuzzy systems (Zadeh, 1965, 1988) opened a new field of information science — the creation of new types of hybrid systems that combine the learning ability of neural networks, at a lower level of information processing, and the reasoning and explanation ability of fuzzy rule-based systems, at the higher level. An exemplar system is shown in Figure 11.1 where, at a lower level, a neural network (NN) module predicts the level of a stock index and, at a higher level, a fuzzy reasoning module combines the predicted values with some macro-economic

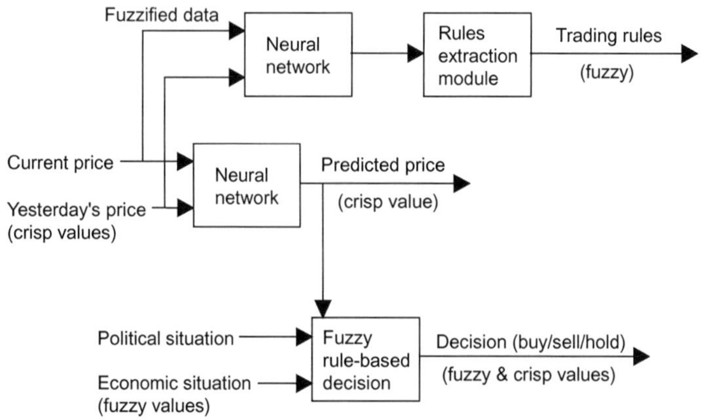

Figure 11.1: A hybrid NN-fuzzy rule-based expert system for financial decision support (Kasabov, 1996).

variables, using the following types of fuzzy rules (Kasabov, 1996).

$$\begin{aligned} &\mathit{IF} < \textit{the predicted by the NN module stock is high} > \\ &\quad \mathit{AND} < \textit{the economic situation is good} > \\ &\mathit{THEN} < \textit{buy stock} >. \end{aligned} \tag{1}$$

These fuzzy expert systems continued the development of the hybrid NN- rule-based expert systems that used crisp propositional and fuzzy rules (Hopfield, 1995; Izhikevich, 2004; Kasabov and Shishkov, 1993).

The integration of neural networks and fuzzy systems into expert systems attracted many researchers to join this theme. The low-level integration of fuzzy rules into a single neuron model and larger neural network structures, tightly coupling learning and fuzzy reasoning rules into connectionists structures, was initiated by Professor Takeshi Yamakawa and other Japanese scientists and promoted at a series of IIZUKA conferences in Japan (Yamakawa *et al.*, 1992; Zadeh, 1965). Many models of fuzzy neural networks were developed based on these principles (Furuhashi *et al.*, 1993; Lin and Lee, 1996; Kasabov, 1996, 1998; Kasabov *et al.*, 1997; Angelov, 2002; Angelov *et al.*, 2010)).

11.2. Evolving Connectionist Systems (ECOS)

11.2.1. *Principles of ECOS*

The evolving neuro-fuzzy systems developed these ideas further, where instead of training a fixed connectionist structure, the structure and its functionality were evolving from incoming data, often in an online, one-pass learning mode. This is the case with the evolving connectionist systems, ECOS (Kasabov, 1998, 2001, 2003; Kasabov *et al.*, 1997; Kasabov and Song, 2002; Angelov, 2002).

ECOS are modular connectionist-based systems that evolve their structure and functionality in a continuous, self-organized, online, adaptive, interactive way from incoming information (Kasabov, 1998). They can process both data and knowledge in a supervised and/or unsupervised way. ECOS learn local models from data through clustering of the data and associating a local output function for each cluster represented in a connectionist structure. They can learn incrementally single data items or chunks of data and also incrementally change their input features (Kasabov, 2003, 2007). Elements of ECOS have been proposed as part of the classical NN models, such as SOM, RBF, FuzyARTMap, Growing neural gas, neuro-fuzzy systems, RAN (for a review, see Kasabov, 2003). Other ECOS models, along with their applications, have been reported in (Watts, 2009; Futschik and Kasabov, 2002).

The principle of ECOS is based on *local learning* — neurons are allocated as centers of data clusters and the system creates local models in these clusters. Fuzzy clustering, as a mean to create local knowledge-based systems, was stimulated by the pioneering work of Bezdek, Yager and Filev (Bezdek, 1987; Yager and Filev, 1994).

To summarize, the following are the main principles of ECOS as stated in Kasabov (1998):

(1) Fast learning from large amount of data, e.g., using 'one-pass' training, starting with little prior knowledge;
(2) Adaptation in a real time and in an online mode where new data is accommodated as it comes based on local learning;
(3) 'Open', evolving structure, where new input variables (relevant to the task), new outputs (e.g., classes), new connections and neurons are added/evolved 'on the fly';
(4) Both data learning and knowledge representation are facilitated in a comprehensive and flexible way, e.g., supervised learning, unsupervised learning, evolving clustering, 'sleep' learning, forgetting/pruning, fuzzy rule insertion and extraction;
(5) Active interaction with other ECOSs and with the environment in a multi-modal fashion;
(6) Representing both space and time in their different scales, e.g., clusters of data, short- and long-term memory, age of data, forgetting, etc.;
(7) System's self-evaluation in terms of behavior, global error and success and related knowledge representation.

In 1998, Walter Freeman, who attended the ICONIP conference, commented on the proposed ECOS concepts: "... Through the 'chemicals' and let the system grow ...".

The development of ECOS as a trend in neural networks and computational intelligence that started in 1998 (Kasabov, 1998) continued as many improved or new computational *methods* that use the ECOS principles have been developed along many *applications.*

11.2.2. *Neuro-Fuzzy ECOS: EFuNN and DENFIS*

Here we will briefly illustrate the concepts of ECOS on two implementations: EFuNN (Kasabov, 2001) and DENFIS (Kasabov and Song, 2002). Examples of EFuNN and DENFIS are shown in Figures 11.2 and 11.3 respectively. In ECOS, clusters of data are created based on similarity between data samples either in the input space (this is the case in some of the ECOS models, e.g., the dynamic neuro-fuzzy inference system DENFIS), or in both the input and output space (this is the case e.g., in the EFuNN models). Samples (examples) that have a distance to an existing node (cluster center, rule node) less than a certain threshold are allocated to the same cluster. Samples that do not fit into existing clusters form new clusters. Cluster centers are continuously adjusted according to new data samples, and new clusters are created incrementally. ECOS learn from data and automatically create or update a local fuzzy model/function, e.g.,

$$IF < data\ is\ in\ a\ fuzzy\ cluster\ Ci > THEN < the\ model\ is\ Fi >, \quad (2)$$

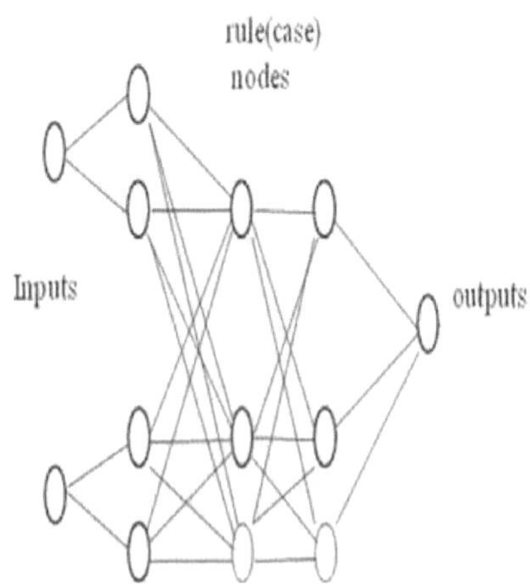

Figure 11.2: An example of EFuNN model.
Source: Kasabov (2001).

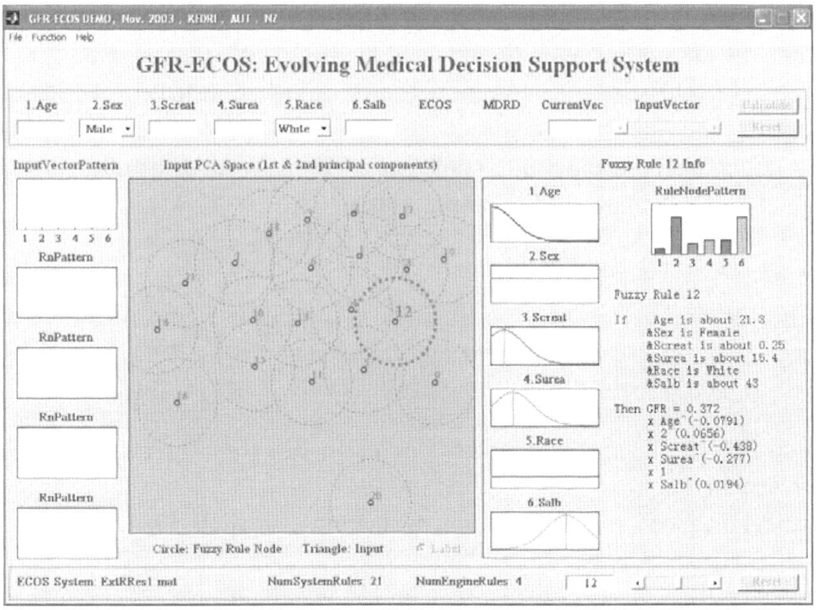

Figure 11.3: An example of DENFIS model.
Source: Marshall *et al.* (2005); Kasabov (2002, 2003).

where Fi can be a fuzzy value, a logistic or linear regression function (Figure 11.3) or a NN model (Kasabov and Song, 2002; Kasabov, 2003)

A special development of ECOS is *transductive reasoning and personalized modeling*. Instead of building a set of local models (e.g., prototypes) to cover the whole problem space and then use these models to classify/predict any new input vector, in transductive modeling for every new input vector, a new model is created based on selected nearest neighbor vectors from the available data. Such ECOS models are NFI and TWNFI (Song and Kasabov, 2006). In TWNFI, for every new input vector, the neighborhood of closets data vectors is optimized using both the distance between the new vector and the neighboring ones and the weighted importance of the input variables, so that the error of the model is minimized in the neighborhood area (Kasabov and Hu, 2010).

11.2.3. *Methods that Use Some ECOS Principles*

Among other methods that use or have been inspired by the ECOS principles are (publications are available from www.ieeexplore.ieee.org; Google Scholar; Scopus):

— Evolving Self-organized Maps (ESOM) (Deng and Kasabov, 2003);
— Evolving Clustering Method (ECM) (Song and Kasabov, 2002);

— Incremental feature learning in ECOS (Ozawa *et al.*, 2010);
— Online ECOS optimization (Minku and Ludemir, 2005; Chan *et al.*, 2004);
— Evolving Takagi–Sugeno fuzzy model based on switching to neighboring models (Angelov and Filev, 2004);
— Clustering and co-evolution to construct neural network ensembles: An experimental study (Minku and Ludermir, 2006).

11.2.4. *ECOS-Based Applications*

Based on the ECOS concepts and methods, sustained engineering applications have been developed, some of them are included in the list below and presented in (Kasabov, 2007) in detail:

— Discovery of diagnostic markers for early detection of cancer, (see also, www.pebl.co.nz);
— Medical diagnosis of renal function evaluation using DENFIS (also in Marshall *et al.*, 2005);
— Risk analysis and discovery of evolving economic clusters in Europe (see Kasabov, 2003);
— Adaptive robot control system based on ECOS (see Huang, 2008);
— Personalized modeling systems (see Kasabov and Hu, 2010)
Other applications include:
— Phoneme-base speech recognition;
— EEG signal processing;
— Adaptive image processing;
— Language modeling;
— Ecological event prediction;
— Decision support in economics;
— A software agent framework to overcome malicious host threats and uncontrolled agent clones (Sujitha and Amudha, 2012);
— Autonomous visual self-localization in completely unknown environment using evolving fuzzy rule-based classifier (Zhou and Angelov, 2007).

While the ECOS methods presented above use McCulloch and Pitts model of a neuron, the further developed evolving spiking neural network (eSNN) architectures use a spiking neuron model applying the same or similar ECOS principles and applications.

11.3. Evolving Spiking Neural Networks (eSNN)

11.3.1. *Main Principles, Methods and Examples of eSNN*

A single biological neuron and the associated synapses is a complex information processing machine that involves short term information processing, long-term

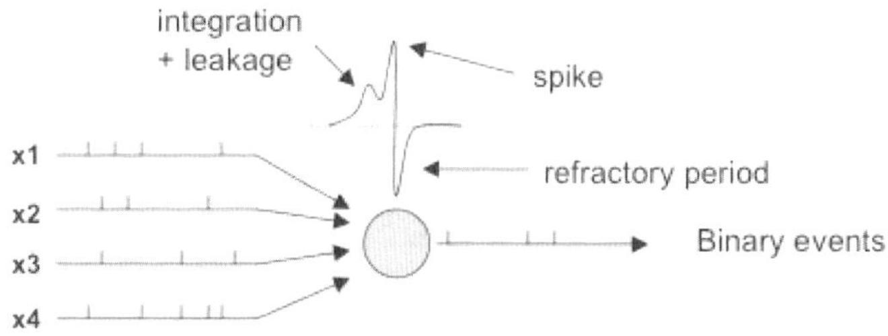

Figure 11.4: The structure of the LIFM.

information storage, and evolutionary information stored as genes in the nucleus of the neuron. A spiking neuron model assumes input information represented as trains of spikes over time. When sufficient input information is accumulated in the membrane of the neuron, the neuron's post synaptic potential exceeds a threshold and the neuron emits a spike at its axon (Figure 11.4).

Some of the-state-of-the-art models of a spiking neuron include: early models by Hodgkin and Huxley (1952); more recent models by Maas, Gerstner, Kistler, Izhikevich and others, e.g., Spike Response Models (SRM); Integrate-and-Fire Model (IFM) (Figure 11.4); Izhikevich models; adaptive IFM; probabilistic IFM (for details, see: Hebb, 1949; Gerstner, 1995; Hopfield, 1995; Izhikevich, 2004; Kasabov, 2010).

Based on the ECOS principles, an evolving spiking neural network architecture (eSNN) was proposed (Kasabov, 2007; Wysoski *et al.*, 2010). It was initially designed as a visual pattern recognition system. The first eSNNs were based on the Thorpe's neural model (Thorpe and Delorme, 2001), in which the importance of early spikes (after the onset of a certain stimulus) is boosted, called rank-order coding and learning. Synaptic plasticity is employed by a fast supervised one-pass learning algorithm. Different eSNN models were developed, including:

— Reservoir-based eSNN for spatio- and spectro-temporal pattern recognition shown in Figure 11.5 (following the main principles from Verstraeten *et al.*, 2007);
— Dynamic eSNN (deSNN) (Kasabov *et al.*, 2013a) a model that uses both rank-order and time-based STDP learning (Song *et al.*, 2000) to account for spatio-temporal data;

and many more (for references, see Schliebs and Kasabov, 2013):

Extracting fuzzy rules from an eSNN would make the eSNN not only efficient learning models, but also knowledge-based models. A method was proposed (Soltic and Kasabov, 2010) and illustrated in Figures 11.6 and 11.7. Based on the connection weights (W) between the receptive field layer (L1) and the class output neuron

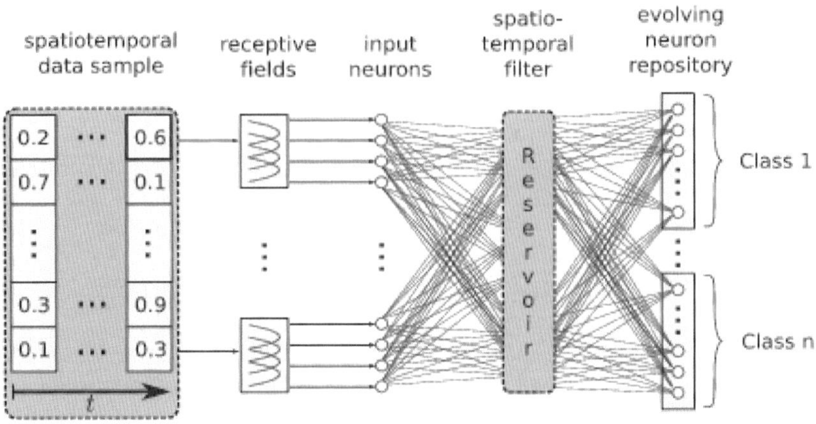

Figure 11.5: A reservoir-based eSNN for spatio-temporal pattern classification.

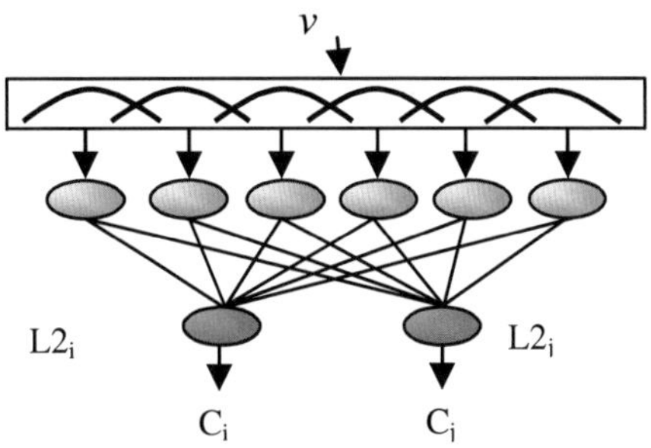

Figure 11.6: A simplified structure of an eSNN for two-class classification showing only one input variable using six receptive fields to convert the input values into spike trains.

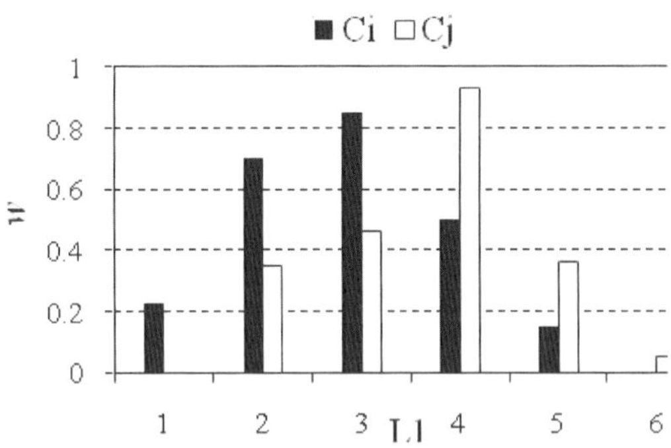

Figure 11.7: The connection weights of the connections to class *Ci* and *Cj* output neurons respectively are interpreted as fuzzy rules (Equation (3)).

layer (L2), the following fuzzy rules are extracted:

$$\begin{aligned} &IF\ (input\ variable\ v\ is\ SMALL)\ THEN\ class\ C_i; \\ &IF\ (v\ is\ LARGE)\ THEN\ class\ C_j. \end{aligned} \tag{3}$$

In principle, eSNN uses spike information representation, spiking neuron models and SNN learning and encoding rules and the structure is evolving to capture spatio-temporal relationship from data. The eSNNs have been further developed as computational neurogenetic models as discussed below.

11.3.2. *Quantum Inspired Optimization of eSNN*

eSNNs have several parameters that need to be optimized for an optimal performance. Several successful methods have been proposed for this purpose, among them are: Quantum-inspired evolutionary algorithm, QiEA (Defoin-Platel *et al.*, 2009); and Quantum inspired particle swarm optimization method, QiPSO (Nuzly *et al.*, 2010).

Quantum inspired optimization methods use the principle of superposition of states to represent and optimize features (input variables) and parameters of the eSNN (Kasabov, 2007). Features and parameters are represented as qubits that are in a superposition of 1 (selected), with a probability α, and 0 (not selected) with a probability β. When the model has to be calculated, the quantum bits 'collapse' in 1 or 0.

11.3.3. *Some Applications Based on eSNN*

Numerous applications based on the different eSNN models have been reported, among them:

— Advanced spiking neural network technologies for neurorehabilitation (Chen *et al.*, 2013);
— Object movement recognition (EU FP7 Marie Curie EvoSpike project 2011–2012, INI/ETH/UZH, http://ncs.ethz.ch/projects/evospike);
— Multimodal audio and visual information processing (Wysoski *et al.*, 2010);
— Ecological data modeling and prediction of the establishment of invasive species (Schliebs *et al.*, 2009);
— Integrated brain data analysis (Kasabov, 2014);
— Predictive modeling method and case study on personalized stroke occurrence prediction (Kasabov, *et al.*, 2014d);
— Financial time series prediction (Widiputra *et al.*, 2011);
— Other applications (Schliebs and Kasabov, 2013).

11.4. Computational Neuro-Genetic Models (CNGM) Based on eSNN

11.4.1. *Main Principles*

A neurogenetic model of a neuron is proposed in (Kasabov, 2007) and studied in (Benuskova and Kasabov, 2007). It utilizes information about how some proteins and genes affect the spiking activities of a neuron such as *fast excitation, fast inhibition, slow excitation, and slow inhibition*. An important part of the model is a dynamic gene/protein regulatory network (GRN) model of the dynamic interactions between genes/proteins over time that affect the spiking activity of the neuron — Figure 11.8.

New types of neuro-genetic fuzzy rules can be extracted from such CNGM in the form of:

$$\begin{aligned} &\mathit{IF} < \mathit{GRN\ is\ represented\ by\ a\ function\ F} > \mathit{AND} < \mathit{input\ is\ Small} > \\ &\quad \mathit{THEN} < \mathit{Class\ C} >. \end{aligned} \tag{4}$$

This type of eSNN is further developed into a comprehensive SNN framework called NeuCube for spatio/spectro temporal data modeling and analysis as presented in the next section.

11.4.2. *The NeuCube Architecture*

The latest development of neurogenetic systems is NeuCube (Kasabov, 2014), initially designed for spatio-temporal brain data modeling, but then it was used for climate data modeling, stroke occurrence prediction and other applications (Kasabov, *et al.*, 2015).

The NeuCube framework is depicted in Figure 11.9. It consists of the following functional parts (modules):

— Input information encoding module;
— 3D SNN reservoir module (SNNr);

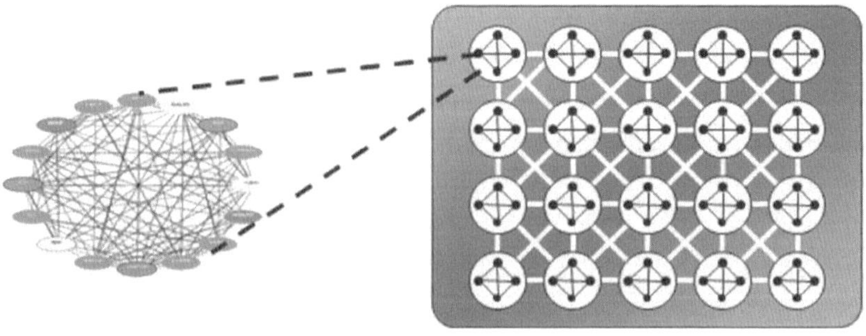

Figure 11.8: A schematic diagram of a CNGM framework, consisting of a GRN as part of a eSNN (Benuskova and Kasabov, 2007).

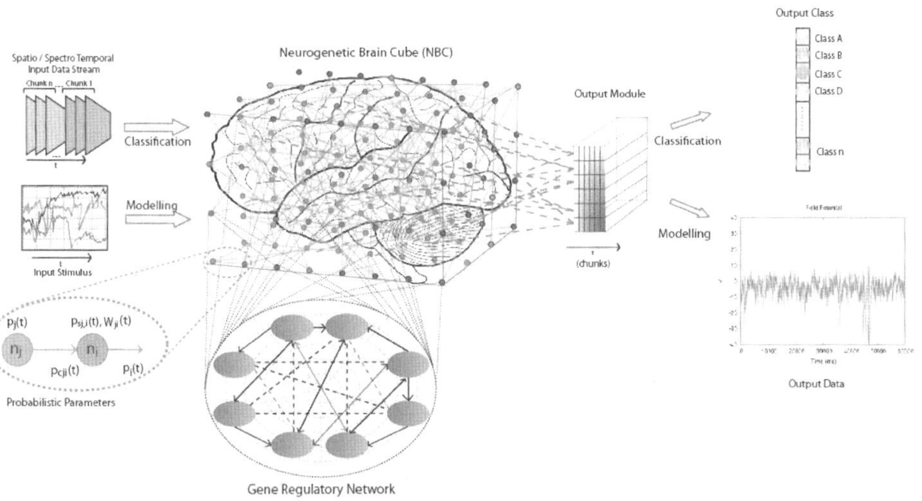

Figure 11.9: A block diagram of the NeuCube architecture (from Kasabov, 2014).

— Output (e.g., classification) module;
— Gene regulatory network (GRN) module (Optional);
— Optimization module.

The input module transforms input data into trains of spikes. Spatio-temporal data (such as EEG, fMRI, climate) is entered into the main module — the 3D SNN cubes (SNNc). Input data is entered into *pre-designated spatially located* areas of the SNNc that correspond to the spatial location in the origin where data was collected (if there is such).

Learning in the SNN is performed in two stages:

— Unsupervised training, where spatio-temporal data is entered into relevant areas of the SNNc over time. Unsupervised learning is performed to modify the initially set connection weights. The SNNc will learn to activate same groups of spiking neurons when similar input stimuli are presented, also known as a *polychronization* effect (Izhikevich, 2004).
— Supervised training of the spiking neurons in the output classification module, where the same data that was used for unsupervised training is now propagated again through the trained SNNc and the output neurons are trained to classify the spatio-temporal spiking pattern of the SNNc into pre-defined classes (or output spike sequences). As a special case, all neurons from the SNN are connected to every output neuron. Feedback connections from output neurons to neurons in the SNN can be created for reinforcement learning. Different SNN methods can be used to learn and classify spiking patterns from the SNNr, including the deSNN (Kasabov *et al.*, 2013b) and SPAN models (Mohemmed *et al.*, 2013).

The latter is suitable for generating spike trains in response to certain patterns of activity of the SNNc.

Memory in the NeuCube architecture is represented as a combination of the three types of memory described below, which are mutually interacting:

— Short-term memory, represented as changes of the PSP and temporary changes of synaptic efficacy;
— Long-term memory, represented as a stable establishment of synaptic efficacy — LTP and LTD;
— Genetic memory, represented as a genetic code.

In NeuCube, similar activation patterns (called 'polychronous waves') can be generated in the SNNc with recurrent connections to represent short term memory. When using STDP learning connection weights change to form LTP or LTD, which constitute long-term memory. Results of the use of the NeuCube suggest that the NeuCube architecture can be explored for learning long (spatio-) temporal patterns and to be used as associative memory. Once data is learned, the SNNc retains the connections as a long-term memory. Since the SNNc learns functional pathways of spiking activities represented as structural pathways of connections, when only a small initial part of input data is entered the SNNc will 'synfire' and 'chain-fire' *learned connection pathways* to reproduce *learned functional pathways.* Thus, a NeuCube can be used as an associative memory and as a predictive system.

11.4.3. *Neuromorphic Implementations*

The different types of eSNN and neurogenetic systems, especially the NeuCube architecture, are suitable to be implemented as a neuromorphic hardware system for embedded applications. For this purpose, both digital (e.g., Furber, 2012) and analogue (e.g., Indiveri *et al.*, 2011) realizations can be used.

11.5. Conclusion

This chapter presents briefly the methods of ECOS. ECOS facilitate adaptive learning and knowledge discovery from complex data. ECOS principles are derived from neural networks, fuzzy systems, evolutionary computation, quantum computing and brain information processing. ECOS applications are manifold, but perhaps most welcome in the environmental and health sciences, where the diagnostic phenomena are chaotic in nature and the datasets are massive and often incomplete. In the field of sustainability science, whether it is in analyzing issues related to sustainable resource utilization, countering global environmental issues, or the assurance of the continuity of life, (particularly human life) on earth, the speed of transformation is most rapid. Massive datasets with the characteristics just described need to be analyzed, virtually in real time, for prognoses to be made and solutions to the issues sought at a level of urgency. In this sense, evolving connectionist systems for adaptive learning and knowledge discovery can make a great contribution to the methodologies of intelligent evolving systems (Angelov *et al.*, 2010). In the future, new methods of ECOS can be developed based on the integration of principles from computational intelligence, bioinformatics and neuroinformatics (Kasabov, 2014).

Acknowledgment

The work on this chapter is supported by the Knowledge Engineering and Discovery Research Institute (KEDRI, http://www.kedri.aut.ac.nz). Some of the methods, techniques and applications are publicly available from: http://www.kedri.aut.ac.nz; http://www.theneucom.com; http://www.kedri.aut.ac.nz/neucube/. I would like to acknowledge the work of many authors who developed methods and applications of ECOS referring to the presented here material in more than 10,000 citations (Google Scholar, September 2015). I have not been able to reference all or even part of their work. Many of them have contributed greatly to the development and the applications of ECOS e.g., S. Amari, T. Yamakawa, W. Freeman, J. Taylor, S. Grossberg, P. Angelov, D. Filev, J. Pratt, T. Ludemir, S. Ozawa, P. Pang, Lughofer, B. Gabrys, M. Watts, Dovzan and Skrjanc, F. Gomide, Ang and Quek, Rubio, Aznarte, Cetisli, Subramian and Suresh, Babu and Suresh, Tung, Boubacar, Yamauchi, Hayashi, L.Goh, Ishibuchi, Hwang and Song, Capo, Vachkov, Rutkowski and Cpalka, Han and Qiao, Zanchettin, O'Hora, Hernandez and Castaeda, Guzaitis, and many more. I would like to acknowledge the editor of this volume Plamen Angelov for his incredible energy and efforts to put all these chapters together.

References

Amari, S. (1967). A theory of adaptive pattern classifiers. *IEEE Trans. Electron. Comput.*, 16, pp. 299–307.

Amari, S. (1990). Mathematical foundations of neurocomputing. *Proc. IEEE*, 78, pp. 1143–1163.

Angelov, P. (2002). *Evolving Rule-based Models: A Tool for Design of Flexible Adaptive Systems*. Heidelberg, Germany: Springer-Verlag.

Angelov, P. and Filev, D. (2004). An approach to on-line identification of evolving Takagi–Sugeno models. *IEEE Trans. Systems, Man and Cybernetics, Part B*, 34(1), pp. 484–498.

Angelov, P., Filev, D. and Kasabov, N. (eds.). (2010). *Evolving Intelligent Systems*. USA: IEEE Press and Wiley.

Benuskova, L and Kasabov, N. (2007). *Computational Neuro-Genetic Modeling*. New York: Springer.

Bezdek, J. (ed.). (1987). *Analysis of Fuzzy Information, Volumes 1–3*. Boca Raton, Florida: CRC Press.

Chan, Z. and Kasabov, N. (2004). Evolutionary computation for on-line and off-line parameter tuning of evolving fuzzy neural networks. *Int. J. Comput. Intell. Appl.*, 4(3), pp. 309–319.

Chen, Y., Hu, J., Kasabov, N., Hou, Z. and Cheng, L. (2013). NeuroCubeRehab: a pilot study for EEG classification in rehabilitation practice based on spiking neural networks. *Proc. ICONIP 2013, Springer LNCS*, 8228, pp. 70–77.

Defoin-Platel, M., Schliebs, S. and Kasabov, N. (2009). Quantum-inspired evolutionary algorithm: a multi-model EDA. *IEEE Trans. Evol. Comput.*, 13(6), pp. 1218–1232.

Deng, D. and Kasabov, N. (2003). On-line pattern analysis by evolving self-organizing maps. *Neurocomput.*, 51, pp. 87–103.

EU FP7 Marie Curie EvoSpike project (2011–2012). INI/ETH/UZH. (http://ncs.ethz.ch/projects/evospike).

Furber, S. (2012). To build a brain. *IEEE Spectr.*, 49(8), pp. 39–41.

Furuhashi, T., Hasegawa, T., Horikawa, S. and Uchikawa, Y. (1993). An adaptive fuzzy controller using fuzzy neural networks. In *Proc. Fifth IFSA World Congr.*, pp. 769–772.

Futschik, M. and Kasabov, N. (2002) Fuzzy clustering in gene expression data analysis. *Proc. World Congr. Comput. Intell. WCCI'2002*, May 2002. Hawaii: IEEE Press.

Gerstner, W. (1995). Time structure of the activity of neural network models. *Phys. Rev.*, 51, pp. 738–758.

Hebb, D. (1949). *The Organization of Behavior*. New York: John Wiley and Sons.

Hodgkin, A. L. and Huxley, A. F. (1952). A quantitative description of membrane current and its application to conduction and excitation in nerve. *J. Physiol.*, 117, pp. 500–544.

Hopfield, J. (1995). Pattern recognition computation using action potential timing for stimulus representation. *Nature*, 376, pp. 33–36.

Huang, L. (2008). Evolving connectionist system based role allocation for robotic soccer. *Int. J. Adv. Robot. Syst.*, 5(1), pp. 59–62.

Indiveri, G., Linares-Barranco, B., Hamilton, T., Van Schaik, A., Etienne-Cummings, R., Delbruck, T., Liu, S., Dudek, P., Hafliger, P. and Renaud, S. (2011). Neuromorphic silicon neuron circuits. *Front. Neurosci.*, 5, pp. 1–23.

Izhikevich, E. M. (2004). Which model to use for cortical spiking neurons? *IEEE TNN*, 15(5), pp. 1063–1070.

Kasabov, N. (1991). Incorporating neural networks into production systems and a practical approach towards the realisation of fuzzy expert systems. *Comput. Sci. Inf.*, 21(2), pp. 26–34.

Kasabov, N. (1993). Hybrid connectionist production systems. *J. Syst. Eng.*, 3(1), pp. 15–21.

Kasabov, N. (1994). Connectionist fuzzy production systems. *LNCS/AI*, 847, pp. 114–128.

Kasabov, N. (1995). Hybrid connectionist fuzzy production systems: Towards building comprehensive AI. *Intell. Autom. Soft Comput.*, 1(4), pp. 351–360.

Kasabov, N. (1996). *Foundations of Neural Networks, Fuzzy Systems and Knowledge Engineering*. Cambridge, Massachussets: MIT Press, p. 550.

Kasabov, N. (1998). Evolving fuzzy neural networks: Algorithms, applications and biological motivation. In Yamakawa, T. and Matsumoto, G. (eds.), *Methodologies for the Conception, Design and Application of Soft Computing*. Singapore: World Scientific, pp. 271–274.

Kasabov, N. (2001). Evolving fuzzy neural networks for on-line supervised/unsupervised, knowledge-based learning. *IEEE Trans. SMC/B*, Cybern., 31(6), pp. 902–918.

Kasabov, N. (2003). *Evolving Connectionist Systems: Methods and Applications in Bioinformatics, Brain Study and Intelligent Machines*. London, New York, Heidelberg: Springer Verlag.

Kasabov, N. (2007). *Evolving Connectionist Systems: The Knowledge Engineering Approach*. Berlin, Heidelberg: Springer.

Kasabov, N. (2010). To spike or not to spike: A probabilistic spiking neural model. *Neural Networks*, 23(1), pp. 16–19.

Kasabov, N. (2014). NeuCube: a spiking neural network architecture for mapping, learning and understanding of spatio-temporal brain data. *Neural Netw.*, 52, pp. 62–76. http://dx.doi.org/10.1016/j.neunet.2014.01.006.

Kasabov, N. (ed.) (2014). *The Springer Handbook of Bio- and Neuroinformatics*. New York: Springer.

Kasabov, N. *et al.* (2015). Design methodology and selected applications of evolving spatio-temporal data machines in the NeuCube neuromorphic framework. *Neural Networks*, in print.

Kasabov, N. and Hu, Y. (2010). Integrated optimization method for personalized modeling and case study applications. *Int. J. Funct. Inf. Person. Med.*, 3(3), pp. 236–256.

Kasabov, N. and Shishkov, S. (1993). A connectionist production system with partial match and its use for approximate reasoning. *Connect. Sci.*, 5(3/4), pp. 275–305.

Kasabov, N., Kim, J. S., Watts, M. and Gray, A. (1997). FuNN/2: a fuzzy neural network architecture for adaptive learning and knowledge acquisition. *Inf. Sci. Appl.*, 101(3–4), pp. 155–175.

Kasabov, N. and Song, Q. (2002). DENFIS: dynamic, evolving neural-fuzzy inference systems and its application for time-series prediction. *IEEE Trans. Fuzzy Syst.*, 10, pp. 144–154.

Kasabov, N., Liang, L., Krishnamurthi, R., Feigin, V., Othman, M., Hou, Z. and Parmar, P. (2014). Evolving spiking neural networks for personalized modeling of spatio-temporal data and early prediction of events: a case study on stroke. *Neurocomputing*, 134, pp. 269–279.

Kasabov, N., Dhoble, K., Nuntalid, N. and Indiveri, G. (2013b). Dynamic evolving spiking neural networks for on-line spatio- and spectro-temporal pattern recognition. *Neural Netw.*, 41, pp. 188–201.

Lin, C. T. and Lee, C. S. G. (1996). *Neuro Fuzzy Systems*. US: Prentice Hall.

Marshall, M. R. *et al.* (2005). Evolving connectionist system versus algebraic formulae for prediction of renal function from serum creatinine. *Kidney Int.*, 6, pp. 1944–1954.

Minku, F. L. and Ludermir, T. B. (2006). EFuNNs ensembles construction using a clustering method and a coevolutionary genetic algorithm. *Proc. IEEE Congress on Evolutionary Computation*, Vancouver, July 16–21, IEEE Press, pp. 5548–5555.

Minku, F. L. and Ludermir, T. B. (2005). Evolutionary strategies and genetic algorithms for dynamic parameter optimisation of evolving fuzzy neural networks. *Proc. IEEE Congress on Evolutionary Computation* (CEC), Edinburgh, September, pp. 1951–1958.

Mohemmed, A., Schliebs, S., Matsuda, S. and Kasabov, N. (2013). Evolving spike pattern association neurons and neural networks. *Neurocomputing*, 107, pp. 3–10.

Nuzly, H., Kasabov, N. and Shamsuddin, S. (2010). Probabilistic evolving spiking neural network optimization using dynamic quantum inspired particle swarm optimization. In *Springer LNCS*, 6443.

Ozawa, S., Pang, S. and Kasabov, N. (2008). Incremental learning of chunk data for on-line pattern classification systems. *IEEE Trans. Neural Networks*, 19(6), pp. 1061–1074.

Schliebs, S. and Kasabov, N. (2013). Evolving spiking neural network — a survey. *Evolving Systems*, 4(2), pp. 87–98.

Schliebs, S. *et al.* (2009). Integrated feature and parameter optimization for evolving spiking neural networks: exploring heterogeneous probabilistic models. *Neural Netw.*, 22, pp. 623–632.

Soltic, S. and Kasabov, N. (2010). Knowledge extraction from evolving spiking neural networks with rank order population coding. *Int. J. Neural Syst.*, 20(6), pp. 437–445.

Song, Q. and Kasabov, N. (2006). TWNFI: A transductive neuro-fuzzy inference system with weighted data normalization for personalized modeling. *Neural Netw.*, 19(10), pp. 1591–1596.

Song, S., Miller, K. and Abbott, L. (2000). Competitive hebbian learning through spike-timing-dependent synaptic plasticity. *Nature Neurosci.*, 3, pp. 919–926.

Sujitha, G. A. and Amudha, T. (2012). *Int. J. Adv. Inf. Technol.*, 2(2), pp. 13–27.

Thorpe, S. and Delorme, A. (2001). Spike-based strategies for rapid processing. *Neural Netw.*, 14(6–7), pp. 715–725.

Verstraeten, D., Schrauwen, B., D'Haene, M. and Stroobandt, D. (2007). An experimental unification of reservoir computing methods. *Neural Netw.*, 20(3), pp. 391–403.

Watts, M. (2009). A decade of Kasabov's evolving connectionist systems: a review. *IEEE Trans. Syst. Man Cybern. Part C: Appl. Rev.*, 39(3), pp. 253–269.

Widiputra, H., Pears, R. and Kasabov, N. (2011). Multiple time-series prediction through multiple time-series relationships profiling and clustered recurring trends. *Springer LNAI*, 6635(2), pp. 161–172.

Wysoski, S., Benuskova, L. and Kasabov, N. (2010). Evolving spiking neural networks for audiovisual information processing. *Neural Netw.*, 23(7), pp. 819–835.

Yager, R. R. and Filev, D. (1994). Generation of fuzzy rules by mountain clustering. *J. Intell. Fuzzy Syst.*, 2, pp. 209–219.

Yamakawa, T., Uchino, E., Miki, T. and Kusanagi, H. (1992). A neo fuzzy neuron and Its application to system identification and prediction of the system behavior. *Proc. Second Int. Conf. Fuzzy Log. Neural Netw.*, Iizuka, Japan, pp. 477–483.

Zadeh, L. (1965). Fuzzy Sets. *Inf. Control*, 8, pp. 338–353.

Zadeh, L. A. (1988). Fuzzy Logic. *IEEE Comput.*, 21, pp. 83–93.

Zanchettin, C. and Ludermir, T. B. (2004). Evolving fuzzy neural networks applied to odor recognition in an artificial nose. *Proc. IEEE Int. Joint Conf. Neural Networks*, Budapest, July 26–29, IEEE Press.

Zhou, X. and Angelov, P. (2006). Real-time joint landmark recognition and classifier generation by an evolving fuzzy system. *Proc. of IEEE Int. Conf. Fuzzy Systems*, Vancouver, July 16–21, IEEE Press, pp. 6314–6321.

Chapter 12

Reinforcement Learning with Applications in Automation Decision and Feedback Control

Kyriakos G. Vamvoudakis, Frank L. Lewis and Draguna Vrabie

This book chapter is interested in showing how ideas from Control Systems Engineering and Computational Intelligence have been combined to obtain a new class of control techniques. Since reinforcement learning involves modifying the control policy based on responses from an unknown environment, we have the initial feeling that it is closely related to adaptive control. Moreover, reinforcement learning methods allow learning of optimal solutions relative to prescribed cost/payoff metrics by measuring data in real time along system trajectories, hence it also has relations to optimal feedback control. This book chapter is an exposition of research results that clarify these relations.

12.1. Background

Adaptive control is one of the most widespread techniques for feedback control of modern engineered systems since the 1960s. Its effective and reliable use in aerospace systems, the industrial process industry, vehicle control, communications, and elsewhere is firmly established. Optimal control is equally widespread since it enables the design of feedback controllers with the purpose of minimizing energy, fuel consumption, performance time, or other premium quantities.

Optimal controllers are normally designed offline by solving Hamilton–Jacobi–Bellman (HJB) equations, for example, the Riccati equation, using complete knowledge of the system dynamics. Optimal control policies for nonlinear systems can be obtained by solving nonlinear HJB equations that cannot usually be solved. By contrast, adaptive controllers learn online to control unknown systems using data measured in real time along the system trajectories. Adaptive controllers are generally not optimal in the sense of minimizing user-prescribed performance functions. Indirect adaptive controllers have been designed that use system identification techniques to first identify the system parameters, then use the obtained model to solve optimal design equations (Astrom and Wittenmark, 1995). It is shown that adaptive controllers may satisfy certain inverse optimality conditions (Ioannou and

Fidan, 2006). The design of adaptive controllers that learn online, in real time, the solutions to user-prescribed optimal control problems can be studied by means of reinforcement learning and adaptive dynamic programming techniques, and forms the object of this book chapter which is a condensation of the paper that appeared in IEEE Control Systems Magazine in December 2012 (Lewis *et al.*, 2012a).

The real-time learning of optimal controllers for unknown systems occurs in nature. The limits within which living organisms can survive are often quite narrow and the resources available to most species are meager. Therefore, most organisms occurring in nature act in an optimal fashion to conserve resources while achieving their goals. Living organisms learn by acting on their environment, observing and evaluating the resulting reward stimulus, and adjusting their actions accordingly to improve the reward.

Inspired by natural learning mechanisms, that is, those occurring in biological organisms including animals and humans, reinforcement learning techniques for machine learning and artificial intelligence have been developed and used mainly in the Computational Intelligence community (Lewis *et al.*, 2012b; Li and Krstic, 1997; Powell, 2011; Sutton and Barto, 1998; Werbos, 1991). The purpose of this book chapter is to give an exposition of the usefulness of reinforcement learning techniques in designing feedback controllers for engineered systems, where optimal actions may be driven by objectives such as minimum fuel, minimum energy, minimum risk, maximum reward, and so on. We specifically focus on a family of techniques known as approximate or adaptive dynamic programming (ADP) (Balakrishnan *et al.*, 2008; Barto and Powell, 2004; Busoniu *et al.*, 2009; Lewis and Liu, 2013; Lewis *et al.*, 2008; Prokhorov, 2008; Wang *et al.*, 2009). We show that reinforcement learning ideas can be used to design a family of adaptive control algorithms that converge in real time to optimal control solutions while using data measured along the system trajectories. Such techniques may be referred to as optimal adaptive control. The use of reinforcement learning techniques provides optimal control solutions for linear or nonlinear systems using adaptive control techniques. In effect, reinforcement learning methods allow the solution of HJB equations, or for linear quadratic design, the Riccati equation, online and without knowing the full system dynamics.

In machine learning, reinforcement learning (Lewis *et al.*, 2012b; Powell, 2011; Sutton and Barto, 1998) refers to the set of optimization problems that involve an actor or agent that interacts with its environment and modifies its actions, or control policies, based on stimuli received in response to its actions. reinforcement learning is based on evaluative information from the environment and could be called action-based learning.

Reinforcement learning implies a cause and effect relationship between actions and reward or punishment. It implies goal directed behavior at least insofar as the agent has an understanding of reward versus lack of reward or punishment. The idea behind reinforcement learning is that of modifying actions or behavior policy in order to reduce the prediction error between anticipated future rewards and actual performance as computed based on observed rewards. The reinforcement learning algorithms are constructed on the idea that effective control decisions must be remembered, by means of a reinforcement signal, such that they become more likely to be used a second time. Although the idea originates from experimental animal learning, where it is observed that the dopamine neurotransmitter acts as a reinforcement informational signal that favors learning at the level of the neuron (Doya *et al.*, 2001; Schultz, 2004), reinforcement learning is strongly connected from a theoretical point of view with adaptive control and optimal control methods.

Although RL algorithms have been widely used to solve the optimal regulation problems, some research efforts considered solving the optimal tracking control problem for discrete-time (Zhang *et al.*, 2008) and continuous-time systems (Dierks and Jagannathan, 2010; Zhang *et al.*, 2011). Moreover, existing methods require the exact knowledge of the system dynamics a priori while finding the feedforward part of the control input using the dynamic inversion concept. In order to attain the required knowledge of the system dynamics, in Zhang *et al.* (2011), a plant model was first identified and then an RL-based optimal tracking controller was synthesized using the identified model.

One class of reinforcement learning methods is based on the actor-critic structure shown in Figure 12.1, where an actor component applies an action, or control policy,

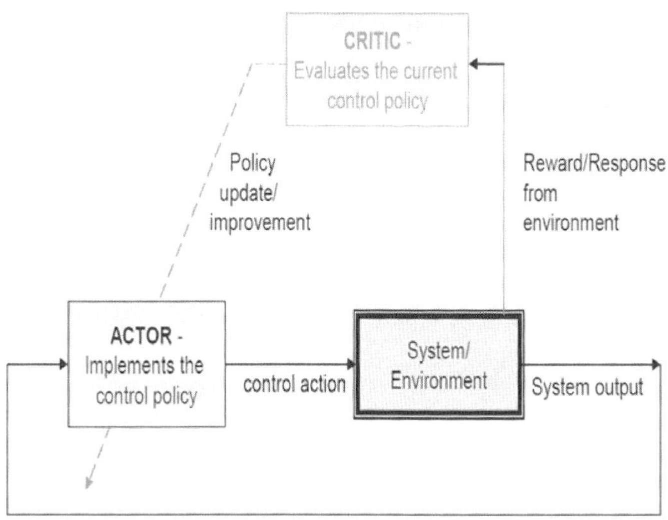

Figure 12.1: Reinforcement learning with an actor/critic structure. This structure provides methods for learning optimal control solutions online based on data measured along the system trajectories.

to the environment, and a critic component assesses the value of that action. Based on this assessment of the value, one of several schemes can then be used to modify or improve the action, or control policy, in the sense that the new policy yields a value that is improved relative to the previous value. The learning mechanism supported by the actor-critic structure implies two steps, namely, policy evaluation, executed by the critic, followed by policy improvement, performed by the actor. The policy evaluation step is performed by observing from the environment the results of applying current actions.

It is of interest to study reinforcement learning systems that have an actor-critic structure wherein the critic assesses the value of current policies based on some sort of optimality criteria (Busoniu *et al.*, 2009; Cao, 2007; Sutton and Barto, 1998; Werbos, 1992). It is worth noting that the actor-critic structure is similar to one encountered in adaptive control. However, adaptive control schemes make use of system identification mechanisms to first obtain a model of the system dynamics and then use this model to guide adaptation of the parameters of the controller/actor. In contrast, in the optimal reinforcement learning algorithm case the learning process is moved to a higher level, having no longer as object of interest the details of a system's dynamics, but a performance index that quantifies how close to optimality the closed loop control system operates. In this scheme, reinforcement learning is a means of learning optimal behaviors by observing the real-time responses from the environment to non-optimal control policies. Two new research monographs on this subject are Vrabie *et al.* (2012) and Zhang *et al.* (2013).

The intention of this book chapter is to present the main ideas and algorithms of reinforcement learning and approximate dynamic programming and to show how they are applied in the design of optimal adaptive feedback controllers. A few connections are also shown between reinforcement learning and decision and control on systems distributed over communication graphs, including shortest path problems, relaxation methods, and cooperative control. In fact, we show that reinforcement learning provides connections between optimal control, adaptive control, and cooperative control and decisions on finite graphs. This book chapter presents an expository development of ideas from reinforcement learning and ADP and their applications in automatic control systems. Surveys of ADP are given in (Barto *et al.* (1983); Bertsekas and Tsitsiklis, 1996; Bellman, 1957; Vrabie and Lewis (2009); Werbos, 1989).

12.2. Markov Decision Processes and Stochasticity

A framework for studying reinforcement learning is provided by Markov decision processes (MDP). In fact, dynamical decision problems can be cast into the framework of MDP. Included are feedback control systems for human engineered systems, feedback regulation mechanisms for population balance and survival of species (Prokhorov and Wunsch, 1997), the balance of power between nations, decision-making in multi-player games, and economic mechanisms for regulation of global financial markets. Therefore, we provide a development of MDP here.

Consider the MDP (X, U, P, R) where X is a set of states and U is a set of actions or controls. The transition probabilities $P : X \times U \times X \to [0, 1]$ give for each state $x \in X$ and action $u \in U$ the conditional probability $P^u_{x,x'} = Pr\{x'|x, u\}$ of transitioning to state $x' \in X$ given the MDP is in state x and takes action u. The cost function $R : X \times U \times X \to \mathbb{R}$ gives the expected immediate cost $R^u_{xx'}$ paid after transition to state $x' \in X$ given the MDP starts in state $x \in X$ and takes action $u \in U$. The Markov property refers to the fact that transition probabilities $P^u_{x,x'}$ depend only on the current state x and not on the history of how the MDP attained that state.

The basic problem for MDP is to find a mapping $\pi : X \times U \to [0, 1]$ that gives for each state x and action u the conditional probability $\pi(x, u) = Pr\{u|x\}$ of taking action u given the MDP is in state x. Such a mapping is termed a closed-loop control or action strategy or policy. The strategy or policy is called stochastic or mixed if there is a non-zero probability of selecting more that one control when in state x. We can view mixed strategies as probability distribution vectors having as component i the probability of selecting the ith control action while in state $x \in X$. If the mapping $\pi : X \times U \to [0, 1]$ admits only one control with probability 1, when in every state x the mapping is called a deterministic policy. Then $\pi(x, u) = Pr\{u|x\}$ corresponds to a function mapping states into controls $\mu(x) : X \to U$.

12.2.1. *Optimal Sequential Decision Problems*

Dynamical systems evolve causally through time. Therefore, we consider sequential decision problems and impose a discrete stage index k such that the MDP takes an action and changes states at nonnegative integer stage values k. The stages may correspond to time or more generally to sequences of events. We refer to the stage value as the time. Denote state values and actions at time k by x_k, u_k. MDP evolve in discrete time. It is often desirable for human engineered systems to be optimal in terms of conserving resources such as cost, time, fuel, energy. Thus, the notion of optimality should be captured in selecting control policies for MDP. Define, therefore, a stage cost at time k by $r_k \equiv r_k(x_k, u_k, x_{k+1})$. Then $R^u_{xx'} = E\{r_k|x_k = x, u_k = u, x_{k+1} = x'\}$, with $E\{\cdot\}$ the expected value operator. Define a performance index as the sum of future costs over the time interval $[k, k + T]$, $T > 0$,

$$J_{k,T} = \sum_{i=0}^{T} \gamma^i r_{k+1} \equiv \sum_{i=k}^{k+T} \gamma^{i-k} r_i, \tag{1}$$

where $0 \leq \gamma < 1$ is a discount factor that reduces the weight of costs incurred further in the future.

Usage of MDP in the fields of computational intelligence and economics usually considers r_k as a reward incurred at time k, also known as utility and $J_{k,T}$ as a discounted return also known as strategic reward. We refer instead to state costs and discounted future costs to be consistent with objectives in the control of dynamical systems. For convenience we call r_k the utility.

Consider that an agent selects a control policy $\pi_k(x_k, u_k)$ and uses it at each stage k of the MDP. We are primarily interested in stationary policies, where the conditional probabilities $\pi_k(x_k, u_k)$ are independent of k. Then $\pi_k(x, u) \equiv \pi(x, u) = Pr\{u|x\}$, $\forall k$. Non-stationary deterministic policies have the form $\pi = \{\mu_0, \mu_1, \ldots\}$, where each entry is a function $\mu_k(x) : X \to U; k = \{0, 1, \ldots\}$. Stationary deterministic policies are independent of time so that $\pi = \{\mu, \mu, \ldots\}$.

Select a fixed stationary policy $\pi(x, u) = Pr\{u|x\}$. Then the 'closed-loop' MDP reduces to a Markov chain with state space X. That is, the transition probabilities between states are fixed with no further freedom of choice of actions. The transition probabilities of this Markov chain are given by,

$$\mathrm{p}_{x,x'} \equiv P^{\pi}_{x,x'} = \sum_u Pr\{x'|x, u\} Pr\{u|x\} = \sum_u \pi(x, u) P^{u}_{x,x'}, \tag{2}$$

where the Chapman–Kolmogorov identity is used (Papoulis, 2002).

A Markov chain is ergodic if all the states are positive recurrent and aperiodic (Papoulis, 2002). Under the assumption that the Markov chain corresponding to each policy, with transition probabilities given as in Equation (2), is ergodic, it can be shown that every MDP has a stationary deterministic optimal policy (Al-Tamimi *et al.*, 2008; Bellman, 1957; Bertsekas and Tsitsiklis, 1996; Liu *et al.*, 2013; Papoulis, 2002; Prokhorov and Wunsch, 1997; Vrabie *et al.*, 2009; Werbos, 1989; Wheeler and Narendra, 1986). Then for a given policy there exists a stationary distribution $p_\pi(x)$ over X that gives the steady-state probability the Markov chain is in state x.

The value of a policy is defined as the conditional expected value of future cost when starting in state x at time k and following policy $\pi(x, u)$ thereafter,

$$V_k^{\pi}(x) = E_\pi\{J_{k,T}|x_k = x\} = E_\pi\left\{\sum_{i=k}^{k+T} \gamma^{i-k} r_i | x_k = x\right\}, \tag{3}$$

where $V^\pi(x)$ is known as the value function for policy $\pi(x, u)$.

A main objective of MDP is to determine a policy $\pi(x, u)$ to minimize the expected future cost,

$$\pi^*(x, u) = \arg\min_\pi V_k^\pi(x) = \arg\min_\pi E_\pi\left\{\sum_{i=k}^{k+T} \gamma^{i-k} r_i | x_k = x\right\}. \tag{4}$$

This policy is termed as optimal policy, and the corresponding optimal value is given as,

$$V_k^*(x) = \min_\pi V_k^\pi(x) = \min_\pi E_\pi\left\{\sum_{i=k}^{k+T} \gamma^{i-k} r_i | x_k = x\right\}. \tag{5}$$

In computational intelligence and economics, the interest is in utilities and rewards and the interest is in maximizing the expected performance index.

12.2.2. *A Backward Recursion for the Value*

By using the Chapman–Kolmogorov identity and the Markov property, we can write the value of policy $\pi(x, u)$ as,

$$V_k(x) = \sum_u \pi(x,u) \sum_{x'} P_{xx'}^u \left[R_{xx'}^u + \gamma V_{k+1}^\pi(x')\right]. \tag{6}$$

This equation provides a backwards recursion for the value at time k in terms of the value at time $k+1$.

12.2.3. *Dynamic Programming*

The optimal cost can be written as,

$$V_k^* = \min_\pi V_k^\pi(x) = \min_\pi \sum_u \pi(x,u) \sum_{x'} P_{xx'}^u \left[R_{xx'}^u + \gamma V_{k+1}^\pi(x')\right]. \tag{7}$$

Bellman's optimality principle (Bellman, 1957) states that "An optimal policy has the property that no matter what the previous control actions have been, the remaining controls constitute an optimal policy with regard to the state resulting from those previous controls". Therefore we can write,

$$V_k^* = \min_\pi V_k^\pi(x) = \min_\pi \sum_u \pi(x,u) \sum_{x'} P_{xx'}^u \left[R_{xx'}^u + \gamma V_{k+1}^*(x')\right]. \tag{8}$$

Suppose an arbitrary control u is now applied at time k and the optimal policy is applied from time $k+1$ on. Then Bellman's optimality principle says that the optimal control policy at time k is given by,

$$\pi^*(x,u) = \arg\min_\pi \sum_u \pi(x,u) \sum_{x'} P_{xx'}^u \left[R_{xx'}^u + \gamma V_{k+1}^*(x')\right]. \tag{9}$$

Under the assumption that the Markov chain corresponding to each policy with transition probabilities given as in Equation (2) is ergodic, every MDP has a stationary deterministic optimal policy. Then we can equivalently minimize the conditional expectation over all actions u in state x. Therefore,

$$V_k^* = \min_u \sum_{x'} P_{xx'}^u \left[R_{xx'}^u + \gamma V_{k+1}^*(x')\right], \tag{10}$$

$$u_k^* = \arg\min_u \sum_{x'} P_{xx'}^u \left[R_{xx'}^u + \gamma V_{k+1}^*(x')\right]. \tag{11}$$

The backwards recursion, Equation (10), forms the basis for dynamic programming which gives offline methods for working backwards in time to determine optimal policies (Lewis *et al.*, 2012b). DP is an offline procedure (Howard, 1960) for finding the optimal value and optimal policies that requires knowledge of the complete system dynamics in the form of transition probabilities $P_{xx'}^u = Pr\{x'|x, u\}$ and expected costs, $R_{xx'}^u = E\{r_k|x_k = x, u_k = u, x_{k+1} = x'\}$.

12.2.4. *Bellman Equation and Bellman Optimality Equation*

Dynamic programming is a backwards in time method for finding the optimal value and policy. By contrast, reinforcement learning is concerned with finding optimal policies based on causal experience by executing sequential decisions that improve control actions based on the observed results of using a current policy. This procedure requires the derivation of methods for finding optimal values and optimal policies that can be executed forward in time. The key to this is the Bellman equation, which we now develop. References for this subsection include (Barto *et al.*, 1983; Busoniu *et al.*, 2009; Powell, 2011; Sutton and Barto, 1998). To derive forward-in-time methods for finding optimal values and optimal policies, set now the time horizon T to $+\infty$ and define the infinite-horizon cost,

$$J_k = \sum_{i=0}^{\infty} \gamma^i r_{k+1} = \sum_{i=k}^{\infty} \gamma^{i-k} r_i. \tag{12}$$

The associated infinite-horizon value function for *policy* $\pi(x, u)$ is,

$$V^\pi(x) = E_\pi \left\{\gamma^{i-k} r_i | x_k = x\right\}. \tag{13}$$

By using (6) with $T = \infty$ it is seen that the value function for policy $\pi(x, u)$ satisfies the Bellman equation,

$$V^\pi(x) = \sum_u \pi(x, u) \sum_{x'} P_{xx'}^u \left[R_{xx'}^u + \gamma V^\pi(x')\right]. \tag{14}$$

The key to deriving this equation is that the same value function appears on both sides, which is due to the fact that the infinite-horizon cost is used. Therefore, the Bellman equation, Equation (14), can be interpreted as a consistency equation that must be satisfied by the value function at each time stage. It expresses a relation between the current value of being in state x and the value of being in next state x' given that policy $\pi(x, u)$ is used. The solution to the Bellman equation is the value given by the infinite sum in Equation (13).

The Bellman equation, Equation (14), is the starting point for developing a family of reinforcement learning algorithms for finding optimal policies by using causal experiences received stage-wise forward in time. The Bellman optimality equation, Equation (8), involves the minimum operator, and so does not contain any specific policy $\pi(x, u)$. Its solution relies on knowing the dynamics, in the form of transition probabilities. By contrast, the form of the Bellman equation is simpler than that of the optimality equation, and it is easier to solve. The solution to the Bellman equation yields the value function of a specific policy $\pi(x, u)$. As such, the Bellman equation is well suited to the actor-critic method of reinforcement learning shown in Figure 12.1. It is shown subsequently that the Bellman equation provides methods for implementing the critic in Figure 12.1, which is responsible for evaluating the performance of the specific current policy. Two key ingredients remain to be put in place. First, it is shown that methods known as policy iteration and value iteration use the Bellman equation to solve optimal control problems forward in time. Second, by approximating the value function in Equation (14) by a parametric structure, these methods can be implemented online using standard adaptive control system identification algorithms such as recursive least-squares.

In the context of using the Bellman equation, Equation (14), for reinforcement learning, $V^\pi(x)$ may be considered as a predicted performance $\sum_u \pi(x, u) \sum_{x'} P^u_{xx'} R^u_{xx'}$, the observed one step reward and $V^\pi(x')$ a current estimate of future behavior. Such notions can be capitalized on in the subsequent discussion of temporal different learning, which uses them to apply adaptive control algorithms that can learn optimal behavior online in real-time applications.

If the MDP is finite and has N states then the Bellman equation, Equation (14), is a system of N simultaneous linear equations for the value $V^\pi(x)$ of being in each state x given the current policy $\pi(x, u)$.

The optimal value satisfies,

$$V^*(x) = \min_\pi V^\pi(x) = \min_\pi \sum_u \pi(x, u) \sum_{x'} P^u_{xx'} \left[R^u_{xx'} + \gamma V^\pi(x)\right], \tag{15}$$

while the Bellman's optimality principle gives the Bellman optimality equation,

$$V^*(x) = \min_\pi V^\pi(x) = \min_\pi \sum_u \pi(x, u) \sum_{x'} P^u_{xx'} \left[R^u_{xx'} + \gamma V^*(x)\right], \tag{16}$$

Now under the assumption of ergodicity on the Markov chains corresponding to each action/policy, the Bellman optimality equation, Equation (16), can be written as,

$$V^*(x) = \min_u \sum_{x'} P^u_{xx'} \left[R^u_{xx'} + \gamma V^*(x')\right], \tag{17}$$

which is known as Hamilton–Jacobi–Bellman (HJB) equation in control systems. The optimal control is given by,

$$u^* = \arg\min_u \sum_{x'} P^u_{xx'}\big[R^u_{xx'} + \gamma V^*(x')\big]. \tag{18}$$

Equations (17)–(18) can be written in the context of feedback control of dynamical systems. In the Linear Quadratic Regulator (LQR) case the Bellman equation, Equation (14), becomes a Lyapunov equation and the optimality equation, Equation (16), becomes the well known algebraic Riccati equation.

We shall see in the subsequent subsection two different algorithmic methods to solve the Bellman equation, Equation (14).

12.2.5. *Policy Iteration and Value Iteration*

Given a current policy $\pi(x, u)$, its value, Equation (13), can be determined by solving Equation (14). This procedure is known as policy evaluation. Moreover, given the value for some policy $\pi(x, u)$ we can always use it to find another policy that is at least no worse. This step is known as policy improvement. Specifically, suppose $V^\pi(x)$ satisfies Equation (14). Then define a new policy $\pi'(x, u)$ by

$$\pi'(x, u) = \arg\min_\pi \sum_{\pi'} P^u_{xx'}\big[R^u_{xx'} + \gamma V^\pi(x')\big] \tag{19}$$

and it can be shown that the value is monotonically decreasing (Bertsekas and Tsitsiklis, 1996; Sutton and Barto, 1998). The policy, Equation (19), is said to be greedy with respect to the value function. In the special case that $V^{\pi'}(x) = V^\pi(x)$ in Equation (19), then the value and the policy satisfy Equations (17)–(18). In computational intelligence, greedy refers to quantities determined by optimizing over short or 1-step horizons, without regards to potential impacts far into the future. Now we will form the basis for the policy and value iteration algorithms in the form of two steps, a policy evaluation and a policy improvement. The policy evaluation step can be written as,

$$V^\pi(x) = \sum_u \pi(x, u) \sum_{\pi'} P^u_{xx'}\big[R^u_{xx'} + \gamma V^\pi(x')\big],\ \forall x \in S \subseteq X, \tag{20}$$

and the policy improvement step as,

$$\pi'(x, u) = \arg\min_\pi \sum_{\pi'} P^u_{xx'}\big[R^u_{xx'} + \gamma V^\pi(x')\big],\ \forall x \in S \subseteq X. \tag{21}$$

Here, S is a suitably selected subspace of the state space, to be discussed later. We call an application of Equation (20) followed by an application of Equation (21) one step. This terminology is in contrast to the decision time stage k defined above.

At each step of such algorithms, we obtain a policy that is no worse than the previous policy. Therefore, it is not difficult to prove convergence under fairly mild conditions to the optimal value and optimal policy. Most such proofs are based on the Banach Fixed Point Theorem. Note that Equation (17) is a fixed point equation for $V^*(\cdot)$. Then the two equations, Equations (20)–(21), define an associated map that can be shown under mild conditions to be a contraction map (Bertsekas and Tsitsiklis, 1996; Mehta and Meyn, 2009; Powell, 2011) which converges to the solution of Equation (17). A large family of algorithms is available that implement the policy evaluation and policy improvement procedures in different ways, or interleave them differently, or select subspace $S \subseteq X$ in different ways, to determine the optimal value and optimal policy. The relevance for feedback control systems of this discussion is that these two procedures can be implemented for dynamical systems online in real time by observing data measured along the system trajectories. The result is a family of adaptive control algorithms that converge to optimal control solutions. Such algorithms are of the actor-critic class of reinforcement learning systems, shown in Figure 12.1. There, a critic agent evaluates the current control policy using methods based on Equation (20). After this evaluation is completed, the action is updated by an actor agent based on Equation (21).

One method of reinforcement learning for using Equations (20)–(21) to find the optimal value and policy is called policy iteration and is described next.

Algorithm 1: Policy Iteration

---

procedure

  Given an initial admissible policy π_0

  while $\| V^{\pi^{(j)}} - V^{\pi^{(j-1)}} \| \geq \epsilon_{\text{ac}}$ **do**

    Solve for the value $V_j(x)$ using Bellman's equation

$$V_j(x) = \sum_u \pi_j(x, u) \sum_{x'} P^u_{xx'} \left[R^u_{xx'} + \gamma V_j(x') \right], \ \forall x \in X$$

    Update the control policy $\pi_{(j+1)}$ using

$$\pi_{(j+1)}(x, u) = \arg\min_{\pi} \sum_{\pi'} P^u_{xx'} \left[R^u_{xx'} + \gamma V_j(x') \right], \ \forall x \in X$$

    $j := j + 1$

  end while

end procedure

In Algorithm 1, ϵ_{ac} is a small number used to terminate the algorithm when two consecutive value functions differ by less than ϵ_{ac}.

At each step j, the policy iteration algorithm determines the solution of the Bellman equation to compute the value $V_j(x)$ of using the current policy $\pi_j(x, u)$. This value corresponds to the infinite sum, Equation (13) for the current policy. Then the policy is improved. The steps are continued until there is no change in the value or the policy. Note that j is not the time or stage index k, but a policy iteration step iteration index. As detailed in the next sections, policy iteration can be implemented for dynamical systems online in real time by observing data measured along the system trajectories. Data for multiple times k are needed to solve the Bellman equation at each step j. The policy iteration algorithm must be suitably initialized to converge. The initial policy $\pi_0(x, u)$ and value V_0 must be selected so that $V_1 \leq V_0$. Then, for finite Markov chains with N states, policy iteration converges in a finite number of steps, less than or equal to N, because there are only a finite number of policies (Bertsekas and Tsitsiklis, 1996).

If the MDP is finite and has N states, then the policy evaluation equation is a system of N simultaneous linear equations, one for each state. Instead of directly solving the Bellman equation, it can be solved by an iterative policy evaluation procedure.

A second method for using Equations (20) and (21) in reinforcement learning is value iteration.

Algorithm 2: Value Iteration

1: **procedure**
2: Given an initial policy π_0
3: **while** $\| V^{\pi^j} - V^{\pi^{(j-1)}} \| \geq \epsilon_{\text{ac}}$ **do**
4: Solve for the value $V_j(x)$ using Bellman's equation

$$V_{j+1}(x) = \sum_u \pi_j(x, u) \sum_{x'} P^u_{xx'}\big[R^u_{xx'} + \gamma V_j(x')\big], \ \forall x \in S_j \subseteq X$$

5: Update the policy π_{j+1} using

$$\pi_{j+1}(x, u) = \arg\min_{\pi} \sum_{\pi'} P^u_{xx'}\big[R^u_{xx'} + \gamma V_j(x')\big], \ \forall x \in S_j \subseteq X$$

6: $j := j + 1$
7: **end while**
8: **end procedure**

In Algorithm 2, ϵ_{ac} is a small number used to terminate the algorithm when two consecutive value functions differ by less than ϵ_{ac}.

In subsequent sections, we show how to implement value iteration for dynamical systems online in real time by observing data measured along the system trajectories. Data for multiple times k are needed to solve the Bellman equation for each step j. Standard value iteration takes the update set as $S_j = X$, for all j. That is, the value and policy are updated for all states simultaneously. Asynchronous value iteration methods perform the updates on only a subset of the states at each step. In the extreme case, updates can be performed on only one state at each step.

It is shown in Bertsekas and Tsitsiklis (1996) that standard value iteration, which has, $S_j = X, \forall j$, converges for finite MDP for all initial conditions when the discount factor satisfies $0 < \gamma < 1$. When $S_j = X, \forall j$ and $\gamma = 1$, an absorbing state is added and a 'properness' assumption is needed to guarantee convergence to the optimal value. When a single state is selected for value and policy updates at each step, the algorithm converges, for all choices of initial value, to the optimal cost and policy if each state is selected for update infinitely often. More universal algorithms result if value update is performed multiple times for different choices of S_j prior to a policy improvement. Then, it is required that the updates are performed infinitely often for each state, and a monotonicity assumption must be satisfied by the initial starting value.

Considering Equation (16) as a fixed point equation, value iteration is based on the associated iterative map, which can be shown under certain conditions to be a contraction map.

In contrast to policy iteration, which converges under certain conditions in a finite number of steps, value iteration usually takes an infinite number of steps to converge (Bertsekas and Tsitsiklis, 1996). Consider finite MDP and consider the transition probability graph having probabilities (2) for the Markov chain corresponding to an optimal policy $\pi^*(x, u)$. If this graph is acyclic for some $\pi^*(x, u)$, then value iteration converges in at most N steps when initialized with a large value. Having in mind the dynamic programming equation, Equation (6), and examining the value iteration value update $V_j(x')$ can be interpreted as an approximation or estimate for the future stage cost-to-go from the future state x'. Those algorithms wherein the future cost estimate are themselves costs or values for some policy are called roll-out algorithms in Bertsekas and Tsitsiklis (1996). Such policies are forward looking and self-correcting. It is shown that these methods can be used to derive algorithms for receding horizon control (Zhang *et al.*, 2009). MDP, policy iteration, and value iteration are closely tied to optimal and adaptive control.

12.2.6. *Generalized Policy Iteration*

In policy iteration, the system of linear equations (see Algorithm 1) is completely solved at each step to compute the value Equation (13) of using the current policy $\pi_j(x, u)$. This solution can be accomplished by running iterations of the policy evaluation step until convergence. By contrast, in value iteration one takes only one iteration in the value update step. Generalized policy iteration algorithms make several iterations in their value update step. Usually, policy iteration converges to the optimal value in fewer steps j since it does more work in solving equations at each step. On the other hand, value iteration is the easiest to implement as it only takes one iteration of a recursion. Generalized policy iteration provides a suitable compromise between computational complexity and convergence speed. Generalized policy iteration is a special case of the value iteration algorithm given above, where we select $S_j = X, \forall j$ and perform value update multiple times before each policy update.

12.2.7. *Q-Learning*

The conditional expected value in Equation (10) at iteration k is

$$\begin{aligned} Q_k^*(x, u) &= \sum_{x'} P_{xx'}^u \left[R_{xx'}^u + \gamma V_{k+1}^*(x') \right] \\ &= E_\pi \left\{ r_k + \gamma V_{k+1}^*(x') | x_k = x, u_k = u \right\}, \end{aligned} \tag{22}$$

and is known as optimal Q function (Watkins, 1989; Watkins and Dayan, 1992). In other words the Q function is equal to the expected return for taking an arbitrary action u at time k in state x and thereafter following an optimal policy. The Q function is a function of the current state x and the action u.

In terms of the Q function, the Bellman optimality equation has the particularly simple form,

$$V_k^*(x) = \min_u Q_k^*(x, u), \tag{23}$$

and

$$u_k^* = \arg\min_u Q_k^*(x, u), \tag{24}$$

Given some fixed policy $\pi(x, u)$ define the Q function for that policy as,

$$\begin{aligned} Q_k^\pi(x, u) &= E_\pi \left\{ r_k + \gamma V_{k+1}^\pi(x') | x_k = x, u_k = u \right\} \\ &= \sum_{x'} P_{xx'}^u \left[R_{xx'}^u + \gamma V_{k+1}^\pi(x') \right], \end{aligned} \tag{25}$$

where this function is equal to the expected return for taking an arbitrary action u at time k in state x and thereafter following the existing policy $\pi(x, u)$.

Note that $V_k^\pi(x) = Q_k^\pi(x, \pi(x, u))$ hence Equation (25) can be written as the backwards recursion in the Q function,

$$Q_k^\pi(x, u) = \sum_{x'} P_{xx'}^u \left[R_{xx'}^u + \gamma Q_{k+1}^\pi(x', \pi(x', u')) \right]. \tag{26}$$

The Q function is a two-dimensional function of both the current state x and the action u. By contrast, the value function is a one-dimensional function of the state. For finite MDP, the Q function can be stored as a 2D lookup table at each state/action pair. Note that direct minimization in Equations (8)–(9) requires knowledge of the state transition probabilities, which correspond to the system dynamics, and costs. By contrast, the minimization in Equations (23)–(24) requires knowledge only of the Q function and not the system dynamics. The utility of the Q function is twofold. First, it contains information about control actions in every state. As such, the best control in each state can be selected using Equation (24) by knowing only the Q function. Second, the Q function can be estimated online in real time directly from date observed along the system trajectories, without knowing the system dynamics information, that is, the transition probabilities. We shall see how this is accomplished later. The infinite horizon Q function for a prescribed fixed policy is given by,

$$Q^\pi(x, u) = \sum_{x'} P_{xx'}^u \left[R_{xx'}^u + \gamma V^\pi(x') \right] \tag{27}$$

which also satisfies the Bellman equation. Note that for a fixed policy $\pi(x, u)$

$$V^\pi(x) = Q^\pi(x, \pi(x, u)), \tag{28}$$

whence according to Equation (27) the Q function satisfies the Bellman equation,

$$Q^\pi(x, u) = \sum_{x'} P_{xx'}^u \left[R_{xx'}^u + \gamma Q^\pi(x', \pi(x', u')) \right]. \tag{29}$$

The Bellman optimality equation for the Q function is given by

$$Q^*(x, u) = \sum_{x'} P_{xx'}^u \left[R_{xx'}^u + \gamma \min_{u'} Q^*(x', u') \right]. \tag{30}$$

It is interesting to compare Equations (17) and (30) where the minimum operator and the expected value operator are reversed.

The algorithms defined in the previous subsections, namely, policy iteration and value iteration are really easy to implement in terms of the Q function, Equation (25) as follows,

---

Algorithm 3: Policy Iteration Using Q Function

---

procedure
    Given an initial admissible policy π_0
    while $\|Q^{\pi^j} - Q^{\pi^{(j-1)}}\| \geq \epsilon_{\text{ac}}$ **do**
        Solve for $Q_j(x)$ using

$$Q_j(x) = \sum_u \pi_j(x,u) \sum_{x'} P^u_{xx'}\big[R^u_{xx'} + \gamma Q_j(x', \pi(x', u'))\big], \ \forall x \in X$$

        Update the policy π_{j+1} using

$$\pi_{j+1}(x,u) = \arg\min_{\pi} Q_j(x,u), \ \forall x \in X$$

        $j := j + 1$
    end while
end procedure

Algorithm 4: Value Iteration Using Q Function

---

procedure
    Given an initial policy π_0
    while $\|Q^{\pi^j} - Q^{\pi^{(j-1)}}\| \geq \epsilon_{\text{ac}}$ **do**
        Solve for the value $Q_j(x)$ using Bellman's equation

$$Q_{j+1}(x) = \sum_u \pi_j(x,u) \sum_{x'} P^u_{xx'}\big[R^u_{xx'} + \gamma Q_j(x', \pi(x', u'))\big], \ \forall x \in S_j \subseteq X$$

        Update the policy π_{j+1} using

$$\pi_{j+1}(x,u) = \arg\min_{\pi} Q_j(x,u), \ \forall x \in S_j \subseteq X$$

        $j := j + 1$
    end while
end procedure

In Algorithms 3 and 4, ϵ_{ac} is a small number used to terminate the algorithm when two consecutive Q functions differ by less than ϵ_{ac}.

As we show, the utility of the Q function is that these algorithms can be implemented online in real-time, without knowing the system dynamics, by measuring data along the system trajectories. They yield optimal adaptive control algorithms, that is, adaptive control algorithms that converge online to optimal control solutions.

12.3. Methods for Implementing Policy Iteration and Value Iteration

Different methods are available for performing the value and policy updates for policy iteration and value iteration (Bertsekas and Tsitsiklis, 1996; Powell, 2011; Sutton and Barto, 1998) The main three are exact computation, Monte Carlo methods, and temporal difference learning. The last two methods can be implemented without the knowledge of the system dynamics. Temporal difference learning is the means by which optimal adaptive control algorithms can be derived for dynamical systems.

Policy iteration requires solution at each step of the Bellman equation for the value update. For a finite MDP with N states, this is a set of linear equations in N unknowns, namely, the values of each state. Value iteration requires performing the one-step recursive update at each step for the value update. Both of these can be accomplished exactly if we know the transition probabilities $P^u_{x,x'}$ and costs $R^u_{xx'}$ of the MDP, which corresponds to knowing full system dynamics information. Likewise, the policy improvements can be explicitly computed if the dynamics are known.

Monte Carlo learning is based on the definition, Equation (13), for the value function, and uses repeated measurements of data to approximate the expected value. The expected values are approximated by averaging repeated results along sample paths. An assumption on the ergodicity of the Markov chain with transition probabilities, Equation (2), for the given policy being evaluated is implicit. This assumption is suitable for episodic tasks, with experience divided into episodes (Sutton and Barto, 1998), namely, processes that start in an initial state and run until termination, and are then restarted at a new initial state. For finite MDP, Monte Carlo methods converge to the true value function if all states are visited infinitely often. Therefore, in order to ensure accurate approximations of value functions, the episode sample paths must go through all the states $x \in X$ many times. This issue is called the problem of maintaining exploration. Several methods are available to ensure this, one of which is to use 'exploring starts', in which every state has non-zero probability of being selected as the initial state of an episode. Monte Carlo techniques are useful for dynamic systems control because the episode sample paths can be interpreted as system trajectories beginning in a prescribed initial state. However, no updates to the value function estimate or the control policy are made until after an episode terminates. In fact, Monte Carlo learning methods are closely related to repetitive or iterative learning control (Moore, 1993). They do not learn in real time along a trajectory, but learn as trajectories are repeated.

12.4. Temporal Difference Learning and its Application to Feedback Control

It is now shown that the temporal difference method (Sutton and Barto, 1998) for solving Bellman equations leads to a family of optimal adaptive controllers, that is, adaptive controllers that learn online the solutions to optimal control problems without knowing the full system dynamics. Temporal difference learning is true online reinforcement learning, wherein control actions are improved in real time based on estimating their value functions by observing data measured along the system trajectories.

Policy iteration requires solution at each step of N linear equations. Value iteration requires performing a recursion at each step. Temporal difference reinforcement learning methods are based on the Bellman equation without using any systems dynamics knowledge, but using data observed along a single trajectory of the system. Therefore, temporal difference learning is applicable for feedback control applications. Temporal difference updates the value at each time step as observations of data are made along a trajectory. Periodically, the new value is used to update the policy. Temporal difference methods are related to adaptive control in that they adjust values and actions online in real time along system trajectories. Temporal difference methods can be considered to be stochastic approximation techniques whereby the Bellman equation, Equation (14), is replaced by its evaluation along a single sample path of the MDP. Then, the Bellman equation becomes a deterministic equation that allows the definition of a temporal difference error. Equation (6) is used to write the Bellman equation, Equation (14) for the infinite-horizon value, Equation (13). An alternative form for the Bellman equation is,

$$V^{\pi}(x_k) = E_{\pi}\{r_k|x_k\} + \gamma E_{\pi}\{V_{\pi}(x_{k+1})|x_k\}, \tag{31}$$

which is the basis for temporal difference learning.

Temporal difference reinforcement learning uses one sample path, namely the current system trajectory, to update the value. Then, Equation (31) is replaced by the deterministic Bellman equation,

$$V^{\pi}(x_k) = r_k + \gamma V_{\pi}(x_{k+1}), \tag{32}$$

which holds for each observed data experience set (x_k, x_{k+1}, r_k) at each time step k. This dataset consists of the current state x_k the observed cost r_k and the next state x_{k+1}. Hence, we can define the temporal difference error as

$$e_k = -V^{\pi}(x_k) + r_k + \gamma V^{\pi}(x_{k+1}), \tag{33}$$

and the value estimate is updated to make the temporal difference error small.

In the context of temporal difference learning, the interpretation of the Bellman equation is shown in Figure 12.2, where $V^{\pi}(x_k)$ may be considered as a predicted performance or value, r_k as the observed one step reward, and $\gamma V^{\pi}(x_{k+1})$ as a current estimate of future value. The Bellman equation can be interpreted as a consistency equation that holds if the current estimate for the predicted value $V^{\pi}(x_k)$ is correct. Temporal difference methods update the predicted value estimate $\hat{V}^{\pi}(x_k)$ to make the temporal difference error small. The idea, based on stochastic approximation, is that if we use the deterministic version of Bellman's equation repeatedly in policy iteration or value iteration, then on average these algorithms converge towards the solution of the stochastic Bellman equation.

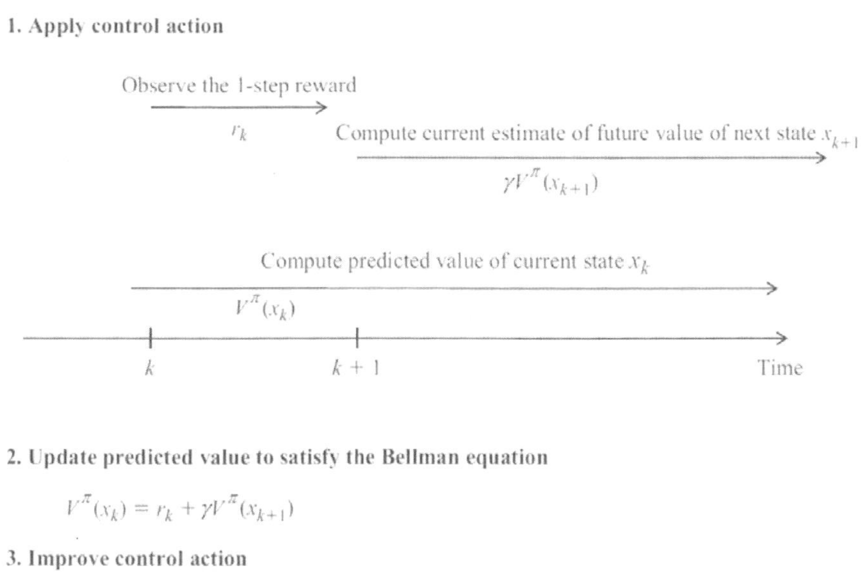

Figure 12.2: Temporal difference interpretation of Bellman equation. Shows how use of the Bellman equation captures the action, observation, evaluation, and improvement mechanisms of reinforcement learning.

12.5. Optimal Adaptive Control for Discrete-Time Deterministic Systems

A family of optimal adaptive control algorithms can now be developed for dynamical systems. These algorithms determine the solutions to Hamilton–Jacobi (HJ) design equations online in real-time without knowing the system drift dynamics. In the LQR case, this means they solve the Riccati equation online without knowing the system A matrix. Physical analysis of dynamical systems using Lagrangian mechanics or Hamiltonian mechanics produces system descriptions in terms of nonlinear ordinary differential equations. Discretization yields nonlinear difference equations. Most research in reinforcement learning is conducted for systems that operate in discrete time (Sutton and Barto, 1998; Werbos, 1992; Wheeler and Narendra, 1986). Therefore, we cover discrete-time dynamical systems first, then continuous time systems.

Temporal difference learning is a stochastic approximation technique based on the deterministic Bellmans equation, Equation (32). Therefore, we lose little by considering deterministic systems here. Therefore, consider a class of discrete-time systems described by deterministic nonlinear dynamics in the affine state space difference equation form,

$$x_{k+1} = f(x_k) + g(x_k)u_k, \quad k = 0, 1, \ldots, \tag{34}$$

with state $x_k \in \mathrm{IR}^n$ and control input $u_k \in \mathrm{IR}^m$. We use this form because its analysis is convenient. The following development can be generalized to the sampled-data form $x_{k+1} = F(x_k, u_k)$.

A deterministic control policy is defined as a function from state space to control space $h(\cdot) : \mathrm{IR}^n - \mathrm{IR}^m$. That is, for every state x_k, the policy defines a control action,

$$u_k = h(x_k), \tag{35}$$

which is a feedback controller.

The value function with a deterministic cost function can be written as,

$$V^h(x_k) = \sum_{i=k}^{\infty} \gamma^{i-k} r(x_i, u_i) = \sum_{i=k}^{\infty} \gamma^{i-k} \big(Q(x_i) + u_i^T R u_i\big), \tag{36}$$

where $0 < \gamma \leq 1$ is a discount factor, $Q(x_k) > 0$, $R > 0$ and $u_k = h(x_k)$ is a prescribed feedback control policy. That is, the stage cost is

$$r(x_k, u_k) = Q(x_k) + u_k^T Q u_k, \tag{37}$$

which is taken as quadratic in u_k to simplify the developments but can be any positive definite function of the control. We assume that the system is stabilizable on some set $\Omega \in \mathrm{IR}^n$, that is there exists a control policy $u_k = h(x_k)$ such that the closed-loop system $x_{k+1} = f(x_k) + g(x_k)h(x_k)$ is asymptotically stable on Ω.

For the deterministic value (36), the optimal value is given by Bellman's optimality equation,

$$v^*(x_k) = \min_{h(\cdot)}(r(x_k, h(x_k)) + \gamma V^*(x_{k+1})), \tag{38}$$

which is just the discrete time Hamilton–Jacobi–Bellman (HJB) equation. The optimal policy is then given as,

$$h^*(x_k) = \arg\min_{h(\cdot)}(r(x_k, h(x_k)) + \gamma V^*(x_{k+1})). \tag{39}$$

In this setup, the deterministic Bellman's equation, Equation (32) is,

$$\begin{aligned} V^h(x_k) &= r(x_k, u_k) + \gamma V^h(x_{k+1}) \\ &= Q(x_k) + \mu_k^T R u_k + \gamma V^h(x_{k+1}), \quad V^h(0) = 0, \end{aligned} \tag{40}$$

which is a difference equation equivalent of the value, Equation (36). That is, instead of evaluating the infinite sum, Equation (36), the difference equation, Equation (40), can be solved with boundary condtion $V(0) = 0$ to obtain the value of using a current policy $u_k = h(x_k)$.

The discrete-time Hamiltonian function can be defined as,

$$H(x_k, h(x_k), \Delta V_k) = r(x_k, h(x_k)) + \gamma V^h(x_{k+1}) - V^h(x_k), \tag{41}$$

where $\Delta V_k \equiv \gamma V^h(x_{k+1}) - V^h(x_k)$ is the forward difference operator. The Hamiltonian function captures the energy content along the trajectories of a system as reflected in the desired optimal performance. In fact, the Hamiltonian is the temporal difference error, Equation (33). The Bellman equation requires that the Hamiltonian be equal to zero for the value associated with a prescribed policy.

For the discrete-time linear quadratic regulator case we have,

$$x_{k+1} = Ax_k + Bu_k, \tag{42}$$

$$V^h(x_k) = \frac{1}{2}\sum_{i=k}^{\infty} \gamma^{i-k}\left(x_i^T Q x_i + u_i^T R u_i\right) \tag{43}$$

and the Bellman equation can be easily derived.

12.5.1. *Policy Iteration and Value Iteration for Discrete-Time Deterministic Dynamical Systems*

Two forms of reinforcement learning can be based on policy iteration and value iteration.

Algorithm 5: Policy Iteration Using Temporal Difference Learning

procedure
  Given an initial admissible policy $h_0(x_k)$
  while $\|V^{h^j} - V^{h^{(j-1)}}\| \geq \epsilon_{\text{ac}}$ **do**
    Solve for $V_j(x_k)$ using

$$V_{j+1}(x_k) = r(x_k, h_j(x_k)) + \gamma V_{j+1}(x_{k+1})$$

    Update the policy h_{j+1} using

$$h_{j+1}(x_k) = -\frac{\gamma}{2} R^{-1} g^T(x_k) \nabla V_{j+1}(x_{k+1}),$$

    $j := j + 1$
  end while
end procedure

Algorithm 6: Value Iteration Using Temporal Difference Learning

procedure
  Given an initial policy $h_0(x_k)$
  while $\|V^{h^j} - V^{h^{(j-1)}}\| \geq \epsilon_{\text{ac}}$ **do**
    Solve for $V_j(x_k)$ using

$$V_{j+1}(x_k) = r(x_k, h_j(x_k)) + \gamma V_j(x_{k+1})$$

    Update the policy h_{j+1} using

$$h_{j+1}(x_k) = -\frac{\gamma}{2} R^{-1} g^T(x_k) \nabla V_{j+1}(x_{k+1}),$$

    $j := j + 1$
  end while
end procedure

In Algorithms 5 and 6, ϵ_{ac} is a small number used to terminate the algorithm when two consecutive value functions differ by less than ϵ_{ac} and $\nabla V(x) = \frac{\partial V(x)}{\partial x}$. Note that in value iteration we can select any initial control policy, not necessarily admissible or stabilizing. The policy iteration and value iteration algorithms just described are offline design methods that require knowledge of the discrete-time dynamics. By contrast, we next desire to determine online methods for implementing policy iteration and value iteration that do not require full dynamics information.

Policy iteration and value iteration can be implemented for finite MDP by storing and updating lookup tables. The key to implementing policy iteration and value iteration online for dynamical systems with infinite state and action spaces is to approximate the value function by a suitable approximator structure in terms of unknown parameters. Then, the unknown parameters are tuned online exactly as in system identification. This idea of value function approximation (VFA) is used by Werbos (1989, 1992), and called approximate dynamic programming (ADP) or adaptive dynamic programming. The approach is used by Bertsekas and Tsitsiklis (1996) and called neuro-dynamic programming (Bertsekas and Tsitsiklis, 1996; Busoniu *et al.*, 2009; Powell, 2011). For nonlinear systems, Equation (34), the value function contains higher order nonlinearities. Then, we assume the Bellman equation, Equation (40), has a local smooth solution (Van der Schaft, 1992). Then, according to the Weierstrass Higher Order Approximation Theorem, there exists a dense basis set $\phi_i(x)$ such that,

$$V(x) = W^T \phi(x) + \epsilon_L(x), \tag{44}$$

where $\phi(x) = [\phi_1(x)\phi_2(x)\ldots\phi_L(x)] : \mathbb{R}^n \to \mathbb{R}^L$ and $\epsilon_L(x)$ converges uniformly to zero as the basis sets $L \to \infty$. Note that in the LQR case the weight vector consists of the elements of the symmetric Riccati matrix P. We are now in a position to present several adaptive control algorithms based on temporal difference reinforcement learning that converge online to the optimal control solution.

Algorithm 7: Optimal Adaptive Control Using Policy Iteration

1: **procedure**
2: Given an initial admissible policy $h_0(x_k)$
3: **while** No convergence **do**
4: Determine the least squares solution W_{j+1} using

$$W_{j+1}^T(\phi(x_k) - \gamma\phi(x_{k+1})) = r(x_k, h_j(x_k))$$

5: Update the policy h_{j+1} using

$$h_{j+1}(x_k) = -\frac{\gamma}{2}R^{-1}g^T(x_k)\nabla\phi^T(x_{k+1})W_{j+1},$$

6: $j := j + 1$
7: **end while**
8: **end procedure**

Algorithm 8: Optimal Adaptive Control Using Value Iteration

1: **procedure**
2: Given an initial policy $h_0(x_k)$
3: **while** No convergence **do**
4: Determine the least squares solution W_{j+1} using

$$W_{j+1}^T \phi(x_k) = r(x_k, h_j(x_k)) + \gamma W_j^T \phi(x_{k+1})$$

5: Update the policy h_{j+1} using

$$h_{j+1}(x_k) = -\frac{\gamma}{2} R^{-1} g^T(x_k) \nabla\phi^T(x_{k+1}) W_{j+1},$$

6: $j := j + 1$
7: **end while**
8: **end procedure**

12.5.2. *Introducing a Second 'Actor' Neural Network*

Using value function approximation (VFA) allows standard system identification techniques to be used to find the value function parameters that approximately solve the Bellman equation. The approximator structure just described that is used for approximation of the value function is known as the critic neural network, as it determines the value of using the current policy. Using VFA, the policy iteration reinforcement learning algorithm solves a Bellman equation during the value update portion of each iteration step j by observing only the dataset $(x_k, x_{k+1}, r(x_k, h_j(x_k)))$ at each time along the system trajectory. In the case of value iteration, VFA is used to perform a value update.

The critic network solves the Bellman equation using observed data without knowing the system dynamics. However, note that in the Linear Quadratic Case (systems of the form $x_{k+1} = Ax_k + Bu_k$ with quadratic costs) case the policy update is given by

$$K^{j+1} = -(B^T P^{j+1} B + R)^{-1} B^T P^{j+1} A, \tag{45}$$

which requires full knowledge of the dynamics.

This problem can be solved by introducing a second neural network for the control policy, known as the actor neural network (Al-Tamimi *et al.*, 2008; Vrabie and Lewis, 2009; Werbos, 1989). Therefore, consider a parametric approximator structure for the control action,

$$u_k = h(x_k) = U^T \sigma(x_k) \tag{46}$$

with $\sigma(x) : \mathrm{IR}^n \mathrm{IR}^m$ a vector of M activation functions and $U \in \mathrm{IR}^{M \times m}$ a matrix of weights or unknown parameters. Note that in the LQR case the basis set can be taken as the state vector. After convergence of the critic neural network parameters to W_{j+1} in policy iteration or value iteration, it is required to perform the policy update. To achieve this aim, we can use a gradient descent method for tuning the actor weights U such as,

$$U_{j+1}^{i+1} = U_{j+1}^{i} - \beta \sigma(x_k) \left(2R \left(U_{j+1}^{i} \right)^T \sigma(x_k) + \gamma g^T(x_k) \nabla \phi^T(x_{k+1}) W_{j+1} \right)^T, \tag{47}$$

where $\beta \in \mathrm{IR}^+$ is a tuning parameter. The tuning index i can be incremented with the time index k.

Note that the tuning of the actor neural network requires observations at each time k of the dataset x_k, x_{k+1}, that is, the current state and the next state. However, as per the formulation Equation (46), the actor neural network yields the control u_k at time k in terms of the state x_k at time k. The next state x_{k+1} is not needed in Equation (46). Thus, after Equation (47) converges, Equation (46) is a legitimate feedback controller. Note also that, in the LQR case, the actor neural network Equation (46) embodies the feedback gain computation Equation (45). Equation (45) contains the state internal dynamics A, but Equation (46) does not. Therefore, the A matrix is not needed to compute the feedback control. The reason is that the actor neural network learns information about A in its weights, since x_k, x_{k+1} are used in its tuning. Finally, note that only the input function $g(\cdot)$ or, in the LQR case, the B matrix, is needed in Equation (47) to tune the actor neural network. Thus, introducing a second actor neural network completely avoids the need for knowledge of the state drift dynamics $f(\cdot)$, or A in the LQR case.

12.6. Actor/Critic Structures for Optimal Adaptive Control

The implementation of reinforcement learning using two neural networks, one as a critic and one as an actor, yields the actor/critic reinforcement learning structure shown in Figure 12.1. In this control system, the critic and the actor are tuned online using the observed data $(x_k, x_{k+1}, r(x_k, h_j(x_k)))$ along the system trajectory. The critic and actor are tuned sequentially in both the policy iteration and the value iteration algorithms. That is, the weights of one neural network are held constant while the weights of the other are tuned until convergence. This procedure is repeated until both neural networks have converged. Thus, the controller learns the optimal controller online. This procedure amounts to an online adaptive optimal control system wherein the value function parameters are tuned online and the convergence is to the optimal value and control. The convergence of value iteration using two neural networks for the discrete-time nonlinear system Equation (34) is proven in (Al-Tamimi *et al.*, 2008).

According to reinforcement learning principles, the optimal adaptive control structure requires two loops, a critic and an actor, and operates at multiple timescales. A fast loop implements the control action inner loop, a slower timescale operates in the critic loop, and a third timescale operates to update the policy. Several actor/critic structures for optimal adaptive control have been proposed in Ferrari and Stengel (2002); Prokhorov *et al.* (1995) and Hanselmann *et al.* (2007).

12.6.1. *Q-learning for Optimal Adaptive Control*

It has just been seen how to implement an optimal adaptive controller using reinforcement learning that only requires knowledge of the system input function $g(x_k)$. The Q learning reinforcement learning method gives an adaptive control algorithm that converges online to the optimal control solution for completely unknown systems. That is, it solves the Bellman equation, Equation (40), and the HJB equation, Equation (38), online in real time by using data measured along the system trajectories, without any knowledge of the dynamics $f(x_k)$, $g(x_k)$. Writing the Q function Bellman equation, Equation (29) along a sample path gives,

$$Q^{\pi}(x_k, u_k) = r(x_k, u_k) + \gamma Q^{\pi}(x_{k+1}, h(x_{k+1})), \tag{48}$$

which defines a temporal difference error,

$$e_k = -Q^{\pi}(x_k, u_k) + r(x_k, u_k) + \gamma Q^{\pi}(x_{k+1}, h(x_{k+1})). \tag{49}$$

The Q function is updated using the algorithm,

$$\begin{aligned} Q_k(x_k, u_k) &= Q_{k-1}(x_k, u_k) \\ &\quad + \alpha_k\big[r(x_k, u_k) + \gamma \min_u Q_{k-1}(x_{k+1}, u_k) - Q_{k-1}(x_k, u_k)\big], \end{aligned} \tag{50}$$

with α_k a tuning parameter. This algorithm is developed for finite MDP and the convergence proven by Watkins (1989) using Stochastic Approximation (SA) methods. The Q learning algorithm Equation (50) is similar to SA methods of adaptive control or parameter estimation used in control systems. Let us now derive methods for Q learning for dynamical systems that yield adaptive control algorithms that converge to optimal control solutions. Policy iteration and value iteration algorithms can be given using the Q function. A Q learning algorithm is easily developed for discrete-time dynamical systems using Q function approximation

(Bradtke *et al.*, 1994; Werbos, 1989, 1991, 1992). Assume therefore that for nonlinear systems the Q function is parameterized as,

$$Q(x,u) = W^T \phi(z), \tag{51}$$

where $z_k \equiv \left[x_k^T \; u_k^T\right]^T$, W is the unknown parameter vector and $\phi(z)$ is the basis set vector. Substituting the Q-function approximation into the temporal difference error Equation (49) yields,

$$e_k = -W^T \phi(z_k) + r(x_k, u_k) + \gamma W^T \phi(z_{k+1}), \tag{52}$$

on which either policy iteration or value iteration algorithms can be based. Considering the policy iteration algorithm defined before the Q-function evaluation step is,

$$W_{j+1}^T(\phi(z_k) - \gamma\phi(z_{k+1})) = r(x_k, h_j(x_k)), \tag{53}$$

and the policy improvement step,

$$h_{j+1}(x_k) = \arg\min_u \left(W_{j+1}^T \phi(x_k, u)\right), \quad \forall x \in X. \tag{54}$$

Now using value iteration, the Q learning is given by,

$$W_{j+1}^T \phi(z_k) = r(x_k, h_j(x_k)) + \gamma W_j^T \phi(z_{k+1}), \tag{55}$$

and Equation (54). Note that these equations do not require knowledge of the dynamics.

12.6.2. *Approximate Dynamic Programming Using Output feedback*

The methods discussed have relied on full state variable feedback. Little work has been done in applications of reinforcement learning for feedback control using output feedback. This corresponds to partially observable Markov processes. Design of an ADP controller that uses only output feedback is given in Lewis and Vamvoudakis (2011).

12.7. Integral Reinforcement Learning for Optimal Adaptive Control of Deterministic Continuous-Time Systems

Reinforcement learning is considerably more difficult for continuous-time systems (Doya, 2000) than for discrete-time systems, and fewer results are available. See Abu-Khalaf *et al.* (2006) for the development of an offline policy iteration method for continuous-time systems. Using a method known as integral reinforcement learning (IRL) (Vrabie and Lewis, 2009; Vrabie *et al.*, 2009; Vrabie and Vamvoudakis, 2012; Zhang *et al.*, 2013) allows the application of reinforcement learning to formulate online optimal adaptive control methods for continuous-time systems.

These methods find solutions to optimal HJ design equations and Riccati equations online in real-time without knowing the system drift dynamics $f(x)$, or in the LQR case without knowing the A matrix.

Consider the continuous-time nonlinear dynamical system,

$$\dot{x} = f(x) + g(x)u, \tag{56}$$

where $x \in \mathbb{R}^n$ is the state, $u \in \mathbb{R}^m$ is the control input. Also consider as $x = 0$ an equilibrium point e.g., $f(0) = 0$ and $f(x) + g(x)u$ Lipschitz on a set $\Omega \subseteq \mathbb{R}^n$ that contains the origin. We assume the system is stabilizable on Ω, that is, there exists a continuous control input function $u(t)$ such that the closed-loop system is asymptotically stable on Ω.

Define a performance measure or cost function that has the value associated with the feedback control policy $u = \mu(x)$ given by,

$$V^{\mu}(x(t)) = \int_t^{\infty} r(x(\tau), u(\tau))d\tau, \tag{57}$$

where $r(x, u) = Q(x) + u^T Ru$ the utility function, $Q(x) > 0$, $\forall x$ and $x = 0 \to Q(x) = 0$, and $R = R^T$ positive definite matrix.

For the continuous-time LQR, we have,

$$\dot{x} = Ax + Bu, \tag{58}$$

$$V^{\mu}(x(t)) = \frac{1}{2}\int_t^{\infty} \left(x^T Qx + u^T Ru\right) d\tau. \tag{59}$$

If the cost is smooth, then an infinitesimal equivalent to Equation (57) can be found by Leibnizs formula to be,

$$0 = r(x, \mu(x)) + (\nabla V^{\mu})^T (f(x) + g(x)\mu(x)), \quad V^{\mu}(0) = 0, \tag{60}$$

where ∇V^{μ} denotes the column gradient vector with respect to x.

This is the continuous-time Bellman equation. This equation is defined based on the continuous-time Hamiltonian function,

$$H(x, \mu(x), \nabla V^{\mu}) = r(x, \mu(x)) + (\nabla V^{\mu})^T (f(x) + g(x)\mu(x)) \tag{61}$$

and the HJB equation is given by

$$0 = \min_{\mu} H(x, \mu(x), \nabla V^*) \tag{62}$$

with an optimal control,

$$\mu^* = \arg\min_{\mu} H(x, \mu(x), \nabla V^*). \tag{63}$$

We now see the problem with continuous-time systems immediately. Comparing the continuous-time Hamiltonian Equation (61) to the discrete-time Hamiltonian equation (41), it is seen that Equation (61) contains the full system dynamics $f(x)+g(x)u$, while Equation (41) does not. What this means is that the continuous-time Bellman equation, Equation (86) cannot be used as a basis for reinforcement learning unless the full dynamics are known. Reinforcement learning methods based on Equation (60) can be developed (Mehta and Meyn, 2009). These have limited use for adaptive control purposes because the system dynamics must be know, state derivatives must be measured, or integration over an infinite horizon is required. In another approach, Euler's method can be used to discretize the continuous-time Bellman equation, Equation (60) [see (Baird, 1994)]. Noting that

$$0 = r(x, \mu(x)) + (\nabla V^{\mu})^{T}(f(x) + g(x)\mu(x)) = r(x, \mu(x)) + \dot{V}^{\mu}, \qquad (64)$$

we use Euler's forward method to discretize this partial differential equation (PDE) to obtain,

$$0 = r(x, \mu(x)) + \frac{V^{\mu}(x_{k+1}) - V^{\mu}(x_k)}{T} \equiv \frac{r_S(x_k, u_k)}{T} + \frac{V^{\mu}(x_{k+1}) - V^{\mu}(x_k)}{T}, \qquad (65)$$

where $T > 0$ is a sample period i.e., $t = kT$ and $r_S(x_k, u_k) = Tr(x_k, u_k)$.

Now note that the discretized continuous-time Bellman equation, Equation (65) has the same form as the discrete-time Bellman equation, Equation (40). Therefore, all the reinforcement learning methods just described for discrete-time systems can be applied.

However, this equation is an approximation only. An alternative exact method for continuous-time reinforcement learning is given in Vrabie and Lewis (2009); Vrabie *et al.* (2009). That method is termed integral reinforcement learning (IRL). Note that the cost Equation (57) can be written in the integral reinforcement form,

$$V^{\mu}(x(t)) = \int_{t}^{t+T} r(x(\tau), u(\tau))d\tau + V^{\mu}(x(t+T)), \qquad (66)$$

for some $T > 0$. This equation is exactly in the form of the discrete-time Bellman equation, Equation (40). According to Bellmans principle, the optimal value is given in terms of this construction as (Lewis *et al.*, 2012b),

$$V^{*}(x(t)) = \min_{\overline{u}(t:t+T)} \left(\int_{t}^{t+T} r(x(\tau), u(\tau))d\tau + V^{*}(x(t+T)) \right)$$

where $\overline{u}(t:t+T) = \{u(\tau) : t \leq \tau < t+T\}$ and the optimal control is given by,

$$\mu^*(x(t)) = \arg \min_{\bar{u}(t:t+T)} \left(\int_t^{t+T} r(x(\tau), u(\tau))d\tau + V^*(x(t+T)) \right).$$

It is shown in Vrabie *et al.* (2009) that the Bellman equation, Equation (60), is equivalent to the integral reinforcement form Equation (66). That is, the positive definite solution of both is the value Equation (57) of the policy $u = \mu(x)$. The integral reinforcement form Equation (66) serves as a Bellman equation for continuous-time systems, and is a fixed point equation. Therefore, the temporal difference error for continuous-time systems can be defined as,

$$e(t:t+T) = \int_t^{\infty} r(x(\tau), u(\tau))d\tau + V^{\mu}(x(t+T)) - V^{\mu}(x(t)), \tag{67}$$

which is an equation that does not involve the system dynamics. Now, it is direct to formulate policy iteration and value iteration for continuous-time systems. The following algorithms are termed integral reinforcement learning for continuous time systems in Vrabie and Lewis (2009); Vrabie *et al.* (2009). Both algorithms give optimal adaptive controllers for continuous time systems, that is, adaptive control algorithms that converge to optimal control solutions.

Algorithm 9: IRL Optimal Adaptive Control Using Policy Iteration

---

1: **procedure**
2: Given an initial admissible policy $\mu_0(x)$
3: **while** $\| V^{\mu^j} - V^{\mu^{(j-1)}} \| \geq \epsilon_{\text{ac}}$ **do**
4: Solve for V_j using

$$V_{j+1}(x(t)) = \int_t^{t+T} r(x(s), \mu_j(x(s)))ds + V_{j+1}(x(t+T)), \; V_{j+1}(0) = 0$$

5: Update the policy μ_{j+1} using

$$\mu_{j+1}(x_k) = -\frac{1}{2}R^{-1}g^T(x)\nabla V_{j+1},$$

6: $j := j+1$
7: **end while**
8: **end procedure**

Algorithm 10: IRL Optimal Adaptive Control Using Value Iteration

procedure
  Given an initial policy $\mu_0(x)$
  while $\| V^{\mu^j} - V^{\mu^{(j-1)}} \| \geq \epsilon_{\mathrm{ac}}$ **do**
    Solve for V_j using

$$V_{j+1}(x(t)) = \int_{t}^{t+T} r(x(s), \mu_j(x(s)))ds + V_j(x(t+T))$$

    Update the policy μ_{j+1} using

$$\mu_{j+1}(x) = -\frac{1}{2}R^{-1}g^T(x)\nabla V_{j+1},$$

    $j := j+1$
  end while
end procedure

In Algorithms 9 and 10, ϵ_{ac} is a small number used to terminate the algorithm when two consecutive value functions differ by less than ϵ_{ac} and note that neither algorithm requires knowledge about the system drift dynamics function $f(x)$. That is, they work for partially unknown systems. Convergence of IRL policy iteration is proved in Vrabie *et al.* (2009). An IRL algorithm for nonlinear systems has been proposed in Liu *et al.* (2013).

12.7.1. *Online Implementation of IRL — a Hybrid Optimal Adaptive Controller*

Both of these IRL algorithms can be implemented online by reinforcement learning techniques using value function approximation $V(x) = W^T\phi(x)$ in a critic approximator network. Using VFA in the policy iteration algorithm just defined yields

$$W_{j+1}^T[\phi(x(t)) - \phi(x(t+T))] = \int_{t}^{\infty} r(x(s), \mu_j(x(s)))ds. \tag{68}$$

Using VFA in the value iteration algorithm just defined yields

$$W_{j+1}^T\phi(x(t)) = \int_{t}^{\infty} r(x(s), \mu_j(x(s)))ds + W_j^T\phi(x(t+T))]. \tag{69}$$

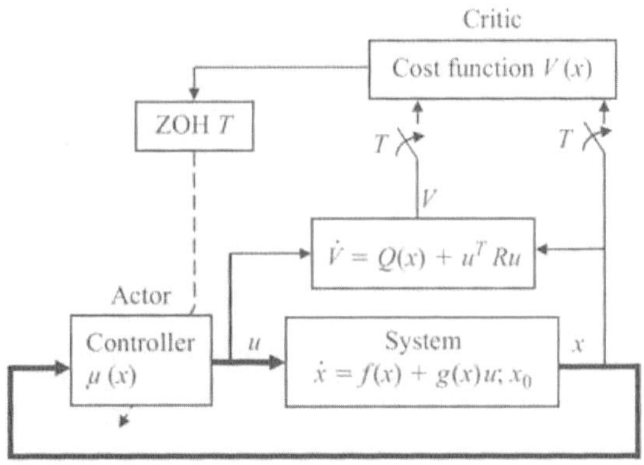

Figure 12.3: Hybrid optimal adaptive controller based on Integral Reinforcement Learning. Shows the two-time scale hybrid nature of the IRL controller. The integral reinforcement signal $\rho(t)$ is added as an extra state and functions as the memory of the controller. The Critic runs on a slow time scale and learns the value of using the current control policy. When the Critic converges, the Actor control policy is updated to obtain an improved value.

Then RLS or least-squares batch is used to update the value function parameters in these equations. On convergence of the value parameters, the action is updated.

IRL provides an optimal adaptive controller, that is, an adaptive controller that measures data along the system trajectories and converges to optimal control solutions. Note that only the system input coupling dynamics $g(x)$ is needed to implement these algorithms. The drift dynamics $f(x)$ is not needed. The implementation of IRL optimal adaptive control is shown in Figure 12.3. The time is incremented at each iteration by the period T. The reinforcement learning time interval T need not be the same at each iteration. T can be changed depending on how long it takes to receive meaningful information from the observations and is not a sample period in the standard meaning. The measured data at each time increment are $(x(t), x(t+T), \rho(t:t+T))$ where,

$$\rho(t:t+T) = \int_{t}^{t+T} r(x(\tau), u(\tau))d\tau \tag{70}$$

is the integral reinforcement measured on each time interval. The integral reinforcement can be computed in real time by introducing an integrator $\dot{\rho} = r(x(t), u(t))$ as shown in Figure 12.3. That is, the integral reinforcement $\rho(t)$ is added as an extra continuous-time state. It functions as the memory or controller dynamics. The remainder of the controller is a sampled-data controller. Note that the control policy $\mu(t)$ is updated periodically after the critic weights have converged to the solution to Equation (68) or Equation (69). Therefore, the policy is piecewise constant in time. On the other hand, the control varies continuously with the state between each policy update. It is seen that IRL for continuous-time systems is in fact a hybrid continuous-time/discrete-time adaptive controller that converges to the optimal control solution in real-time without knowing the drift dynamics $f(x)$. The optimal adaptive controller has multiple control loops and several timescales. The inner control action loop operates in continuous-time. Data is sampled at intervals of length T. The critic network operates at a slower timescale depending on how long it takes to solve Equation (68) or Equation (69). Due to the fact that the policy update for continuous-time systems does not involve the drift dynamics $f(x)$, no actor neural network is needed in IRL. Only a critic neural network is needed for VFA.

12.8. Synchronous Optimal Adaptive Control for Continuous-Time System

The IRL controller just gives tunes to the critic neural network for determining the value while holding the control policy fixed. Then, a policy update is performed. Now we develop an adaptive controller that has two neural networks, one for value function approximation and one to approximate the control. We could call these the critic neural network and actor neural network. The two neural networks are tuned simultaneously, that is, synchronously in time. This procedure is more nearly in line with accepted practice in adaptive control. Though this synchronous controller does require knowledge of the dynamics, it converges to the approximate local solutions to the HJB equation and the Bellman equation online, yet does not require explicitly solving either one. The HJB is usually impossible to solve for nonlinear systems except for special cases.

Based on the continuous-time Hamiltonian equation (61) and the stationarity condition $0 = \frac{\partial H(x,u,\nabla V^{\mu})}{\partial \mu}$ a policy iteration algorithm for continuous-time systems could be written based on the policy evaluation step,

$$\begin{aligned} 0 &= H(x, \mu_j(x), \nabla V_{j+1}) \\ &\equiv r(x, \mu_j(x)) + (\nabla V_{j+1})^T (f(x) + g(x)\mu_j(x)), \; V_{j+1}(0) = 0 \end{aligned} \tag{71}$$

and the policy improvement step

$$\mu_{j+1} = \arg\min_{\mu} H(x, \mu, \nabla V_{j+1}). \tag{72}$$

Unfortunately, Equation (71) is a nonlinear partial differential equation and cannot usually be solved analytically. However, this policy iteration algorithm provides the structure needed to develop another adaptive control algorithm that can be implemented online using measured data along the trajectories and converges to the optimal control. Specifically, select a value function approximation (VFA), or critic neural network, structure as

$$V(x) = W_1^T \phi(x) \tag{73}$$

and a control action approximation structure or actor neural network as

$$u(x) = -\frac{1}{2}R^{-1}g^T(x)\nabla\phi^T W_2. \tag{74}$$

These approximators could be, for instance, two neural networks with unknown parameters or weights W_1, W_2, and $\phi(x)$ the basis set or activation functions of the first neural network. The structure of the second action neural network comes from the policy iteration algorithm. Then tuning the neural network weights as

$$\dot{W}_1 = -\alpha_1 \frac{\sigma}{(\sigma^T\sigma + 1)^2}\left[\sigma^T W_1 + Q(x) + u^T R u\right], \tag{75}$$

and

$$\dot{W}_2 = -\alpha_2 \left\{(F_2 W_2 - F_2 \bar{\sigma}^T W_1) - \frac{1}{4}D(x) W_2 m^T(x) W_1\right\}, \tag{76}$$

guarantees stability as well as convergence to the optimal value and control (Vamvoudakis and Lewis, 2010). In these parameter estimation algorithms α_1, α_2, F_1, F_2 are positive tuning parameters, $D(x) = \nabla\phi(x)g(x)R^{-1}g^T(x)\nabla\phi^T(x)$, $\sigma = \nabla\phi(f + gu)$, $\bar{\sigma} = \frac{\sigma}{\sigma^T\sigma+1}$ and $m(x) = \frac{\sigma}{(\sigma^T\sigma+1)^2}$. A Persistence of Excitation condition on $\bar{\sigma}(t)$ is needed to achieve convergence to the optimal value.

This synchronous policy iteration controller is an adaptive control algorithm that requires full knowledge of the system dynamics $f(x)$, $g(x)$, yet converges to the optimal control solution. That is, it solves, locally approximately, the HJB equation, which is usually intractable for nonlinear systems. In the continuous-time LQR case, it solves the ARE using data measured along the trajectories and knowledge of A, B. The utility of this algorithm is that it can approximately solve the HJB equation for nonlinear systems using data measured along the system trajectories in real time. The HJB is usually impossible to solve for nonlinear systems except in some special cases.

The VFA tuning algorithm for W_1 is based on gradient descent, while the control action tuning algorithm is a form of backpropagation (Werbos, 1989) that is, however, also tuned by the VFA weights W_i. This adaptive structure is similar to the actor-critic reinforcement learning structure in Figure 12.1. However, in contrast to IRL, this algorithm is a continuous-time optimal adaptive controller with two parameter estimators tuned simultaneously, that is, synchronously and continuously in time. An algorithm that combines the advantages of the synchronous policy iteration algorithm and IRL has been proposed in Vamvoudakis *et al.* (2013). The authors in Jiang and Jiang (2012) have proposed a model-free IRL algorithm while the authors in Bhasin *et al.* (2013) have used neural network-based identifiers for a model-free synchronous policy iteration.

12.9. Using Reinforcement Learning for Multi-Player Nash and Stackelberg Games

The ideas presented in this book chapter can be applied to multi-player games and H-infinity control. Game theory provides an ideal environment to study multi-player decision and control problems, and offers a wide range of challenging and engaging problems. Game theory has been successful in modeling strategic behavior, where the outcome for each player depends on the actions of himself and all the other players. Every player chooses a control to minimize independently from the others his own performance objective. Multi-player cooperative games rely on solving coupled Hamilton–Jacobi (HJ) equations, which in the linear quadratic case reduce to the coupled algebraic Riccati equations. Reinforcement learning techniques have been applied to design adaptive controllers that converge to the solution of two-player zero-sum games in Vrabie and Lewis (2011); Zhang *et al.* (2013), of multi-player nonzero-sum games in Vamvoudakis and Lewis (2011); Vamvoudakis *et al.* (2012a) and of Stackelberg games in Vamvoudakis *et al.* (2012b). In these cases, the adaptive control structure has multiple loops, with action networks and critic networks for each player. The adaptive controller for zero-sum games finds the solution to the H-infinity control problem online in real time. A Q-learning approach to finding the H-infinity controller online is given in Kim and Lewis (2010). This adaptive controller does not require any systems dynamics information.

12.10. Conclusion

This book chapter uses computational intelligence techniques to bring together adaptive control and optimal control. Adaptive controllers do not generally converge to optimal solutions, and optimal controllers are designed offline using full dynamics information by solving matrix design equations. The book chapter shows that methods from reinforcement learning can be used to design new types of adaptive controllers that converge to optimal control solutions online in real time by measuring data along the system trajectories. These are called optimal adaptive controllers, and they have multi-loop, multi-timescale structures that come from reinforcement learning methods of policy–iteration and value iteration. These controllers learn the solutions to Hamilton-Jacobi design equations such as the Riccati equation online without knowing the full dynamical model of the system. A method known as Q learning allows the learning of optimal control solutions online, in the discrete-time case, for completely unknown systems. Q learning has not yet been fully investigated for continuous-time systems.

References

Abu-Khalaf, M., Lewis, F. L. and Huang, J. (2006). Policy iterations on the Hamilton–Jacobi–Isaacs equation for state feedback control with input saturation. *IEEE Trans. Autom. Control*, 51(12), pp. 1989–1995.

Al-Tamimi, A., Lewis, F. L. and Abu-Khalaf, M. (2008). Discrete-time nonlinear HJB solution using approximate dynamic programming: convergence proof. *IEEE Trans. Syst. Man Cybern. Part B*, 38(4), pp. 943–949, special issue on ADP/RL.

Astrom, K. J. and Wittenmark, B. (1995). *Adaptive Control*. UK: Addison-Wesley.

Baird, L. C. (1994). Reinforcement learning in continuous time: advantage updating. *Proc. Int. Conf. Neural Netw.*, Orlando, FL, June, pp. 2448–2453.

Balakrishnan, S. N., Ding, J. and Lewis, F. L. (2008). Issues on stability of ADP feedback controllers for dynamical systems. *IEEE Trans. Syst. Man Cybern. Part B*, 38(4), pp. 913–917, special issue on ADP/RL, invited survey paper.

Barto, A. G., Sutton, R. S. and Anderson, C. (1983). Neuron-like adaptive elements that can solve difficult learning control problems. *IEEE Trans. Syst. Man Cybern.*, pp. 834–846.

Bellman, R. E. (1957) *Dynamic Programming*. Princeton, NJ: Princeton University Press.

Bertsekas, D. P. and Tsitsiklis, J. N. (1996). *Neuro-Dynamic Programming*. MA: Athena Scientific.

Bhasin, S., Kamalapurkar, R., Johnson, M., Vamvoudakis, K. G., Lewis, F. L. and Dixon, W. E. (2013). A novel actor–critic–identifier architecture for approximate optimal control of uncertain nonlinear systems. *Autom.*, 49(1), pp. 82–92.

Bradtke, S., Ydstie, B. and Barto, A. (1994). Adaptive linear quadratic control using policy iteration. *Proc. Am. Control Conf.*, Baltimore, pp. 3475–3479.

Busoniu, L., Babuska, R., De Schutter, B. and Ernst, D. (2009). *Reinforcement Learning and Dynamic Programming Using Function Approximators*. Boca Raton: CRC Press.

Cao, X. (2007). *Stochastic Learning and Optimization*. Berlin: Springer-Verlag.

Dierks, T. and Jagannathan, S. (2010). Optimal control of affine nonlinear continuous-time systems. *Proc. Am. Control Conf.*, pp. 1568–1573.

Doya, K. (2000). Reinforcement learning in continuous time and space. *Neural Comput.*, 12, pp. 219–245.

Doya, K., Kimura, H. and Kawato, M. (2001). Neural mechanisms for learning and control. *IEEE Control Syst. Mag.*, pp. 42–54.

Ferrari, S. and Stengel, R. F. (2002). An adaptive critic global controller. *Proc. Am. Control Conf.*, May, pp. 2665–2670.

Hanselmann, T., Noakes, L. and Zaknich, A. (2007). Continuous-time adaptive critics. *IEEE Trans. Neural Netw.*, 18(3), pp. 631–647.

Howard, R. A. (1960). *Dynamic Programming and Markov Processes*. Cambridge, MA: MIT Press.

Ioannou, P. and Fidan, B. (2006). *Adaptive Control Tutorial*. Philadelphia: SIAM Press.

Jiang, Y. and Jiang, Z. P. (2012). Computational adaptive optimal control for continuous-time linear systems with completely unknown dynamics. *Autom.*, 48, pp. 2699–2704.

Kim, J. H. and Lewis, F. L. (2010). Model-free H-infinity control design for unknown linear discrete-time systems via Q-learning with LMI. *Autom.*, 46(8), pp. 1320–1326.

Lewis, F. L. and Liu, D. (2013). Reinforcement learning and approximate dynamic programming for feedback control. *IEEE Press Series on Computational Intelligence*.

Lewis, F. L. and Vamvoudakis, K. G. (2011). Reinforcement learning for partially observable dynamic processes: adaptive dynamic programming using measured output data. *IEEE Trans. Syst. Man Cybern.-Part B*, 41(1), pp. 14–25.

Lewis, F. L., Lendaris, G. and Liu, D. (2008) Special issue on approximate dynamic programming and reinforcement learning for feedback control. *IEEE Trans. Syst. Man Cybern. Part B*, 38(4).

Lewis, F. L., Vrabie, D., Vamvoudakis, K. G. (2012a). Reinforcement learning and feedback control: using natural decision methods to design optimal adaptive controllers. *IEEE Control Syst. Mag.*, 32(6), pp. 76–105.

Lewis, F. L., Vrabie, D. and Syrmos, V. (2012b). *Optimal Control, Third Edition*. New York: John Wiley.

Li, Z.-H. and Krstic, M. (1997). Optimal design of adaptive tracking controllers for nonlinear systems. *Autom.*, 33(8), pp. 1459–1473.

Liu, D., Yang, X. and Li, H. (2013). Adaptive optimal control for a class of continuous-time affine nonlinear systems with unknown internal dynamics, to appear in *Neural Comput. Appl.*

Mehta, P. and Meyn, S. (2009). Q-learning and Pontryagin's minimum principle. *Proc. IEEE Conf. Decis. Control*, pp. 3598–3605.

Mendel, J. M. and MacLaren, R. W. (1970). Reinforcement learning control and pattern recognition systems. In Mendel, J. M. and Fu, K. S. (eds.), *Adaptive, Learning, and Pattern Recognition Systems: Theory and Applications*. New York: Academic Press, pp. 287–318.

Moore, K. L. (1993). *Iterative Learning Control for Deterministic Systems*. London: Springer-Verlag.

Papoulis, A. (2002). *Probability, Random Variables and Stochastic Processes*. New York: McGraw-Hill.

Powell, W. B. (2011). *Approximate Dynamic Programming, Second edition*. Hoboken: Wiley.

Prokhorov, D. (2008). (ed.), *Computational Intelligence in Automotive Applications*, Heidelberg: Springer.

Prokhorov, D. and Wunsch, D. (1997). Adaptive Critic Designs. *IEEE Trans. Neural Netw.*, 8(5), pp. 997–1007.

Prokhorov, D., Santiago, R. A. and Wunsch II, D. C. (1995). Adaptive critic designs: A case study for neurocontrol. *Neural Netw.*, 8(9), pp. 1367–1372.

Schultz, W. (2004). Neural coding of basic reward terms of animal learning theory, game theory, microeconomics and behavioral ecology. *Curr. Opinion Neurobiol.*, 14, pp. 139–147.

Si, J., Barto, A., Powell, W. and Wunsch, D. (2004). *Handbook of Learning and Approximate Dynamic Programming*. USA: IEEE Press.

Sutton, R. S. and Barto, A. G. (1998). *Reinforcement Learning — An Introduction*. Cambridge, Massachusetts: MIT Press.

Vamvoudakis, K. G. and Lewis, F. L. (2010). Online actor-critic algorithm to solve the continuous-time infinite horizon optimal control problem. *Autom.*, 46(5), pp. 878–888.

Vamvoudakis, K. G. and Lewis, F. L. (2011). Multi-player non-zero sum games: online adaptive learning solution of coupled Hamilton-Jacobi equations. *Autom.*, 47, pp. 1556–1569.

Vamvoudakis, K. G., Lewis, F. L. and Hudas, G. R. (2012). Multi-agent differential graphical games: online adaptive learning solution for synchronization with optimality. *Autom.*, 48(8), pp. 1598–1611.

Vamvoudakis, K. G., Lewis, F. L., Johnson, M. and Dixon, W. E. (2012). Online Learning Algorithm for Stackelberg Games in Problems with Hierarchy. *Proc. 51st IEEE Conf. Decis. Control.* Maui, HI, pp. 1883–1889.

Vamvoudakis, K. G., Vrabie, D. and Lewis, F. L. (2013). Online learning algorithm for optimal control with integral reinforcement learning, to appear in *Int. J. Robust Nonlin. Control.*

Van der Schaft, A. J. (1992). L2-gain analysis of nonlinear systems and nonlinear state feedback H∞ control. *IEEE Trans. Autom. Control*, 37(6), pp. 770–784.

Vrabie, D. and Lewis, F. L. (2009). Neural network approach to continuous-time direct adaptive optimal control for partially-unknown nonlinear systems. *Neural Netw.*, 22(3), pp. 237–246.

Vrabie, D. and Lewis, F. L. (2011). Adaptive dynamic programming for online solution of a zero-sum differential game. *J. Control Theory Appl.*, 9(3), pp. 353–360.

Vrabie, D., Pastravanu, O., Abu-Khalaf, M. and Lewis, F. L. (2009). Adaptive optimal control for continuous-time linear systems based on policy iteration. *Autom.*, 45, pp. 477–484.

Vrabie, D., Vamvoudakis, K. G. and Lewis, F. L. (2012). *Optimal Adaptive Control and Differential Games by Reinforcement Learning Principles, Control Engineering Series.* IET Press.

Wang, D., Liu, D., Wei, Q. (2012). Finite-horizon neuro-optimal tracking control for a class of discrete-time nonlinear systems using adaptive dynamic programming approach. *Neurocomputing*, 78, p. 1422.

Wang, F. Y., Zhang, H. and Liu, D. (2009). Adaptive dynamic programming: an introduction. *IEEE Comput. Intell. Mag.*, pp. 39–47.

Watkins, C. (1989). *Learning from Delayed Rewards.* Ph.D. Thesis. Cambridge, England: Cambridge University.

Watkins, C. J. C. H. and Dayan, P. (1992). Q-learning. *Mach. Learn.*, 8, pp. 279–292.

Werbos, P. J. (1989). Neural networks for control and system identification. *Proc. IEEE Conf. Decis. Control.*

Werbos, P. J. (1991). A menu of designs for reinforcement learning over time. In Miller, W. T., Sutton, R. S. and Werbos, P. J. (eds.), *Neural Networks for Control.* Cambridge: MIT Press.

Werbos, P. J. (1992). Approximate dynamic programming for real-time control and neural modeling. In White, D. A. and Sofge, D. A. (eds.), *Handbook of Intelligent Control.* New York: Van Nostrand Reinhold.

Wheeler, R. M. and Narendra, K. S. (1986). Decentralized learning in finite Markov chains. *IEEE Trans. Autom. Control*, 31(6).

Zhang, H., Cui, L., Zhang, X. and Luo, X. (2011). Data-driven robust approximate optimal tracking control for unknown general nonlinear systems using adaptive dynamic programming method. *IEEE Trans. Neural Netw.*, 22, pp. 2226–2236.

Zhang, H., Huang, J. and Lewis, F. L. (2009). Algorithm and stability of ATC receding horizon control. *Proc. IEEE Symp. ADPRL.* Nashville, March, pp. 28–35.

Zhang, H., Liu, D., Luo, Y. and Wang, D. (2013). *Adaptive Dynamic Programming for Control: Algorithms and Stability*. Heidelberg: Springer.

Zhang, H., Wei, Q., Luo, Y. (2008). A novel infinite-time optimal tracking control scheme for a class of discrete-time nonlinear systems via the greedy HDP iteration algorithm. *IEEE Trans. Syst. Man Cybern. Part B: Cybern.*, 38, pp. 937–942.

Chapter 13

Kernel Models and Support Vector Machines

Denis Kolev, Mikhail Suvorov and Dmitry Kangin

Though linear models remain very attractive for researchers in the area of pattern recognition, they cannot meet some of the emerging difficulties of classification and regression problems. In this chapter, the authors discuss kernel methods as a theoretically justified tool, introducing non-linearity into originally linear models while preserving the overall model structure.Based on solid theoretical foundations, they describe some interesting kernel models and then focus on the SVM framework as it is a particularly important family of models within the area of kernel methods.

13.1. Introduction

Nowadays, the amount of information produced by different sources is steadily growing. For that reason, statistical data analysis and pattern recognition algorithms become more and more pervasive and highly demanded (Bishop, 2006; Hastie *et al.*, 2003). The most studied and widely applied approaches are based on parametric linear models. They combine learning and evaluation simplicity and well-grounded theoretical basis. On the other hand, linear methods impose strong restrictions on the data structure model, significantly reducing, in some cases, performance. Nonlinear methods provide more flexible models but usually they suffer from very complex, time demanding learning procedures and possible overfitting.

In this chapter, we discuss a framework for parametric linear methods that determine nonlinear models: kernel methods. These methods preserve theoretical basis of the linear models providing, at the same time, more flexibility. This framework extends linear machine learning methods.

Support vector machines (SVMs) play a significant role in the scope of linear and kernel methods. It is one of the most popular approaches for regression and classification problems due to a large number of reasons. The given approach is theoretically well-grounded and studied that helps to adapt it to various problems. SVMs are known to be universal approximators in some specific conditions. Also, due to the sparseness of the model (described further), SVMs are widely used for processing of streaming/large data. SVM classifier is rated as one of the best-performance machine learning algorithms (Wu *et al.*, 2008). A number of problem specific techniques are based on "SVM-driven" ideas. In this chapter, we discuss the SVM method and its extensions focusing on their relationship with kernel methods.

The rest of the chapter is structured as follows. In the second section, we discuss theoretical basis of kernel methods and give illustrative examples. In the third section, we list main kernel machines explaining their principles. The fourth section is focused on the SVM method and its extensions.

13.2. Basic Concepts and Theory

Here, we present a brief overview of the basic concepts and theorems about kernels and kernel models. Hereafter, we will use the following notation, unless stated otherwise.

$\boldsymbol{X} \subseteq \mathbb{R}^n$ — set of objects/vectors, Universum.
n — dimensionality of the object space.
$Y \subseteq \mathbb{R}^m$ — set of responses.
m — dimensionality of responses.
$\boldsymbol{X}_N = \{(\boldsymbol{x}_1, y_1), \ldots, (\boldsymbol{x}_N, y_N)\}$ — sample, where,

$\boldsymbol{x}_i \in \boldsymbol{X}$ — sample object/vector, $i = 1, \ldots, N$,
$y_i \in Y$ — response to $\boldsymbol{x}_i$, $i = 1, \ldots, N$.

$\mathcal{H}$ — Hilbert space of functions or Reproducing Kernel Hilbert Space.
$K(\boldsymbol{x}, \boldsymbol{t})$ — kernel function defined on $\boldsymbol{X} \times \boldsymbol{X}$.

13.2.1. *Regression and Classification Problems*

In many real-world problems, the classical approach of building a mathematical model of relationship between inputs and outputs turns to be unsound. Complicated dependencies, inputs of complex structure and noise are all the reasons that hinder mathematical modeling. In fact, development of a strict mathematical model is often infeasible or is related to strong performance and application constraints, which often limits the model's scalability. The alternative is information models that allow for restoring rather complex input–output relationships, dealing with noise and outliers. In this chapter, we speak about regression and classification problems (Bishop, 2006), and kernel approaches to solve them.

Inputs and outputs of real-world problems have various complicated structures. But in many cases they can be quantified. So hereafter we consider sets of data objects as subsets of $\mathbb{R}^n$. Here, we state the problem of recognition.

Consider a subset $\boldsymbol{X} \subseteq \mathbb{R}^n$. We refer its elements as *objects*. Coordinates x_i of object $\boldsymbol{x} \in \boldsymbol{X}$ are called *features* and marked by Roman script i. Each object $\boldsymbol{x}$ is associated with a vector $y \in Y \subseteq \mathbb{R}^m$, regarded as a kind of characteristic of objects in $\boldsymbol{X}$. We assume that there exists a law f that puts objects and their characteristics in correspondence. So f can be regarded as a map $\boldsymbol{X} \to Y$ and

$$y = f(\boldsymbol{x}), \quad \boldsymbol{x} \in \boldsymbol{X}, \ y \in Y.$$

We have some assumptions about this law/mapping and a *training set*. Training set is a very important concept in recognition theory as it is the main source of recovering f or at least its approximation $\hat{f}$. Usually, we assume that mapping $\hat{f}$ belongs to a certain family of maps $F \subseteq X^Y$. Then the training set is used to choose one mapping from this family. More formally, *training set* is a set $\boldsymbol{X}_N$ of pairs $(\boldsymbol{x}_i, y_i)$:

$$\boldsymbol{X}_N = \{(\boldsymbol{x}_i, y_i) | y_i = f(\boldsymbol{x}_i), \ i = 1, \ldots, N\}.$$

Then learning algorithm can be regarded as a mapping μ, so that

$$\hat{f} = \mu(\boldsymbol{X}_N), \\ \hat{f} \in F.$$

When Y is a finite set,

$$Y = \{L_1, \ldots, L_R\},$$

then the problem is called classification problem. L_r are called *labels*.

When $Y \subseteq \mathbb{R}$ and contains innumerable number of elements, then the problem is called a regression problem.

13.2.2. *Support Vector Machines, Classification Problem, Separating Hyperplane*

To illustrate recognition problem discussed above, we will give a simple example of a classification problem inspired by Vapnik and Chervonenkis (Vapnik, 1995; Vapnik and Chervonenkis, 1964). Let $\boldsymbol{X} = \mathbb{R}^2$, $Y = \{-1, 1\}$. Then objects can be regarded as two-dimensional points represented by either squares ($y = -1$), or circles ($y = 1$). Following Vapnik and Chervonenkis, we start with considering a simple case of linearly separable training set, presented in Figure 13.1. As points of training set of different classes are linearly divisible, the goal is to find a hyperplane

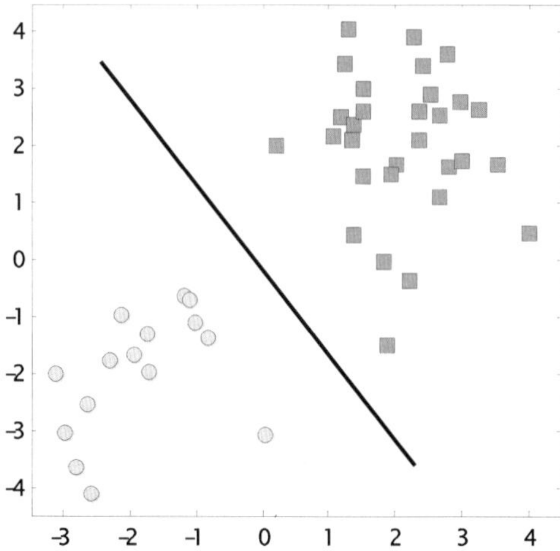

Figure 13.1: Linearly separable case.

H that will divide $\boldsymbol{X}$ into two parts H_+ and H_-. Hyperplane is determined by its normal vector $\boldsymbol{w}$ and intercept ρ. Then a vector $\boldsymbol{x}$ belongs to the hyperplane if and only if

$$\langle \boldsymbol{w}, \boldsymbol{x} \rangle - \rho = 0.$$

The hyperplane can be chosen in different ways. Vapnik and Chervonenkis proposed to choose an some optimal hyperplane. They formalized optimality using the notation of separating band, which is the space between two hyperplanes parallel to H, that contain no points of the training set $\boldsymbol{X}_N$. They showed that the width of this band equals (for proof refer to Section 13.4.1).

$$\frac{2}{\|\boldsymbol{w}\|}.$$

Then, they stated the problem of quadratic programming

$$\begin{aligned} &\|\boldsymbol{w}\|^2 \to \min_{w} \\ &\text{w.r.t.} \\ &y_i(\langle \boldsymbol{w}, \boldsymbol{x}_i \rangle - \rho) \geq 1, \\ &i = 1, \ldots, N. \end{aligned}$$

This can be generalized for the case of a linearly non-separable training set by introducing the so called *slack* variables $\xi_i \geq 0$ that allow violating the constraint

$$y_i(\langle \boldsymbol{w}, \boldsymbol{x}_i \rangle - \rho) \geq 1 - \xi_i.$$

So the final version of the problem becomes

$$\|\boldsymbol{w}\|^2 + C\sum_{i=1}^{N}\xi_i \to \min_{\boldsymbol{w},\xi}$$

$$\text{w.r.t.}$$

$$y_i(\langle \boldsymbol{w}, \boldsymbol{x}_i\rangle - \rho) \geq 1 - \xi_i,$$

$$\xi_i \geq 0,$$

$$i = 1, \ldots, N.$$

Formally speaking, in the case of linearly non-separable sample, the set of the optimization problem constraints defines an empty set. Introduction of slack variables prevents such situation allowing misclassifications, which are penalized by the functional under optimization.

13.2.3. *SVM Solver, Towards Nonlinearity, Polynomial Kernel*

In this section, we do not investigate the main properties of the problem solution. Instead, we focus on the techniques that introduce nonlinearity into the model, describing briefly the background theory and most vital theorems.

Consider the solution of the optimization problem stated by two-class SVM classifier. Earlier, we have presented the convex quadratic programming problem, which has a single solution. Usually, the SVM model is investigated from the point of the dual optimization problem (Boyd and Vandenberghe, 2004), which is formulated as follows:

$$-\frac{1}{2}\boldsymbol{\alpha} Q \boldsymbol{\alpha}^T + \sum_{i=1}^{N}\alpha_i \to \max_{\alpha}$$

$$\text{w.r.t.}$$

$$\begin{cases} 0 \leq \alpha_i \leq C, \quad \forall i = 1, \ldots, N, \\ \sum_{i=1}^{N}\alpha_i y_i = 0. \end{cases}$$

Here the N-dimensional vector $\boldsymbol{\alpha} \in \mathbb{R}^N$ represents the vector of Lagrange multipliers, corresponding to each constraint in the primal problem. Matrix $Q \in \mathbb{R}^{N\times N}$ is a matrix of "class-corresponding" inner products with elements

$$Q_{ij} = \langle \boldsymbol{x}_i, \boldsymbol{x}_j\rangle y_i y_j.$$

According to the differential Karush–Kuhn–Tucker conditions of the primal problem (it will be detailed further), the normal vector of the resulting hyperplane can be expressed as

$$\boldsymbol{w} = \sum_{i=1}^{N} y_i \alpha_i \boldsymbol{x}_i.$$

Therefore, the class label of arbitrary vector $\boldsymbol{x}$ can be evaluated as

$$y(\boldsymbol{x}) = \text{sign}\left(\sum_{i=1}^{N} \alpha_i y_i \langle \boldsymbol{x}_i, \boldsymbol{x} \rangle - \rho\right).$$

Thus, one can see that the optimization problem depends on the values of the Lagrange multipliers and inner products between the vectors from the learning set and classified vector. This information is sufficient for performing classification.

The SVM classifier discussed here is linear, which means that it performs adequately only in the cases when the classes in the learning set (and in the Universum at all) are linearly separable. However, this limitation can be overcome. There are a lot of specially developed techniques that can be applied, for instance, feature engineering, mixture of experts, etc. But for the SVM model (and a wide range of other machine learning methods) there is a special approach, which keeps the overall linear model structure, but allows fitting nonlinear separation surfaces. This approach is referred as "mapping to linearization space" or just "kernel trick" (Silverman, 1986).

Coming back to the SVM's dual optimization problem and final separating function we note that the optimization problem depends on pairwise inner products in the learning set. The final classification rule also depends only on the inner products between vectors in the learning set and vector classified. It gives the way to the described approach. The idea is to replace the standard inner product by a two argument nonlinear function (Schölkopf *et al.*, 1999), so that

$$\langle \boldsymbol{x}, \boldsymbol{t} \rangle \to K(\boldsymbol{x}, \boldsymbol{t}),$$
$$Q_{ij} = K(\boldsymbol{x}_i, \boldsymbol{x}_j) y_i y_j,$$
$$y(\boldsymbol{x}) = \text{sign}\left(\sum_{i=1}^{N} \alpha_i y_i K(\boldsymbol{x}_i, \boldsymbol{x}) - \rho\right).$$

A simple example can be provided. Suppose that the replacement is

$$\langle \boldsymbol{x}, \boldsymbol{t} \rangle \to (\langle \boldsymbol{x}, \boldsymbol{t} \rangle + 1)^2.$$

Then, the decision rule becomes a second-order polynomial, i.e.,

$$y(\boldsymbol{x}) = \operatorname{sign}\left(\sum_{i=1}^{N} \alpha_i y_i \langle \boldsymbol{x}, \boldsymbol{x}_i \rangle^2 + 2\sum_{i=1}^{N} \alpha_i y_i \langle \boldsymbol{x}, \boldsymbol{x}_i \rangle + \sum_{i=1}^{N} \alpha_i y_i - \rho\right).$$

However, two important questions must be answered to ensure a proper use of such approach:

(1) What function $K(\boldsymbol{x}, \boldsymbol{t})$ can be used in place of the inner product?
(2) What is the set of possible separating surfaces that can be fitted using given $K(\boldsymbol{x}, \boldsymbol{t})$?

13.2.4. *Kernel Function Discussion*

Kernel trick can be defined in different ways. Consider a function Φ that maps the data from the initial space $\mathbb{R}^n$ to a Hilbert space $\mathcal{H}$, $\Phi: \mathbb{R}^n \to \mathcal{H}$. Inner product in the space $\mathcal{H}$ is denoted by $\langle \cdot, \cdot \rangle_{\mathcal{H}}$. In general case, the space $\mathcal{H}$ can be infinite-dimensional.

Classification model is learned in the space $\mathcal{H}$ using mapped data as a learning set,

$$\Phi(\boldsymbol{X}_N) = \{\Phi(\boldsymbol{x}_1), \ldots, \Phi(\boldsymbol{x}_N)\}.$$

It is supposed that for all $\boldsymbol{x}, \boldsymbol{t} \in \mathbb{R}^n$, the inner product for the mapped vectors is evaluated as

$$\langle \Phi(\boldsymbol{x}), \Phi(\boldsymbol{t}) \rangle_{\mathcal{H}} = K(\boldsymbol{x}, \boldsymbol{t}),$$

where $K(\boldsymbol{x}, \boldsymbol{t})$ is a symmetric two-argument function, in general nonlinear, defined for vectors in $\mathbb{R}^n$. $\Phi(\boldsymbol{x})$ can be considered as a new feature map, that makes "kernel trick" similar to the feature engineering.

Therefore, the final classification model can be expressed as

$$\begin{aligned} y(\boldsymbol{x}) &= \operatorname{sign}\left(\sum_{i=1}^{N} \alpha_i y_i \langle \Phi(\boldsymbol{x}_i), \Phi(\boldsymbol{x}) \rangle_{\mathcal{H}} - \rho\right) \\ &= \operatorname{sign}\left(\sum_{i=1}^{N} \alpha_i y_i K(\boldsymbol{x}_i, \boldsymbol{x}) - \rho\right). \end{aligned}$$

Kernel trick helps building linear classification model in a different space resulting in a generally nonlinear classification model in the initial data space. For that reason, the function $K(\boldsymbol{x}, \boldsymbol{t})$ must be an inner product of the $\Phi(\boldsymbol{x})$ and $\Phi(\boldsymbol{t})$ in a Hilbert space for all $\boldsymbol{x}, \boldsymbol{t} \in \mathbb{R}^n$. Such functions are usually referred as "kernels" (this is not a strict definition) and there are a lot of examples of such functions:

- Linear kernel $K(\boldsymbol{x}, \boldsymbol{t}) = \langle \boldsymbol{x}, \boldsymbol{t} \rangle$,
- Polynomial kernel $K(\boldsymbol{x}, \boldsymbol{t}) = \langle \boldsymbol{x}, \boldsymbol{t} \rangle^d$ or $K(\boldsymbol{x}, \boldsymbol{t}) = (\langle \boldsymbol{x}, \boldsymbol{t} \rangle + \beta)^d$,
- Exponential kernel $K(\boldsymbol{x}, \boldsymbol{t}) = \exp\left(-\frac{\|\boldsymbol{x}-\boldsymbol{t}\|^2}{2\sigma^2}\right)$,
- Student-type RBF kernel $K(\boldsymbol{x}, \boldsymbol{t}) = (\beta + \gamma \|\boldsymbol{x} - \boldsymbol{t}\|^2)^{-\alpha}$, $\beta > 0,\ \gamma > 0,\ \alpha > 0$.

Discussing the diversity of the set of SVM's separating functions that can be learned using a given kernel function, it is essential to point that the classification rule is based on a linear combination of kernel functions with one fixed input argument. Therefore, the set of functions that can be obtained is limited by the linear spectrum of the kernel:

$$\operatorname{span}(K) = \left\{ f : \mathbb{R}^n \to \mathbb{R} | \exists \boldsymbol{x}1, \ldots, \boldsymbol{x}_N \in \mathbb{R}^n : f(\boldsymbol{x}) = \sum_{i=1}^{N} \alpha_i K(\boldsymbol{x}, \boldsymbol{x}_i) \right\}.$$

Further, we investigate the underlying theory of the "kernel trick" in detail, including the criteria for a function to be a kernel and the importance of the spectrum of the kernels. We finalize the chapter by the representer theorem, showing the significance of the kernel theory for the machine learning.

13.2.5. *Kernel Definition via Matrix*

This discussion leads us to the following definition of a kernel function.

Definition 1 (Cuturi, 2010)**:** *Function $K : \boldsymbol{X} \times \boldsymbol{X} \to \mathbb{R}$ is called a positive definite kernel if for any finite subset $\boldsymbol{X}_N = \{\boldsymbol{x}_1, \ldots, \boldsymbol{x}_N\} \subset \boldsymbol{X}$ the corresponding matrix $K(\boldsymbol{X}_N, \boldsymbol{X}_N)$,*

$$K(\boldsymbol{X}_N, \boldsymbol{X}_N) = \begin{bmatrix} K(\boldsymbol{x}_1, \boldsymbol{x}_1) & \cdots & K(\boldsymbol{x}_1, \boldsymbol{x}_N) \\ \vdots & \ddots & \vdots \\ K(\boldsymbol{x}_N, \boldsymbol{x}_1) & \cdots & K(\boldsymbol{x}_N, \boldsymbol{x}_N) \end{bmatrix},$$

is symmetric, i.e., $K(\boldsymbol{X}_N, \boldsymbol{X}_N) = K(\boldsymbol{X}_N, \boldsymbol{X}_N)^T$, and nonnegative definite.

The latter we understand as for any $\boldsymbol{t} \in \mathbb{R}^N$

$$\langle K(\boldsymbol{X}_N, \boldsymbol{X}_N)\boldsymbol{t}, \boldsymbol{t} \rangle \geq 0.$$

Directly from the definition it follows that

$$\begin{aligned} &\forall \boldsymbol{x}, \boldsymbol{t} \in \boldsymbol{X}, \\ &K(\boldsymbol{x}, \boldsymbol{t}) \geq 0, \\ &K(\boldsymbol{x}, \boldsymbol{t}) = K(\boldsymbol{t}, \boldsymbol{x}). \end{aligned}$$

It should be pointed that this fact provides important link to kernel SVM, as non-negative matrix $K(\boldsymbol{X}_N, \boldsymbol{X}_N)$ ensures the concavity of the dual problem, which is essential for the optimization.

13.2.6. *Reproducing Kernel (RKHS) via Linear Operator*

Up to this moment we introduced the definition of the positive definite kernel. Now we consider one of the most important entities in the theory of reproducing kernels — Reproducing Kernel Hilbert space (RKHS) (Aronszajn, 1950).

Let $\boldsymbol{X}$ be a non-empty subset of $\mathbb{R}^n$. Then let $\mathcal{H}$ be a Hilbert space of functions over $\boldsymbol{X}$:

$$f : \boldsymbol{X} \to \mathbb{R}.$$

Definition 2: *A function $K : \boldsymbol{X} \times \boldsymbol{X} \to \mathbb{R}$ is called a reproducing kernel of $\mathcal{H}$ if and only if*

1. $\forall \boldsymbol{x} \in \boldsymbol{X}\ K(\cdot, \boldsymbol{x}) \in \mathcal{H}$.
2. $\forall f \in \mathcal{H}\ \langle f, K(\cdot, \boldsymbol{x})\rangle_{\mathcal{H}} = f(\boldsymbol{x})$.

The function $K(\cdot, \boldsymbol{x})$ is called reproducing kernel for point $\boldsymbol{x}$. Here, $\langle\cdot, \cdot\rangle_{\mathcal{H}}$ is a voluntarily chosen function meeting the inner product definition. From the definition, it follows that the reproducing kernel is a symmetric function as

$$\begin{aligned} K(\boldsymbol{x}, \boldsymbol{t}) &= \langle K(\cdot, \boldsymbol{t}), K(\cdot, \boldsymbol{x})\rangle_{\mathcal{H}} \\ &= \{\text{property of real} - \text{valued inner product}\} \\ &= \langle K(\cdot, \boldsymbol{x}), K(\cdot, \boldsymbol{t})\rangle_{\mathcal{H}} = K(\boldsymbol{t}, \boldsymbol{x}). \end{aligned}$$

The reproducing property may be defined in a different way. Consider a functional $L_x : \mathcal{H} \to \mathbb{R}$, so that

$$\forall f \in \mathcal{H} \quad L_x f = f(\boldsymbol{x}).$$

The "evaluation functional" L_x can be defined for any $\boldsymbol{x} \in \boldsymbol{X}$. It is easy to show that L_x is a linear functional. Using this notation, we introduce another definition of RKHS.

Definition 3: *A Hilbert space of functions $\mathcal{H}$ is a RKHS if and only if $\forall \boldsymbol{x} \in \boldsymbol{X}$ the evaluation functional L_x is bounded, i.e.,*

$$\forall \boldsymbol{x} \in \boldsymbol{X}\ \exists C_x : \forall f \in \mathcal{H} : |L_x f| \leq C_x \|f\|_{\mathcal{H}} = C_x \sqrt{\langle f, f\rangle_{\mathcal{H}}}.$$

So, it means that if two functions f and g are close in terms of RKHS norm, they will be close at every point:

$$|f(\boldsymbol{x}) - g(\boldsymbol{x})| = |L_x(f - g)| \leq C_x \|f - g\|_{\mathcal{H}}.$$

Now we can state a theorem linking two definitions.

Theorem 1. *Hilbert space $\mathcal{H}$ is a RKHS $\Leftrightarrow$ it has a reproducing kernel.*

According to Riesz–Frechet theorem, for every bounded linear functional $A : \mathcal{H} \to \mathbb{R}$ there exists an element $\theta \in \mathcal{H} : \forall f \in \mathcal{H}\ Af = \langle f, \theta \rangle_{\mathcal{H}}$. In our case, $A \equiv L_{\boldsymbol{x}}$. Therefore, one side of the theorem ($\Rightarrow$) is a specific case of Riesz–Frechet theorem. The other side ($\Leftarrow$) can be proved using Cauchy–Schwartz inequality.

13.2.7. *Moore–Aronszajn Theorem: Equivalence*

The problem of selecting a reproducing kernel arises. The Moore–Aronszajn theorem builds a correspondence between positive definite kernels and RKHS.

Theorem 2 (*Moore–Aronszajn* (Aronszajn, 1950)). *Suppose $K : \boldsymbol{X} \times \boldsymbol{X} \to \mathbb{R}$ is a positive definite kernel $\Rightarrow \exists!$ Hilbert space $\mathcal{H}$ of functions over $\boldsymbol{X}$, where K is a reproducing kernel.*

Therefore, for each positive definite kernel there is a unique corresponding RKHS.

13.2.8. *Mercer's Theorem*

We further investigate properties of positive definite kernels in the RKHSs. For this purpose we introduce a strictly positive Borel measure μ on $\boldsymbol{X}$. We define $L^2_\mu(\boldsymbol{X})$ as a linear space of square-integrable functions, i.e.,

$$f \in L^2_\mu(\boldsymbol{X}) : \int_X |f(\boldsymbol{x})|^2 d\mu(\boldsymbol{x}) < \infty.$$

A symmetric positive definite kernel $K : \boldsymbol{X} \times \boldsymbol{X} \to \mathbb{R}$, which is square integrable, i.e.,

$$\int_X \int_X K^2(\boldsymbol{x}, \boldsymbol{t}) d\mu(\boldsymbol{x}) d\mu(\boldsymbol{t}) < \infty,$$

induces (Minh *et al.*, 2006) a linear operator $L_K : L^2_\mu(\boldsymbol{X}) \to L^2_\mu(\boldsymbol{X})$ defined by

$$L_K f(\boldsymbol{x}) = \int_X K(\boldsymbol{x}, \boldsymbol{t}) f(\boldsymbol{t}) d\mu(\boldsymbol{t}).$$

It possesses a countable system of eigenfunctions $\{\phi_k\}_{k=1}^{\infty}$ forming an orthonormal basis of $L^2_\mu(\boldsymbol{X})$ with corresponding eigenvalues $\{\lambda_k\}_{k=1}^{\infty}$.

Theorem 3 (Mercer, 1909). *Let $\boldsymbol{X} \subset \mathbb{R}^n$ be closed, μ a strictly positive Borel measure on $\boldsymbol{X}$, which means that this measure of every nonempty subset in $\boldsymbol{X}$ is* *positive, K a square integrable continuous function on $\boldsymbol{X} \times \boldsymbol{X}$ being a positive definite kernel. Then*

$$K(\boldsymbol{x}, \boldsymbol{t}) = \sum_{k=1}^{\infty} \lambda_k \phi_k(\boldsymbol{x}) \phi_k(\boldsymbol{t}).$$

This series converges absolutely for each pair $(\boldsymbol{x}, \boldsymbol{t}) \in \boldsymbol{X} \times \boldsymbol{X}$ and uniformly on each compact subset of $\boldsymbol{X}$.

This theorem allows building a map $\Phi : \boldsymbol{X} \to \ell^2$, where ℓ^2 is a Hilbert space of square summable sequences, so that

$$[\Phi(\boldsymbol{x})]_k = \sqrt{\lambda_k} \phi_k(\boldsymbol{x}).$$

Then kernel K can be regarded as a scalar product in ℓ^2:

$$K(\boldsymbol{x}, \boldsymbol{t}) = \langle \Phi(\boldsymbol{x}), \Phi(\boldsymbol{t}) \rangle_{\ell^2} = \sum_{k=1}^{\infty} ([\Phi(\boldsymbol{x})]_k [\Phi(\boldsymbol{t})]_k) = \sum_{k=1}^{\infty} \lambda_k \phi_k(\boldsymbol{x}) \phi_k(\boldsymbol{t}).$$

As kernel K is supposed to be continuous, the feature map Φ is also continuous. Coming back to the SVM example, Mercer's theorem provides an explanation of the correctness of the positive definite kernels usage. Any square integrable positive definite kernel can be considered as an inner product between maps of two vectors in some Hilbert space (namely ℓ^2) replacing the inner product in the initial space $\mathbb{R}^n$. $\Phi(\boldsymbol{x})$ can be regarded as a feature map to the transformed feature space,

$$\Phi : \boldsymbol{X} \to \ell^2.$$

Thus, SVM builds a linear classifier in the ℓ^2 space.

13.2.9. *Polynomial Kernel Example*

To illustrate the discussed theory we return to polynomial kernel example. This will build a link between RKHS reproducing kernel, positive definite kernel and "kernel trick".

Consider a problem of fitting a linear regression in a two-dimensional space. For training set $\boldsymbol{X}_N = \{(\boldsymbol{x}_1, y_1), \ldots, (\boldsymbol{x}_N, y_N)\}, \boldsymbol{x}_i \in \mathbb{R}^2, y_i \in \mathbb{R}$ the goal is to restore parameter $\boldsymbol{w}$ so that $\forall i = 1, \ldots, N$, the output value of parametric function $f(\boldsymbol{x}_i, \boldsymbol{w})$ is close to y_i. The word "close" can be understood as an (sub)optimal solution of any regular empirical error measure like least squares, SVM-type measure, etc. For the current example, assume least-squares optimization is used as a learning procedure, i.e.,

$$\sum_{i=1}^{N} (f(\boldsymbol{x}_i, \boldsymbol{w}) - y_i)^2 \to \min_{w}.$$

We choose function $f(\boldsymbol{x}, \boldsymbol{w})$ to be linear:

$$f(\boldsymbol{x}, \boldsymbol{w}) = \langle \boldsymbol{x}, \boldsymbol{w} \rangle = \sum_{i=1}^{2} x_i w_i, \quad \boldsymbol{w} \in \mathbb{R}^2.$$

Suppose that "kernel trick" is performed, so regression is transformed to second order polynomial, i.e.,

$$\langle \boldsymbol{x}, \boldsymbol{t} \rangle_{\mathbb{R}^2} \to K(\boldsymbol{x}, \boldsymbol{t}) = [\langle \boldsymbol{x}, \boldsymbol{t} \rangle_{\mathbb{R}^2}]^2 = \langle \Phi(\boldsymbol{x}), \Phi(\boldsymbol{t}) \rangle_{\mathcal{H}}.$$

Then, the feature map $\Phi(\boldsymbol{x})$ is defined as

$$\Phi : \boldsymbol{x} = \begin{bmatrix} x_1 \\ x_2 \end{bmatrix} \to \begin{bmatrix} x_1^2 \\ x_2^2 \\ \sqrt{2} x_1 x_2 \end{bmatrix} \in \mathbb{R}^3.$$

Thus, $\mathcal{H}$ may be understood as $\mathbb{R}^3$. Inner product in this space is evaluated as,

$$\langle \Phi(\boldsymbol{x}), \Phi(\boldsymbol{t}) \rangle_{\mathbb{R}^3} = x_1^2 t_1^2 + x_2^2 t_2^2 + 2 x_1 x_2 t_1 t_2 = [\langle \boldsymbol{x}, \boldsymbol{t} \rangle_{\mathbb{R}^2}]^2.$$

In this case, parameter $\boldsymbol{w} \in \mathbb{R}^3$ is growing in dimension. But the function model still depends linearly on $\boldsymbol{w}$, and this usually simplifies learning procedure. The model function is,

$$f(\boldsymbol{x}, \boldsymbol{w}) = \sum_{i=1}^{3} w_i [\Phi(\boldsymbol{x})]_i = w_1 x_1^2 + w_2 x_2^2 + w_3 \sqrt{2} x_1 x_2,$$

where $[\Phi(\boldsymbol{x})]_i$ denotes ith coordinate in the transformed feature map.

If we consider $f(\boldsymbol{x}, \boldsymbol{w})$ as a function-member of the Hilbert space of second-order polynomials over $\mathbb{R}^2$, $P^2(\mathbb{R}^2)$, then every function in $P^2(\mathbb{R}^2)$ can be specified by its three coefficients, i.e.,

$$g(\boldsymbol{u}) = a u_1^2 + b u_2^2 + c u_1 u_2 \leftrightarrow \begin{bmatrix} a \\ b \\ \frac{c}{\sqrt{2}} \end{bmatrix}.$$

Here, $\leftrightarrow$ denotes some schematic correspondence of the polynomial to vectors from $\mathbb{R}^3$. Factor $\sqrt{2}$ is introduced for future convenience. We denote inner product in $P^2(\mathbb{R}^2)$ as a sum of pairwise multiplications of the corresponding coefficients,

$$\langle g_1, g_2\rangle_{P^2(\mathbb{R}^2)} = a_1a_2 + b_1b_2 + \frac{c_1c_2}{2},$$

where $g_i(\boldsymbol{u}) = a_iu_1^2 + b_iu_2^2 + c_iu_1u_2 \in P^2(\mathbb{R}^2)$.

One can see that the polynomial

$$K(\boldsymbol{u}, \boldsymbol{x}) = x_1^2u_1^2 + x_2^2u_2^2 + 2x_1x_2u_1u_2 \leftrightarrow \begin{bmatrix} x_1^2 \\ x_2^2 \\ \sqrt{2}x_1x_2 \end{bmatrix},$$

$$K(\cdot, \boldsymbol{x}) \in P^2(\mathbb{R}^2)\ \forall \boldsymbol{x} \in \mathbb{R}^2,$$

is a reproducing kernel of $P^2(\mathbb{R}^2)$.

Indeed,

$$\forall g \in P^2(\mathbb{R}^2)\quad \langle g, K(\cdot, \boldsymbol{x})\rangle_{P^2(\mathbb{R}^2)} = ax_1^2 + bx_2^2 + \frac{2x_1x_2c}{2} = g(\boldsymbol{x}).$$

Therefore, mapping $\Phi : \mathbb{R}^2 \to \mathbb{R}^3$ is equivalent to mapping $\Psi : \mathbb{R}^2 \to P^2(\mathbb{R}^2)$, where

$$\Psi(\boldsymbol{x}) = K(\cdot, \boldsymbol{x}).$$

Inner product between the data mapped by Ψ is evaluated as $\langle\Psi(\boldsymbol{x}), \Psi(\boldsymbol{t})\rangle_{P^2(\mathbb{R}^2)}$. Mapping Ψ is equivalent to mapping Φ as

$$K(\boldsymbol{x}, \boldsymbol{t}) = \langle\Phi(\boldsymbol{x}), \Phi(\boldsymbol{t})\rangle_{\mathbb{R}^3} = \langle\Psi(\boldsymbol{x}), \Psi(\boldsymbol{t})\rangle_{P^2(\mathbb{R}^2)}\ \forall \boldsymbol{x}, \boldsymbol{t} \in \mathbb{R}^2.$$

Therefore, the regression learning procedure is reduced to the search of the polynomial

$$\pi \in P^2(\mathbb{R}^2), \quad \pi \leftrightarrow \begin{bmatrix} \pi_1 \\ \pi_2 \\ \dfrac{\pi_3}{\sqrt{2}} \end{bmatrix},$$

so that $\forall i = 1, \ldots, N \langle\pi, \Psi(\boldsymbol{x}_i)\rangle_{P^2(\mathbb{R}^2)} = \pi_1x_1^2 + \pi_2x_2^2 + \pi_3x_1x_2$ is close to y_i. However, due to the fact that π is defined by three coefficients, the function model is linear with respect to its parameters. Final optimization ("learning") procedure is

$$\sum_{i=1}^{N}\left(\pi_1x_{i1}^2 + \pi_2x_{i2}^2 + \pi_3x_{i1}x_{i2} - y_i\right)^2 \to \min_{\pi},$$

where x_i corresponds to ith entry of ith learning sample.

The result provided here can be generalized. Every "kernel trick" is equivalent to defining a new feature map, where K is a reproducing kernel of the linearization space. However, the fitted parameters are not always included into the RKHS inner product in a linear way, which may cause problem during optimization. For instance, if we map the data into the space of all continuous functions, the learning procedure becomes equivalent to the variational optimization over all continuous functions. However, further we will show that in most of the cases this problem can be overcome and it is possible to leave the model linear with respect to the optimized parameters.

13.2.10. *RKHS Approximation*

The next question we address is an arbitrary separating surface using kernel K. Consider a RKHS $\mathcal{H}$, Hilbert space of real valued functions over $\boldsymbol{X} \subseteq \mathbb{R}^n$, where K is a reproducing kernel. If $\boldsymbol{X}$ is a compact subset, we are able to form the space of kernel sections

$$K(\boldsymbol{X}) = \overline{\text{span}}\{K_{\boldsymbol{t}}, \boldsymbol{t} \in \boldsymbol{X}\},$$

which is a closure of a linear span of functions $K_{\boldsymbol{t}}(\cdot) = K(\cdot, \boldsymbol{t})$. It is clear that $K(\boldsymbol{X}) \subseteq \mathcal{H}$. But if we would like to build an arbitrary function (specifying a separating surface) we must call for the opposite embedding $\mathcal{H} \supseteq K(\boldsymbol{X})$. In other terms, for any positive number ε and any function $f \in \mathcal{H}$ there should exist such a function $g \in K(\boldsymbol{X})$ that function f is well approximated by g, i.e.,

$$\|f - g\|_{\mathcal{H}} \leq \varepsilon.$$

Returning to RKHS it may be shown that $K(\boldsymbol{X})$ is dense in $\mathcal{H}$, which means that any function from the RKHS can be approximated with any given precision ε by linear combination of reproducing kernels. Formally speaking (Micchelli *et al.*, 2006),

$$\forall \varepsilon > 0, \quad \forall f \in \mathcal{H}\, \exists N > 0, \boldsymbol{x}_1, \ldots, \boldsymbol{x}_N \in \boldsymbol{X}, \alpha_1, \ldots, \alpha_N \in \mathbb{R}:$$

$$\left\| f - \sum_{i=1}^{N} \alpha_i K(\cdot, \boldsymbol{x}_i) \right\|_{\mathcal{H}} \leq \varepsilon.$$

Thus, if we return to the SVM model we can state that the diversity of possible decision function forms is limited by the RKHS of the selected kernel.

In practice, most of the kernels are parametric functions. Thus it is reasonable to analyze how corresponding RKHS depends on kernel parameters. Consider a family of parameterized positive definite kernel functions

$$\mathcal{K} = \{K(\cdot, \cdot|\boldsymbol{\theta}) : \boldsymbol{X} \times \boldsymbol{X} \to \mathbb{R} \mid \boldsymbol{\theta} \in \boldsymbol{\Theta}\},$$

where $\boldsymbol{\Theta}$ is a set of acceptable values for $\boldsymbol{\theta}$. As an example of such a family, we can take Gaussian kernel with different variance values. A natural question that arises is whether corresponding RKHS depends on kernel parameters. In general, the answer is "yes", but not in all cases. For instance, Gaussian kernel with different variances corresponds to the RKHS of all continuous real-valued functions, which is independent from variance parameters. At the same time, polynomial kernels with different degrees correspond to different RKHS (spaces of polynomials with different degrees).

13.2.11. *Universal Kernels and Examples*

Using the notation from the previous subsection, we introduce the property of the *universality* of the kernel (Micchelli *et al.*, 2006).

Definition 4: *Positive definite kernel* $K : \boldsymbol{X} \times \boldsymbol{X} \to \mathbb{R}, \boldsymbol{X} \subseteq \mathbb{R}^n$ *is called universal if it is a reproducing kernel of RKHS* $\mathbb{R}(\boldsymbol{X})$ *— space of all continuous real-valued functions defined on* $\boldsymbol{X}$.

Using the previous result, we can state that any continuous real-valued function $f \in \mathbb{R}(\boldsymbol{X})$ can be approximated with any given precision by a function $g \in K(\boldsymbol{X})$.

So, the question is which kernels possess this property of universality. A number of universality criteria exist, but in this work we present just a number of examples of universal kernels and some sufficient conditions of universality.

Definition 5: *Kernel* $K : \boldsymbol{X} \times \boldsymbol{X} \to \mathbb{R}$ *is strictly positive definite if it is a positive definite kernel and for any finite subset* $\boldsymbol{X}_N = \{\boldsymbol{x}_1, \ldots, \boldsymbol{x}_N\} \subset \boldsymbol{X}$ *the corresponding matrix* $K(\boldsymbol{X}_N, \boldsymbol{X}_N)$,

$$K(\boldsymbol{X}_N, \boldsymbol{X}_N) = \begin{bmatrix} K(\boldsymbol{x}_1, \boldsymbol{x}_1) & \cdots & K(\boldsymbol{x}_1, \boldsymbol{x}_N) \\ \vdots & \ddots & \vdots \\ K(\boldsymbol{x}_N, \boldsymbol{x}_1) & \cdots & K(\boldsymbol{x}_N, \boldsymbol{x}_N) \end{bmatrix},$$

is strictly positive definite.

Theorem 4. *If positive definite kernel is strictly positive definite, it is a universal kernel.*

The following positive definite kernels are the examples of the universal kernels:

- Exponential kernel $K(\boldsymbol{x}, \boldsymbol{t}) = \exp\left(-\frac{\|\boldsymbol{x}-\boldsymbol{t}\|^2}{2\sigma^2}\right)$,
- Survival kernel $K(\boldsymbol{x}, \boldsymbol{t}) = \prod_{i=1}^{n} \min(x_i, t_i)$,
- $K(\boldsymbol{x}, \boldsymbol{t}) = (\beta + \gamma \|\boldsymbol{x} - \boldsymbol{t}\|^2)^{-\alpha}, \beta > 0, \gamma > 0, \alpha > 0$.

13.2.12. *Why Span? Representer Theorem*

Here, we will present a very strong and a very general result, which is essential for the kernel learning and which extends the possibility of applying the "kernel trick" to a very wide range of machine learning models.

Theorem 5 (Representer theorem (Schölkopf *et al.*, 2001)). *Let $\boldsymbol{X}$ be a non-empty set, K is a positive definite kernel over $\boldsymbol{X}$ and a reproducing kernel of RKHS $\mathcal{H}$ of functions over $\boldsymbol{X}$. Given a training sample $\boldsymbol{X}_N = \{(\boldsymbol{x}_1, y_1), \ldots, (\boldsymbol{x}_N, y_N)\}, \boldsymbol{x}_i \in \boldsymbol{X}, y_i \in \mathbb{R}, i = 1, \ldots, N$, a strictly monotonically increasing function $g : [0, +\infty) \to \mathbb{R}$. Then, for any arbitrary empirical risk function $E : (\boldsymbol{X} \times \mathbb{R}^2)^N \to \mathbb{R}$ if f^* is a solution of optimization problem*

$$E((\boldsymbol{x}_1, y_1, f(\boldsymbol{x}_1)), \ldots, (\boldsymbol{x}_N, y_N, f(\boldsymbol{x}_N))) + g(\|f\|_H) \to \min_{f \in \mathcal{H}},$$

then f^* has the structure

$$f^*(\cdot) = \sum_{i=1}^{N} \alpha_i K(\cdot, \boldsymbol{x}_i).$$

Summand $g(\|f\|)$ in the functional under optimization corresponds to regularization term that is usually added for noise-stability purposes.

The theorem is very significant as it presents a parametric linear model of generally nonlinear function, which is an optimal solution for a very wide range of machine learning problems.

However, the theorem does not present the exact kernel form. It just states that such a reproducing kernel exists. Therefore, the theorem simplifies but does not remove the "model selection" problem.

13.3. Kernel Models and Applications

In this part of the chapter, we discuss kernel models, their properties and their applications to regression, density estimation, dimensionality reduction, filtering and finally clustering. Kernels provide elegant approach for incorporating nonlinearity into linear models, dramatically broadening the area of application for many algorithms, such as, linear regression, PCA, k-means, etc.

13.3.1. *Kernel Density Estimation*

One of the common problems in data mining is the probability density estimation aiming to restore an unknown probability distribution function basing on some given data points, which are supposed to be generated from the target distribution.

Formally, let $\boldsymbol{X}_N = \{\boldsymbol{x}_1, \ldots, \boldsymbol{x}_N\}$ be an i.i.d. sample in $\mathbb{R}^n$ drawn from an unknown distribution $p(x)$. The aim is to build an estimate distribution $\hat{p}(x)$. In general, $\hat{p}(x)$ should be a consistent estimate at every point.

Such problems appear as a subtask in many different practical applications such as classification, clustering, etc. Kernel models are widely used for probability density functions (pdf) estimation.

Kernel density estimation is closely related to the histogram-based density estimation approach which is also referred as histogram method. For one-dimensional data, the estimator is calculated as

$$\hat{p}_h(x) = \frac{1}{N} \frac{\sum_{i=1}^{N} \mathrm{I}\left[x - \frac{h}{2} < x_i < x + \frac{h}{2}\right]}{h},$$

where h is the bandwidth parameter or window size, I denotes indicator function, i.e.,

$$\mathrm{I}[c] = \begin{cases} 1, & \text{if } c \text{ is true;} \\ 0, & \text{if } c \text{ is false.} \end{cases}$$

The estimate is very sensitive to the bandwidth parameter, as it may cause over- or underfitting. Examples of estimates for different bandwidths are shown in Figure 13.2. The original pdf is solid line, while its estimates are dashed lines. Too small bandwidth $h = 0.1$ results in very rough approximation. Too large bandwidth $h = 2$ leads to oversmoothing. Bandwidth $h = 0.56$ seems to be a compromise between too small and too large windows.

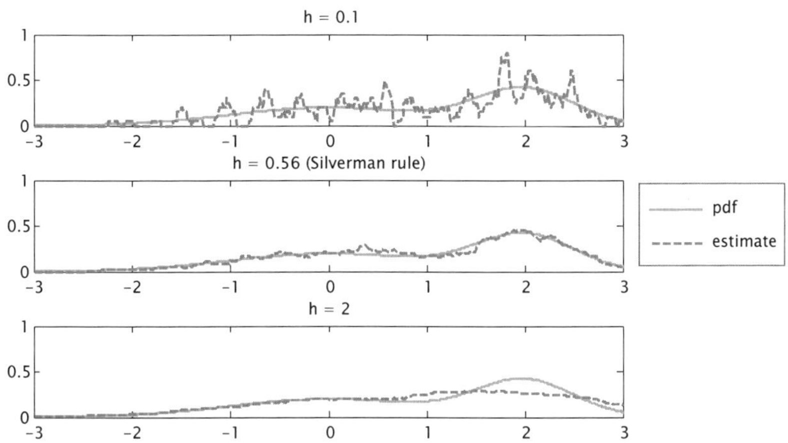

Figure 13.2: Kernel density estimation.

However, in the cases of small learning datasets histogram approach leads to unacceptable solutions. For this reason, the histogram function is often replaced by a nonnegative symmetric smooth function $K(\boldsymbol{x})$, normalized at 1, i.e.,

$$\int K(\boldsymbol{x})d\boldsymbol{x} = 1.$$

Then the estimate becomes

$$\hat{p}_h(\boldsymbol{x}) = \frac{1}{N}\frac{\sum_{i=1}^{N} K\left(\frac{\boldsymbol{x}-\boldsymbol{x}_i}{h}\right)}{h} = \frac{1}{N}\sum_{i=1}^{N} K_h(\boldsymbol{x}-\boldsymbol{x}_i),$$

where $K_h(\boldsymbol{x}) = \frac{1}{h}K\left(\frac{\boldsymbol{x}}{h}\right)$, usually referred as a scaled kernel. This approach is known as Parzen–Rosenblatt method. Notice that the histogram estimation is a special case of Parzen–Rosenblatt method (Parzen, 1962; Rosenblatt, 1956).

Such modification results in a smooth function. An example illustrating difference between regular histogram window and Gaussian kernel estimation is shown in Figure 13.3.

As Figure 13.2 shows, density estimation relies on good bandwidth parameter selection. There is a number (Jones *et al.*, 1996; Park and Marron, 1990; Park and Turlach, 1992; Sheather and Jones, 1991; Sheather, 1992) of different approaches but practically for one-dimensional data all of them are based on the result that the window size decreases as $O(N^{-\frac{1}{5}})$. Optimal bandwidth for kernel K estimating one-dimensional density p can be determined by minimizing asymptotic mean integrated

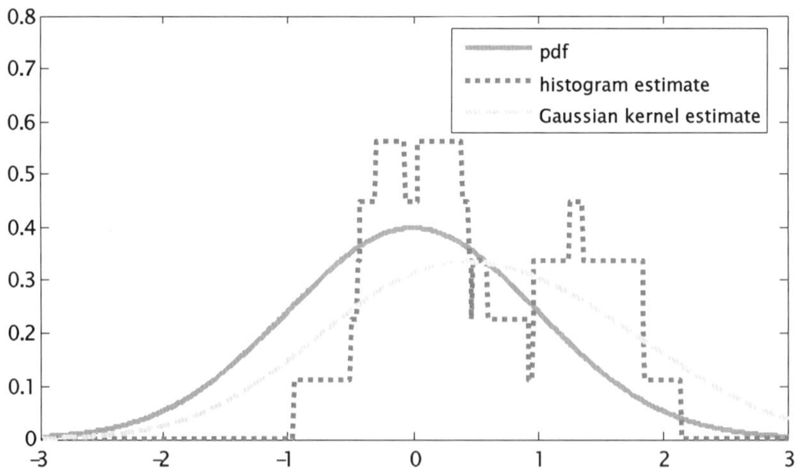

Figure 13.3: Kernel density estimation from 10 points, $h = 0.9$.

squared error (AMISE):

$$h^* = \frac{R(K)^{\frac{1}{5}}}{s(K)^{\frac{2}{5}} R\left(\frac{\partial^2 p}{\partial x^2}\right)^{\frac{1}{5}} N^{\frac{1}{5}}},$$

where

$$R(f) = \int f^2(x)dx,$$

$$s(f) = \int x^2 f(x)dx.$$

However, such estimate cannot be applied directly because it requires some prior knowledge about the estimated distribution (in particular, density$p(x)$). For some distributions this bandwidth estimate is known. For Gaussian distribution the following value, known as Silverman's rule of thumb (Silverman, 1986), is commonly used:

$$h^* = \left(\frac{4\hat{\sigma}^5}{3N}\right)^{\frac{1}{5}}.$$

It can be obtained from the asymptotic formula by direct substitution of the parametric variance by its estimate $\hat{\sigma}^2$.

13.3.2. *The Nadaraya–Watson Kernel Regression*

In 1964, (Nadaraya, 1964) and (Watson, 1964) proposed a method for kernel regression which is a nonparametric regression technique. Having a sample of pairs $\{(\boldsymbol{x}_i, y_i)\}_{i=1}^N$, we look forward for finding the most expected value of y for any value of $\boldsymbol{x}$. Assuming that pairs $(\boldsymbol{x}_i, y_i)$ come from some distribution f on $\boldsymbol{X} \times Y$, where $\boldsymbol{x}_i \in \boldsymbol{X}$, $y_i \in Y \subseteq \mathbb{R}$, regression problem is formulated in terms of finding conditional expectation $\bar{y}$:

$$\bar{y} = \mathbb{E}(y|\boldsymbol{x}) = \int y f(y|\boldsymbol{x}) dy = \frac{\int y f(\boldsymbol{x}, y) dy}{f(\boldsymbol{x})}.$$

Kernel density estimation helps us estimate the joint distribution $f(\boldsymbol{x}, y)$ of two random variables (that can be, in fact, multivariate variables) $\boldsymbol{x}$ and y,

$$\hat{f}(\boldsymbol{x}, y) = \frac{1}{N h_x h_y} \sum_{i=1}^{N} K\left(\frac{\boldsymbol{x} - \boldsymbol{x}_i}{h_x}\right) K\left(\frac{y - y_i}{h_y}\right),$$

and the marginal distribution $f(\boldsymbol{x})$,

$$\hat{f}(\boldsymbol{x}) = \frac{1}{Nh_x} \sum_{i=1}^{N} K\left(\frac{\boldsymbol{x} - \boldsymbol{x}_i}{h_x}\right).$$

Here h_x and h_y are corresponding bandwidths of the kernels.

Now these estimators are used to calculate the conditional expectation

$$\bar{y} = \frac{\int y\hat{f}(\boldsymbol{x}, y)dy}{\hat{f}(\boldsymbol{x})} = \frac{\sum_{i=1}^{N} K\left(\frac{x - x_i}{h_x}\right) y_i}{\sum_{i=1}^{N} K\left(\frac{x - x_i}{h_x}\right)},$$

assuming that $\int yK\left(\frac{y-y_i}{h_y}\right) dy = h_y y_i$.

Bandwidth selection addresses the same approaches as were discussed in the previous section.

Figure 13.4 illustrates dependency of Nadaraya–Watson estimator on the bandwidth parameter h_x. Again, too large bandwidth leads to over-smoothing, while too small bandwidth makes estimate excessively sensitive to outliers.

Speaking about kernel regression, we must mention a rather relative approach — locally weighted regression (LWR) (Atkeson *et al.*, 1997). LWR also makes use of kernels but in a different way, weighting examples by kernel function K. Linear regression weights $\boldsymbol{w}$ become a function of data, i.e.,

$$\boldsymbol{w}(\boldsymbol{x}) = \arg\min_{w} \sum_{i=1}^{N} K(\boldsymbol{x}, \boldsymbol{x}_i)(\langle \boldsymbol{w}, \boldsymbol{x}_i \rangle - y_i)^2,$$

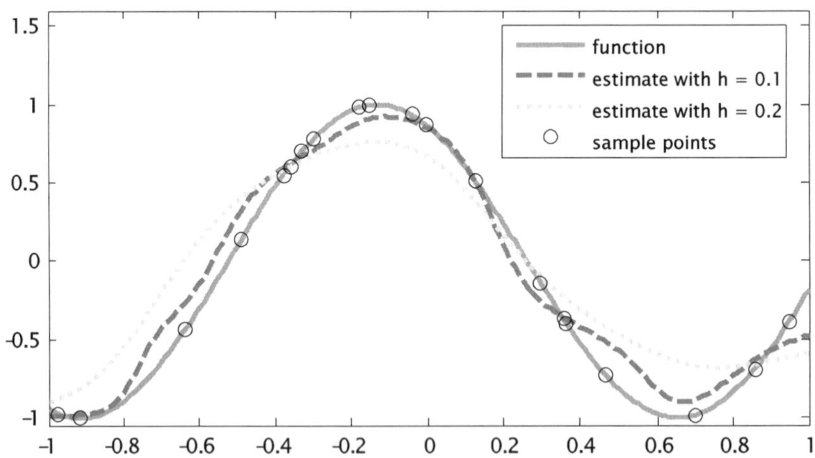

Figure 13.4: Nadaraya–Watson regression.

and

$$y(\boldsymbol{x}) = \langle \boldsymbol{w}(\boldsymbol{x}), \boldsymbol{x} \rangle.$$

Linear regression function $\langle \boldsymbol{w}(\boldsymbol{x}), \boldsymbol{x} \rangle$ may be replaced with an arbitrary $f(\boldsymbol{x}, \boldsymbol{w})$ resulting in more complex models. It was shown that for a uniformly (or regularly) distributed data LWR is equivalent to kernel regression, while for non-uniform (irregular) data LWR outperforms kernel regression (Atkeson *et al.*, 1997; Jones *et al.*, 1999; Müller, 1987).

13.3.3. *Kernel PCA*

Another example of kernel methods is a kernel extension of principal component analysis (PCA). PCA is a feature aggregation technique aiming on finding a projection to an optimal linear subspace which occurs to be a span of eigenvectors of data matrix. Let

$$\boldsymbol{X}_N = (\boldsymbol{x}_1, \ldots, \boldsymbol{x}_N) \in \mathbb{R}^{n \times N}, \quad \boldsymbol{x}_i \in \mathbb{R}^n, \ i \in \{1, \ldots, N\},$$

be a data matrix. PCA finds its decomposition in two matrices of lower rank

$$\boldsymbol{X}_N \approx GW.$$

Columns of G represent an orthonormal basis of a linear L-dimensional subspace. W is a weight matrix determining projection onto this subspace. Subspace and orthogonal projection are chosen so that

$$\|\boldsymbol{X}_N - GW\|^2 \to \min_{G,W}.$$

Initially linear, PCA approach can be easily extended to nonlinear cases (Schölkopf *et al.*, 1999).

Solution of PCA is based on eigenvalue decomposition of covariance matrix $C = \boldsymbol{X}_N \boldsymbol{X}_N^T$, which finds eigenvectors $\boldsymbol{g}$ and eigenvalues λ,

$$C\boldsymbol{g} = \boldsymbol{X}_N \boldsymbol{X}_N^T g = \lambda \boldsymbol{g}.$$

For any kernel K there exists a map Φ and we can rewrite covariance matrix as

$$C_\Phi = \sum_{i=1}^{N} \Phi(\boldsymbol{x}_i)\Phi(\boldsymbol{x}_i)^T,$$

and find its eigenvalue decomposition. It gives us the first L eigenvectors $\boldsymbol{g}_1, \ldots, \boldsymbol{g}_L$ so that

$$C_\Phi \boldsymbol{g}_l = \lambda_l \boldsymbol{g}_l.$$

As it is in a linear case of PCA eigenvectors are linear combinations of $\Phi(\boldsymbol{x}_i)$, i.e.,

$$\boldsymbol{g}_l = \sum_{i=1}^{N} \alpha_{il} \Phi(\boldsymbol{x}_i).$$

Vectors $\boldsymbol{\alpha}_l$ can be calculated by eigenvalue decomposition of the pairwise inner product matrix $K = K[\boldsymbol{X}_N, \boldsymbol{X}_N]$, $K_{ij} = K(\boldsymbol{x}_i, \boldsymbol{x}_j)$, namely

$$K\boldsymbol{\alpha}_l = \lambda_l \boldsymbol{\alpha}_l.$$

By normalizing eigenvectors so that $\langle \boldsymbol{g}_l, \boldsymbol{g}_l \rangle_{\mathcal{H}} = 1$, we obtain a rule for finding nonlinear projection of any data vector $\boldsymbol{x}$ on each basis vector as

$$\langle \boldsymbol{g}_l, \Phi(\boldsymbol{x}) \rangle_{\mathcal{H}} = \sum_{i=1}^{N} \alpha_{il} \langle \Phi(\boldsymbol{x}_i), \Phi(\boldsymbol{x}) \rangle_{\mathcal{H}}.$$

Note, we do not have to know an implicit form of the map Φ, just the corresponding kernel K, which is used for calculation of inner products.

Expression for C_Φ is tricky as, in general case, RKHS corresponding to the mapping Φ is infinite dimensional. Thus, transpose operator is incorrect. Then C_Φ can be understood as a linear operator

$$C_\Phi z = \sum_{i=1}^{N} \Phi(\boldsymbol{x}_i) \langle \Phi(\boldsymbol{x}_i), z \rangle_{\mathcal{H}}, \quad \forall z \in \mathcal{H}.$$

Kernel PCA allows finding nonlinear dependencies inside data. This property is illustrated in Figure 13.5. In the original feature space, two-dimensional data points form three concentric circles, which are not linearly separated. Introduction of Gaussian or polynomial kernels into PCA allows obtaining linearly separable dataset.

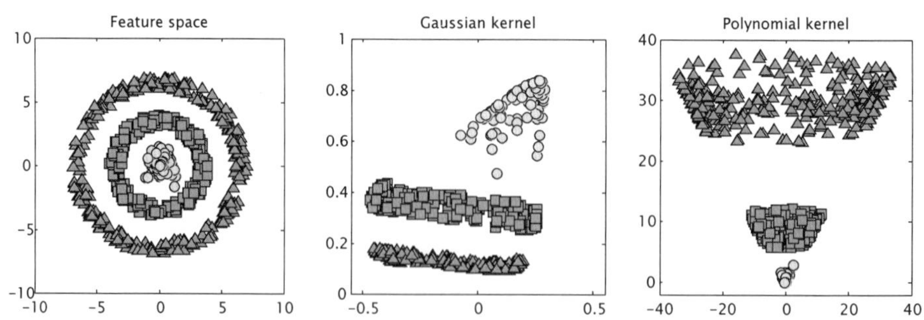

Figure 13.5: Kernel PCA with different kernels.

13.3.4. *Kernel Linear Discriminant Analysis*

Linear discriminant analysis relates to classification problem, i.e., for a given learning set

$$\boldsymbol{X}_N = \{(\boldsymbol{x}_1, y_1), \ldots, (\boldsymbol{x}_N, y_N)\},$$

$\boldsymbol{x}_i \in \mathbb{R}^n$, $y_i \in Y$, where $Y = \{L_1, \ldots, L_R\}$ is a set of class labels, the aim is to recover the labelling function $f : \mathbb{R}^n \to Y$.

Linear Discriminant Analysis finds the normal vector $\boldsymbol{w}$ of the "optimal" (in terms of given quality function) separating plane in the data space. The projection of the data on the resulting vector gives a good separation of classes.

For two-class classification problems, i.e., $R = 2$, the optimal vector is determined as a solution of the following problem

$$\frac{\boldsymbol{w}^T S_B \boldsymbol{w}}{\boldsymbol{w}^T S_W \boldsymbol{w}} \to \max_{\boldsymbol{w} \in \mathbb{R}^n},$$

where

$$S_B = (\boldsymbol{\mu}_1 - \boldsymbol{\mu}_2)(\boldsymbol{\mu}_1 - \boldsymbol{\mu}_2)^T \in \mathbb{R}^{n \times n},$$

is the between-class covariance matrix,

$$S_W = \sum_{r=1}^{2} \sum_{i:y_i = L_r} (\boldsymbol{\mu}_r - \boldsymbol{x}_i)(\boldsymbol{\mu}_r - \boldsymbol{x}_i)^T \in \mathbb{R}^{n \times n},$$

is the within-class covariance matrix, $\boldsymbol{\mu}_r$ is an arithmetic mean of sample vectors of the class L_r,

$$\boldsymbol{\mu}_r = \frac{1}{N_r} \sum_{i:y_i = L_r} \boldsymbol{x}_i,$$

where N_r is a number of samples in class L_r.

It can be shown that the resulting vector

$$\boldsymbol{w} \propto S_W^{-1}(\boldsymbol{\mu}_1 - \boldsymbol{\mu}_2).$$

Similarly to the previous examples, kernel trick can be applied to the given model (Mika *et al.*, 1999). Suppose, there is a mapping between the initial data space and a Hilbert space: $\Phi : \mathbb{R}^n \to \mathcal{H}$, where

$$\langle \Phi(\boldsymbol{x}), \Phi(\boldsymbol{t}) \rangle_{\mathcal{H}} = K(\boldsymbol{x}, \boldsymbol{t}).$$

In this Hilbert space, the sample vectors class means are calculated as

$$\boldsymbol{\mu}_r^{\Phi} = \frac{1}{N_r} \sum_{i:y_i = L_r} \Phi(\boldsymbol{x}_i).$$

Therefore, an inner product of the mean with the map of any arbitrary vector $\boldsymbol{x} \in \mathbb{R}^n$ is

$$\left\langle \Phi(\boldsymbol{x}), \boldsymbol{\mu}_r^{\Phi} \right\rangle_{\mathcal{H}} = \frac{1}{N_r} \sum_{i:y_i = L_r} \langle \Phi(\boldsymbol{x}), \Phi(\boldsymbol{x}_i) \rangle_{\mathcal{H}} = \frac{1}{N_r} \sum_{i:y_i = L_r} K(\boldsymbol{x}, \boldsymbol{x}_i).$$

Definition of the covariance matrix in the mapped feature space is more complex, as it defines a linear operator in $\mathcal{H}$. However, we can determine the linear operator by its values over the vectors from the span of Φ. For example, Hilbert space within-class covariance matrix is "schematically" defined as

$$S_W^{\Phi} = \sum_{r=1}^{2} \sum_{i:y_i = L_r} \left[\left(\Phi(\boldsymbol{x}_i) - \boldsymbol{\mu}_r^{\Phi} \right) \left(\Phi(\boldsymbol{x}_i) - \boldsymbol{\mu}_r^{\Phi} \right)^T \right].$$

Suppose that

$$\boldsymbol{w}^{\Phi} = \sum_{i=1}^{N} \alpha_i \Phi(\boldsymbol{x}_i),$$

then

$$S_W^{\Phi} \boldsymbol{w}^{\Phi} = \sum_{r=1}^{2} \sum_{j:y_j = L_r} \left\langle \Phi(\boldsymbol{x}_j) - \boldsymbol{\mu}_r^{\Phi}, \boldsymbol{w}^{\Phi} \right\rangle_{\mathcal{H}} \left[\Phi(\boldsymbol{x}_j) - \boldsymbol{\mu}_r^{\Phi} \right].$$

The coefficient $\langle \Phi(\boldsymbol{x}_j) - \boldsymbol{\mu}_r^{\Phi}, \boldsymbol{w}^{\Phi} \rangle_{\mathcal{H}}$ can be easily computed using the properties of the inner product,

$$\left\langle \Phi(\boldsymbol{x}_j) - \boldsymbol{\mu}_r^{\Phi}, \boldsymbol{w}^{\Phi} \right\rangle_{\mathcal{H}} = \sum_{i=1}^{N} \alpha_i \left[K(\boldsymbol{x}_j, \boldsymbol{x}_i) - \left\langle \boldsymbol{\Phi}(\boldsymbol{x}_i), \boldsymbol{\mu}_r^{\Phi} \right\rangle_{\mathcal{H}} \right].$$

The result is a weighted sum of elements of $\mathcal{H}$. In a similar way a second-order function $\langle \boldsymbol{w}^{\Phi}, S_W^{\Phi} \boldsymbol{w}^{\Phi} \rangle_{\mathcal{H}}$ can be calculated. The optimal values of $\alpha_i, i = 1, \ldots N$, are still to be defined. Therefore, the resulting Kernel LDA optimization problem is to find maximum

$$\frac{\langle \boldsymbol{w}^{\Phi}, S_B^{\Phi} \boldsymbol{w}^{\Phi} \rangle_{\mathcal{H}}}{\langle \boldsymbol{w}^{\Phi}, S_W^{\Phi} \boldsymbol{w}^{\Phi} \rangle_{\mathcal{H}}} \to \max_{\alpha_i \in \mathbb{R}, i=1,\ldots,N},$$

w.r.t.

$$\boldsymbol{w}^{\Phi} = \sum_{i=1}^{N} \alpha_i \Phi(\boldsymbol{x}_i).$$

Optimal solution of the stated Kernel LDA problem is

$$\boldsymbol{\alpha} \propto Q^{-1}(\boldsymbol{M}_1 - \boldsymbol{M}_2),$$

where

$$\boldsymbol{M}_r \in \mathbb{R}^N, \quad (\boldsymbol{M}_r)_i = \frac{1}{N_r} \sum_{j:y_j=L_r} K(\boldsymbol{x}_j, \boldsymbol{x}_i),$$

$$Q = \sum_{r=1}^{2} K_r(\mathbf{I} - \mathbf{E}_{N_r})K_r^T,$$

$\mathbf{E}_{\mathbf{N_r}} \in \mathbb{R}^{\mathbf{N_r} \times \mathbf{N_r}}$ is a matrix with elements equal to $\frac{1}{N_r}$,
$K_r \in \mathbb{R}^{N \times N_r}$, $(K_r)_{ij} = K(\boldsymbol{x}_i, \boldsymbol{x}_j^r)$, $\boldsymbol{x}_j^r$ – jth vector in the rth class.

As it was pointed previously, projection of the data on the optimal vector leads to the optimal separation. In terms of Kernel LDA, the projection of the $\Phi(\boldsymbol{x})$ on the vector $\boldsymbol{w}^\Phi$ is defined by the inner product

$$\langle \boldsymbol{w}^\Phi, \Phi(\boldsymbol{x}) \rangle_{\mathcal{H}} = \sum_{i=1}^{N} \alpha_i K(\boldsymbol{x}, \boldsymbol{x}_i).$$

Separating property of the Kernel LDA method is illustrated in Figure 13.6.

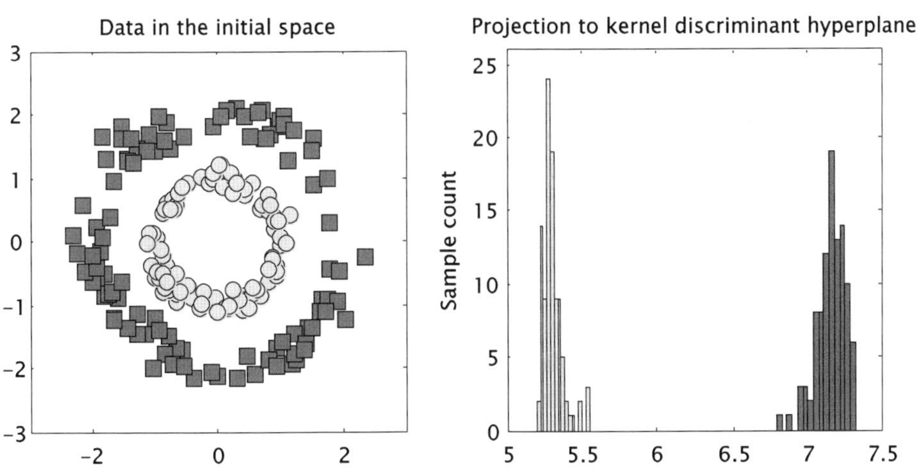

Figure 13.6: Kernel LDA projection example. Chart on the left demonstrates the distribution of the data in the initial space. Right chart demonstrates the histogram of the data samples projected on optimal vector in the feature map space.

13.3.5. *Kernelization of an Arbitrary Linear Model*

In fact, any linear model can be "kernelized" by replacing inner products $\langle \boldsymbol{x}, \boldsymbol{t} \rangle$ with kernel values $K(\boldsymbol{x}, \boldsymbol{t})$. Here, we show the idea on an example of the ridge regression model. Recall the classical ridge regression with target function

$$\sum_{i=1}^{N} (y_i - \langle \boldsymbol{w}, \boldsymbol{x}_i \rangle)^2 + \lambda \|\boldsymbol{w}\|^2 \to \min_{\boldsymbol{w}}.$$

Here, pairs $(\boldsymbol{x}_i, y_i)$ belong to the training sample $\boldsymbol{X}_N$. This optimization problem can be solved analytically. With the help of linear algebra, we get

$$\boldsymbol{w} = \left(\sum_{i=1}^{N} \boldsymbol{x}_i \boldsymbol{x}_i^T + \lambda \mathbf{I} \right)^{-1} \left(\sum_{i=1}^{N} y_i \boldsymbol{x}_i \right).$$

Now, with an appropriate kernel we perform mapping $\boldsymbol{x}_i \to \Phi(\boldsymbol{x}_i)$. Therefore,

$$\sum_{i=1}^{N} (y_i - \langle \boldsymbol{w}, \Phi(\boldsymbol{x}_i) \rangle_{\mathcal{H}})^2 + \lambda \|\boldsymbol{w}\|^2 \to \min_{\boldsymbol{w} \in \mathcal{H}}.$$

Assuming that $\boldsymbol{w} = \sum_{i=1}^{N} \alpha_i \Phi(\boldsymbol{x}_i)$, we can reformulate the optimization problem as

$$\sum_{i=1}^{N} \left(y_i - \sum_{j=1}^{N} \alpha_j \langle \Phi(\boldsymbol{x}_j), \Phi(\boldsymbol{x}_i) \rangle_{\mathcal{H}} \right)^2 + \lambda \boldsymbol{\alpha}^T K(\boldsymbol{X}_N, \boldsymbol{X}_N) \boldsymbol{\alpha} \to \min_{\boldsymbol{\alpha} \in \mathbb{R}^N}.$$

Here, we denote matrix of pairwise inner products of the training sample as $K(\boldsymbol{X}_N, \boldsymbol{X}_N)$,

$$[K(\boldsymbol{X}_N, \boldsymbol{X}_N)]_{ij} = K(\boldsymbol{x}_i, \boldsymbol{x}_j).$$

Then, the optimal solution of the stated problem is given by

$$\boldsymbol{\alpha} = (K(\boldsymbol{X}_N, \boldsymbol{X}_N) + \lambda \mathbf{I})^{-1} \bar{y}.$$

This result can be interpreted as a special case of the representer theorem application.

Again, for calculating y value for an arbitrary $\boldsymbol{x}$ the exact form of the mapping Φ is not needed, we just have to know the corresponding kernel function.

$$y = \langle \boldsymbol{w}, \Phi(\boldsymbol{x}) \rangle = \boldsymbol{\alpha}^T K(\boldsymbol{X}_N, \boldsymbol{x}) = \sum_{i=1}^{N} \alpha_i K(\boldsymbol{x}_i, \boldsymbol{x}).$$

Vector $K(\boldsymbol{X}_N, \boldsymbol{x})$ consists of inner products of the training sample objects and the object being evaluated.

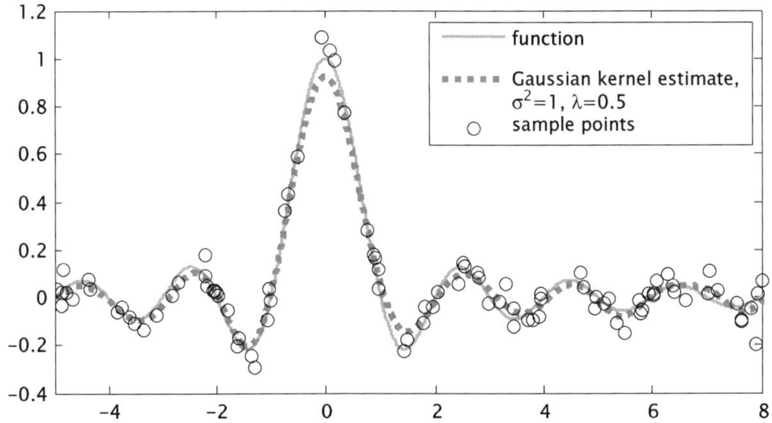

Figure 13.7: Kernel ridge regression with Gaussian kernel, $\sigma^2 = 1, \lambda = 0.5$.

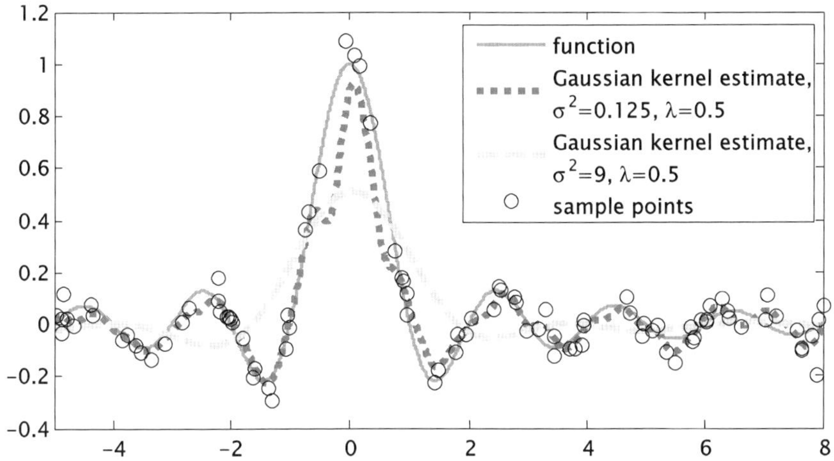

Figure 13.8: Kernel ridge regression with Gaussian kernel and different σ^2.

Figure 13.7 shows an example of kernel ridge regression for a model

$$y = \frac{\sin \pi x}{\pi x} + \varepsilon,$$

where $\varepsilon \sim \mathcal{N}(0, s^2)$ is a normally distributed noise with zero mean and variance s^2 imposed on signal.

Kernel ridge regression significantly depends on the selection of kernel and its parameters. In the case of Gaussian kernel (Hastie *et al.*, 2003; Vapnik, 1995), too large values of spread σ^2 lead to an oversmoothed solution, while too small σ^2 results in an over-fitting. These effects are shown in Figure 13.8.

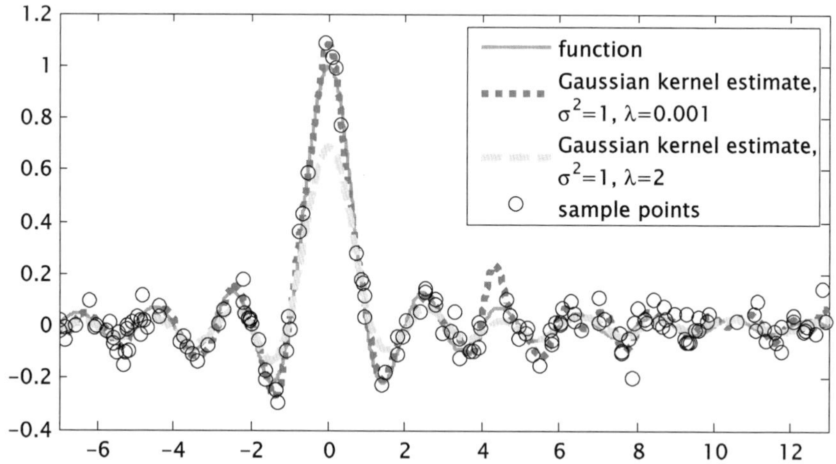

Figure 13.9: Kernel ridge regression with Gaussian kernel and different λ.

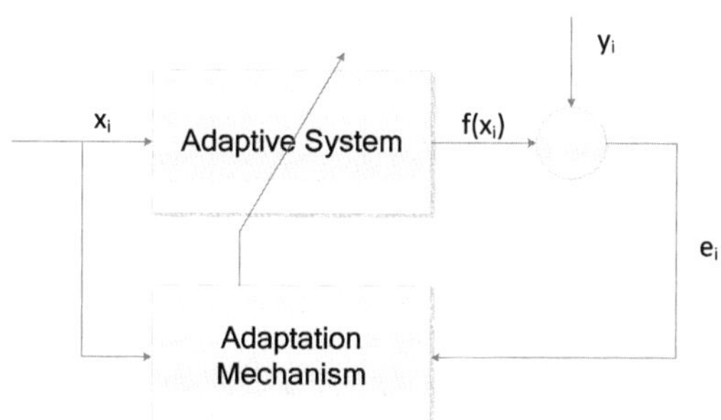

Figure 13.10: Adaptive system.

The same is with regression parameter λ: its growth will lead to smoothing and its decrease will lead to a very sensitive model, as it can be seen in Figure 13.9. To tune the parameters of the kernel ridge regression, cross-validation technique may be applied (Exterkate *et al.*, 2013).

13.3.6. *Adaptive Kernel Filtering*

Described kernel models are applicable to adaptive filter design (Hayes, 1996). Adaptive kernel filtering admits online learning of the nonlinear filters. Learning procedure is computationally cheap, as the optimization is convex.

Consider a system that takes as input streaming data vectors $\boldsymbol{x}_i \in \mathbb{R}^n$ drawn independently from an unknown probability distribution and produces output $f(\boldsymbol{x}_i)$ aiming to predict corresponding outcome y_i. One of the possible representations of such a system is shown in Figure 13.10.

The learning procedure is performed in online way. In case of the linear model, the output can be represented as an inner product

$$f(\boldsymbol{x}_i) = \langle \boldsymbol{x}_i, \boldsymbol{w} \rangle.$$

Learning can be performed using any online fitting procedure, such as stochastic gradient descent (Hayes, 1996), Recursive Least Squares (Bottou, 1998), etc. But that approach limits the resulting filter output to a linear combination of the data vector components, i.e., a linear function.

This limitation can be overcome by the kernel trick. Hereafter, we use least squares functional

$$E(\boldsymbol{X}_N, f) = \sum_{i=1}^{N} (f(\boldsymbol{x}_i) - y_i)^2.$$

Consider stochastic gradient descent as a learning algorithm. Suppose that the target function is an inner product in the Hilbert space $\mathcal{H}$:

$$f(\boldsymbol{x}) = \langle \Phi(\boldsymbol{x}), \boldsymbol{w} \rangle_{\mathcal{H}},$$

where $\Phi : \mathbb{R}^n \to \mathcal{H}$ is a map from the data space to a Hilbert space. Similar to the previous examples, we assume that

$$\forall \boldsymbol{x}, \boldsymbol{t} \in \mathbb{R}^n \ \langle \Phi(\boldsymbol{x}), \Phi(\boldsymbol{t}) \rangle_{\mathcal{H}} = K(\boldsymbol{x}, \boldsymbol{t}).$$

As a new learning pair $(\boldsymbol{x}_i, y_i)$ comes, parameter vector $\boldsymbol{w}_{i-1}$ is updated according to gradient of $(\langle \Phi(\boldsymbol{x}_i), \boldsymbol{w}_{i-1} \rangle_{\mathcal{H}} - y_i)^2$:

$$\boldsymbol{w}_i = \boldsymbol{w}_{i-1} - \nu(\langle \Phi(\boldsymbol{x}_i), \boldsymbol{w}_{i-1} \rangle_{\mathcal{H}} - y_i)\Phi(\boldsymbol{x}_i) = \boldsymbol{w}_{i-1} + \alpha_i \Phi(\boldsymbol{x}_i).$$

Here, ν is a gradient descent step. Therefore, the resulting function f can be expressed as

$$f(\boldsymbol{x}) = \sum_{i=1}^{N} \alpha_i K(\boldsymbol{x}, \boldsymbol{x}_i).$$

The overall algorithm is presented in Table 13.1.

Parameter ν usually affects convergence and, specifically, convergence speed. The required condition for convergence is

$$\nu < \frac{N}{\xi_{\max}} \Longrightarrow \nu < \frac{N}{\sum_{i=1}^{N} K(\boldsymbol{x}_i, \boldsymbol{x}_i)} = \frac{N}{\operatorname{tr}(K(\boldsymbol{X}_N, \boldsymbol{X}_N))} < \frac{N}{\xi_{\max}}.$$

Table 13.1: Adaptive kernel filtering algorithm.

Kernel Least Mean Squares Algorithm
Input: $X_N = \{(\boldsymbol{x}_1, y_1), \ldots, (\boldsymbol{x}_N, y_N)\}, \boldsymbol{x}_i \in \mathbb{R}^n, y_i \in \mathbb{R}$ **Output**: $\alpha_1, \ldots, \alpha_N$ **1.** $\boldsymbol{w}_0 = \boldsymbol{0} \in \mathcal{H}$ — zero vector in the Hilbert space **2.** **for** $\alpha_1, \ldots, \alpha_N$ **2.1.** $e_i = (\langle \Phi(\boldsymbol{x}_i), \boldsymbol{w}_{i-1} \rangle_{\mathcal{H}} - y_i) = \left(\sum_{j=1}^{i-1} \alpha_j K(\boldsymbol{x}_i, \boldsymbol{x}_j) - y_i\right)$ **2.2.** $\alpha_i = -\nu e_i$

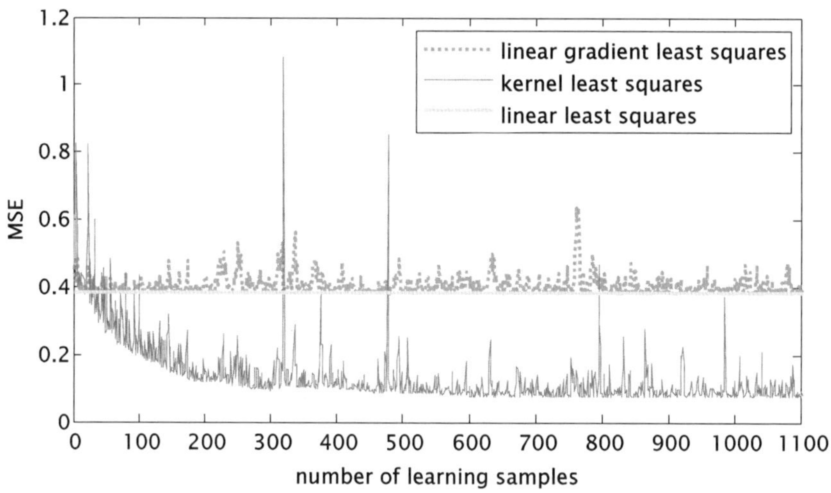

Figure 13.11: Adaptive kernel filtering.

Here, $\xi_{\max}$ is the maximal eigenvalue of the matrix $K(\boldsymbol{X}_N, \boldsymbol{X}_N) \in \mathbb{R}^{N \times N}$ of samples' Hilbert space inner products, i.e.,

$$[K(\boldsymbol{X}_N, \boldsymbol{X}_N)]_{ij} = K(\boldsymbol{x}_i, \boldsymbol{x}_j).$$

An example of kernel least mean squares performance is presented in Figure 13.11. The input of the system was generated from uniform distribution over unit 10-dimentional cube. The output was defined as the sine of the squared norm of the corresponding input vector, i.e.,

$$\boldsymbol{x}_i \in \mathbb{R}^{10}, \quad y_i = \sin(\|\boldsymbol{x}_i\|^2).$$

Thin and dotted lines represent the mean squared error (MSE) over the testing set depending on the number of learning samples used by an adaptive filter for kernel LMS and linear stochastic LMS correspondingly. Thick line represents the

MSE for the linear least squares algorithm, which is a theoretical minimum for the linear model. Kernel model converges slower, but significantly outperforms the linear model in terms of MSE.

However, one of the most significant drawbacks of the system is the order of the filter, which increases with each new accumulated learning data sample. This can be overcome by a number of approaches limiting the order of the filter (Liu *et al.*, 2010).

Kernel methods are widely applied in the area of adaptive filtering. There exist techniques for regularized regression fitting, kernel extended least squares algorithms and many other kernel data mining models.

13.3.7. *Spectral Clustering*

Spectral clustering (Balakrishnan *et al.*, 2011; Dhillon *et al.*, 2004; Luxburg, 2007; Ng *et al.*, 2001) is a clustering technique based on analysis of the data similarity matrix spectrum. Now it is considered to be one of the most popular clustering methods as it can be simply implemented and efficiently solved by standard linear algebra methods and outperforms many other clustering approaches in different domains (Balakrishnan *et al.*, 2011; Luxburg, 2007). Originally, the idea comes from weighted graph analysis, but it can be shown that it has connection to kernel methods.

The starting point of spectral clustering is building a similarity $N \times N$ matrix S of dataset $\{\boldsymbol{x}_1, \ldots, \boldsymbol{x}_N\}$, where $s_{ij} > 0$ is similarity between $\boldsymbol{x}_i$ and $\boldsymbol{x}_j$. These relationships can be represented in form of the similarity graph $G = (V, E)$, where vertex $v_i \in V$ corresponds to $\boldsymbol{x}_i$ and edge $e_{ij} \in E$ is weighted by s_{ij}. This graph can be fully connected, i.e., all $s_{ij} > 0$, or each vertex can be connected to k nearest neighbors only, i.e., all other edges have $s_{ij} = 0$, resulting in a sparse matrix (Luxburg, 2007). The problem of clustering then can be reformulated in terms of partitioning of the graph. And edges of the partition between different groups are expected to have low weights.

Following the graph theory, we denote a degree of a vertex v_i as

$$d_i = \sum_{j=1}^{N} s_{ij}.$$

The degree matrix D is a diagonal matrix with $d_1, \ldots, d_N$ on the diagonal.

Spectral clustering algorithms are based on eigenvalue decomposition of graph Laplacian matrix. There are several ways to calculate it.

1. The unnormalized graph Laplacian matrix (Mohar, 1991; Mohar *et al.*, 1997) is defined as

$$L = D - S.$$

2. The symmetric normalized graph Laplacian matrix (Chung, 1997) is defined as
$$L = D^{-\frac{1}{2}}(D - S)D^{-\frac{1}{2}} = \mathbf{I} - D^{-\frac{1}{2}}SD^{-\frac{1}{2}}.$$
3. The random walk normalized graph Laplacian matrix (Chung, 1997) is defined as
$$L = D^{-1}(D - S) = \mathbf{I} - D^{-1}S.$$
4. In (Ng *et al.*, 2001), the authors define graph Laplacian matrix as
$$L = D^{-\frac{1}{2}}SD^{-\frac{1}{2}},$$
which has the same eigenvectors as the symmetric normalized graph Laplacian matrix and eigenvalues λ_i, corresponding to $1 - \lambda_i$ of the latter.

After calculating the graph Laplacian matrix of the data, eigenvalue decomposition is performed. Ordinary decomposition may be replaced with a generalized eigenvalue decomposition as it is in Shi and Malik spectral clustering (Shi and Malik, 2000). Eigenvectors, which are vector columns, corresponding to k smallest eigenvalues form matrix $V^{N\times k}$ containing new descriptions of the original objects as vector rows.

Finally, these row vectors are clustered, for instance, using simple k-means algorithm. Ng *et al.* (2001) suggest normalizing vector rows to have norm 1.

Spectral clustering can be easily implemented and solved by standard linear algebra methods. Numerous experiments show that spectral clustering algorithms, though there is no theoretical proof, can be applied to clusters with arbitrary shapes (Luxburg, 2007). Intuitively, it follows from the fact that spectral clustering explores the spectrum of the similarity matrix. Thus, an appropriate similarity metric will lead to a reasonably good result.

Two examples of spectral clustering performance on datasets of complicated structures are given in Figure 13.12.

In the end of the section, we show that spectral clustering has relationship with the kernel k-means,
$$\sum_{j=1}^{k}\sum_{x\in\pi_j} w(\boldsymbol{x})\|\Phi(\boldsymbol{x}) - \boldsymbol{\mu}_j\|^2 \rightarrow \min_{\pi_j,\boldsymbol{\mu}_j},$$
where $\pi = \{\pi_j\}_{j=1}^{k}$ is a partitioning of data into clusters π_j. For fixed partition, cluster centers are calculated similarly to standard k-means,
$$\boldsymbol{\mu}_j = \arg\min_{\boldsymbol{\mu}} \sum_{x\in\pi_j} w(\boldsymbol{x})\|\Phi(\boldsymbol{x}) - \boldsymbol{\mu}\|^2$$

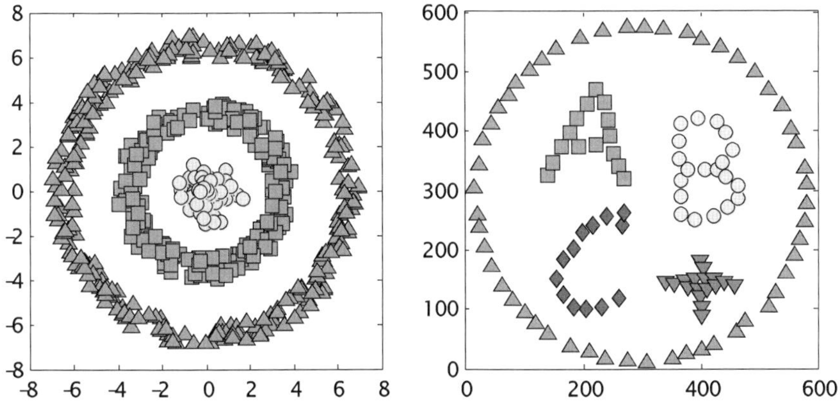

Figure 13.12: Spectral clustering result on different datasets.

and $\boldsymbol{x} \in \boldsymbol{X}_N$. Function $w(\boldsymbol{x})$ assigns some nonnegative weight to each object $\boldsymbol{x}$. Mapping Φ is determined by some kernel function K. Note that there is no need in computing this mapping as $\|\cdot\|$ depends only on inner products computed by K.

Normalized spectral clustering, as having close connection to normalized graph cut problem, can be expressed as the matrix trace maximization problem (Dhillon *et al.*, 2004),

$$\text{trace}(V^T L V) \to \max_{V \in \mathbb{R}^{N \times k}, V^T V = \mathbf{I}},$$

where $L = D^{-\frac{1}{2}} S D^{-\frac{1}{2}}$.

Denoting diagonal matrix formed by weights $w(\boldsymbol{x}_i), i = 1, \ldots, N$, as W, weighted kernel k-means optimization problem takes the form of

$$\text{trace}\left(V^T W^{\frac{1}{2}} K(\boldsymbol{X}_N, \boldsymbol{X}_N) W^{\frac{1}{2}} V\right) \to \max_{V \in \mathbb{R}^{N \times k}, V^T V = \mathbf{I}},$$

which is close to that in normalized spectral clustering.

13.4. Support Vector Machines

Support vector machines are one of the most pervasive techniques for solving data mining problems, including classification, regression, anomaly detection, and metric learning. Initially invented as a linear classification problem solver in the mid-1960s by Soviet scientists Vapnik and Chervonenkis (1964), it was further developed to a framework of statistical methods with common optimization approaches. SVM plays a significant role in the scope of kernel machines due to the "sparsity" of the method, because the size of the learning set is the main limitation for such types of algorithms. Subsequent part of the chapter is composed as follows: we describe in more detail the SVM classifier (Vapnik, 1995) and its relation to kernel machines, introduce several types of support vector machines for binary classification, regression, and multiclass classification. Finally, we provide some approaches for anomaly detection, incremental SVM learning and metric fitting.

13.4.1. *Support Vector Classifier*

As it was pointed in the first chapter, the main idea behind the SVM is to build a maximal margin classifier. Suppose that we have a labelled sample $\boldsymbol{X}_N = \{(\boldsymbol{x}_1, y_1), \ldots, (\boldsymbol{x}_N, y_N)\}, \boldsymbol{x}_i \in \mathbb{R}^n, y_i \in \{1, -1\}$, and we need to solve a two class classification problem. Assume that linear classification is considered, i.e., the algorithm's decision rule can be presented as

$$f(\boldsymbol{x}) = \operatorname{sign}(\langle \boldsymbol{w}, \boldsymbol{x}\rangle - \rho),$$

where $\boldsymbol{w} \in \mathbb{R}^n$, $\rho \in \mathbb{R}$. Therefore, the problem can be stated as finding of $\boldsymbol{w}$ and ρ, or defining a hyperplane that separates the objects of different classes. It is also supposed that the sample set is linearly separable meaning that

$$\exists \boldsymbol{w} \in \mathbb{R}^n, \quad \exists \rho \in \mathbb{R} : \sum_{i=1}^{N} \mathrm{I}[(\langle \boldsymbol{w}, \boldsymbol{x}_i\rangle - \rho)y_i \leq 0] = 0,$$

i.e., all the objects are classified correctly. Margin function is defined as

$$M(\boldsymbol{x}_i, y_i) = (\langle \boldsymbol{w}, \boldsymbol{x}_i\rangle - \rho)y_i \begin{cases} \leq 0, & \text{if } f(\boldsymbol{x}_i) \neq y_i, \\ > 0, & \text{if } f(\boldsymbol{x}_i) = y_i. \end{cases}$$

However, there could be infinitely many possible ways to define the hyperplane as illustrated in Figure 13.13 where two possible separation lines for two-dimensional classification problem are shown.

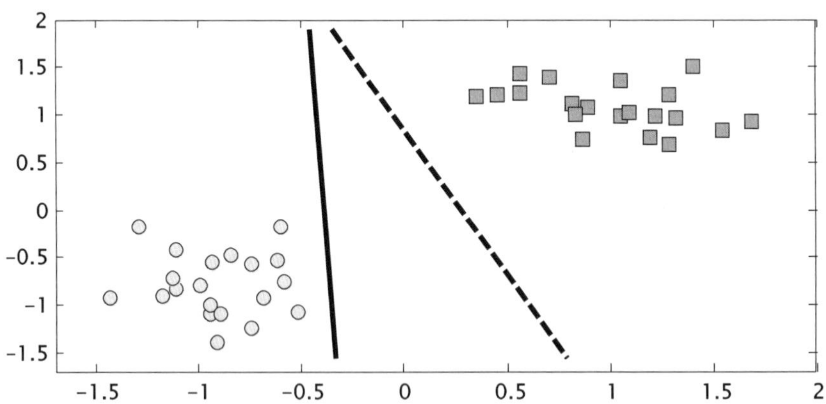

Figure 13.13: Different ways to define a hyperplane for the dataset.

Vladimir Vapnik *et al.* suggested "maximum margin" approach (Boser *et al.*, 1992), according to which the hyperplane is placed as far as possible from the closest objects of both classes. So, linear two-class SVM finds a "hyper-band" between two classes with maximal width.

Consider the maximal bandwidth problem in more detail. Actually, distance from a given point $\boldsymbol{x}_0 \in \mathbb{R}^n$ to the plane $P(\boldsymbol{w}, \rho)$, defined by the equation

$$\langle \boldsymbol{x}, \boldsymbol{w} \rangle - \rho = 0,$$

can be calculated as

$$d(P(\boldsymbol{w}, \rho), \boldsymbol{x}_0) = \frac{|\langle \boldsymbol{x}_0, \boldsymbol{w} \rangle - \rho|}{\|\boldsymbol{w}\|}.$$

In order to find the best separating bandwidth, we maximize the distance from the closest data point in the learning set taking into account class separation constraints. Therefore, the optimization problem for SVM is stated as

$$\max_{\boldsymbol{w},\rho} \min_{x_i \in X_N} \frac{|\langle \boldsymbol{x}_i, \boldsymbol{w} \rangle - \rho|}{\|\boldsymbol{w}\|},$$

$$\text{w.r.t.}$$

$$y_i(\langle \boldsymbol{x}_i, \boldsymbol{w} \rangle - \rho) > 0, \quad \forall (\boldsymbol{x}_i, y_i) \in \boldsymbol{X}_N.$$

Note that for all $\alpha > 0$ terms $\alpha \boldsymbol{w}$, $\alpha \rho$ define the same separating hyperplane. So, we can strengthen the constraints of the problem:

$$\forall (\boldsymbol{x}_i, y_i) \in \boldsymbol{X}_N (\langle \boldsymbol{w}, \boldsymbol{x}_i \rangle - \rho) y_i \geq 1,$$

i.e., for the objects closest to the hyperplane the inequality turns into equality. It is possible to show that there should be at least two closest objects (with the same distance) from both of the classes. Suppose $P(\boldsymbol{w}^*, \rho^*) \equiv P^*$ is the optimal. Let the closest vector from the class "-1" be denoted as $\boldsymbol{x}_{-1}$, and one from the class "1" as $\boldsymbol{x}_{+1}$. Without loss of generality, let us suppose that

$$d(P(\boldsymbol{w}^*, \rho^*), \boldsymbol{x}_{+1}) < d(P(\boldsymbol{w}^*, \rho^*), \boldsymbol{x}_{-1}).$$

Denote $\varepsilon = d(P^*, \boldsymbol{x}_{-1}) - d(P^*, \boldsymbol{x}_{+1})$ and consider a plane

$$P\left(\boldsymbol{w}^*, \left(\rho^* - \frac{\varepsilon}{2}\right)\right) = P^*_\varepsilon.$$

This hyperplane fits to the learning set constraints (all the vectors are correctly classified), but the distance of each "-1" class sample is reduced by $\frac{\varepsilon}{2}$, the distance of each "$+1$" class sample is enlarged by $\frac{\varepsilon}{2}$ comparing to P^*. It is obvious that the object which is the closest to the hyperplane P_ε^* is still $\boldsymbol{x}_{+1}$, but

$$d(P^*, \boldsymbol{x}_{+1}) < d(P^*, \boldsymbol{x}_{+1}) + \frac{\varepsilon}{2} = d(P_\varepsilon^*, \boldsymbol{x}_{+1}),$$

that contradicts to "maximum distance" statement. Thus, objects from classes "1" and "-1", closest to the hyperplane, are equidistant to it.

Therefore, the separation bandwidth is

$$h = \left\langle \boldsymbol{x}_{+1} - \boldsymbol{x}_{-1}, \frac{\boldsymbol{w}}{\|\boldsymbol{w}\|} \right\rangle = \frac{(\langle \boldsymbol{x}_{+1}, \boldsymbol{w}\rangle - \rho) - (\langle \boldsymbol{x}_{-1}, \boldsymbol{w}\rangle - \rho)}{\|\boldsymbol{w}\|} = \frac{2}{\|\boldsymbol{w}\|}.$$

This value is to be maximized, i.e.,

$$\frac{2}{\|\boldsymbol{w}\|} \to \max_{w}.$$

The formulation is easily converted to the standard SVM optimization problem

$$\frac{1}{2}\|\boldsymbol{w}\|^2 \to \min_{w,\rho}$$

$$\text{w.r.t.}$$

$$y_i(\langle \boldsymbol{w}, \boldsymbol{x}_i\rangle - \rho) \geq 1, \quad i = 1, \ldots, N.$$

However, it does not allow solving classification problem for linearly non-separable classes. From the mathematical perspective, it comes from the point that the set defined by constraints $y_i(\langle \boldsymbol{w}, \boldsymbol{x}_i\rangle - \rho) \geq 1$ may be empty. In order to overcome this issue, the so-called "slack variables" ξ_i are introduced.

$$\tfrac{1}{2}\|\boldsymbol{w}\|^2 + C\sum_{i=1}^{N} \xi_i \to \min_{w,\rho,\xi}$$

$$\text{w.r.t.}$$

$$y_i(\langle \boldsymbol{w}, \boldsymbol{x}_i\rangle - \rho) \geq 1 - \xi_i,$$

$$\xi_i \geq 0, \quad i = 1, \ldots, N.$$

In this case, the set of constraints defines an open set (because $\forall \boldsymbol{w}, \rho$ there exist slack variables ξ_i high enough for constraints to be met). The problem is defined as quadratic-programming optimization. Usually it is solved in its dual formulation. If we write down the Lagrangian and derive the Karush–Kuhn–Tucker (KKT) conditions we get the dual optimization problem,

$$-\frac{1}{2}\boldsymbol{\alpha} Q \boldsymbol{\alpha}^T + \sum_{i=1}^{N} \alpha_i \to \max_{\boldsymbol{\alpha}}$$

w.r.t.

$$\begin{cases} 0 \le \alpha_i \le C \quad \forall i = 1, \dots, N, \\ \sum_{i=1}^{N} \alpha_i y_i = 0, \end{cases}$$

where $\boldsymbol{\alpha} \in \mathbb{R}^N$ is a vector of Lagrangian multipliers, $Q_{ij} = y_i y_j \langle \boldsymbol{x}_i, \boldsymbol{x}_j \rangle$.

KKT conditions play an essential role in solving optimization problems and explaining the properties of the approach. We focus on two main consequences of KKT conditions for the SVM.

The first KKT condition leads to an explicit representation of vector $\boldsymbol{w}$,

$$\boldsymbol{w} = \sum_{i=1}^{N} y_i \alpha_i \boldsymbol{x}_i,$$

which can be interpreted as special case of the representer theorem with Lagrangian regarded as a regularized loss function. One of the key properties of the SVM is that most of the α_i will be reduced to zero. Only a relatively small subset of samples has corresponding nonzero alpha entries. Such samples are called *support vectors*.

High number of zero entries in $\boldsymbol{\alpha}$ can be explained by second consequence of KKT conditions. It can be shown that vectors in the learning set can be split into three categories

$$\begin{cases} M(\boldsymbol{x}_i, y_i) > 1, & \alpha_i = 0, & \xi_i = 0 : C - \text{group}, \\ M(\boldsymbol{x}_i, y_i) = 1, & 0 < \alpha_i < C, & \xi_i = 0 : M - \text{group}, \\ M(\boldsymbol{x}_i, y_i) < 1, & \alpha_i = C, & \xi_i > 0 : E - \text{group}, \end{cases}$$

where $M(\boldsymbol{x}_i, y_i) = (\langle \boldsymbol{w}, \boldsymbol{x}_i \rangle - \rho) y_i$. C-group (*correct*) defines a subset of vectors from $\boldsymbol{X}_N$ lying beyond the boundaries of the separation band and, thus, are well-separated. M- (*margin*) and E- (*error*) groups are the subsets of the vectors lying on the border and within the separation band, respectively. These groups are related to less separable vectors (E-group may contain misclassified vectors).

Therefore, all the vectors that lie beyond the boundaries of the separation band (C-group) have zero alpha entries. Taking into account that the algorithm aims to minimize the sum of ξ_i, the number of vectors in M- and E-groups should be relatively small. Otherwise it could be a sign of poor classification model selection..

Other explanation for the sparsity of the SVM can be referred as "geometrical". Constraints of the primal optimization problem define a set, limited by a hyper-polyline (maybe, hyper-polygon) in the space of $\boldsymbol{w}$. Each vector $\boldsymbol{x}_i$ in the sample set determines a linear function in the space of $\boldsymbol{w}$

$$f_i(\boldsymbol{w}, \rho) = y_i \langle \boldsymbol{x}_i, \boldsymbol{w} \rangle - y_i \rho - 1,$$

defining a half-space $f_i(\boldsymbol{w}, \rho) \geq 0$, but not each of linear functions is involved into forming the broken hyperplane, which represents a border of the set

$$\{\boldsymbol{w}, \rho | f_i(\boldsymbol{w}, \rho) \geq 0 \quad \forall i = 1, \ldots, N\}.$$

An example with a sample set of five vectors is illustrated in Figure 13.14.

It is assumed that each hyperplane defines a half-space above it. Only three lines of five construct the border polyline.

13.4.2. *Kernel Trick: Examples*

Let us now consider application of kernels to SVM more carefully. The so-called "*kernel trick*" (Aizerman *et al.*, 1964) is a powerful tool that introduces nonlinearity into a model allowing to separate data that cannot be separated linearly.

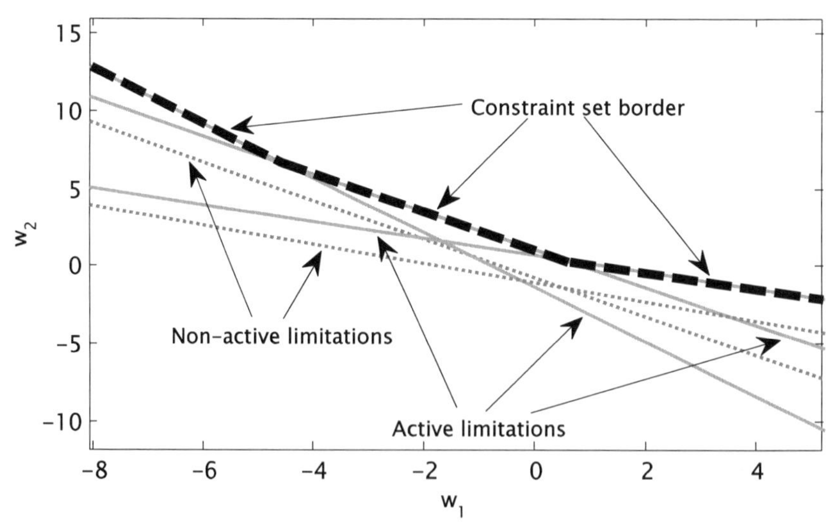

Figure 13.14: Active and nonactive constraints.

In linear SVM, we have

$$\frac{1}{2}\|\boldsymbol{w}\|^2 + C\sum_{i=1}^{N}\xi_i \to \min_{\boldsymbol{w},\xi,\rho},$$
$$\text{w.r.t.}$$
$$y_i(\langle \boldsymbol{w}, \boldsymbol{x}_i\rangle - \rho) \geq 1 - \xi_i,$$
$$\xi_i \geq 0, \quad i = 1, \ldots, N.$$

Slack variables ξ_i make the problem consistent even for linearly non-separable cases, but still linear hyperplane can have poor discriminative ability with classes being separated by a nonlinear surface. We may hope that with a map $\Phi : \boldsymbol{X} \to \mathcal{H}$ the problem will become linearly separable in the feature space $\mathcal{H}$. Due to the fact different feature space that target function and conditions in SVM depend only on inner products thus they can be calculated in $\mathcal{H}$ using the corresponding kernel function K without the evaluation of map Φ,

$$K(\boldsymbol{x}, \boldsymbol{t}) = \langle \Phi(\boldsymbol{x}), \Phi(\boldsymbol{t})\rangle_{\mathcal{H}}.$$

In other words, we are trying to find such a feature space $\mathcal{H}$ with corresponding reproducing kernel K so that the dividing function f in the input space can be represented as a linear combination

$$f(\boldsymbol{x}) = \sum_{i=1}^{N} \hat{\alpha}_i K(\boldsymbol{x}, \boldsymbol{x}_i).$$

The dual form of the linear SVM provides an elegant solution for determining linear coefficients $\hat{\alpha}_i$. Actually, from KKT conditions, we have

$$\boldsymbol{w} = \sum_{i=1}^{N} \alpha_i y_i \boldsymbol{x}_i.$$

The image of $\boldsymbol{w}$ to the Hilbert space can be written as

$$\boldsymbol{w}_{\mathcal{H}} = \sum_{i=1}^{N} \alpha_i y_i \Phi(\boldsymbol{x}_i).$$

Then the inner product $\langle \boldsymbol{w}, \boldsymbol{x}\rangle$ that determines a linear separating plane in the initial space is replaced by a nonlinear separating surface determined by function

$$f(\boldsymbol{x}) = \langle \boldsymbol{w}_{\mathcal{H}}, \Phi(\boldsymbol{x})\rangle_{\mathcal{H}} = \sum_{i=1}^{N} \alpha_i y_i \langle \Phi(\boldsymbol{x}), \Phi(\boldsymbol{x}_i)\rangle_{\mathcal{H}} = \sum_{i=1}^{N} \alpha_i y_i K(\boldsymbol{x}, \boldsymbol{x}_i).$$

Then the following quadratic program is to be solved instead of the initial one.

$$\sum_{i=1}^{N} \alpha_i - \frac{1}{2} \sum_{i,j=1}^{N} \alpha_i \alpha_j y_i y_j K(\boldsymbol{x}_i, \boldsymbol{x}_j) \to \max_{\alpha},$$

w.r.t.

$$0 \le \alpha_i \le C,$$

$$\sum_{i=1}^{N} \alpha_i y_i = 0.$$

The computation effectiveness of the kernel SVM arises from a relatively small number of non-zero α_i, corresponding to support vectors. It dramatically reduces the number of kernel function calculations.

Here, we illustrate the kernel SVM technique by two examples. The first one in Figure 13.15 shows the ability of polynomial kernel

$$K(\boldsymbol{x}, \boldsymbol{t}) = (\langle \boldsymbol{x}, \boldsymbol{t} \rangle + 1)^2,$$

to restore quadratic discriminant line. True class labels of the data are marked with different color and form. Quadratic discriminant line of the kernel SVM is in red. Filled points are support vectors.

The second example in Figure 13.16 illustrates performance of Radial Basis Function SVM on data come from the mixture of Gaussians. Once again, true class

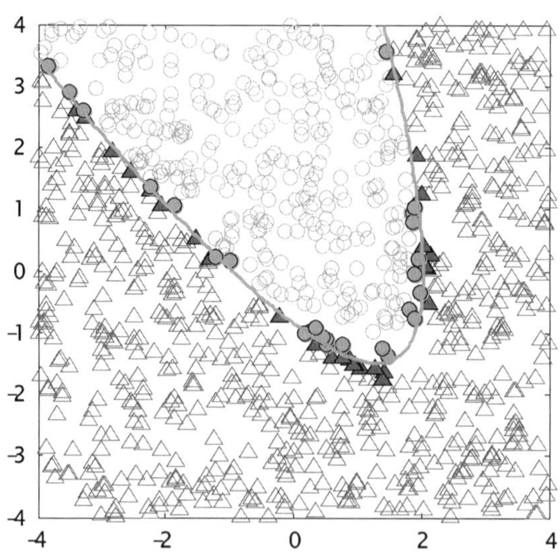

Figure 13.15: Polynomial kernel SVM example.

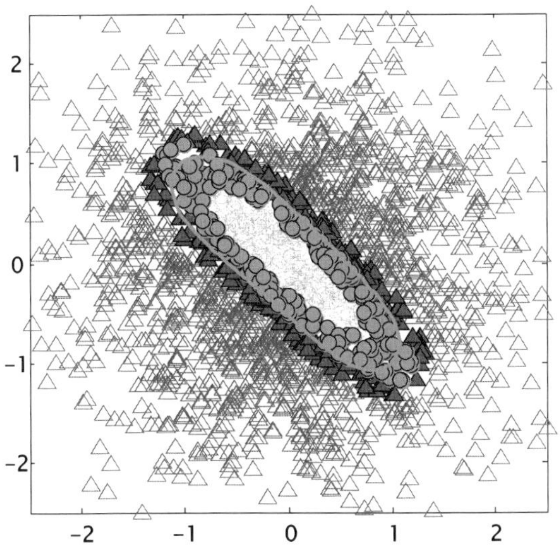

Figure 13.16: RBF SVM example.

labels of the data are marked with color and form while discriminant line of RBF SVM is in red filled points represent support vectors.

13.4.3. *ν-SVM and C-SVM*

As we mentioned before, we can state the optimization problem to find an optimal margin in the form

$$\frac{1}{2}\|\boldsymbol{w}\|^2 \to \min_{\boldsymbol{w},\rho},$$
$$y_i(\langle \boldsymbol{w}, \boldsymbol{x}_i\rangle - \rho) \geq 1, \quad i = 1, \ldots, N.$$

This statement, however, does not allow data to be misclassified, but the dataset is not guaranteed to be exactly divisible in the proposed model.

For this purpose, we relax the constraints to allow data to be misclassified. We introduce slack variables, penalizing misclassifications,

$$\frac{1}{2}\|\boldsymbol{w}\|^2 + C\sum_{i=1}^{N} \xi_i \to \min_{\boldsymbol{w},\rho,\xi},$$
w.r.t.
$$y_i(\langle \boldsymbol{w}, \boldsymbol{x}_i\rangle - \rho) \geq 1 - \xi_i,$$
$$\xi_i \geq 0, \quad i = 1, \ldots, N,$$

where C is a parameter, controlling the value of misclassification penalty. The constraints imposed on each of the dataset elements are often referred as *soft margin constraints*, in contrast to *hard margin constraints*, imposed on the problem.

Then we can write the Lagrangian of the problem as

$$
\begin{aligned}
&L(\boldsymbol{w}, \rho, \boldsymbol{\xi}, \boldsymbol{\alpha}, \boldsymbol{\beta}) \\
&\quad = \frac{1}{2}\|\boldsymbol{w}\|^2 + C\sum_{i=1}^{N} \xi_i - \sum_{i=1}^{N} \alpha_i (y_i(\langle \boldsymbol{w}, \boldsymbol{x}_i\rangle - \rho) - 1 + \xi_i) - \sum_{i=1}^{N} \beta_i \xi_i,
\end{aligned}
$$

where α_i, β_i are Lagrangian multipliers, with corresponding set of KKT conditions:

$$
\begin{aligned}
&\alpha_i (y_i(\langle \boldsymbol{w}, \boldsymbol{x}_i\rangle - \rho) - 1 + \xi_i) = 0, \\
&\beta_i \xi_i = 0, \\
&y_i(\langle \boldsymbol{w}, \boldsymbol{x}_i\rangle - \rho) - 1 + \xi_i \geq 0, \\
&\alpha_i \geq 0, \quad \beta_i \geq 0, \quad \xi_i \geq 0.
\end{aligned}
$$

Differentiating the Lagrangian, we obtain

$$
\begin{aligned}
&\frac{\partial L(\boldsymbol{w}, \rho, \boldsymbol{\xi}, \boldsymbol{\alpha}, \boldsymbol{\beta})}{\partial \boldsymbol{w}} = 0 \Rightarrow \boldsymbol{w} = \sum_{i=1}^{N} \alpha_i y_i \boldsymbol{x}_i, \\
&\frac{\partial L(\boldsymbol{w}, \rho, \boldsymbol{\xi}, \boldsymbol{\alpha}, \boldsymbol{\beta})}{\partial \rho} = 0 \Rightarrow \sum_{i=1}^{N} \alpha_i y_i = 0, \\
&\frac{\partial L(\boldsymbol{w}, \rho, \boldsymbol{\xi}, \boldsymbol{\alpha}, \boldsymbol{\beta})}{\partial \xi_i} = 0 \Rightarrow C - \beta_i = \alpha_i,
\end{aligned}
$$

and then we switch to the dual problem

$$
\begin{aligned}
&\tilde{L}(\boldsymbol{\alpha}) = \sum_{i=1}^{N} \alpha_i - \frac{1}{2}\sum_{i=1}^{N}\sum_{j=1}^{N} \alpha_i \alpha_j y_i y_j \langle \boldsymbol{x}_i, \boldsymbol{x}_j\rangle \rightarrow \max_{\boldsymbol{\alpha}}, \\
&\text{w.r.t.} \\
&0 \leq \alpha_i \leq C, \quad i = 1, \ldots, N, \\
&\sum_{i=1}^{N} \alpha_i y_i = 0.
\end{aligned}
$$

This approach is named C-SVM (Cortes and Vapnik, 1995). The dual representation gives a rise to an alternative technique to tackle with misclassification, ν-SVM

(Schölkopf *et al.*, 2000). For this approach, the primal problem is stated as

$$\frac{1}{2}\|\boldsymbol{w}\|^2 - \nu\gamma + \frac{1}{N}\sum_{i=1}^{N}\xi_i \to \min_{\boldsymbol{w},\rho,\gamma},$$

w.r.t.

$$y_i(\langle \boldsymbol{w}, \boldsymbol{x}_i\rangle - \rho) \geq \gamma - \xi_i,$$

$$\xi_i \geq 0, \quad i = 1, \ldots, N,$$

and the dual problem is

$$\tilde{L}(\boldsymbol{\alpha}) = -\frac{1}{2}\sum_{i=1}^{N}\sum_{j=1}^{N}\alpha_i\alpha_j y_i y_j (\boldsymbol{x}_i, \boldsymbol{x}_j) \to \max_{\boldsymbol{\alpha}},$$

w.r.t.

$$0 \leq \alpha_i \leq \frac{1}{N}, \quad i = 1, \ldots, N,$$

$$\sum_{i=1}^{N}\alpha_i y_i = 0, \quad \sum_{i=1}^{N}\alpha_i \geq \nu.$$

Here, the parameter ν gives a lower bound for the fraction of support vectors, as well as an upper bound for the fraction of margin errors in case of $\gamma > 0$. Actually, the first statement can be justified by noting that the maximum contribution to the last KKT inequality of each of the vectors is $\frac{1}{N}$, thus the overall count of support vectors cannot be lower than νN. The last statement can be proven using the KKT conditions of the primal problem (Schölkopf *et al.*, 2000). This formulation of the task can be proved to be equivalent to C-SVM with $C = \frac{1}{N\gamma}$, if $\gamma > 0$.

13.4.4. *ε-SVR and ν-SVR*

The support vector machines do not restrict only to classification problems, but can be addressed to regression problems as well. This family of methods is referred as Support Vector Regression (SVR).

Given a learning dataset $\boldsymbol{X}_N = \{(\boldsymbol{x}_1, y_1), \ldots, (\boldsymbol{x}_N, y_N)\}$, $y_i \in \mathbb{R}$, we aim to find a regression function $\hat{f}(\boldsymbol{x})$, approximating an unknown target function $f : \boldsymbol{X} \to \mathbb{R}$, in the form

$$\hat{f}(\boldsymbol{x}) = \langle \boldsymbol{w}, \boldsymbol{x}\rangle - \rho.$$

We state the problem as minimization of the regularized error function

$$E_1\big(\hat{f}, \boldsymbol{w}\big) = \frac{1}{2}\sum_{i=1}^{N} E\big\{\hat{f}(\boldsymbol{x}_i) - y_i\big\} + \frac{\lambda\|\boldsymbol{w}\|^2}{2}, \quad \lambda \geq 0.$$

Here, we do not use a standard error function

$$E\{\hat{f}(\boldsymbol{x}_i) - y_i\} = \left(\hat{f}(\boldsymbol{x}_i) - y_i\right)^2,$$

as we aim to obtain a sparse solution, but state

$$E\{\hat{f}(\boldsymbol{x}_i) - y_i\} = \begin{cases} \left|\hat{f}(\boldsymbol{x}_i) - y_i\right| - \varepsilon, & \text{if } \left|\hat{f}(\boldsymbol{x}_i) - y_i\right| > \varepsilon, \\ 0, & \text{else.} \end{cases}$$

Again, the statement is augmented by slack variables, penalizing the exit from

$$\left|\hat{f}(\boldsymbol{x}_i) - y_i\right| < \varepsilon$$

Introducing slack variables, we turn the problem into the form

$$E(\boldsymbol{\xi}^1, \boldsymbol{\xi}^2, \boldsymbol{w}) = C\sum_{i=1}^{N}\{\xi_i^1 + \xi_i^2\} + \frac{\|\boldsymbol{w}\|^2}{2} \to \min_{\boldsymbol{\xi}^1, \boldsymbol{\xi}^2, \boldsymbol{w}},$$
$$\hat{f}(\boldsymbol{x}_i) - y_i \geq -\varepsilon - \xi_i^1, \quad \xi_i^1 \geq 0\; \forall\, i \in 1, \ldots, N,$$
$$\hat{f}(\boldsymbol{x}_i) - y_i \leq \varepsilon + \xi_i^2, \quad \xi_i^2 \geq 0\; \forall\, i \in 1, \ldots, N.$$

Here, $C = \frac{1}{2}\lambda^{-1}$.

As before, we introduce Lagrangian to turn the problem into dual representation

$$\begin{aligned} &L(\boldsymbol{w}, \boldsymbol{\xi}^1, \boldsymbol{\xi}^2, \boldsymbol{\beta}^1, \boldsymbol{\beta}^2, \boldsymbol{\alpha}^1, \boldsymbol{\alpha}^2, \rho), \\ &= C\sum_{i=1}^{N}\{\xi_i^1 + \xi_i^2\} + \frac{\|\boldsymbol{w}\|^2}{2} - \sum_{i=1}^{N}\{\beta_i^1\xi_i^1 + \beta_i^2\xi_i^2\} \\ &\quad - \sum_{i=1}^{N}\alpha_i^1\{\varepsilon + \xi_i^1 + \hat{f}(\boldsymbol{x}_i) - y_i\} - \sum_{i=1}^{N}\alpha_i^2\{\varepsilon + \xi_i^2 - \hat{f}(\boldsymbol{x}_i) + y_i\}. \end{aligned}$$

Differentiating, we obtain

$$\frac{\partial L}{\partial \boldsymbol{w}} = \boldsymbol{0} \Rightarrow \boldsymbol{w} = \sum_{i=1}^{N}\boldsymbol{x}_i\left(\alpha_i^1 - \alpha_i^2\right),$$
$$\frac{\partial L}{\partial \xi_i^1} = 0 \Rightarrow C = \alpha_i^1 + \beta_i^1,$$
$$\frac{\partial L}{\partial \xi_i^2} = 0 \Rightarrow C = \alpha_i^2 + \beta_i^2,$$
$$\frac{\partial L}{\partial \rho} = 0 \Rightarrow \sum_{i=1}^{N}\left(\alpha_i^1 - \alpha_i^2\right) = 0.$$

Finally, utilizing the KKT conditions, we can obtain the final expression of the dual problem:

$$\tilde{L}(\boldsymbol{\alpha}^1, \boldsymbol{\alpha}^2) = -\frac{1}{2}\sum_{i=1}^{N}\sum_{j=1}^{N}\left(\alpha_i^1 - \alpha_i^2\right)\left(\alpha_j^1 - \alpha_j^2\right)\langle \boldsymbol{x}_i, \boldsymbol{x}_j\rangle$$
$$-\varepsilon\sum_{i=1}^{N}\left(\alpha_i^1 + \alpha_i^2\right) + \sum_{i=1}^{N}\left(\alpha_i^1 - \alpha_i^2\right)y_i \to \max_{\boldsymbol{\alpha}^1, \boldsymbol{\alpha}^2},$$
$$\alpha_i^1 \geq 0, \quad \alpha_i^1 \leq C, \quad \alpha_i^2 \geq 0, \quad \alpha_i^2 \leq C.$$

Also it should be mentioned, that as the Lagrangian is dependent of scalar products, one can apply standard kernel trick.

The described approach is referred as ε-SVR (Drucker *et al.*, 1996).

Similar to ν-SVM, we can define the ν-SVR method (Schölkopf *et al.*, 2000). The primal problem for it is formulated as follows:

$$E(\boldsymbol{\xi}^1, \boldsymbol{\xi}^2, \boldsymbol{w}, \varepsilon) = \frac{C}{N}\sum_{i=1}^{N}\left\{\xi_i^1 + \xi_i^2\right\} + C\varepsilon\nu + \frac{\|\boldsymbol{w}\|^2}{2} \to \min_{\boldsymbol{\xi}^1, \boldsymbol{\xi}^2, \boldsymbol{w}, \varepsilon},$$
$$\hat{f}(\boldsymbol{x}_i) - y_i \geq -\varepsilon - \xi_i^1, \quad \xi_i^1 \geq 0 \;\forall\, i \in 1, \ldots, N,$$
$$\hat{f}(\boldsymbol{x}_i) - y_i \leq \varepsilon + \xi_i^2, \quad \xi_i^2 \geq 0 \;\forall\, i \in 1, \ldots, N,$$
$$\varepsilon \geq 0.$$

The dual problem in this case is written as

$$L(\boldsymbol{\alpha}^1, \boldsymbol{\alpha}^2) = -\frac{1}{2}\sum_{i=1}^{N}\sum_{j=1}^{N}\left(\alpha_i^1 - \alpha_i^2\right)\left(\alpha_j^1 - \alpha_j^2\right)\langle \boldsymbol{x}_i, \boldsymbol{x}_j\rangle \to \max_{\boldsymbol{\alpha}^1, \boldsymbol{\alpha}^2},$$
$$0 \leq \alpha_i^1 \leq \frac{C}{N}, \quad 0 \leq \alpha_i^2 \leq \frac{C}{N},$$
$$\sum_{i=1}^{N}\left(\alpha_i^1 - \alpha_i^2\right) = 0, \quad \sum_{i=1}^{N}\left(\alpha_i^1 + \alpha_i^2\right) \leq \nu C.$$

ε-SVR regression for the function $y = x^2$ is shown in Figures 13.17–13.19. We compare the models for different count of the learning points. The support vectors are marked by black boxes around learning points. The Gaussian radial basis kernel is chosen for this example. Prediction gets better while increasing the number of the points. Here, we can see that sparsity of the solution is exposed again. In Figure 13.19, we have 30 learning points, but only 18 of them are support vectors.

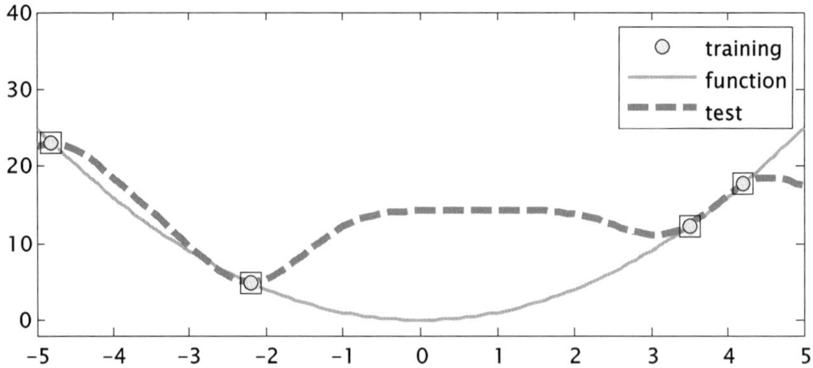

Figure 13.17: ε-SVR regression of the function $y = x^2$, 4 learning points.

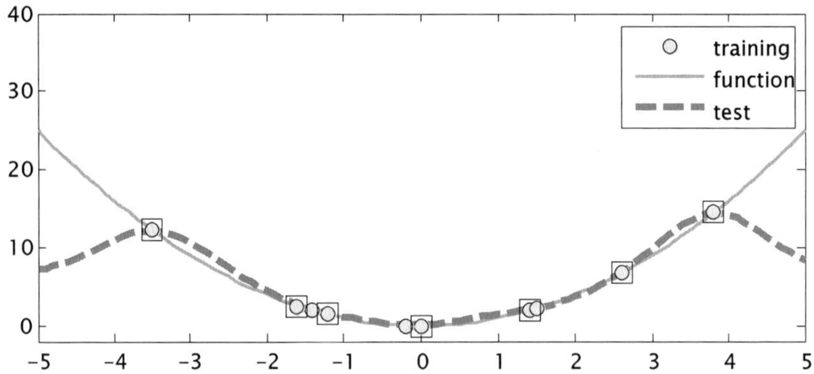

Figure 13.18: ε-SVR regression of the function $\boldsymbol{y} = \boldsymbol{x}^2$, 10 learning points.

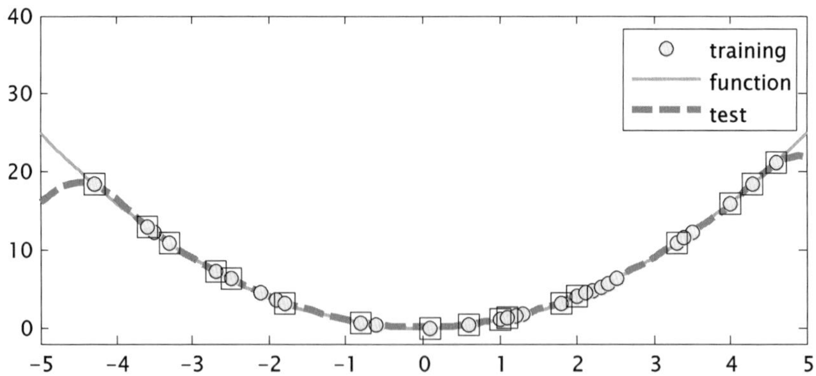

Figure 13.19: ε-SVR regression of the function $y = x^2$, 30 learning points.

13.4.5. *Multiclass SVM*

Multiclass SVM classifier is assumed to assign labels to the input objects, where the set of labels is finite and can consists of two or, generally, more elements. Formally, the classifier is trained over the sample set

$$X_N = \{(\boldsymbol{x}_1, y_1), \ldots, (\boldsymbol{x}_N, y_N)\}, \quad \boldsymbol{x}_i \in \mathbb{R}^n, \; y_i \in \{L_1, \ldots, L_R\}, \; R \geq 2.$$

SVM classification model was initially adapted for two-class problems, and there is no common approach for multiclass classification problems.

We present three main approaches for SVM adaptation for multiclass classification problems.

- One-versus-all approach: For each of the R classes, two-class SVM classifier is trained to separate the given class from all the rest classes. If we denote the model separating rth class as

$$y_r(\boldsymbol{x}) = \text{sign}(f_r(\boldsymbol{x})) = \text{sign}\left(\sum_{i=1}^{N} y_i^r \alpha_i^r K(\boldsymbol{x}, \boldsymbol{x}_i) + \rho_r\right),$$

$$y_i^r = \begin{cases} 1, & \text{if } y_j = L_r, \\ -1, & \text{otherwise,} \end{cases}$$

  the classification of the input vector $\boldsymbol{x}$ is performed using winner-takes-all strategy:

$$y(\boldsymbol{x}) = L_{r^*}, \quad r^* = \arg\max_{r=1,\ldots,R}[f_r(\boldsymbol{x})].$$

  The proposed method requires training of R classifiers. However, this architecture suffers from the so-called imbalanced learning problem, which appears when the training set for one of the class has much less samples, that all the rest in sum.
- One-versus-one strategy: For each unordered pair of classes $(L_r, L_{r'})$, a two-class SVM classifier is trained, which separates objects from class L_r from objects from $L_{r'}$, disregarding all the rest classes. Let us denote such pairwise classifiers by

$$y_{rr'}(\boldsymbol{x}), \quad y_{rr'} : \mathbb{R}^n \to \{L_r, L_{r'}\}.$$

  In order to classify a new incoming object $\boldsymbol{x}$, the following procedure is performed. First, we need to calculate how many times each class occurs as a winner in pair classification:

$$n_r(\boldsymbol{x}) = |\{L_{r'} | y_{rr'}(\boldsymbol{x}) = L_r\}|.$$

Then, a class with maximal "pairwise wins" is selected:

$$y(\boldsymbol{x}) = L_{r^*}, \quad r^* = \arg\max_{r=1,\ldots R}[n_r(\boldsymbol{x})].$$

Such approach requires $\frac{R(R-1)}{2}$ classifiers to be trained, which is computationally complex for large R. This architecture can be exceptionally useful to tackle an imbalanced learning problem, where the samples count from all the classes but one have a clear majority over this one class. To cope with it, weighted voting procedure can be applied with some pre-defined preference matrix with confidence weights for different pairs of classifiers (Hüllermeier and Brinker, 2008). Comparison between different strategies is given by Lughofer and Buchtala (2013).

- Directed acyclic graph classification (Platt *et al.*, 2000). The approach is similar to the one-versus-one strategy, because a classifier for each pair of classes should be fitted. However, the final decision of the input label is produced not by applying all the $\frac{R(R-1)}{2}$ classifiers, but just $R - 1$. For classification, a decision tree is produced, so that each class corresponds to one leaf. Each node of the graph is linked to some of $\frac{R(R-1)}{2}$ classifiers, each outgoing edge is linked to corresponding classifier's result. One of the nodes is selected as a root. Starting from the root, the classification process is descending to one of the leaves. An example of DAG for four classes is Figure 13.20.

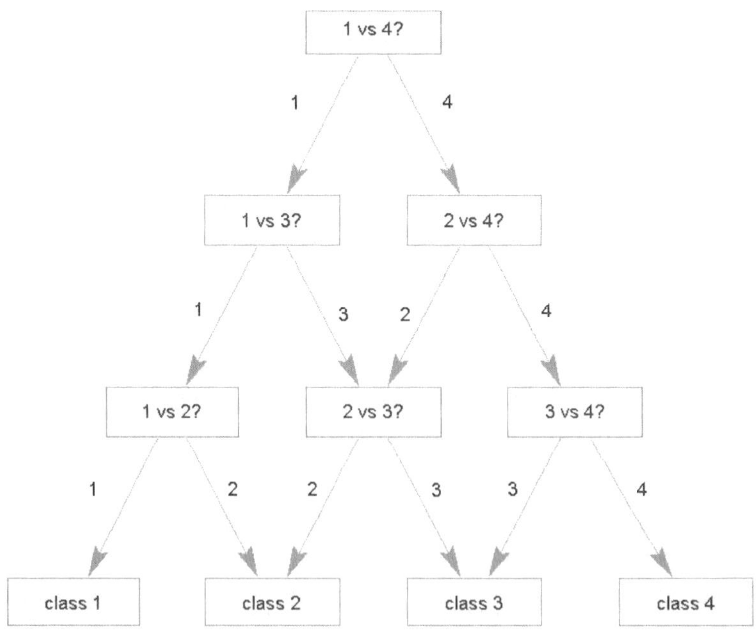

Figure 13.20: Directed acyclic graph (DAG) classification.

The main advantage of the approach is its learning simplicity against one-versus-one strategy. However, usually the classification results are not so stable as only a subpart of classifiers is engaged into the decision-making.

13.4.6. *One-Class SVM*

A special case of classification problems is one-class classification. This classification problem aims to distinguish between "normal" data and outliers. Such problems emerge with the training set consisting of one class examples only and an assumption of other classes existing. Either one class may be well structured and described while other being unstructured and unclear. This problem can be seen as a kind of probability distribution estimation or anomaly detection as well.

Schölkopf *et al.* (2001) showed that SVM-based approach is applicable to this class of problems. The idea of one-class SVM is to map the data into a feature space corresponding to a given kernel and to separate it from the origin with maximum margin. The quadratic program, implementing this approach, is given as follows:

$$
\begin{aligned}
&\frac{1}{2}\|\boldsymbol{w}\|^2 + \frac{1}{\nu N}\sum_{i=1}^{N}\xi_i - \rho \to \min_{\boldsymbol{w},\xi,\rho}, \\
&\text{w.r.t.} \\
&\langle \boldsymbol{w}, \Phi(\boldsymbol{x}_i)\rangle \geq \rho - \xi_i, \\
&\xi_i \geq 0, \;\; i = 1, \ldots, N.
\end{aligned}
$$

The decision function

$$
f(\boldsymbol{x}) = \operatorname{sign}(\langle \boldsymbol{w}, \Phi(\boldsymbol{x})\rangle - \rho),
$$

describes the desired class (i.e., probability distribution or membership function, normal state opposite to anomalies), i.e., is positive for most examples in the training set.

To transfer to the dual form of the problem, we express the weights via KKT conditions:

$$
\begin{aligned}
&\boldsymbol{w} = \sum_{i=1}^{N}\alpha_i \Phi(\boldsymbol{x}_i), \\
&0 \leq \alpha_i \leq \frac{1}{\nu N}, \quad \sum_{i=1}^{N}\alpha_i = 1.
\end{aligned}
$$

Then the decision function can be rewritten as

$$f(\boldsymbol{x}) = \operatorname{sign}\left(\sum_{i=1}^{N} \alpha_i K(\boldsymbol{x}, \boldsymbol{x}_i) - \rho\right).$$

Those objects with $\alpha_i > 0$ are Support Vectors. It can be proven that for any $\boldsymbol{x}_i$ with $0 < \alpha_i < \frac{1}{\nu N}$ it holds $\langle \boldsymbol{w}, \Phi(\boldsymbol{x}_i)\rangle = \rho$ at the optimum and

$$\rho = \langle \boldsymbol{w}, \Phi(\boldsymbol{x}_i)\rangle = \sum_{j=1}^{N} \alpha_j K(\boldsymbol{x}_i, \boldsymbol{x}_j).$$

Finally, the dual problem is given as

$$\frac{1}{2}\sum_{i,j=1}^{N} \alpha_i \alpha_j K(\boldsymbol{x}_i, \boldsymbol{x}_j) \to \min_{\alpha},$$

w.r.t.

$$0 \le \alpha_i \le \frac{1}{\nu N}, \quad \sum_{i=1}^{N} \alpha_i = 1.$$

Parameter ν is of a special interest as it possesses the following theoretically proven ν-property. If the solution of one-class SVM problem satisfies $\rho \neq 0$, then

(1) ν is an upper bound on the fraction of outliers in the learning set (vectors $\boldsymbol{x}_i$ for which $\alpha_i = \frac{1}{\nu N}$);
(2) ν is a lower bound on the fraction of SVs in the learning set (vectors $\boldsymbol{x}_i$ for which $\alpha_i > 0$);
(3) if, additionally, data is generated independently from distribution which does not contain discrete components and the kernel is analytic and non-constant then with probability 1, asymptotically, ν equals both the fraction of SVs and the fraction of outliers.

Figure 13.21 shows isolines provided by one-class SVM learned on a set of two-dimensional points come from Gaussian mixture

$$p(\boldsymbol{x}) = 0.5 \times p(\boldsymbol{x}|\boldsymbol{\mu}_1, \Sigma_1) + 0.5 \times p(\boldsymbol{x}|\boldsymbol{\mu}_2, \Sigma_2),$$

where $\boldsymbol{\mu}_1 = (3, 3)^T$, Σ_1 is an identity matrix, $\boldsymbol{\mu}_2 = (-3, -3)^T$,

$$\Sigma_2 = \begin{pmatrix} 1 & -0.5 \\ -0.5 & 2 \end{pmatrix}.$$

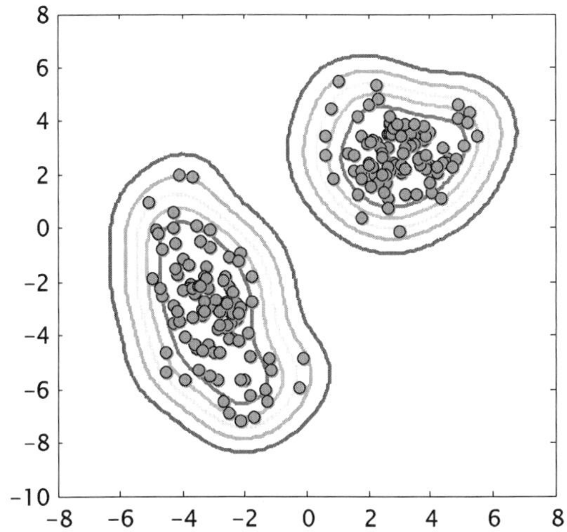

Figure 13.21: Density estimation by one-class SVM.

13.4.7. *Incremental SVM Learning*

Most of the SVM-type models admit incremental learning (Cauwenberghs and Poggio, 2001). It means that the model can be fitted sample-per-sample or in batch mode, but the model requires all the previous learning set to be stored. However, such algorithms could be useful in the cases when the learning data is not provided at one moment, but is split into batches coming sequentially, for instance in streaming data analysis.

In this part, we provide the algorithm for incremental SVM learning, i.e., adding one more sample to the learning set for SVM classifier. Suppose that we have a two-class C-SVM classifier defined by its parameters $(\boldsymbol{w}, \rho)$, estimated for the kernel $K(\boldsymbol{x}, \boldsymbol{t})$ over learning sample $\boldsymbol{X}_N$.

Assume that we need to add the new sample $(\boldsymbol{x}_{N+1}, y_{N+1})$ to the dataset. Therefore, we need to assign a corresponding value α_{N+1}, and to update all previous values $\alpha_i, i = 1, \ldots, N$, and ρ. These parameters should be changed so that KKT conditions are met, which is necessary and sufficient condition for the optimality.

Before we discuss the algorithm itself, we should refer once again to the KKT conditions for the two-class SVM, defining three groups of samples from $\boldsymbol{X}_N$ and the constraints to be met.

(1) Margin group (M-group, $\boldsymbol{M} \subset \boldsymbol{X}_N$) — subset of vectors $\boldsymbol{x}_m$ at the border of the dividing band, the corresponding KKT condition for $\boldsymbol{x}_m$ is

$$M(\boldsymbol{x}_m) = \sum_{i=1}^{N} \alpha_i y_m y_i K(\boldsymbol{x}_i, \boldsymbol{x}_m) + \rho y_m = 1 \Leftrightarrow \alpha_m \in (0, C).$$

(2) Correct group (C-group, $\boldsymbol{C} \subset \boldsymbol{X}_N$) — subset of vectors $\boldsymbol{x}_c$ correctly classified by the model,

$$M(\boldsymbol{x}_c) = \sum_{i=1}^{N} \alpha_i y_c y_i K(\boldsymbol{x}_i, \boldsymbol{x}_c) + \rho y_c > 1 \Leftrightarrow \alpha_c = 0.$$

(3) Error-group (E-group, $\boldsymbol{E} \subset \boldsymbol{X}_N$) — subset of vectors lying within the dividing band or even misclassified,

$$\boldsymbol{x}_e\colon M(\boldsymbol{x}_e) = \sum_{i=1}^{N} \alpha_i y_e y_i K(\boldsymbol{x}_i, \boldsymbol{x}_e) + \rho y_e < 1 \Leftrightarrow \alpha_e = C.$$

Additional KKT condition that should be considered is

$$\sum_{i=1}^{N} \alpha_i y_i = 0.$$

Here, we should mention that KKT conditions are necessary and sufficient for a point to be a solution of the dual optimization problem.

Initially, we assign $\alpha_{N+1} = 0$, leaving all the rest values $\boldsymbol{\alpha} \in \mathbb{R}^N, \rho \in \mathbb{R}$ without changes. If margin $M(\boldsymbol{x}_{N+1}) > 1$ (see C-group), then all KKT conditions are met and, therefore, learning is finished.

If margin $M(\boldsymbol{x}_{N+1}) \leq 1$, then KKT conditions are violated, we increase α_{N+1} so that

i. margins of all points from M-group stay equal to 1,

$$\forall \boldsymbol{x}_m \in M \quad M(\boldsymbol{x}_m) = 1;$$

ii. $\sum_{i=1}^{N} \alpha_i y_i + \alpha_{N+1} y_{N+1} = 0$;

iii. margins of all points from C-group stay above 1,

$$\forall \boldsymbol{x}_c \in C \quad M(\boldsymbol{x}_c) > 1;$$

iv. margins of all points from E-group stay below 1,

$$\forall \boldsymbol{x}_e \in E \quad M(\boldsymbol{x}_e) < 1.$$

Therefore, during the change of all the parameters $(\boldsymbol{\alpha}, \rho)$ only α_{N+1} violates the KKT conditions.

We denote the ith vector from C-, E-, and M-group $\boldsymbol{x}_i^c$, $\boldsymbol{x}_i^e$, $\boldsymbol{x}_i^m$ with labels y_i^c, y_i^e, y_i^m respectively.

Consider first two limitations. Assume that at the previous iteration we have the model $\boldsymbol{\alpha}_{\text{old}}, \rho_{\text{old}}$. Suppose that $\boldsymbol{\alpha}_{\text{old}}^m \in \mathbb{R}^{|M|}$ is a sub-vector of $\boldsymbol{\alpha}_{\text{old}}$ related to the vectors from M-group. Once again, as the new learning data $\boldsymbol{x}_{N+1}$ arrives, we have to update all the previous parameters of the classifier, and calculate α_{N+1} iteratively. First, we assign $\alpha_{N+1} = 0$, that can violate KKT conditions, as mentioned before. Therefore, we have to change the α values. First, we fix the values of α for C-group to 0, and for E-group to C. Hence, we change only $\boldsymbol{\alpha}^m$ values. If we increase α_{N+1} by $\Delta\alpha_{N+1} > 0$, we can calculate corresponding $\Delta\boldsymbol{\alpha}^m$, $\Delta\rho$ while holding i and ii.

$$F^m \begin{bmatrix} \boldsymbol{\alpha}^m_{\text{old}} + \Delta\boldsymbol{\alpha}^m \\ \rho + \Delta\rho \end{bmatrix} + \boldsymbol{k}^{\text{m}}_{N+1}(\alpha_{N+1} + \Delta\alpha_{N+1}) = 1,$$

where

$$F^m = \begin{bmatrix} (\boldsymbol{y}^m)^T & 0 \\ Q^{mm} & \boldsymbol{y}^m \end{bmatrix} \in \mathbb{R}^{|M|+1\times|M|+1},$$

$$\boldsymbol{y}^m = \left[y_1^m, \ldots, y_i^m, \ldots, y_{|M|}^m\right]^T,$$

$$\boldsymbol{k}^m_{N+1} \in \mathbb{R}^{|M|+1}, \quad \boldsymbol{k}^m_{N+1} = \begin{bmatrix} y_{N+1} \\ y_{N+1}y_1^m\left\langle \boldsymbol{x}_1^m, \boldsymbol{x}_{N+1}\right\rangle \\ \cdots \\ y_{N+1}y_i^m\left\langle \boldsymbol{x}_i^m, \boldsymbol{x}_{N+1}\right\rangle \\ \cdots \\ y_{N+1}y_{|M|}^m\left\langle \boldsymbol{x}_{|M|}^m, \boldsymbol{x}_{N+1}\right\rangle \end{bmatrix},$$

$$Q_{ij}^{mm} = y_i^m y_j^m \langle \boldsymbol{x}_i^m, \boldsymbol{x}_j^m \rangle, \quad i, j = 1, \ldots, |M|.$$

Q^{mm} is a matrix of inner products of the objects in the M-group.

Therefore, taking into account that conditions i–ii are met for $\boldsymbol{\alpha}_{\text{old}}$, ρ_{old} and α_{N+1}, we can derive that

$$\begin{bmatrix} \Delta\boldsymbol{\alpha}^m \\ \Delta\rho \end{bmatrix} = -(F^m)^{-1}\boldsymbol{k}^m_{N+1}\Delta\alpha_{N+1}.$$

However, taking into account the conditions i–iv, we can claim that $\Delta\alpha_{N+1}$ is bounded and we increase it until one of the following conditions is met:

(1) For one of the data vectors in the C-group, the value of $M\left(\boldsymbol{x}_i^c\right)$ reaches 1. Then this data vector is moved to the M-group with corresponding α_i^c set to 0, α_{N+1} is increased by corresponding $\Delta\alpha_{N+1}$, procedure continues with the new structure of the data subsets.

(2) For one of the data vectors in the E-group, the value of $M\left(\boldsymbol{x}_i^e\right)$ reaches 1. Then this data vector is moved to the M-group with corresponding α_i^e set to 0, α_{N+1} is

increased by corresponding $\Delta\alpha_{N+1}$, procedure continues with the new structure of the data subsets.

(3) For one of the data vectors in the M-group, the value of α_i^m reaches value $\alpha_i^m = C$. Then this data vector is moved to the E-group with corresponding α_i^m set to C, α_{N+1} is increased by corresponding $\Delta\alpha_{N+1}$, procedure continues with the new structure of the data subsets.

(4) For one of the data vectors in the M-group, the value of α_i^m gets value 0. Then this data vector is moved to the C-group with corresponding α_i^m set to 0, α_{N+1} is increased by corresponding $\Delta\alpha_{N+1}$, procedure continues with the new structure of the data subsets.

(5) $\alpha_{N+1} = C$. Then the new data vector is moved to the E-group, and the algorithm terminates.

(6) $M(\boldsymbol{x}_{N+1}) = 1$. Then the new data vector is moved to the M-group with the current value of α_{N+1}, and the algorithm terminates.

If conditions (1)–(4) are met, then the structure of the groups $\boldsymbol{E}$, $\boldsymbol{C}$, and $\boldsymbol{M}$ should be re-arranged. It means that vector $\boldsymbol{\alpha}^m$ should be increased by $\Delta\boldsymbol{\alpha}^m$ and augmented/reduced by the corresponding α of the migrating vector. Matrix F^m should be recalculated. α_{N+1} is increased by $\Delta\alpha_{N+1}$. Then a new iteration of the described procedure is performed taking into account new structures of the sets $\boldsymbol{C}$, $\boldsymbol{E}$, $\boldsymbol{M}$. Iterations are repeated until KKT conditions are met, which is equivalent to conditions (5) and (6).

For each condition from (1)–(4), the effective computational technique exists, which allows the inverse inner product matrix $(F^m)^{-1}$ for the M-group to be calculated iteratively using Woodbury formula. However, usually M-group is relatively small.

13.4.8. *Metric Learning*

At a first glance, the problem of Metric Learning stands far from the area of SVM applications. But it appears to be that SVM approach can be fruitful for learning a metric.

The problem of Metric Learning is to find a metric that pulls objects of the same class closer and pushes objects from different class as far as possible from one another. It is common to find this metric in a family of Mahalanobis metrics parameterized by positive semidefinite matrix $M \in \mathbb{R}^{n \times n}$,

$$\rho_M(\boldsymbol{x}, \boldsymbol{t}) = (\boldsymbol{x} - \boldsymbol{t})^T M(\boldsymbol{x} - \boldsymbol{t}), \quad M = M^T, \quad M \geq 0.$$

Though Mahalanobis metric was initially used to measure distance between two random vectors, it can be seen as a Euclidean distance in a linearly transformed space, i.e., for any Mahalanobis metric ρ_M there exists a linear map specified by matrix $L \in \mathbb{R}^{k \times n}$ so that

$$\rho_M(\boldsymbol{x}, \boldsymbol{t}) = (\boldsymbol{x} - \boldsymbol{t})^T M (\boldsymbol{x} - \boldsymbol{t}) = (\boldsymbol{x} - \boldsymbol{t})^T L^T L (\boldsymbol{x} - \boldsymbol{t}) = \|L(\boldsymbol{x} - \boldsymbol{t})\|^2.$$

Starting from this point, most Metric Learning methods try to find the best (with some respect) linear map L.

It may be desired that in the new space for each object its distance to all neighbors of the same class is smaller than its distance to any neighbors of other classes. This leads to the following constraints on Mahalanobis metric ρ_M:

$$\min_{\substack{x_j \in \mathcal{N}(\boldsymbol{x}_i) \\ y_j \neq y_i}} \rho_M(\boldsymbol{x}_i, \boldsymbol{x}_j) \geq \max_{\substack{x_j \in \mathcal{N}(\boldsymbol{x}_i) \\ y_j = y_i}} \rho_M(\boldsymbol{x}_i, \boldsymbol{x}_j) + 1, \quad \forall (\boldsymbol{x}_i, y_i) \in X,$$

where $\mathcal{N}(\boldsymbol{x}_i)$ is a neighborhood of $\boldsymbol{x}_i$ determined by Euclidean distance.

Finding Mahalanobis metric with the smallest possible Frobenius norm results in the MLSVM model (Nguyen and Guo, 2008).

$$\frac{\lambda}{2}\|M\|_F^2 + \frac{1}{N}\sum_{i=1}^{N} \xi_i \to \min_{M \geq 0, \xi \geq 0},$$

w.r.t.

$$\min_{\substack{x_j \in \mathcal{N}(\boldsymbol{x}_i) \\ y_j \neq y_i}} \rho_M(\boldsymbol{x}_i, \boldsymbol{x}_j) \geq \max_{\substack{x_j \in \mathcal{N}(\boldsymbol{x}_i) \\ y_j = y_i}} \rho_M(\boldsymbol{x}_i, \boldsymbol{x}_j) + 1 - \xi_i,$$

$$\xi_i \geq 0.$$

Note that ρ_M depends linearly on the matrix M. This leads to the quadratic programming problem linking MLSVM to SVM approach. Slack variables ξ_i are introduced as it is in SVM to obtain the soft margin constraints. This optimization problem can be solved by a modified Pegasos method (Nguyen and Guo, 2008), without transforming it into a dual form.

Another approach for Metric Learning is to find such a linear transformation L that in the transformed target space neighborhood $\mathcal{N}(\boldsymbol{x}_i)$ consists of objects of the same class as $\boldsymbol{x}_i$ only. Objects $\boldsymbol{x}_j$ in this neighborhood are called target neighbors and denoted as

$$j \rightsquigarrow i.$$

Notice that this motivation leads to better performance of KNN algorithm in the transformed space. In the original space, some objects of different classes may be closer (in Euclidean distance sense) to $\boldsymbol{x}_i$ than target neighbors. These objects are impostors $\boldsymbol{x}_k$ and defined as

$$\|L(\boldsymbol{x}_i - \boldsymbol{x}_k)\|^2 \leq \|L(\boldsymbol{x}_i - \boldsymbol{x}_j)\|^2 + 1, \quad j \rightsquigarrow i, \ y_i \neq y_k.$$

Loss function in this LMNN model (Weinberger and Saul, 2009) differs from one in MLSVM and is represented as a sum of two terms, one pulling target neighbors closer together and the other pushing impostors apart. Denoting

$$y_{ij} = \begin{cases} 1, & y_i = y_j, \\ 0, & y_i \neq y_j, \end{cases}$$

we obtain the following optimization problem

$$\begin{aligned} &(1-\mu) \sum_{j \rightsquigarrow i} \|L(\boldsymbol{x}_i - \boldsymbol{x}_j)\|^2 \\ &\quad + \mu \sum_{i, j \rightsquigarrow i} \sum_k (1 - y_{ik}) \big[1 + \|L(\boldsymbol{x}_i - \boldsymbol{x}_j)\|^2 - \|L(\boldsymbol{x}_i - \boldsymbol{x}_k)\|^2\big]_+ \\ &\quad \to \min_L . \end{aligned}$$

This optimization problem can be converted into a SVM-like form.

$$\begin{aligned} &(1-\mu) \sum_{j \rightsquigarrow i} \|L(\boldsymbol{x}_i - \boldsymbol{x}_j)\|^2 + \mu \sum_{i, j \rightsquigarrow i} \sum_k (1 - y_{ik}) \xi_{ijk} \to \min_{L, \xi}, \\ &\text{w.r.t.} \\ &\|L(\boldsymbol{x}_i - \boldsymbol{x}_k)\|^2 - \|L(\boldsymbol{x}_i - \boldsymbol{x}_j)\|^2 \geq 1 - \xi_{ijk}, \quad \forall\, i,\, j \rightsquigarrow i,\; k\colon y_i \neq y_k, \\ &\xi_{ijk} \geq 0, \quad M = L^T L \geq 0. \end{aligned}$$

Notice that all functions in both models depend on the input objects only through inner products. This allows incorporating kernel trick and nonlinearity into Metric Learning.

13.4.9. *Structured SVM*

Here we expand classification problem, relaxing the restrictions for the labels set in the way it is described by Aizerman *et al.* (1964). As usual, we consider a sample set $\boldsymbol{X} \subseteq \mathbb{R}^n$ and associate each of its elements with some labels from finite set Y. In the algorithms we referred before, it is supposed that label $y \in Y \subseteq \mathbb{R}$, but here we abandon this constraint and allow labels to be any arbitrary objects (e.g., strings, graphs, etc.), often referred as "structured". As before, we define a map $f : \boldsymbol{X} \to Y$, a training set

$$\boldsymbol{X}_N = \{(\boldsymbol{x}_1, y_1), \ldots, (\boldsymbol{x}_N, y_N)\},$$

and we are trying to learn a map $\hat{f} : \boldsymbol{X} \to Y$, giving an approximation of f.

In order to tackle with such complex structured labels, we also define a discriminant function

$$F(\boldsymbol{x}, y|\boldsymbol{w}) : \boldsymbol{X} \times Y \to \mathbb{R},$$

where $\boldsymbol{w}$ is a vector of parameters. This function gives the maximum for the most "suitable" pairs of $\boldsymbol{x}$ and y, so it should represent the map $\hat{f}$ in the form

$$\hat{f}(\boldsymbol{x}|\boldsymbol{w}) = \arg\max_{y \in Y} F(\boldsymbol{x}, y|\boldsymbol{w}).$$

In order to utilize common optimization schemes, we restrict the function $F(\boldsymbol{x}, y|\boldsymbol{w})$ to depend linearly on the parameters:

$$F(\boldsymbol{x}, y|\boldsymbol{w}) = \langle \boldsymbol{w}, \Psi(\boldsymbol{x}, y) \rangle.$$

Here Ψ is a function, dependent of the data samples, referred as the "joint feature map", $\Psi : \boldsymbol{X} \times Y \to \mathbb{R}^K$, $\boldsymbol{w} \in \mathbb{R}^K$. If, for example, $Y = \{1, \ldots, R\} \subset \mathbb{N}$, and

$$\Psi(\boldsymbol{x}, y) = \{[y = 1]\boldsymbol{x}, [y = 2]\boldsymbol{x}, \ldots, [y = R]\boldsymbol{x}\} \in \mathbb{R}^{\mathrm{R} \times n},$$

then the method performs as a multiclass SVM.

The maximization problem can be reformulated (Tsochantaridis *et al.*, 2005) as a maximum margin problem

$$\frac{1}{2}\|\boldsymbol{w}\|^2 \to \min_{w},$$

with respect to constraints defining that maximum is reached only on the given labeling $\hat{f}$. These constraints can be written for all $\boldsymbol{x}_i$, $y_i = f(\boldsymbol{x}_i)$, as

$$\max_{y \in Y \backslash y_i} \{\langle \boldsymbol{w}, \Psi(\boldsymbol{x}_i, y) \rangle\} < \langle \boldsymbol{w}, \Psi(\boldsymbol{x}_i, y_i) \rangle.$$

These constraints ensure us to have an exact labeling. However, they are nonlinear, but they can be replaced by $N(|Y| - 1)$ linear constraints

$$\forall (\boldsymbol{x}_i, y_i) \in \boldsymbol{X}_N, \quad \forall\, y \in Y \backslash y_i$$
$$\langle \boldsymbol{w}, \Delta(\boldsymbol{x}_i, y) \rangle > 0,$$

where $\Delta(\boldsymbol{x}_i, y) = (\Psi(\boldsymbol{x}_i, y_i) - \Psi(\boldsymbol{x}_i, y))$.

As in ordinary SVM, $\boldsymbol{w}$ can be rescaled so that it fulfils the following conditions:

$$\forall \boldsymbol{x}_i, y_i, y \in Y \backslash y_i, \quad \langle \boldsymbol{w}, \Delta(\boldsymbol{x}_i, y) \rangle \geq 1.$$

To allow classifier errors on the dataset, slack variables ξ_i are introduced:

$$\begin{aligned}
&\frac{1}{2}\|\boldsymbol{w}\|^2 + \frac{C}{N}\sum_{i=1}^{N}\xi_i \to \min_{\boldsymbol{w},\boldsymbol{\xi}} \\
&\text{w.r.t.} \\
&\forall \boldsymbol{x}_i, y_i, y \in Y\backslash y_i, \quad \langle \boldsymbol{w}, \Delta(\boldsymbol{x}_i, y)\rangle \geq 1 - \xi_i, \\
&\xi_i \geq 0, \quad 1 \leq i \leq N.
\end{aligned}$$

The dual version of the problem can be derived by introducing Lagrangian multipliers:

$$\begin{aligned}
L(\boldsymbol{w}, \boldsymbol{\xi}, \boldsymbol{\alpha}, \boldsymbol{\beta}) &= \frac{1}{2}\|\boldsymbol{w}\|^2 + \frac{C}{N}\sum_{i=1}^{N}\xi_i \\
&\quad - \sum_{i=1}^{N}\beta_i\xi_i - \sum_{i=1}^{N}\sum_{y\in Y\backslash y_i}\alpha_{iy}\{\langle \boldsymbol{w}, \Delta(\boldsymbol{x}_i, y)\rangle - 1 + \xi_i\}, \\
\frac{\partial L}{\partial \boldsymbol{w}} &= \boldsymbol{w} - \sum_{i=1}^{N}\sum_{y\in Y\backslash y_i}\alpha_{iy}\Delta(\boldsymbol{x}_i, y) = 0, \\
\frac{\partial L}{\partial \xi_i} &= \frac{C}{N} - \beta_i - \sum_{y\in Y\backslash y_i}\alpha_{iy} = 0.
\end{aligned}$$

The kernel trick can be applied and the dual optimization problem should be written as

$$\begin{aligned}
&\sum_{i=1, y\in Y\backslash y_i}^{N}\alpha_{iy} - \frac{1}{2}\sum_{i=1, y\in Y\backslash y_i}^{N}\ \sum_{j=1, y'\in Y\backslash y_j}^{N}\alpha_{iy}\alpha_{jy'}K\big(\Delta(\boldsymbol{x}_i, y), \Delta(\boldsymbol{x}_j, y')\big) \to \max_{\alpha}, \\
&\alpha_{iy} \geq 0, \quad \sum_{i, y\in Y\backslash y_i}\alpha_{iy} \leq \frac{C}{N}\ \forall i = 1, \ldots, N.
\end{aligned}$$

There are several alternative formulations of the problem, different in the way of defining slack variables, but they are not ideologically different and can be found in reference (Aizerman *et al.*, 1964).

A very important problem with the described method is the large amount of constraints, leading to exponential complexity of the optimization algorithm depending on "dimensionality" of the space Y. To avoid this, cutting planes relaxation technique is utilized, which provides polynomial complexity, but takes into account only some of the constraints, giving the most severe restrictions. This means the constraints could be violated by a value not more than some pre-specified value ε. To do this, the optimization is provided within a loop, while the constraint list is complemented until all the constraints are violated not more than on ε.

The structured SVM approach can be used to solve various tasks once a correct feature-specific joint feature map Ψ is chosen, taking contributions both from input and output. Given some problem-specific function Ψ, the structured SVM can be utilized for various image segmentation (Lucchi *et al.*, 2012) and object detection problems (Tsochantaridis *et al.*, 2004), protein alignments structure identification (Joachims *et al.*, 2009) and many others.

For the case of natural grammar analysis, we have a grammar, incorporating grammar rules G_i. String parsing can be seen as a process of grammar rule application. The hierarchy of rule applications is organized into a tree. The function Ψ then represents the histogram of grammar rules application event frequency (Blaschko and Lampert, 2008). Then, the structure $y \in Y$, found by optimization of the function $F(\boldsymbol{x}, y|\boldsymbol{w})$, represents a parse tree prediction.

Let us consider in more detail a problem of image segmentation as structured SVM application. For each of the pixels of the image I, we should assign an integer value $Y = \{1 \ldots K\}$, referred as segment labels. Let us define a graph (V, E), with a set of vertices V, each corresponding to one pixel of the image I, and a set of edges E, giving a neighborhood relation. The assignment of the segment labels can be done within the Conditional Random Field (CRF) framework (Blaschko and Lampert, 2008). Alternatively, it can be interpreted as graph labelling problem for the graph (V, E) with the following energy functional:

$$E_w(Y) = \sum_{v_i \in V} U_i(v_i, y_i) + \sum_{(v_i, v_j) \in E} D_{ij}(v_i, v_j, y_i, y_j) \to \min_Y .$$

Such type of optimization problems are usually solved by algorithms like graph-cuts or α-expansion (Boykov and Kolmogorov, 2004; Boykov *et al.*, 2001).

Here, U is referred as unary potential, and D is pairwise potential. However, there remains a problem to define these potentials. Then, imagine that we have a learning set of the images of the same size with corresponding "ground truth" segmentations, namely

$$\{(I_1, Y_1), (I_2, Y_2), (I_3, Y_3), \ldots, (I_N, Y_N)\}, \quad I_i \in \mathbb{R}^{n \times m}, \quad Y_i \in \{1 \ldots K\}^{n \times m}.$$

Structured SVM enables us to define it as an optimization problem aimed to find a functional, providing the images to be segmented closely to the "ground truth".

For each of the pixels p_{ik} of the image I_k, we associate some feature vector $\boldsymbol{x}_{ik} \in \mathbb{R}^l$, where l is the feature vector dimensionality. Here, $\boldsymbol{x}_{ik}$ can be either SIFT descriptor or simply a color value (RGB), or any other feature.

First, let us define the unary potential for the image I_k as

$$U_i^k(v_i, y_i) = \langle \boldsymbol{w}_{y_i}, \boldsymbol{x}_{ik} \rangle, \quad \boldsymbol{w}_{y_i} \in \mathbb{R}^l.$$

Here, we should mention, that the graph is the same for all the images, as they have the same size. Let us define

$$\boldsymbol{\psi}_i^k(y_i) = \left(I(y_i = 1)\boldsymbol{x}_{ik}^T, \ldots, I(y_i = K)\boldsymbol{x}_{ik}^T \right)^T.$$

If we denote $\boldsymbol{w}^U = (\boldsymbol{w}_1, \boldsymbol{w}_2, \ldots \boldsymbol{w}_K)^T$, then

$$U_i^k(v_i, y_i) = \left\langle \boldsymbol{w}^U, \boldsymbol{\psi}_i^k(y_i) \right\rangle = \langle \boldsymbol{w}_{y_i}, \boldsymbol{x}_{ik} \rangle.$$

Second, define the pairwise potential as $D_{ij}^k(v_i, v_j, y_i, y_j) = w_{y_i, y_j} \in \mathbb{R}$.

Let us define

$$\begin{aligned} &\boldsymbol{\psi}_{ij}(y_i, y_j) \\ &\quad = \big(I(y_i = 1, y_j = 1), \ldots, I(y_i = p, y_j = r), \ldots, I(y_i = K, y_j = K) \big). \end{aligned}$$

Also, suppose

$$\boldsymbol{w}^V = (w_{ij})_{(i,j) \in \{1 \ldots K\}^2}.$$

Then,

$$D_{ij}^k(v_i, v_j, y_i, y_j) = \langle \boldsymbol{w}^V, \boldsymbol{\psi}_{ij}(y_i, y_j) \rangle = w_{y_i, y_j}.$$

We can represent optimized energy function for the image I_k in the following way:

$$\begin{aligned} E_w^k(Y) &= \sum_{v_i \in V} U_i^k(v_i, y_i) + \sum_{(v_i, v_j) \in E} D_{ij}(v_i, v_j, y_i, y_j) \\ &= \sum_{v_i \in V} \left\langle \boldsymbol{w}^U, \boldsymbol{\psi}_i^k(y_i) \right\rangle + \sum_{(v_i, v_j) \in E} \langle \boldsymbol{w}^V, \boldsymbol{\psi}_{ij}(y_i, y_j) \rangle. \end{aligned}$$

Therefore, $E_w^k(Y)$ is a linear function of $\boldsymbol{w} \equiv (\boldsymbol{w}^U, \boldsymbol{w}^V)$. If we define

$$\Psi(I_k, Y) = (\Psi^D(I_k, Y), \Psi^V(Y)) = \left(\sum_{v_i \in V} \boldsymbol{\psi}_i^k(y_i), \sum_{(v_i, v_j) \in E} \boldsymbol{\psi}_{ij}(y_i, y_j) \right),$$

then

$$E_w^k(Y) = \langle \boldsymbol{w}, \Psi(I_k, Y) \rangle.$$

We can state structured SVM problem for the weights $\boldsymbol{w}$, with $-\Psi(I_k, Y)$ as a joint feature map. One should pay attention that for each of the constraints the evaluation of the maximum operator is equivalent to the optimization problem for the energy function $E_w^k(Y)$ which can be a difficult one.

13.5. Conclusion

Kernel methods provide powerful, theoretically proven tools for a broad class of machine learning problems.

The problems we address in this chapter are namely classification, clustering, and regression. While first two problems are aimed to find a discriminant function to divide the dataset to some groups, the last is designated for estimating the function for variables relationship. The question is how accurately these functions can be approximated using information contained in the training set.

Here we use an assumption that such functions can be taken from a Reproducing Kernel Hilbert Space with a corresponding kernel, and evaluated on the given training set. Some of the kernels, called universal kernels, can accurately approximate any function. Mercer's theorem shows kernels as inner products in RKHS. All these developments pave the way to the technique of "kernel trick", which allows replacing inner products in the linear model with kernel function values. The representer theorem presents a parametrically linear model of generally nonlinear function, which is an optimal solution for a very wide range of machine learning problems.

Nowadays, the kernel techniques in machine learning are pervasive. In fact, any linear model based on inner products can be kernelized as it happens with kernel filtering or kernel linear discriminant analysis which is not "linear" at all. We have highlighted usage of kernels for Nadaraya–Watson regression, for density estimation problems. To reveal nonlinear dependencies in data, kernels can be introduced into Principal Component Analysis. Kernelizing of k-means leads to spectral clustering linking kernel methods with graph theory.

Kernels provide an extension for a widely used and deservedly praized Support Vector Machine approach. For the linear kernel, SVM searches the best discriminant hyperplane that divides two classes with the largest possible margin between them. Replacing inner products in SVM model with appropriate kernel values results in implicit mapping of input vectors to RKHS where they can be (with a successful kernel choice) linearly separated. In the input space this results in a nonlinear dividing surface.

SVM itself has many interesting extensions. Its model allows control over misclassification rate which is implicit in C-SVM and explicit in ν-SVM where the parameter ν gives an upper bound for the margin errors fraction. SVM can be extended to multiclass problems with one-versus-one or one-versus-all approaches. It can be modified to solve regression tasks resulting in ε-SVR and ν-SVR, or to estimate densities resulting in one-class SVM. Following tendency towards online learning methods, SVM models can be incrementally updated. SVM idea of maximizing margin between classes is applicable in adjacent areas such as metric learning. Finally, the idea of supervised learning can be expanded to composite, structured objects, such as graphs, inaddition to regularly used real valued labels, that are supported by structured SVM models.

References

Aizerman, M., Braverman, E. and Rozonoer, L. (1964). Theoretical foundations of the potential function method in pattern recognition learning. *Automat. Rem. Contr.*, 25, pp. 821–837.

Aronszajn, N. (1950). Theory of Reproducing Kernels. *Trans. Amer. Math. Soc.*, 68(3), pp. 337–404.

Atkeson, C. G., Moore, A. W. and Schaal, S. (1997). Locally weighted learning. *Artif. Intell. Rev.*, 11, pp. 11–73.

Balakrishnan, S., Xu, M., Krishnamurthy, A. and Singh, A. (2011). Noise thresholds for spectral clustering. *NIPS*, pp. 954–962.

Bishop, C. M. (2006). *Pattern Recognition and Machine Learning (Information Science and Statistics)*. Secaucus, NJ, USA: Springer-Verlag.

Blaschko, M. B. and Lampert, C. H. (2008). Learning to localize objects with structured output regression. *Computer Vision: ECCV (2008)*, Berlin, Heidelberg: Springer-Verlag, pp. 2–15.

Boser, B. E., Guyon, I. M. and Vapnik, V. N. (1992). A training algorithm for optimal margin classifiers. In *Proc. 5th. Ann. Workshop on Comput. Learning Theory*, New York: ACM Press, pp. 144–152.

Bottou, L. (1998). Online algorithms and stochastic approximations. *Online Learning and Neural Networks, Edited by David Saad*. Cambridge, UK: Cambridge University Press.

Boyd, S. and Vandenberghe, L. (2004). *Convex Optimization, First Edition*. New York, NY, USA: Cambridge University Press.

Boykov Y. and Kolmogorov, V. (2004). An experimental comparison of min-cut/max-flow algorithms for energy minimization in vision. *IEEE Trans. Pattern Anal. Mach. Intell.*, 26(9), 1124–1137.

Boykov, Y., Veksler, O. and Zabih, R. (2001). Fast approximate energy minimization via graph cuts. *IEEE Trans. Pattern Anal. Mach. Intell.*, 23(11), pp. 1222–1239.

Cauwenberghs G. and Poggio, T. (2001). Incremental and decremental support vector machine learning. In *Adv. Neural Inform. Processing Syst.* (NIPS'2000), 13.

Chung, F. (1997). Spectral graph theory. CMBS, Washington.

Cortes, C. and Vapnik, V. (1995). Support-vector networks. *Mach. Learning*, 20, pp. 273–297.

Cuturi, M. (2010). Positive definite kernels in machine learning.

Dhillon, I. S., Guan, Y. and Kulis, B. (2004). Kernel k-means: Spectral clustering and normalized cuts. In *Proc. Tenth. ACM. SIGKDD. Int. Conf. Knowl. Discov. Data Min. (KDD)*, pp. 551–556.

Drucker, H., Burges, C. J. C., Kaufman, L., Smola, A. J. and Vapnik, V. N. (1997). Support Vector Regression Machines. In *Adv. Neural Inform. Processing Syst.* 9(NIPS 1996), pp. 155–161.

Exterkate, P., Groenen, P. J. F., Heij, C. and van Dijk, D. (2013). *Nonlinear Forecasting With Many Predictors Using Kernel Ridge Regression.* CREATES research papers 2013-16. University of Aarhus, Denmark: School of Economics and Management.

Hastie, T., Tibshirani, R. and Friedman, J. (2003). *The Elements of Statistical Learning: Data Mining, Inference, and Prediction in the Elements of Statistical Learning*, Second Edition. New York: Springer-Verlag.

Hayes, M. H. (1996). *Statistical Digital Signal Processing and Modeling, First Edition.* New York, NY, USA: John Wiley & Sons, Inc.

Hüllermeier, E. and Brinker, K. (2008). Learning valued preference structures for solving classification problems. *Fuzzy Sets Syst.*, pp. 2337–2352.

Joachims, T., Hofmann, T., Yue, Y. and Yu, C.-N. (2009). Predicting structured objects with support vector machines. *Communications of the ACM, Research Highlight*, 52(11), pp. 97–104.

Jones, M. C., Davies, S. J. and Park, B. U. (1994). Versions of kernel-type regression estimators, *J. Am. Stat. Assoc.*, 89(427), pp. 825–832.

Jones, M. C., Marron, J. S. and Sheather, S. J. (1996). A brief survey of bandwidth selection for density estimation. *J. Am. Stat. Assoc.*, 91(433), pp. 401–407.

Liu, W., Príncipe, J. C. and Haykin, S. (2010). Appendix B: Approximate linear dependency and system stability. In *Kernel Adaptive Filtering: A Comprehensive Introduction.* Hoboken, NJ, USA: John Wiley & Sons, Inc.

Lucchi, A., Li, Y., Smith, K. and Fua, P. (2012). Structured image segmentation using kernelized features. *Computer Vision–ECCV*, pp. 400–413.

Lughofer, E. and Buchtala, O. (2013). Reliable all-pairs evolving fuzzy classifiers. *IEEE Trans. Fuzzy Syst.*, 21(4), pp. 625–641.

Luxburg, U. (2007). A tutorial on spectral clustering. *Stat. Comput.*, 17(4), pp. 395–416.

Mercer, J. (1909). Functions of positive and negative type, and their connection with the theory of integral equations. *Phil. Trans. R. Soc. Lond.*, 209, pp. 415–446.

Micchelli, C. A., Xu, Y. and Zhang, H. (2006). Universal Kernels. *J. Mach. Learn. Res.*, 6, pp. 2651–2667.

Mika, S., Ratsch, G., Weston, J., Scholkopf, B. and Muller, K. (1999). Fisher discriminant analysis with Kernels. In Hu, Y.-H., Larsen, J., Wilson, E. and Douglas, S. (eds.), *Neural Networks for Signal Processing*. Piscataway, NJ: IEEE Press, pp. 41–48.

Minh, H. Q., Niyogi, P. and Yao, Y. (2006). *Mercers Theorem, Feature Maps, and Smoothing*. New York: Springer, pp. 154–168.

Mohar, B. (1991). The Laplacian spectrum of graphs. In *COMBGRAF*, 2, pp. 871–898.

Mohar, B. (1997). Some applications of Laplace eigenvalues of graphs. In Hahn, G. and Sabidussi, G. (eds.), *Graph Symmetry: Algebraic Methods and Applications, NATO ASI Series*. Netherlands: Springer, pp. 225–275.

Müller, H.-G. (1987). Weighted local regression and Kernel methods for nonparametric curve fitting. *J. Am. Stat. Assoc.*, 82(397), pp. 231–238.

Nadaraya, E. A. (1964). On estimating regression. *Theor. Probab. Appl.*, 9(1), pp. 141–142.

Ng, A. Y., Jordan, M. I. and Weiss, Y. (2001). On spectral clustering: Analysis and an algorithm. *Adv. Neural Inform. Proc. Syst.*, 14, pp. 849–856.

Nguyen, N. and Guo, Y. (2008). Metric learning: A support vector approach. In *Proceedings of the European conference on Machine Learning and Knowledge Discovery in Databases*. Berlin, Heidelberg: Springer-Verlag, pp. 125–136.

Park, B. U. and Marron, J. S. (1990). Comparison of data-driven bandwidth selectors. *J. Am. Statist. Assoc.*, 85(409), pp. 66–72.

Park, B. U. and Turlach, B. A. (1992). Practical performance of several data driven bandwidth selectors (with discussion). *Comput. Statistics*, 7, pp. 251–270.

Parzen, E. (1962). On estimation of a probability density function and mode. *Ann. Math. Statist.*, 33(3), pp. 1065–1076.

Platt, J. C., Cristianini, N. and Shawe-Taylor, J. (2000). Large Margin DAGs for Multiclass Classification. In *Proc. of Neural Inform. Processing Syst.*, (NIPS'99), pp. 547–553.

Rosenblatt, M. (1956). Remarks on some nonparametric estimates of a density function. *Ann. Math. Statist.*, 27(3), pp. 832–837.

Schölkopf, B., Burges, C. J. C. and Smola, A. J. (1999). *Advances in Kernel Methods: Support Vector Learning*. Cambridge, MA, USA: MIT Press.

Schölkopf, B., Herbrich, R. and Smola, A. J. (2001). A generalized representer theorem. In *Computational Learning Theory*: *Lecture Notes in Computer Science*, 2111, pp. 416–426.

Schölkopf, B., Smola, A., Williamson, R. C. and Bartlett, P. L. (2000). New support vector algorithms. *Neural Comput.*, 12, pp. 1207–1245.

Schölkopf, B., Smola, A. J. and Müller, K.-R. (1999). Kernel principal component analysis, advances in Kernel methods — *Support Vector Learning*. Schölkopf, B., Burges, C. J. C. and Smola, A. J. (eds.). Cambridge, MA: MIT Press, pp. 327–352.

Schölkopf, B., Platt, J., Shawe-Taylor, J., Smola, A. and Williamson, R. (2001). Estimating the support of a high-dimensional distribution. *Neural Comput.*, 13(7), pp. 1443–1472.

Sheather, S. J. and Jones, M. C. (1991). A reliable data-based bandwidth selection method for kernel density estimation. *J. Roy. Stat. Soc.*, 53(Series B), pp. 683–690.

Sheather, S. J. (1992). The performance of six popular bandwidth selection methods on some real datasets (with discussion). *Comput. Statistics*, 7, pp. 225–281.

Shi, J. and Malik, J. (2000). Normalized cuts and image segmentation. *IEEE Trans. Pattern Anal. Mach. Intell.*, 22(8), pp. 888–905.

Silverman, B. W. (1986). *Density Estimation for Statistics and Data Analysis*. London: Chapman & Hall.

Tsochantaridis, I., Hofmann, T., Joachims, T. and Altun, Y. (2004). Support vector machine learning for interdependent and structured output spaces. In *Int. Conf. Mach. Learning* (ICML), ACM, Banff, Alberta, Canada, p. 104.

Tsochantaridis, I., Joachims, T., Hofmann, T. and Altun, Y. (2005). Large margin methods for structured and interdependent output variables. *J. Mach. Learning Res.*, pp. 1453–1484.

Vapnik, V. N. (1995). *The Nature of Statistical Learning Theory*. New York, NY, USA: Springer-Verlag.

Vapnik, V. and Chervonenkis, A. (1964). A note on one class of perceptrons. *Automat. Rem. Contr.*, 25, pp. 112–120.

Watson, G. S. (1964). Smooth regression analysis. *Sankhya*, 26(15), pp. 175–184.

Weinberger, K. Q. and Saul, L. K. (2009). Distance metric learning for large margin nearest neighbor classification. *J. Mach. Learning Res.*, 10, pp. 207–244.

Wu, X., Kumar, V., Quinlan, J. R., Ghosh, J., Yang, Q., Motoda, H., McLachlan, G., Ng, A., Liu, B., Yu, P., Zhou, Z.-H., Steinbach, M., Hand, D. and Steinberg, D. (2008). Top 10 algorithms in data mining. *Knowl. Inform. Syst.*, 14(1), pp. 1–37.

Index

D

K

L

M

N